A Junior Anthology of World Poetry

Edited by *Mark Van Doren*

ASSISTANT PROFESSOR OF ENGLISH, COLUMBIA UNIVERSITY

and *Garibaldi M. Lapolla*

CHAIRMAN, ENGLISH DEPARTMENT, THOMAS JEFFERSON HIGH
SCHOOL, NEW YORK CITY

Albert and Charles Boni

NEW YORK   MCMXXIX

COMPOSITION IN GRANJON TYPE, ELECTRO-
TYPED, PRINTED AND BOUND BY J. J. LITTLE
& IVES COMPANY, NEW YORK, U. S. A.

TO

THE MEMORY OF

JOHN DRYDEN

POET AND TRANSLATOR

PREFACE

The scope of this anthology is so wide—in time from the thirty-fifth century B.C. to the twentieth century A.D. and in space from China and Japan around through India, Persia, Arabia, Palestine, Egypt, Greece, and Rome to Europe and America—that there is no poet in human history who might not have found a place in it had he ever fallen into the hands of a becoming translator. Not all the poets, of course, are here. The book, big as it is, would have been still bigger had I found more material exactly suited to my purpose, which was to provide a collection revealing those riches of the world's poetry thus far gathered into readable English.

For my purpose was not to "represent" these various poetical literatures. My experience with previous collections which have attempted to do such a thing for "The Poets and Poetry of Europe," "The Poets and Poetry of Greece and Rome," and so on has convinced me that nothing is deadlier than a compilation designed with reference to the originals alone. This is an anthology of the world's best poetry in the best English I could unearth, and when I found no good English at all I left the poet out. Pindar, for instance, is absent from these pages not because I was unwilling to accept his great reputation but because I discovered no English version of him which made him seem great—or even, for that matter, readable. Hence also some apparent oddities in the proportions observed, certain minor poets receiving, it would seem, more than their due of space at the expense of ampler figures let off with very little. I simply went by what I found, preferring, if I had to be representative at all, to represent the present state of English translation in these cases, and considering that there might be some interest in the fact that a minor Frenchman, say, had been given more attention in our language than a major Persian or Russian.

Homer is not here because I decided to exclude parts of long narrative poems, and indeed never —though I broke the rule in a few inconspicuous instances—to offer abridgements. Virgil, Dante, Firdawsi, and Kalidasa appear only through their shorter works; and Goethe, like the Greek tragic dramatists, is represented in his masterpiece solely by lyrics which may be said to stand alone. I might add at this point that I have confined myself to translations in verse. Much good work has been done in prose, but for various reasons I disregarded it.

If the book does after all fairly represent the poetry of the world, and I am sanguine enough to think that it does on a scale not hitherto attempted, the credit goes to a race of translators which runs back at least as far as Chaucer. The index of their names at the end of the volume is almost a list of the best British and American poets, and indeed an interesting comparison might be made between that index and the succession of names to be found under the last three headings in the table of contents, where it will be seen that I have assembled, in order to make good my title, an anthology of original poems in the English language.

That this comparison should be extended to the poetry itself I do not suggest, since I am as much convinced as anybody that translation does not give us what creation gives. Yet I finish the anthology in the faith that it spreads a rich and beautiful feast, and in doing so I must yield to the temptation to point out some of the better and longer things—some of them hitherto not generally accessible—that are here provided. FitzGerald's Omar Khayyam and the Song of Songs take their places as a matter of course; but Lafcadio Hearn's The River of Heaven from the Manyō Shū, E. Powys Mathers's Black Marigolds from Bilhana, Lady Anne Blunt's and Wilfrid Scawen Blunt's Ode from Imr El Kais, Robert Hillyer's twenty-seven prayers from the Egyptian Book of the Dead, Thomas Stanley's Vigil of Venus, and Rossetti's New Life from Dante were not matters of course, and I should be happy if this volume helped to make them as widely known as they deserve to be. I am further tempted to speak of certain famous English poems which will introduce themselves to some readers now for the first time, perhaps, as translations. But I will resist that temptation and leave the pleasure of discovery to those readers.

I trust the volume will be easy to use. Towards that end I have made the table of contents complete and have supplied full indexes. The arrangement is by countries, or rather by languages, and within each section the order of poets is chronological, the name of the translator being given at the end of each poem in parentheses. Occasionally I have prefixed a note to a poet's work in its proper place, not so much to give information about that poet as to suggest his quality and to make him stand out. Further than that there is no apparatus. The poetry is expected to speak for itself. The things which might be said about all these poets are so numerous, and sometimes so difficult to say, that no one I like to think could have said them in the space available.

Horace, Catullus, Heine, Hafiz, Sappho, and others are each rendered by various—perhaps too various—hands. There would have been an advantage in presenting a single poet through a single translator, but on the whole I preferred variety, and I found the comparison of methods an engaging game. As usual, too, I was interested only in what seemed to me the best versions, and was content to take them from as many sources as might be.

I have much courteous assistance to acknowledge in another place, but wish to make particular mention now of the kindness of William Ellery Leonard, Max Eastman, and Allen Tate in giving me unpublished material for my collection. To Ludwig Lewisohn, E. Powys Mathers, Robert Hillyer, Jethro Bithell, Howard Mumford Jones, Ezra Pound, Havelock Ellis, Ford Madox Ford, A. E. Housman, and Louis Untermeyer I am indebted for generous and helpful letters. And to one of my publishers, Mr. Albert Boni, I am under greater obligations than I can well state. The book was his idea long ago; with it in mind he had collected an extensive library which was put entirely at my disposal; and throughout the labor of compilation he was an invaluable advisor.

MARK VAN DOREN.

New York, 1928

ACKNOWLEDGMENTS

The editor and publishers herewith render thanks to the following individuals for permission to use their poems and translations:

Hilda Aldington ("H. D."), Mary Austin, Florence Ayscough, John Bailey, Henry Adams Bellows, Jethro Bithell, Lothar von Eichhorn for Daisy Broicher, G. K. Chesterton, Padraic Colum, C. Fillingham Coxwell, L. Cranmer-Byng, Walter de la Mare, Babette Deutsch and Avrahm Yarmolinsky, John Dos Passos, Max Eastman, Havelock Ellis, William Dudley Foulke, Ford Madox Ford, Robert Frost, H. W. Garrod, H. J. C. Grierson, G. B. Grundy, Robert Hillyer, A. E. Housman, Aldous Huxley, Douglas Hyde, A. V. Williams Jackson, Robinson Jeffers, Howard Mumford Jones, Margaret Jourdain, Richard Le Gallienne, Jessie Lemont, William Ellery Leonard, Ludwig Lewisohn, Vachel Lindsay, Edward Marsh, E. Powys Mathers, P. E. Matheson, Paul Elmer More, T. Sturge Moore, Sir Gilbert Murray, Margarete Munsterberg, R. A. Nicholson, Seumas O'Sullivan, Ezra Pound, Curtis Hidden Page, Edwin Arlington Robinson, W. H. D. Rouse, George William Russell ("A. E."), Arthur W. Ryder, Maurice Samuel, Carl Sandburg, George Santayana, Joseph T. Shipley, Constance Lindsay Skinner, Dulcie L. Smith, Herbert J. Spinden, James Stephens, Marie Syrkin, Wilfrid Thorley, J. B. Trend, Louis Untermeyer, Arthur Waley, Charles Whibley, and F. A. Wright;

And to the following publishers, agents, or individuals holding copyright on the poems specified for permission to reprint:

To the American-Scandinavian Foundation for Henry Adams Bellows's translation of "Voluspo" from *The Poetic Edda,* and for Robert Hillyer's translation of "There is a Charming Land" from *A Book of Danish Verse.*

To D. Appleton & Company, New York, for Aldous Huxley's translation of "L'Après-Midi d'un Faune" from *Selected Poems,* for Margarete Munsterberg's translations of "A Lovely Rose is Sprung," "The Hostess' Daughter," and "Voice in Darkness" from *A Harvest of German Verse;* and for H. A. Giles's translations of "Tempus Fugit" and "Ode" from *A History of Chinese Literature.*

To Mary Austin for her translations from *The American Rhythm.*

To Jethro Bithell for his translations in the French and German sections.

To Boni & Liveright for Robinson Jeffers's "Night" and "Continent's End" from *Roan Stallion, Tamar and Other Poems;* for Ezra Pound's "Dieu qu'il la fait," "Rome," three translations from Heine, "The Garden," and "The River Merchant's Wife" from *Personae;* for "H. D.'s" "Adonis," "Oread," and two choruses of Euripides from *Collected Poems;* and for Ludwig Lewisohn's translation of "The Thought Eternal" from *The Creative Life.*

To Brandt & Brandt for Edna St. Vincent Millay's sonnet, "Euclid Alone has Looked on Beauty Bare," from *The Harp Weaver and Other Poems,* published by Harper & Brothers, copyright 1920, 1921, 1922, 1923, by Edna St. Vincent Millay.

To Brentano's for Francis Ledwidge's "Lament for the Poets" and "Ardan Mor," and for Lafcadio Hearn's translation of "Clarimonde."

To the B. J. Brimmer Company for Robert Hillyer's translations from "The Coming Forth by Day, or The Book of the Dead."

To the Bureau of American Ethnology for Alice C. Fletcher's translation of the "Song to the Mountains" from *Hako.*

To the Cambridge University Press, England, for translations by R. A. Nicholson and T. R. Glover.

To the University of Chicago Press for five translations by Arthur W. Ryder from *The Panchatantra,* and for Frank C. Nicholson's translation of "Parting at Morning" from *Old German Love Songs.*

To Margaret Carleton, executor to the late Wilfrid Scawen Blunt, for the ode by Imr el Kais translated from the original Arabic by Lady Anne Blunt and done into English verse by Wilfrid Scawen Blunt.

To Constable & Company, London, for four translations from Helen Waddell's Chinese Lyrics.

To Bridgham Curtis for five translations by Natalie Curtis from *The Indians' Book,* copyright, 1907, by Natalie Curtis, copyright 1923 by Paul Burlin, published by Harper & Brothers.

To Dodd, Mead & Company for the poems and translations by Arthur Symons, Ernest Dowson, and W. H. Mallock in the Latin, Spanish, French, and English sections. Used by permission of Dodd, Mead & Company, Inc.

To Doubleday, Doran & Company for "First Philosopher's Song" from *Leda,* by Aldous Huxley, by special permission of the publishers, Doubleday, Doran & Company, Inc.; for four translations of Antonio Machado from *Rosinante to the Road Again,* by John Dos Passos, copyright, 1922, George H. Doran Company; for translations of "Carpe Diem" and "Xanthias Jollied" from *Tobogganing on Parnassus,* by Franklin P. Adams, copyright, 1911, Doubleday, Page & Company.

To Greenberg, Publisher, for Joseph T. Shipley's translations in the French section.

To Harcourt, Brace & Company for Maurice Samuel's translations of Bialik and Judah Ha-Levi from *The Jewish Anthology;* for "Three Spring Notations on Bipeds" from *Smoke and Steel,* by Carl Sandburg; for four translations of Horace by Louis Untermeyer from *Including Horace,* and for ten translations of Heine by Louis Untermeyer from *Poems of Heinrich Heine.*

To Haldeman-Julius Company for Ludwig Lewisohn's translations of Dehmel, Holz, George, von Hofmannsthal, Rilke, Nietzsche, von Lilliencron, Busse, Bulke, Hesse, Schaukal, Mombert, Vollmoeller, Falke, and Bierbaum from *Modern German Poetry* (*Little Blue Book No. 775*).

To Messrs. Heinemann, London, and to Mr. Philip Gosse for translations by Sir Edmund Gosse in the Spanish, French, and Scandinavian sections.

To the Hispanic Society of America for Thomas Walsh's translation of "Villancico" from the *Hispanic Anthology*.

To Henry Holt & Company for Robert Frost's "The Old Man's Winter Night," "The Tuft of Flowers," "The Oven Bird," and "The Runaway" from *Selected Poems;* for Walter de la Mare's "The Listeners" from *Collected Poems;* for Carl Sandburg's "Grass" from *Cornhuskers;* and for A. E. Housman's "With Rue my Heart is Laden," "White is the Moon," "Loveliest of Trees," and "Far in a Western Brookland" from *A Shropshire Lad*.

The selections from Amy Lowell, Amy Lowell and Florence Ayscough, John Hay, Curtis Hidden Page, Lafcadio Hearn (in the Japanese section), Paul Elmer More, A. J. Butler, Wilfrid Thorley, Havelock Ellis, E. Powys Mathers (with the exception of "Black Marigolds"), Ralph Waldo Emerson, and Henry Wadsworth Longfellow are used by permission of, and by arrangement with, Houghton Mifflin Company, the authorized publishers.

To International Publishers Company for translations by Babette Deutsch and Avrahm Yarmolinsky in the Russian section.

To The Jewish Publication Society of America for translations of Judah Ha-Levi by Nina Salaman and of Solomon Ibn Gabirol by Israel Zangwill.

To the Johns Hopkins Press for translations by Kirby Flower Smith in the Latin section.

To Alfred A. Knopf, Inc., for translations by J. B. Trend, Lorna De' Lucchi, James Elroy Flecker, and Arthur Waley (from *The Temple* and *More Translations from the Chinese*). "Remembering Golden Bells," "Fighting South of the Castle," "Old and New," "A Gentle Wind," "The Scholar in the Narrow Street," "Shady shady," "I built my Hut," "Sailing Homeward," "Loyang," "On the Birth of his Son," and "Rejoicing at the Arrival of Ch'en Hsiung," are reprinted from *170 Chinese Poems,* by Arthur Waley, by and with permission of and special arrangement with Alfred A. Knopf, Inc., authorized publishers. "The Love Song of J. Alfred Prufrock," "Morning at the Window," and "The Hippopotamus" are reprinted from *Poems,* by T. S. Eliot, by and with permission of and special arrangement with Alfred A. Knopf, Inc., authorized publishers.

To Richard Le Gallienne for four translations from *Odes from the Divan of Hafiz*.

To Jessie Lemont for two translations from *Poems: Rainer Maria Rilke*.

To Little, Brown & Company for four poems by Emily Dickinson.

To John W. Luce & Company for two poems by J. M. Synge.

To the Macmillan Company for "A Birthday," "Remember," and "When I am Dead, My Dearest" from *Collected Poems,* by Christina Rossetti, copyright by The Macmillan Company, New

xiv ACKNOWLEDGMENTS

York; for "Drummer Hodge," "Hap," "Let Me Enjoy," and "On an Invitation to the United States" from *Collected Poems,* by Thomas Hardy, copyright by The Macmillan Company, New York; for "Beauty," translation of Sonnet by Francesco de Quevedo y Villegas, and translation of Becquer's "They Closed Her Eyes," from *Collected Poems* by John Masefield, copyright by The Macmillan Company, New York; for "A Mountain Wind," "A Holy Hill," "The Lonely," and "Immortality" from *Collected Poems,* by George William Russell ("A. E."), copyright by The Macmillan Company, New York; for "The Daisies," "The Goat Paths," and "Deirdre" from *Collected Poems,* by James Stephens, copyright by The Macmillan Company, New York; for "To an Isle in the Water," "When You Are Old," "The Everlasting Voices," "The Cold Heaven," and "To a Friend" from *Early Poems* and *Later Poems,* by William Butler Yeats, copyright by The Macmillan Company, New York; for "Corrymeela" from *Songs from the Glens of Antrim,* by Moira O'Neill, copyright by The Macmillan Company, New York; for "A Drover" and "River Mates" from *Wild Earth,* by Padraic Colum, copyright by The Macmillan Company, New York; for "Mr. Flood's Party," "The Sheaves," "The Dust of Timas," "The Old Story," "An Inscription by the Sea," "Doricha," "The Raven," and "A Happy Man" from *Collected Poems,* by Edwin Arlington Robinson, copyright by The Macmillan Company, New York; for a passage from Zoroaster as contained in *Early Persian Poetry* by A. V. Williams Jackson, copyright by The Macmillan Company, New York; for "The Eagle that is Forgotten" from *Collected Poems,* by Vachel Lindsay, copyright by The Macmillan Company, New York.

To Elkin Mathews & Marrot, London, for Daisy Broicher's translation of "No Way too Long" from *German Lyrists of Today,* and for J. E. Flecker's translations of "Litany to Satan," "Hialmar Speaks to the Raven," and "Mignon."

To *The Menorah Journal* for translations by Marie Syrkin and Maurice Samuel.

To Minton, Balch & Company for translations of "Correspondences" and "Farewell to Anactoria" from *Mr. Pope and Other Poems,* by Allen Tate.

To T. Sturge Moore for his translation from Rimbaud.

To John Murray, London, for translations by L. Cranmer-Byng and Dulcie L. Smith.

To *The Nation* for translations by Max Eastman in the Russian section.

To the *Natural History Magazine* and the American Museum of Natural History for H. J. Spinden's translation of "A Lover's Lament."

To the University of North Carolina Press for Howard Mumford Jones's translations of Petronius, Sidonius Apollinaris, and Claudian from *The Romanesque Lyric.*

To The Open Court Publishing Company for William Ellery Leonard's translations of "Æsop" from *Æsop and Hyssop,* and for Howard Mumford Jones's translation of Heine from "The North Sea."

To The Clarendon Press, Oxford, for eleven translations from *Heine's Book of Songs*, by John Todhunter.

To the Paget Literary Agency for "Leisure" by W. H. Davies.

To James B. Pinker and Sons for "Lost Love" by Robert Graves.

To Ezra Pound for translations of "Song of the Virgin Mother" and "Alba Innominata."

To G. P. Putnam's Sons, Publishers, New York and London, for "The Coyote and the Locust," from *Zuni Folk Tales* by Frank Cushing.

To George Routledge & Sons, Ltd., London, for "Hymn to Vishnu" from *Indian Poetry*, by Sir Edwin Arnold, and for "The Peasant and the Sheep" from *Kriloff's Fables*, by C. Fillingham Coxwell.

To Charles Scribner's Sons for poems and translations by George Meredith, George Santayana, Eugene Field, W. E. Henley, and Alice Meynell; and for Edwin Arlington Robinson's "Miniver Cheevy," from *The Town Down the River*, and "Luke Havergal," from *The Children of the Night*.

To Martin Secker, Ltd., London, for translations of "Opportunity," "Pannyra of the Golden Heel," and "Don Juan in Hell" by J. E. Flecker.

To The Talbot Press, Dublin, for Joseph Plunkett's "The Spark," Thomas MacDonagh's "John-John," and Thomas Mac-Donagh's translation of Padraic Pearse's "Ideal."

To The Viking Press for Rimbaud's "The Sleeper in the Valley," Jammes's "The Child Reads an Almanac," and Verhaeren's "The Poor," from *The Poets of Modern France*, by Ludwig Lewisohn, New York, The Viking Press (copyright 1918 by B. W. Huebsch, Inc.); for Arno Holz's "Buddha" from *The Vaunt of Man*, by W. E. Leonard, New York, The Viking Press (copyright 1912 by B. W. Huebsch, Inc.); and for "I Hear an Army" from *Chamber Music*, by James Joyce, New York, The Viking Press (authorized edition, B. W. Huebsch, Inc., 1918).

To A. P. Watt & Son, London, for "Recessional" by Rudyard Kipling, from *The Five Nations*, copyright by Rudyard Kipling.

FOREWORD

This Junior Anthology of World Poetry is offered to the ever-growing numbers of children who have in recent years been learning to enjoy the reading of poetry without the mediation of teacher or parent. It does for our young people what the larger Anthology of World Poetry has done for their elders. In a particularly varied manner it presents a delightful display of the loveliest things in verse done thruout the ages by the poets of all the western and eastern worlds.

It seemed to me as I read the original volume that it was too beautiful a collection not to make it available for our very young people. I read from it to the pupils in my classes and found that they were eager not only to hear more but to obtain the book for their own. So encouraged was I that I submitted the plan of reducing the size of the original volume to the publishers and Mr. Van Doren who were generous enough to see the possibilities of the plan and to try it out.

The book as it stands is complete in itself. It contains all the poems in the original collection which will appeal to young people. It is so rich in the number of poems and the variety and quality of the poems as to make it a storehouse of beauty to which the young boy or girl can go again and again and never find it stale or monotonous. It will grow in meaning as the child grows, and the child will grow in the measure in which he finds joy and delight in the book.

Parents can safely place the collection in the hands of their children with the confidence that the selection of the poems is not only varied and complete but especially suitable for young boys and girls. Every poem which might appeal to them has been retained and all those which would not be suitable excluded. Moreover, as they read they will not only become acquainted with the famous names and the famous poems in English and American literature but they will also learn to know and appreciate the poets who are the most part but the shadows of names to our youngsters. In a very literal sense, the wealth of the world is laid at their feet.

GARIBALDI M. LAPOLLA.

TABLE OF SECTIONS

CONTENTS

CHINESE

CONTENTS

CONTENTS

CONTENTS

CONTENTS

SPANISH

CONTENTS

CONTENTS

GERMAN

CONTENTS

SCANDINAVIAN

CONTENTS xxxvii

ENGLISH

CONTENTS

CONTENTS xli

PAGE

IRISH

AMERICAN

"a Book of Verses
     Underneath the Bough"........

CHINESE

From the Shi King, or Book of Odes

Compiled c. 500 B.C.

The Shi King was compiled by Confucius from earlier collections which had been long existent. It was through the Odes that Confucius taught his own generation to understand the manners and customs and simple feelings of the men of old. These are the natural songs that float upward from the happy valleys and down the sedge-strewn banks of the wandering K'e. They are naïve and bright as on their birthday, with that most precious quality of truth and unconscious art which never lets them tarnish or fade.—L. CRANMER-BYNG.

THE MORNING GLORY

THE morning glory climbs above my head,
Pale flowers of white and purple, blue and red.
    I am disquieted.

Down in the withered grasses something stirred;
I thought it was his footfall that I heard.
    Then a grasshopper chirred.

I climbed the hill just as the new moon showed,
I saw him coming on the southern road.
    My heart lays down its load.

(Helen Waddell)

HOW GOES THE NIGHT?

How goes the night?
Midnight has still to come.
Down in the court the torch is blazing bright;
I hear far off the throbbing of the drum.

How goes the night?
The night is not yet gone.

I hear the trumpets blowing on the height;
The torch is paling in the coming dawn.

How goes the night?
The night is past and done.
The torch is smoking in the morning light,
The dragon banner floating in the sun.

(*Helen Waddell*)

I WAIT MY LORD

THE gourd has still its bitter leaves,
And deep the crossing at the ford.
  I wait my lord.

The ford is brimming to its banks;
The pheasant cries upon her mate.
  My lord is late.

The boatman still keeps beckoning,
And others reach their journey's end.
  I wait my friend.

(*Helen Waddell*)

THE PEAR-TREE

THIS shade-bestowing pear-tree, thou
Hurt not, nor lay its leafage low;
Beneath it slept the Duke of Shaou.

This shade-bestowing pear-tree, thou
Hurt not, nor break one leafy bough;
Beneath it stayed the Duke of Shaou.

This shade-bestowing pear-tree, thou
Hurt not, nor bend one leafy bough,
Beneath it paused the Duke of Shaou.

(*Allen Upward*)

YOU WILL DIE

You have coats and robes,
But you do not trail them;
You have chariots and horses,
But you do not ride them.
By and by you will die,
And another will enjoy them.

You have courtyards and halls,
But they are not sprinkled and swept;
You have bells and drums,
But they are not struck.
By and by you will die,
And another will possess them.

You have wine and food;
Why not play daily on your lute,
That you may enjoy yourself now
And lengthen your days?
By and by you will die,
And another will take your place.

(*H. A. Giles*)

Anonymous

c. 124 B.C.

FIGHTING SOUTH OF THE CASTLE

THEY fought south of the Castle,
They died north of the wall.
They died in the moors and were not buried.
Their flesh was the food of crows.
"Tell the crows we are not afraid;
We have died in the moors and cannot be buried.
Crows, how can our bodies escape you?"
The waters flowed deep
And the rushes in the pool were dark.
The riders fought and were slain:

Their horses wander neighing.
By the bridge there was a house.
Was it south, was it north?
The harvest was never gathered.
How can we give you your offerings?
You served your Prince faithfully,
Though all in vain.
I think of you, faithful soldiers;
Your service shall not be forgotten.
For in the morning you went out to battle
And at night you did not return.

(Arthur Waley)

Tso Ssū

3rd century

THE SCHOLAR IN THE NARROW STREET

FLAP, flap, the captive bird in the cage
Beating its wings against the four corners.
Depressed, depressed the scholar in the narrow street:
Clasping a shadow, he dwells in an empty house.
When he goes out, there is nowhere for him to go:
Bunches and brambles block up his path.
He composes a memorial, but it is rejected and unread,
He is left stranded, like a fish in a dry pond.
Without—he has not a single farthing of salary:
Within—there is not a peck of grain in his larder.
His relations upbraid him for his lack of success:
His friends and callers daily decrease in number.
Su Ch'in used to go preaching in the North
And Li Ssu sent a memorandum to the West.
I once hoped to pluck the fruits of life:
But now alas, they are all withered and dry.
Though one drinks at a river, one cannot drink more
    than a bellyful;
Enough is good, but there is no use in satiety.
The bird in a forest can perch but on one bough,
And this should be the wise man's pattern.

(Arthur Waley)

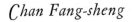

Chan Fang-sheng

4th century

SAILING HOMEWARD

Cliffs that rise a thousand feet
Without a break,
Lake that stretches a hundred miles
Without a wave.
Sands that are white through all the year,
Without a stain,
Pine-tree woods, winter and summer
Ever-green,
Streams that for ever flow and flow
Without a pause,
Trees that for twenty thousand years
Your vows have kept,
You have suddenly healed the pain of a traveler's heart,
And moved his brush to write a new song.

(*Arthur Waley*)

T'ao Ch'ien

365–427

SHADY, SHADY

Shady, shady the wood in front of the Hall:
At midsummer full of calm shadows.
The south wind follows summer's train:
With its eddying puffs it blows open my coat.
I am free from ties and can live a life of retirement.
When I rise from sleep, I play with books and harp.
The lettuce in the garden still grows moist:
Of last year's grain there is always plenty left.
Self-support should maintain strict limits:
More than enough is not what I want.
I grind millet and make good wine:
When the wine is heated, I pour it out for myself.
My little children are playing at my side,
Learning to talk, they babble unformed sounds.

These things have made me happy again
And I forget my lost cap of office.
Distant, distant I gaze at the white clouds:
With a deep yearning I think of the Sages of Antiquity.

(Arthur Waley)

Emperor Ch'ien Wēn-ti

6th century

LO-YANG

A BEAUTIFUL place is the town of Lo-yang:
The big streets are full of spring light.
The lads go driving out with harps in their hands:
The mulberry girls go out to the fields with their baskets.
Golden whips glint at the horses' flanks,
Gauze sleeves brush at the green boughs.
Racing dawn, the carriages come home,—
And the girls with their high baskets full of fruit.

(Arthur Waley)

Li T'ai-po

701–762

It is permitted to very few to live in the hearts of their
countrymen as Li T'ai-po has lived in the hearts of the
Chinese. There is no doubt at all that in Li T'ai-po we
have one of the world's greatest lyrists.—FLORENCE
AYSCOUGH.

THE RIVER-MERCHANT'S WIFE: A LETTER

WHILE my hair was still cut straight across my forehead
I played about the front gate, pulling flowers.
You came by on bamboo stilts, playing horse,
You walked about my seat, playing with blue plums.
And we went on living in the village of Chokan:
Two small people, without dislike or suspicion.

At fourteen I married My Lord you.
I never laughed, being bashful.

Lowering my head, I looked at the wall.
Called to, a thousand times, I never looked back.
At fifteen I stopped scowling,
I desired my dust to be mingled with yours
Forever and forever and forever.
Why should I climb the lookout?

At sixteen you departed,
You went into far Ku-to-yen, by the river of swirling
    eddies,
And you have been gone five months.
The monkeys make sorrowful noise overhead.
You dragged your feet when you went out.
By the gate now, the moss is grown, the different mosses,
Too deep to clear them away!
The leaves fall early this autumn, in wind.
The paired butterflies are already yellow with August
Over the grass in the West garden;
They hurt me. I grow older.
If you are coming down through the narrows of the river
    Kiang,
Please let me know beforehand,
And I will come out to meet you
           As far as Cho-fu-Sa.

                                (Ezra Pound)

CLEARING AT DAWN

THE fields are chill; the sparse rain has stopped;
The colors of Spring teem on every side.
With leaping fish the blue pond is full;
With singing thrushes the green boughs droop.
The flowers of the field have dabbled their powdered
    cheeks;
The mountain grasses are bent level at the waist.
By the bamboo stream the last fragment of cloud
Blown by the wind slowly scatters away.

                                (Arthur Waley)

Tu Fu

712–770

English writers on Chinese literature are fond of an-
nouncing that Li T'ai-po is China's greatest poet; the
Chinese themselves, however, award this place to Tu Fu.
We may put it that Li T'ai-po was the people's poet, and
Tu Fu the poet of scholars.—ARTHUR WALEY.

THE EXCURSION

I

How delightful, at sunset, to loosen the boat!
A light wind is slow to raise waves.
Deep in the bamboo grove, the guests linger;
The lotus-flowers are pure and bright in the cool evening
    air.
The young nobles stir the ice-water;
The Beautiful Ones wash the lotus-roots, whose fibers
    are like silk threads.
A layer of clouds above our heads is black.
It will certainly rain, which impels me to write this
    poem.

II

The rain comes, soaking the mats upon which we are
    sitting.
A hurrying wind strikes the bow of the boat.
The rose-red rouge of the ladies from Yueh is wet;
The Yen beauties are anxious about their kingfisher-
    eyebrows.
We throw out a rope and draw in to the sloping bank.
    We tie the boat to the willow-trees.
We roll up the curtains and watch the floating wave-
    flowers.
Our return is different from out setting out. The wind
    whistles and blows in great gusts.
By the time we reach the shore, it seems as though the
    Fifth Month were Autumn.

(Amy Lowell and Florence Ayscough)

Po Chü-i

772–846

There is a story that he was in the habit of reading his poems to an old peasant woman and altering any expression which she could not understand. The poems of his contemporaries were mere elegant diversions which enabled the scholar to display his erudition, or the literary juggler his dexterity. No poet in the world can ever have enjoyed greater contemporary popularity than Po.— ARTHUR WALEY.

LODGING WITH THE OLD MAN OF THE STREAM

MEN's hearts love gold and jade;
Men's mouths covet wine and flesh.
Not so the old man of the stream;
He drinks from his gourd and asks nothing more.
South of the stream he cuts firewood and grass;
North of the stream he has built wall and roof.
Yearly he sows a single acre of land;
In spring he drives two yellow calves.
In these things he finds great repose;
Beyond these he has no wish or care.
By chance I met him walking by the water-side;
He took me home and lodged me in his thatched hut.
When I parted from him, to seek market and Court,
This old man asked my rank and pay.
Doubting my tale, he laughed loud and long:
"Privy Councillors do not sleep in barns."

(Arthur Waley)

REMEMBERING GOLDEN BELLS

RUINED and ill,—a man of two score;
   Pretty and guileless,—a girl of three.
Not a boy,—but still better than nothing:
To soothe one's feeling,—from time to time a kiss!
There came a day,—they suddenly took her from me;
Her soul's shadow wandered I know not where.

And when I remembered how just at the time she died
She lisped strange sounds, beginning to learn to talk,
Then I know that the ties of flesh and blood
Only bind us to a load of grief and sorrow.
At last, by thinking of the time before she was born,
By thought and reason I drove the pain away.
Since my heart forgot her, many days have passed
And three times winter has changed to spring.
This morning, for a little, the old grief came back,
Because, in the road, I met her foster-nurse.

(*Arthur Waley*)

Yüan Chēn

779–831

THE PITCHER

I DREAMT I climbed to a high, high plain;
And on the plain I found a deep well.
My throat was dry with climbing and I longed to drink,
And my eyes were eager to look into the cool shaft.
I walked round it; I looked right down;
I saw my image mirrored on the face of the pool.
An earthen pitcher was sinking into the black depths;
There was no rope to pull it to the well-head.
I was strangely troubled lest the pitcher should be lost,
And started wildly running to look for help.
From village to village I scoured that high plain;
The men were gone: the dogs leapt at my throat.
I came back and walked weeping round the well;
Faster and faster the blinding tears flowed—
Till my own sobbing suddenly woke me up;
My room was silent, no one in the house stirred;
The flame of my candle flickered with a green smoke;
The tears I had shed glittered in the candle-light.
A bell sounded; I knew it was the midnight-chime;
I sat up in bed and tried to arrange my thoughts:
The plain in my dream was the graveyard at Ch'ang-an,
Those hundred acres of untilled land.

The soil heavy and the mounds heaped high;
And the dead below them laid in deep troughs.
Deep are the troughs, yet sometimes dead men
Find their way to the world above the grave.
And to-night my love who died long ago
Came into my dream as the pitcher sunk in the well.
That was why the tears suddenly streamed from my
    eyes,
Streamed from my eyes and fell on the collar of my dress.

(*Arthur Waley*)

Su Tung-p'o

1036–1101

ON THE BIRTH OF HIS SON

FAMILIES, when a child is born
Want it to be intelligent.
I, through intelligence,
Having wrecked my whole life,
Only hope the baby will prove
Ignorant and stupid.
Then he will crown a tranquil life
By becoming a Cabinet Minister.

(*Arthur Waley*)

Lui Chi

1311–1375

A POET THINKS

THE rain is due to fall,
The wind blows softly.

The branches of the cinnamon are moving,
The begonias stir on the green mounds.

Bright are the flying leaves,
The falling flowers are many.

The wind lifted the dry dust,
And he is lifting the wet dust;
Here and there the wind moves everything.

He passes under light gauze
And touches me.

I am alone with the beating of my heart.

There are leagues of sky,
And the water is flowing very fast.

Why do the birds let their feathers
Fall among the clouds?

I would have them carry my letters,
But the sky is long.

The stream flows east
And not one wave comes back with news.

The scented magnolias are shining still,
But always a few are falling.

I close his box on my guitar of jasper
And lay aside my jade flute.

I am alone with the beating of my heart.

Stay with me to-night,
Old songs.

(E. Powys Mathers)

JAPANESE

From the *Manyo Shū*

Compiled 8th century

Japanese poetry, as an art, may be said to begin with the Manyo Shu ("Ten-thousand-Leaves Collection"). The chief poets of the Manyo were Kakinomoto no Hitomaro and Yamabe no Akahito.—ARTHUR WALEY.

PRINCESS DAIHAKU

7th century

How will you manage
To cross alone
The autumn mountain
Which was so hard to get across
Even when we went the two of us together?

PRINCE YUHARA

7th century

WHAT am I to do with my Sister?
Whom, like the Judas-tree
Which grows in the moon,
I may see with my eyes
But not touch with my hands?

OKURA

660–733

BECAUSE he is young
And will not know the way to go
Would I could bribe
The messenger of the Underworld
That on his shoulders he might carry him!

THE PRIEST HAKUTSU

c. 704

O PINE-TREE standing
At the side of the stone house,
When I look at you,
It is like seeing face to face
The men of old time.

YAKAMOCHI

d. 785

1

WHEN evening comes
I will leave the door open before hand and then
    wait
For him who said he would come
To meet me in my dreams.

2

By way of pretext
I said "I will go
And look at
The condition of the bamboo fence;"
But it was really to see you!

THE LADY OF SAKANOYE

8th century

1

THE dress that my Brother has put on is thin.
O wind from Sao,
Do not blow hard
Till he reaches home.

2

My heart, thinking
"How beautiful he is"
Is like a swift river
Which though one dams it and dams it,
Will still break through.

✗3

Unknown love
Is as bitter a thing
As the maiden-lily
Which grows in the thickets
Of the summer moor.

From the Kokin Shū

Compiled 9th century

✗ONO NO KOMACHI

834–880

A THING which fades
With no outward sign—
Is the flower
Of the heart of man
In this world!

FUJIWARA NO TOSHIYUKI

d. 907

ALTHOUGH it is not plainly visible to the
    eye
That autumn has come,
I am alarmed
By the noise of the wind!

From the Shui Shū

Compiled 10th century

HITOMARO

c. 700

WHEN,
Halting in front of it, I look
At the reflection which is in the depths
Of my clear mirror,
It gives me the impression of meeting
An unknown old gentleman.

KIYOWARA FUKUYABU

c. 900–930

BECAUSE river-fog
Hiding the mountain-base
Has risen,
The autumn mountain looks as though it
    hung in the sky.

From the Hyaku-Nin-Isshu

13th century

PRINCESS SHOKU

I WOULD that even now
    My thread of life were broken—
So should my secret vow
    Remain unspoken.

LADY HORIKAWA

How can one e'er be sure
If true love will endure?
    My thoughts this morning are
    As tangled as my hair.

FUJIWARA NO MICHINOBU

THE day will soon be gone,
    And night come back, I know . . .
Yet how I hate the dawn
    That bids me go.

LADY SANUKI

LIKE a great rock, far out at sea,
    Submerged at even the lowest tide,
Unseen, unknown of man—my sleeve
    Is never for a moment dried.

(*Curtis Hidden Page*)

Bashō

1644–1694

QUICK-FALLING dew,
Ah, let me cleanse in you
   This wretched life.

A lonely pond in age-old stillness sleeps . .
   Apart, unstirred by sound or motion . . . till
Suddenly into it a lithe frog leaps.

Old men, white-haired, beside the ancestral graves,
   All of the household now
Stand lonesome, leaning on their staves.

O cricket, from your cheery cry
   No one could ever guess
How quickly you must die.

(Curtis Hidden Page)

SANSKRIT

From the Rigveda

C. 1500 B.C.

The Rigveda consists of 1,028 hymns, comprising over ten thousand verses. The hymns are generally simple, and betray a childlike and simple faith in the gods, to whom sacrifices are offered and libations of the Soma juice are poured, and who are asked for increase of progeny, cattle, and wealth, and implored to help the Aryans in their still doubtful struggle against the black aborigines of the Punjab.—ROMESH DUTT.

PUSHAN, GOD OF PASTURE

cf.
The 23rd
Psalm

PUSHAN, God of golden day,
Shorten thou the shepherd's way,
Vanquish every foe and stranger,
Free our path from every danger;
Cloud-born Pushan, ever more,
Lead us as you led before!

Smite the wild wolf, fierce and vile,
Lurking in the dark defile,
Smite the robber and the thief,
Stealing forth to take our life;
Cloud-born Pushan, ever more,
Lead us as you led before!

Chase him, Pushan, in thy wrath,
Who infests the lonely path,
Robber with his ruthless heart,
Slayer with his secret dart;
Child of clouds, for ever more,
Lead us as you led before!

Trample with thy heavy tread,
On the darksome man of dread,

18

On the low and lying knave,
Smooth-tongued double-dealing slave;
Child of clouds, for ever more,
Lead us as you led before!

Thou dost pathless forests know,
Thou canst quell the secret foe,
Thou didst lead our fathers right,
Wonder-worker, orb of light;
Grant from thy unfailing store
Wealth and blessings ever more!

Thou hast treasures manifold,
Glittering weapons, arms of gold;
Foremost of the Sons of Light,
Shepherds' God and Leader bright;
Grant from thy unfailing store
Wealth and blessings ever more!

Lead us through the dark defile
Past pursuers dread and vile,
Lead us over pleasant ways
Sheltered by thy saving grace,
Lead us o'er this trackless shore,
And we follow ever more!

Where the grass is rich and green,
And the pasture's beauteous seen,
And the meadow's soft and sweet,
Lead us, safe from scorching heat,
Blessings on thy servants pour,
And we follow ever more!

Fill our hearts with hope and courage,
Fill our homes with food and forage,
Save us from a cruel fate
Feed us and invigorate;
We are suppliants at thy door,
And we follow ever more!

Heart and voice we lift in praise,
Chant our hymns and pious lays,
From the Bright One, good and gracious,
Ask for food and pasture spacious;
Shepherds' God! Befriend the poor,
And we follow ever more!

(*Romesh Dutt*)

From the Panchatantra

2d century B.C., *et seq.*

TRUE FRIENDSHIP

'Tis hard to find in life
A friend, a bow, a wife,
Strong, supple to endure,
In stock and sinew pure,
In time of danger sure.

False friends are common. Yes, but where
True nature links a friendly pair,
The blessing is as rich as rare.

To bitter ends
You trust true friends,
Not wife nor mother,
Not son nor brother.

No long experience alloys
True friendship's sweet and supple joys;
No evil men can steal the treasure;
'Tis death, death only, sets a measure.

(*Arthur W. Ryder*)

FOOL AND FALSE

With the shrewd and upright man
    Seek a friendship rare;
Exercise with shrewd and false
    Superheedful care;

Pity for the upright fool
   Find within your heart;
If a man be fool and false,
   Shun him from the start.

             (Arthur W. Ryder)

Kalidasa

c. 500

Rarely has a man walked the earth who observed the phenomena of living nature as accurately as he. His nature was one of singular balance, equally at home in a splendid court and on a lonely mountain. For something like fifteen hundred years Kalidasa has been more widely read in India than any other author who wrote in Sanskrit.—ARTHUR W. RYDER.

THE SEASONS

AUTUMN

THE autumn comes, a maiden fair
   In slenderness and grace,
With nodding rice-stems in her hair
   And lilies in her face.
In flowers of grasses she is clad;
   And as she moves along,
Birds greet her with their cooing glad
   Like bracelets' tinkling song.

A diadem adorns the night
   Of multitudinous stars;
Her silken robe is white moonlight,
   Set free from cloudy bars;
And on her face (the radiant moon)
   Bewitching smiles are shown:
She seems a slender maid, who soon
   Will be a woman grown.

Over the rice-fields, laden plants
   Are shivering to the breeze;

While in his brisk caresses dance
  The blossomed-burdened trees;
He ruffles every lily-pond
  Where blossoms kiss and part,
And ſtirs with lover's fancies fond
  The young man's eager heart.

(*Arthur W. Ryder*)

Bhartrihari

c. 500

In short verses the Hindus excel. Their maſtery of form, their play of fancy, their depth and tenderness of feeling, are all exquisite. Of the many who wrote such verses, the greateſt is Bhartrihari.—ARTHUR W. RYDER.

TIME

TIME is the root of all this earth;
  These creatures, who from Time had birth,
  Within his bosom at the end
Shall sleep; Time hath nor enemy nor friend.

All we in one long caravan
  Are journeying since the world began;
  We know not whither, but we know
Time guideth at the front, and all muſt go.

Like as the wind upon the field
  Bows every herb, and all muſt yield,
  So we beneath Time's passing breath
Bow each in turn,—why tears for birth or death?

(*Paul Elmer More*)

ARABIAN

From the *Mu'allaqát*

Compiled 8th century

Antara

6th century

ABLA

THE poets have muddied all the little fountains.

Yet do not my strong eyes know you, far house?

O dwelling of Abla in the valley of Gawa,
Speak to me, for my camel and I salute you.

My camel is as tall as a tower, and I make him stand
And give my aching heart to the wind of the desert.

O erstwhile dwelling of Abla in the valley of Gawa;
And my tribe in the valleys of Hazn and Samma
And in the valley of Motethalem!

Salute to the old ruins, the lonely ruins   ·
Since Oum El Aythan gathered and went away.

Now is the dwelling of Abla
In a valley of men who roar like lions.
It will be hard to come to you, O daughter of Makhram.

   ·   ·   ·   ·

Abla is a green rush
That feeds beside the water.

But they have taken her to Oneiza
And my tribe feeds in lazy Ghailam valley.

They fixed the going, and the camels
Waked in the night and evilly prepared.

I was afraid when I saw the camels
Standing ready among the tents
And eating grain to make them swift.

I counted forty-two milk camels,
Black as the wings of a black crow.

White and purple are the lilies of the valley,
But Abla is a branch of flowers.

Who will guide me to the dwelling of Abla?

(E. Powys Mathers)

From the Mufaddaliyat

Compiled 8th century

Alqamah

6th century

HIS CAMEL

So leave her, and cast care from thy heart with a sturdy
    mount—a camel that ambles tireless, carrying riders
    twain; .

To Harith, the generous Lord, I drive her unsparing on,
    with pantings that shake her breast and throb
    through her ribs and flanks:

A fleet runner whose flesh over sides and where neck
    meets hump has vanished beneath noon-tide's hot
    breath and the onward press;

And yet after night's long toil the dawn breaks and finds
    her fresh as antelope, young and strong, that flees
    from the hunter's pack:

They crouched by the *artà*-brake, the hunters, and
    thought to win a safe prey: but she escaped their
    shafts and pursuing hounds.

So travels my beaſt, and makes her objeċt a man far off,
 and little by little gains the way to his bounteous
 hand.
Yet, thou waſt her labor's end—God keep thee from
 curse, O King! and through all the Desert's same-
 ness sped she, beset with fears.
Towards thee the Pole-ſtars led, and there where men's
 feet had passed a track plain to see that wound by
 cairns over ridges scarred.
There bodies of beaſts outworn lay thickly along the
 road, their bones gleaming white, their hides all
 shriveled and hard and dry.
I bring her to drink the dregs of ciſterns all mire and
 draff; and if she mislikes it, all the choice is to
 journey on.

(Sir Charles Lyall)

Khansá

7th century

TEARS

Tears, ere thy death, for many a one I shed,
But thine are all my tears since thou art dead.
To comforters I lend my ear apart,
While pain sits ever closer to my heart.

(R. A. Nicholson)

Ta'Abbata Sharra

7th century

EVER WATCHFUL

Nor exults he nor complains he; silent bears whate'er
 befalls him,
Much desiring, much attempting; far the wanderings of
 his venture.
In one desert noon beholds him; evening finds him in
 another;

As the wild ass lone he crosses o'er the jagged and head-
    long ridges.

Swifter than the wind unpausing, onward yet, nor rest
    nor slackness,

Wild the howling gusts outspeeded in the distance moan
    and falter,

Light the slumber on his eyelids, yet too heavy all he
    deems it;

Ever watchful for the moment when to draw the bitter
    faulchion;

When to plunge it in the heart-blood of the many-
    mustered foemen.

(W. G. Palgrave)

Abd-ar-Rahman I

8th century

THE PALM TREE

In the midst of my garden
Grows a palm-tree;
Born in the West,
Away from the country of palm-trees.

I cried: You are like me,
For you resemble me
In wandering and peregrination,
And the long separation from kith and kin.

You also
Grew up on a foreign soil;
Like me,
You are far from the country of your birth.

May the fertilizing clouds of morning
Water you in exile,
May the beneficent rains besought by the poor
Never forsake you.

(J. B. Trend)

From the Hamâsah
Compiled 9th century

Hittân, son of Al-Mu' Allà of Tayyi

HIS CHILDREN

FORTUNE has brought me down—her wonted way—
    from station great and high to low estate;
Fortune has rent away my plenteous store;
    of all my wealth honor alone is left.
Fortune has turned my joy to tears; how oft
    did Fortune make me laugh with what she gave!
But for these girls, the *kata's* downy brood,
    unkindly thrust from door to door as hard—
Far would I roam and wide to seek my bread
    in Earth that has no end of breadth and length.
Nay, but our children in our midst, what else
    but our hearts are they, walking on the ground?
If but the breeze blow harsh on one of them,
    mine eye says no to slumber all night long.

(Sir Charles Lyall)

Ibn Darrâj Al-Andalûsi
11th century

THE WING OF SEPARATION

THE wing of separation
Bore me away;
The fluttering heart was dismayed
And bore away her senses . . .
Had she but seen me,
When my soul was intent on speeding the journey by
    night,
When my sounding steps
Held converse with the demons of the desert—
When I wandered through the waste

In the shadows of night,
While the roar of the lion was heard
From his lair among the reeds—
When the brilliant Pleiades circled,
Like dark-eyed maidens in the green woods;
And the stars were borne round
Like wine-cups,
Filled by a fair maid
And served by a watchful attendant—
When the Milky Way
Was as the gray hairs of age
Upon the head of gloomy night;
And the ardor of my resolution,
And the piercer of darkness
Were equally terrible;
When the eyelids of the stars
Were closed for weariness—
Ah, then she had known
That fate itself obeyed my will
And that I was worthy of the favor of Ibn Aâmir.

(J. B. Trend)

Mu'tamid, King of Seville

1040–1095

For though his sun of power went down so long ago
that the West has forgotten the colors of his glory, and
though the kingdom for which he gave his blood and
his children and the years of his life now bows to other
rulers, another faith, yet among a beauty-loving race he
still preserves—by reason of those lines which wars have
not scattered nor Time effaced—a gentle eminence.—
DULCIE L. SMITH.

THE FOUNTAIN

THE sea hath tempered it; the mighty sun
Polished the blade,
And from the limpid sheath the sword leaps forth;
Man hath not made
A better in Damascus—though for slaughter
Hath steel somewhat advantage over water.

WOO NOT THE WORLD

Woo not the world too rashly, for behold,
  Beneath the painted silk and broidering,
  It is a faithless and inconstant thing.
(Listen to me, Mu'tamid, growing old.)

And we—that dreamed youth's blade would never
    rust,
  Hoped wells from the mirage, roses from the sand—
  The riddle of the world shall understand
And put on wisdom with the robe of dust.

(Dulcie L. Smith)

From the Thousand and One Nights

13th century ?

DATES

WE grow to the sound of the wind
Playing his flutes in our hair,

Palm tree daughters,
Brown flesh Bedouin,
Fed with light
By our gold father;

We are loved of the free-tented,
The sons of space, the hall-forgetters,
The wide handed, the bright-sworded
Masters of horses.

Who has rested in the shade of our palms
Shall hear us murmur ever above his sleep.

PSALM OF BATTLE

GOD is praise and glory;
Therefore glory and praise be unto Him
Who led me by the hand in stony places,
Who gave me a treasure of gold and a throne of gold
And set a sword of victory in my hand!

He covered the earth with the shadow of my kingdom,
And fed me when I was a stranger
Among strange peoples;
When I was lowly He accounted me
And He has bound my brow about with triumph.

His enemies fled before my face like cattle;
The Lord breathed upon them and they were not!
Not with the ferment of a generous wine
But with death's evil grape
He has sent them drunken into the darkness.

We died, we died in the battle,
But He has set us upon happy grass
Beside an eternal river of scented honey.

DEATH

ONCE he will miss, twice he will miss,
  He only chooses one of many hours;
For him nor deep nor hill there is,
  But all's one level plain he hunts for flowers.

LAMENTS

The Wazir Dandan for Prince Sharkan

WISE to have gone so early to reward,
  Child of the sword;
Wise with a single new-bathed eagle's flight
  To have touched the white
Wild roses spread for feet in paradise.
  Ah, my son, wise
Soon to have drained the new and bitter cup
  Which, once drunk up,
Leads straightway to an old immortal wine
  Pressed from God's vine.

Tumadir Al-Khansa for her Brother

WEEP! Weep! Weep!
These tears are for my brother,

Henceforth that veil which lies between us,
That recent earth,
Shall not be lifted again.
You have gone down to the bitter water
Which all must taste,
And you went pure, saying:
"Life is a buzz of hornets about a lance point."

But my heart remembers, O son of my father and
    mother,
I wither like summer grass,
I shut myself in the tent of consternation.

He is dead, who was the buckler of our tribe
And the foundation of our house,
He has departed in calamity.

He is dead, who was the lighthouse of courageous men,
Who was for the brave
As fires lighted upon the mountains.

He is dead, who rode costly horses,
Shining in his garments.
The hero of the long shoulder belt is dead.
The young man of valiance and beauty breathes no
    more;
The right hand of generosity is withered,
And the beardless king of our tribe shall breathe no
    more.

He shall be cold beneath his rock.

Say to his mare Alwa
That she must weep
As she runs riderless for ever. . . .

When the red millstone ground the flowers of youth,
You shattered a thousand horses against the squadrons;

High on the groaning flanks of Alwa
You lifted the bright skirts of your silver mail.

You made the lances live,
You shook their beams,
You quenched their beams in red,
O tiger of the double panoply.

White women wandered with disordered veils
And you saved them in the morning.
Your captives were as troops of antelopes
Whose beauty troubles the first drops of rain. . . .

How effortless were your rhymes of combat
Chanted in tumult, O my brother!
They pierced like lances,
They live among our hearts for ever.

Let the stars go out,
Let the sun withdraw his rays,
He was our star and sun.

Who now will gather in the strangers at dusk
When the sad North whistles with her winds?
You have laid down and left in the dust, O wanderers,
Him who nourished you with his flocks
And bared his sword for your salvation.
You set him low in the terrible house
Among a few stakes planted,
You threw down boughs of salamah upon him.
He lies among the tombs of our fathers,
Where the days and the years shall pass over him
As they have passed over our fathers.
Your loss is a great distress to me,
Child of the Solamides,
I shall be glad no more. . . .

While you have tears, O daughters of the Solomides,
Weep! Weep! Weep!

From the Arabic

THE DAYS OF OUR YOUTH

These are the days of our youth, our days of glory and
    honor.
  Pleasure begotten of strength is ours, the sword in
    our hand.
Wisdom bends to our will, we lead captivity captive,
  Kings of our lives and love, receiving gifts from men.

Why do I speak of wisdom? The prize is not for the
    wisest.
  Reason, the dull ox, plows a soil which no joy shall
    reap.
Folly is fleeter far 'neath the heel of the fearless rider,
  Folly the bare-backed steed we bestride, the steed of
    the plains.

Mine is a lofty ambition, as wide as the world I covet.
  Vast is the empire I claim for thee, thou spouse of my
    soul.
Show me new lands to win, and, by God in heaven, I
    swear it:
  These shall be mine and thine to-night for all time
    to hold.

Time is our slave and Fortune's. We need not years for
    fruition.
  Here in our hands behold a key which unlocks the
    world.
Each new day is a life. For us there is no to-morrow.
  Love no yesterday knows nor we, but to-day is ours.

See, what a wealth I bring thee, what treasure of myrrh
    and spices!
  Every kingdom of Earth have I sacked to procure
    thee gold.
All the knowledge that fools have learned at the feet of
    women,
  All that the wise have been taught in tears for thy
    sake I know.

Give thyself up to Love. There is naught divine but
  madness.
  Give thyself up to me Love's priest in his inmost
    shrine.
Shut thy eyes on the world, sublime in thy abnegation.
  Only the wise who have bowed their will shall receive
    the prize.

Shut thy eyes on the light. I have nobler dreams to read
  thee,
  Here in the shades of this darkened room, than the
    sun can show.
Is there not light in my eyes to-night more light than
  the dreamlight?
  See it breaks in streams on thy face; it illumes thy
    soul.

Let me persuade thy weakness. I see thee here with my
  reason.
  Let me convince thee of love with thy lips till thou
    cease to think.
Let me enfold thee with words more sweet than the
  prayers of angels,
  Speaking thus with my hand on thy heart till it cease
    to beat.

Let me assuage thy grief with laughter, thy fear with
  kisses.
  Let me cajole thy doubts with surprise, thy pride with
    tears.
Let me outshame the shame of thy face, outblush thy
  blushes.
  Let me teach thee what Love can dare and yet dream
    no shame.

Let me uncover thy bosom and prove to thee its glory.
  Let me preach to thee of thyself the live night long.
Let me chant new hymns to thy praise as I kneel and
  worship,
  Rising still like a god from my knees from eve till
    morn.

Let me discourse of love with my hands and lips and
    bosom.
  Let me explain with my limbs the joy that a soul can
  feel.
Let me unveil to thy bodily sense thy god incarnate
  Taking flesh in a visible form for thy body's need.

Lo, on the mount of Love, the holiest place of holies,
  Incense and prayer and the people's shout and the fires
  have risen.
Love descends on the feast. He mounts the pyre in
  silence,
  Victim and priest and god in one, to thy dreams
  revealed.

There, the rite is accomplished. Whatever Love knows
  thou knowest.
  Sudden the victim staggers and falls. In the dust
  it lies.
See the hot blood flows for thy sake, it o'erflows the altar.
  Dost thou not feel it stream in thy veins? It still lives
  in thee.

These are the days of our youth, the days of our
  dominion.
  All the rest is a dream of death and a doubtful thing.
Here we at least have lived, for love is all life's wisdom,
  Joy of joys for an hour to-day; then away, farewell!

(*Wilfrid Scawen Blunt*)

PERSIAN

Firdawsí

935–1025

ALAS FOR YOUTH

Much have I labored, much read o'er
Of Arabic and Persian lore,
Collecting tales unknown and known;
Now two and sixty years are flown.
Regret, and deeper woe of sin,
'Tis all that youth has ended in,
And I with mournful thoughts rehearse
Bu Táhir Khusrawáni's verse:
"I mind me of my youth and sigh,
Alas for youth, for youth gone by!"

(R. A. Nicholson)

Omar Khayyám

d. 1123

And this, I think, especially distinguishes Omar from all
other Persian poets: That, whereas with them the Poet
is lost in his Song, the Man in Allegory and Abstrac-
tion; we seem to have the Man—the *Bonhomme*—Omar
himself, with all his humors and passions, as frankly before us as if we were really at Table with him, after the
Wine had gone round.—Edward FitzGerald.

RUBAIYAT

(in part)

I

Wake! For the Sun, who scattered into flight
The Stars before him from the Field of Night,
  Drives Night along with them from Heaven, and
    strikes
The Sultàn's Turret with a Shaft of Light.

II

Before the phantom of False morning died,
Methought a Voice within the Tavern cried,
  "When all the Temple is prepared within,
Why nods the drowsy Worshiper outside?"

III

And, as the Cock crew, those who stood before
The Tavern shouted—"Open then the Door!
  You know how little while we have to stay,
And, once departed, may return no more."

VII

Come, fill the Cup, and in the fire of Spring
Your Winter-garment of Repentance fling:
  The Bird of Time has but a little way
To flutter—and the Bird is on the Wing.

VIII

Whether at Naishápúr or Babylon,
Whether the Cup with sweet or bitter run,
  The Wine of Life keeps oozing drop by drop,
The Leaves of Life keep falling one by one.

IX

Each Morn a thousand Roses brings, you say:
Yes, but where leaves the Rose of Yesterday?
  And this first Summer month that brings the Rose
Shall take Jamshyd and Kaikobád away.

X

Well, let it take them! What have we to do
With Kaikobád the Great, or Kaikhosrú?
  Let Zál and Rustum bluster as they will,
Or Hátim call to Supper—heed not you.

XI

With me along the strip of Herbage strown
That just divides the desert from the sown,
    Where name of Slave and Sultán is forgot—
And Peace to Mahmúd on his golden Throne!

✗ XII

A Book of Verses underneath the Bough,
A jug of Wine, a Loaf of Bread—and Thou
    Beside me singing in the Wilderness—
Oh, Wilderness were Paradise enow!

XIII

Some for the Glories of This World; and some
Sigh for the Prophet's Paradise to come;
    Ah, take the Cash, and let the Credit go,
Nor heed the rumble of a distant Drum!

XIV

Look to the blowing Rose about us—"Lo,
Laughing," she says, "into the world I blow,
    At once the silken tassel of my Purse
Tear, and its Treasure on the Garden throw."

XVIII

They say the Lion and the Lizard keep
The Courts where Jamshyd gloried and drank deep
    And Bahrám, that great Hunter—the Wild Ass
Stamps o'er his Head, but cannot break his Sleep.

XIX

I sometimes think that never blows so red
The Rose as where some buried Cæsar bled;
    That every Hyacinth the Garden wears
Dropt in her Lap from some once lovely Head.

xx

And this reviving Herb whose tender Green
Fledges the River-Lip on which we lean—
   Ah, lean upon it lightly! for who knows
From what once lovely Lip it springs unseen!

✗ xxi

Ah, my Belovèd, fill the Cup that clears
To-DAY of paſt Regrets and future Fears:
   To-morrow!—Why To-morrow I may be
Myself with Yeſterday's Seven thousand Years.

xxii

For some we loved, the lovelieſt and the beſt
That from his Vintage rolling Time hath preſt,
   Have drunk their Cup a Round or two before,
And one by one crept silently to reſt.

xxiii

And we, that now make merry in the Room
They left, and Summer dresses in new bloom,
   Ourselves muſt we beneath the Couch of Earth
Descend—ourselves to make a Couch—for whom?

xxiv

Ah, make the moſt of what we yet may spend,
Before we too into the Duſt descend;
   Duſt into Duſt, and under Duſt to lie,
Sans Wine, sans Song, sans Singer, and—sans End!

xxix

Into this Universe, and *Why* not knowing
Nor *Whence,* like Water willy-nilly flowing;
   And out of it, as Wind along the Waſte,
I know not *Whither,* willy-nilly blowing.

XXX

What, without asking, hither hurried *Whence?*
And, without asking, *Whither* hurried hence?
 Oh, many a Cup of this forbidden Wine
Muſt drown the memory of that insolence!

XXXI

Up from Earth's Center through the Seventh Gate
I rose, and on the Throne of Saturn sate,
 And many a Knot unraveled by the Road;
But not the Maſter-knot of Human Fate.

XXXII

There was the Door to which I found no Key;
There was the Veil through which I might not see;
 Some little talk awhile of ME and THEE
There was—and then no more of THEE and ME.

XLIV

Why, if the Soul can fling the Duſt aside,
And naked on the Air of Heaven ride,
 Were 't not a Shame—were 't not a Shame for him
In this clay carcase crippled to abide?

XLV

'Tis but a Tent where takes his one day's reſt
A Sultán to the realm of Death addreſt;
 The Sultán rises, and the dark Ferrásh
Strikes, and prepares it for another Gueſt.

LIV

Waſte not your Hour, nor in the vain pursuit
Of This and That endeavor and dispute;
 Better be jocund with the fruitful Grape
Than sadden after none, or bitter, Fruit.

LV

You know, my Friends, with what a brave Carouse
I made a Second Marriage in my house;
 Divorced old barren Reason from my Bed,
And took the Daughter of the Vine to Spouse.

LVI

For "Is" and "Is-not" though with Rule and Line,
And "Up-and-down" by Logic I define,
 Of all that one should care to fathom, I
Was never deep in anything but—Wine.

LXIII

Oh, threats of Hell and Hopes of Paradise!
One thing at least is certain—*This* Life flies;
 One thing is certain and the rest is Lies;
The Flower that once has blown for ever dies.

LXIV

Strange, is it not? that of the myriads who
Before us passed the door of Darkness through,
 Not one returns to tell us of the Road,
Which to discover we must travel too.

LXV

The Revelations of Devout and Learned
Who rose before us, and as Prophets burned,
 Are all but Stories, which, awoke from Sleep
They told their comrades, and to Sleep returned.

LXVI

I sent my Soul through the Invisible,
Some letter of that After-life to spell:
 And by and by my Soul returned to me,
And answered "I Myself am Heaven and Hell:"

LXVII

Heaven but the Vision of fulfilled Desire,
And Hell the Shadow from a Soul on fire,
    Cast on the Darkness into which Ourselves,
So late emerged from shall so soon expire.

LXVIII

We are no other than a moving row
Of Magic Shadow-shapes that come and go
    Round with the Sun-illumined Lantern held
In Midnight by the Master of the Show;

LXIX

But helpless Pieces of the Game He plays
Upon this Chequer-board of Nights and Days;
    Hither and thither moves, and checks, and slays,
And one by one back in the closet lays.

LXXI

The Moving Finger writes; and, having writ,
Moves on: nor all your Piety nor Wit
    Shall lure it back to cancel half a Line,
Nor all your Tears wash out a Word of it.

LXXII

And that inverted Bowl they call the Sky,
Whereunder crawling cooped we live and die,
    Lift not your hands to *It* for help—for It
As impotently moves as you or I.

XCI

Ah, with the Grape my fading Life provide,
And wash the Body whence the Life has died,
    And lay me, shrouded in the living Leaf,
By some not unfrequented Gardenside

XCII

That even my buried Ashes such a snare
Of Vintage shall fling up into the Air
    As not a True-believer passing by
But shall be overtaken unaware.

XCIII

Indeed the Idols I have loved so long
Have done my credit in this World much wrong:
    Have drowned my Glory in a shallow Cup,
And sold my Reputation for a Song.

XCVI

Yet Ah, that Spring should vanish with the Rose!
That Youth's sweet-scented manuscript should close!
    The Nightingale that in the branches sang,
Ah whence, and whither flown again, who knows!

XCVII

Would but the Desert of the Fountain yield
One glimpse—if dimly, yet indeed, revealed,
    To which the fainting Traveler might spring,
As springs the trampled herbage of the field!

XCVIII

Would but some wingéd Angel ere too late
Arreſt the yet unfolded Roll of Fate,
    And make the ſtern Recorder otherwise
Enregiſter, or quite obliterate!

✗ XCIX

Ah Love! could you and I with Him conspire
To grasp this sorry Scheme of Things Entire,
    Would not we shatter it to bits—and then
Re-mold it nearer to the Heart's Desire!

* * * * * * * *

c

Yon rising Moon that looks for us again—
How oft hereafter will she wax and wane;
  How oft hereafter rising look for us
Through this same Garden—and for *one* in vain!

CI

And when like her, Oh Sáki, you shall pass
Among the Guests Star-scattered on the Grass,
  And in your joyous errand reach the spot
Where I made One—turn down an empty Glass!

(*Edward FitzGerald*)

Sa'di

d. 1291

FROM THE GULISTAN

Sadi's favorite mode is a simplicity and tenderness of
heart, a delicacy of feeling and judgment, and that
exquisitely natural vein in which he relates his many
apologues and parables with a sort of sententious and
epigrammatic turn.—JAMES ROSS.

FRIENDSHIP

HE is no friend who in thine hour of pride
Brags of his love and calls himself thy kin.
He is a friend who hales his fellow in,
And clangs the door upon the wolf outside.

MESNEVI

IF livelihood by knowledge were endowed,
None would be poorer than the brainless crowd;
Yet fortune on the fool bestows the prize,
And leaves but themes for wonder to the wise.

The luck of wealth dependeth not on skill,
But only on the aid of Heaven's will:
So it has happened since the world began—
The witless ape outstrips the learned man;

A poet dies of hunger, grief, and cold;
A fool among the ruins findeth gold.

Courage

Whoever hath washed his hands of living
Utters his mind without misgiving.

In straits which no escape afford
The hand takes hold of the edge of the sword.

Help

Vex no man's secret soul—if that can be—
  The path of life hath far too many a thorn!
Help whom thou may'st—for surely unto thee
  Sharp need of help will e'er the end be borne.

(Sir Edwin Arnold)

FROM THE BUSTAN

The Dancer

I heard how, to the beat of some quick tune,
There rose and danced a Damsel like the moon,
  Flower-mouthed and Pâri-faced; and all around her
Neck-stretching Lovers gathered close; but, soon

A flickering lamp-flame caught her skirt, and set
Fire to the flying gauze. Fear did beget
  Trouble in that light heart! She cried amain.
Quoth one among her worshipers, "Why fret,

Tulip of Love? Th' extinguished fire hath burned
Only one leaf of thee; but I am turned
  To ashes—leaf and stalk, and flower and root—
By lamp-flash of thine eyes!"—"Ah, Soul concerned

"Solely with self!"—she answered, laughing low,
"If thou wert Lover thou hadst not said so.
  Who speaks of the Belov'd's woe as not his
Speaks infidelity, true Lovers know!"

(Sir Edwin Arnold)

Hafiz

d. 1389

Hafiz is the prince of Persian poets, and in his extraordinary gifts adds to some of the attributes of Pindar, Anacreon, Horace, and Burns the insight of a mystic. —RALPH WALDO EMERSON.

ODES

6

THE jewel of the secret treasury
Is still the same as once it was; the seal
Upon Love's treasure casket, and the key,
Are still what thieves can neither break nor steal;
Still among lovers loyalty is found,
And therefore faithful eyes still strew the ground
With the same pearls that mine once strewed for thee.

Question the wandering winds and thou shalt know
That from the dusk until the dawn doth break,
My consolation is that still they blow
The perfume of thy curls across my cheek,
A dart from thy bent brows has wounded me—
Ah, come! my heart still waiteth helplessly,
Has waited ever, till thou heal its pain.

If seekers after rubies there were none,
Still to the dark mines where the gems had lain
Would pierce, as he was wont, the radiant sun,
Setting the stones ablaze. Would'st hide the stain
Of my heart's blood? Blood-red the ruby glows
(And whence it came my wounded bosom knows)
Upon thy lips to show what thou hast done.

Let not thy curls waylay my pilgrim soul,
As robbers use, and plunder me no more!
Years join dead years, but thine extortionate rule
Is still the same, merciless as before.
Sing, Hafiz, sing again of eyes that weep!
For still the fountain of our tears is deep
As once it was, and still with tears is full.

(*Gertrude Lowthian Bell*)

10

THE days of Spring are here! the eglantine,
The rose, the tulip from the dust have risen—
And thou, why liest thou beneath the dust?
Like the full clouds of Spring, these eyes of mine
Shall scatter tears upon the grave thy prison,
Till thou too from the earth thine head shalt thrust.

(Gertrude Lowthian Bell)

11

I HAVE borne the anguish of love, which ask me not
to describe:
I have tasted the poison of absence, which ask me not
to relate.

Far through the world have I roved, and at length
I have chosen
A sweet creature (a ravisher of hearts), whose name ask
me not to disclose.

The flowing of my tears bedews her footsteps
In such a manner as ask me not to utter.

On yesternight from her own mouth with my own ears
I heard
Such words as pray ask me not to repeat.

Why dost thou bite thy lip at me? What dost thou not
hint (*that I may have told?*)
I have devoured a lip like a ruby: but whose, ask me not
to mention.

Absent from thee, and the sole tenant of my cottage,
I have endured such tortures, as ask me not to
enumerate.

Thus am I, HAFIZ, arrived at extremity in the ways of
Love,
Which, alas! ask me not to explain.

(John Hindley)

HEBREW

From the Old Testament

THE BOOK OF PSALMS

PSALM 1

BLESSED is the man that walketh not in the counsel of the ungodly, nor standeth in the way of sinners, nor sitteth in the seat of the scornful.

But his delight is in the law of the Lord; and in his law doth he meditate day and night.

And he shall be like a tree planted by the rivers of water, that bringeth forth his fruit in his season; his leaf also shall not wither; and whatsoever he doeth shall prosper.

The ungodly are not so; but are like the chaff which the wind driveth away.

Therefore the ungodly shall not stand in the judgment, nor sinners in the congregation of the righteous.

For the Lord knoweth the way of the righteous: but the way of the ungodly shall perish.

PSALM 8

O LORD our Lord, how excellent is thy name in all the earth! who hast set thy glory above the heavens.

Out of the mouth of babes and sucklings hast thou ordained strength because of thine enemies, that thou mightest still the enemy and the avenger.

When I consider thy heavens, the work of thy fingers, the moon and the stars, which thou hast ordained;

What is man, that thou art mindful of him? and the son of man, that thou visitest him?

For thou hast made him a little lower than the angels, and hast crowned him with glory and honor.

Thou madeſt him to have dominion over the works of thy hands; thou haſt put all things under his feet:

All sheep and oxen, yea, and the beaſts of the field;

The fowl of the air, and the fish of the sea, and whatsoever passeth through the paths of the seas.

O Lord our Lord, how excellent is thy name in all the earth!

PSALM 19

THE heavens declare the glory of God; and the firmament sheweth his handywork.

Day unto day uttereth speech, and night unto night sheweth knowledge.

There is no speech nor language, where their voice is not heard.

Their line is gone out through all the earth, and their words to the end of the world. In them hath he set a tabernacle for the sun,

Which is as a bridegroom coming out of his chamber, and rejoiceth as a ſtrong man to run a race.

His going forth is from the end of the heaven, and his circuit unto the ends of it; and there is nothing hid from the heat thereof.

The law of the Lord is perfeĉt, converting the soul: the teſtimony of the Lord is sure, making wise the simple.

The ſtatutes of the Lord are right, rejoicing the heart: the commandment of the Lord is pure, enlightening the eyes.

The fear of the Lord is clean, enduring for ever: the judgments of the Lord are true and righteous altogether.

More to be desired are they than gold, yea, than much fine gold: sweeter also than honey and the honeycomb.

Moreover by them is thy servant warned: and in keeping of them there is great reward.

Who can underſtand his errors? cleanse thou me from secret faults.

Keep back thy servant also from presumptuous sins; let them not have dominion over me: then shall I be

upright, and I shall be innocent from the great transgression.

Let the words of my mouth, and the meditation of
my heart, be acceptable in thy sight, O Lord, my strength,
and my redeemer.

PSALM 23

THE Lord is my shepherd; I shall not want.

He maketh me to lie down in green pastures: he
leadeth me beside the still waters.

He restoreth my soul: he leadeth me in the paths of
righteousness for his name's sake.

Yea, though I walk through the valley of the shadow
of death, I will fear no evil: for thou art with me; thy
rod and thy staff they comfort me.

Thou preparest a table before me in the presence of
mine enemies; thou anointest my head with oil; my cup
runneth over.

Surely goodness and mercy shall follow me all the
days of my life: and I will dwell in the house of the
Lord for ever.

PSALM 24

THE earth is the Lord's, and the fullness thereof; the
world, and they that dwell therein.

For he hath founded it upon the seas, and established
it upon the floods.

Who shall ascend into the hill of the Lord? or who
shall stand in his holy place?

He that hath clean hands, and a pure heart; who hath
not lifted up his soul unto vanity, nor sworn de-
ceitfully.

He shall receive the blessing from the Lord, and
righteousness from the God of his salvation.

This is the generation of them that seek him, that
seek thy face, O Jacob.

Lift up your heads, O ye gates; and be ye lift up,
ye everlasting doors; and the King of glory shall come
in.

Who is this King of glory? The Lord strong and mighty, the Lord mighty in battle.

Lift up your heads, O ye gates; even lift them up, ye everlasting doors; and the King of glory shall come in.

Who is this King of glory? The Lord of hosts, he is the King of glory.

Psalm 42

As the hart panteth after the water brooks, so panteth my soul after thee, O God.

My soul thirsteth for God, for the living God: when shall I come and appear before God?

My tears have been my meat day and night, while they continually say unto me, Where is thy God?

When I remember these things, I pour out my soul in me: for I had gone with the multitude, I went with them to the house of God, with the voice of joy and praise, with a multitude that kept holyday.

Why are thou cast down, O my soul? and why art thou disquieted in me? hope thou in God: for I shall yet praise him for the help of his countenance.

O my God, my soul is cast down within me: therefore will I remember thee from the land of Jordan, and of the Hermonites, from the hill Mizar.

Deep calleth unto deep at the noise of thy water-spouts: all thy waves and thy billows are gone over me.

Yet the Lord will command his loving kindness in the daytime, and in the night his song shall be with me, and my prayer unto the God of my life.

I will say unto God my rock, Why hast thou forgotten me? why go I mourning because of the oppression of the enemy?

As with a sword in my bones, mine enemies reproach me; while they say daily unto me, Where is thy God?

Why art thou cast down, O my soul? and why art thou disquieted within me? hope thou in God: for I shall yet praise him, who is the health of my countenance, and my God.

Psalm 95

O come, let us sing unto the Lord: let us make a joyful noise to the rock of our salvation.

Let us come before his presence with thanksgiving, and make a joyful noise unto him with psalms.

For the Lord is a great God, and a great King above all gods.

In his hand are the deep places of the earth: the strength of the hills is his also.

The sea is his, and he made it: and his hands formed the dry land.

O come, let us worship, and bow down: let us kneel before the Lord our maker.

For he is our God; and we are the people of his pasture, and the sheep of his hand. To-day if ye will hear his voice,

Harden not your heart, as in the provocation, and as in the day of temptation in the wilderness:

When your fathers tempted me, proved me, and saw my work.

Forty years long was I grieved with this generation, and said, It is a people that do err in their heart, and they have not known my ways:

Unto whom I swear in my wrath that they should not enter into my rest.

Psalm 103

Bless the Lord, O my soul: and all that is within me, bless his holy name.

Bless the Lord, O my soul, and forget not all his benefits.

Who forgiveth all thine iniquities; who healeth all thy diseases;

Who redeemeth thy life from destruction; who crowneth thee with loving kindness and tender mercies;

Who satisfieth thy mouth with good things; so that thy youth is renewed like the eagle's.

The Lord executeth righteousness and judgment for all that are oppressed.

He made known his ways unto Moses, his acts unto the children of Israel.

The Lord is merciful and gracious, slow to anger, and plenteous in mercy.

He will not always chide: neither will he keep his anger for ever.

He hath not dealt with us after our sins; nor rewarded us according to our iniquities.

For as the heaven is high above the earth, so great is his mercy towards them that fear him.

As far as the east is from the west, so far hath he removed our transgressions from us.

Like as a father pitieth his children, so the Lord pitieth them that fear him.

For he knoweth our frame; he remembereth that we are dust.

As for man, his days are as grass: as a flower of the field, so he flourisheth.

For the wind passeth over it, and it is gone; and the place thereof shall know it no more.

But the mercy of the Lord is from everlasting to everlasting upon them that fear him, and his righteousness unto children's children.

To such as keep his covenant, and to those that remember his commandments to do them,

The Lord hath prepared his throne in the heavens; and his kingdom ruleth over all.

Bless the Lord, ye his angels, that excel in strength, that do his commandments, hearkening unto the voice of his word.

Bless ye the Lord, all ye his hosts; ye ministers of his, that do his pleasure.

Bless the Lord, all his works in all places of his dominion: bless the Lord, O my soul.

PSALM 121

I WILL lift up mine eyes unto the hills, from whence cometh my help.

My help cometh from the Lord, which made heaven and earth.

He will not suffer thy foot to be moved: he that keepeth thee will not slumber.

Behold, he that keepeth Israel shall neither slumber nor sleep.

The Lord is thy keeper: the Lord is thy shade upon thy right hand.

The sun shall not smite thee by day, nor the moon by night.

The Lord shall preserve thee from all evil: he shall preserve thy soul.

The Lord shall preserve thy going out and thy coming in from this time forth, and even for evermore.

Psalm 133

Behold, how good and how pleasant it is for brethren to dwell together in unity!

It is like the precious ointment upon the head, that ran down upon the beard, even Aaron's beard: that went down to the skirts of his garments;

As the dew of Hermon, and as the dew that descended upon the mountains of Zion: for there the Lord commanded the blessing, even life for evermore.

Psalm 137

By the rivers of Babylon, there we sat down, yea, we wept, when we remembered Zion.

We hanged our harps upon the willows in the midst thereof.

For there they that carried us away captive required of us a song; and they that wasted us required of us mirth, saying, Sing us one of the songs of Zion.

How shall we sing the Lord's song in a strange land?

If I forget thee, O Jerusalem, let my right hand forget her cunning.

If I do not remember thee, let my tongue cleave to

the roof of my mouth: if I prefer not Jerusalem above my chief joy.

Remember, O Lord, the children of Edom in the day of Jerusalem; who said, Rase it, rase it, even to the foundation thereof.

O daughter of Babylon, who art to be destroyed: happy shall he be, that rewardeth thee as thou hast served us.

Happy shall he be, that taketh and dasheth thy little ones against the stones.

THE BOOK OF JOB

Job's Curse

Let the day perish wherein I was born, and the night in which it was said, There is a man child conceived.

Let that day be darkness; let not God regard it from above, neither let the light shine upon it.

Let darkness and the shadow of death stain it; let a cloud dwell upon it; let the blackness of the day terrify it.

As for that night, let darkness seize upon it; let it not be joined unto the days of the year, let it not come into the number of the months.

Lo, let that night be solitary, let no joyful voice come therein.

Let them curse it that curse the day, who are ready to raise up their mourning.

Let the stars of the twilight thereof be dark; let it look for light, but have none; neither let it see the dawning of the day:

Because it shut not up the doors of my mother's womb, nor hid sorrow from mine eyes.

Why died I not from the womb? why did I not give up the ghost when I came out of the belly?

Why did the knees prevent me? or why the breasts that I should suck?

For now should I have lain still and been quiet, I should have slept: then had I been at rest

With kings and counsellors of the earth, which built desolate places for themselves;

Or with princes that had gold, who filled their houses with silver:

Or as an hidden untimely birth I had not been; as infants which never saw light.

There the wicked cease from troubling; and there the weary be at rest.

There the prisoners rest together; they hear not the voice of the oppressor.

The small and great are there; and the servant is free from his master.

Wherefore is light given to him that is in misery, and life unto the bitter in soul;

Which long for death, but it cometh not; and dig for it more than for hid treasures;

Which rejoice exceedingly, and are glad, when they can find the grave?

Why is light given to a man whose way is hid, and whom God hath hedged in?

For my sighing cometh before I eat, and my roarings are poured out like the waters.

For the thing which I greatly feared is come upon me, and that which I was afraid of is come unto me.

I was not in safety, neither had I rest, neither was I quiet; yet trouble came.

Job's Entreaty

Man that is born of a woman is of few days, and full of trouble.

He cometh forth like a flower, and is cut down: he fleeth also as a shadow, and continueth not.

And dost thou open thine eyes upon such an one, and bringest me into judgment with thee?

Who can bring a clean thing out of an unclean? not one.

Seeing his days are determined, the number of his months are with thee, thou hast appointed his bounds that he cannot pass;

Turn from him, that he may rest, till he shall accomplish, as an hireling, his day.

For there is hope of a tree, if it be cut down, that it will sprout again, and that the tender branch thereof will not cease.

Though the root thereof wax old in the earth, and the stock thereof die in the ground;

Yet through the scent of water it will bud, and bring forth boughs like a plant.

But man dieth, and wasteth away: yea, man giveth up the ghost, and where is he?

As the waters fail from the sea, and the flood decayeth and drieth up:

So man lieth down, and riseth not: till the heavens be no more, they shall not awake, nor be raised out of their sleep.

O that thou wouldest hide me in the grave, that thou wouldest keep me secret, until thy wrath be past, that thou wouldest appoint me a set time, and remember me!

If a man die, shall he live again? all the days of my appointed time will I wait, till my change come.

Thou shalt call, and I will answer thee: thou wilt have a desire to the work of thine hands.

For now thou numberest my steps: dost thou not watch over my sin?

My transgression is sealed up in a bag, and thou sewest up mine iniquity.

And surely the mountain falling cometh to nought, and the rock is removed out of his place.

The waters wear the stones: thou washest away the things which grow out of the dust of the earth: and thou destroyest the hope of man.

Thou prevailest for ever against him, and he passeth: thou changest his countenance, and sendest him away.

His sons come to honor, and he knoweth it not; and they are brought low, but he perceiveth it not of them.

But his flesh upon him shall have pain, and his soul within him shall mourn.

Then the Lord Answered

Who is this that darkeneth counsel by words without knowledge?

Gird up now thy loins like a man; for I will demand of thee, and answer thou me.

Where wast thou when I laid the foundations of the earth? declare, if thou hast understanding.

Who hath laid the measures thereof, if thou knowest? or who hath stretched the line upon it?

Whereupon are the foundations thereof fastened? or who laid the corner stone thereof;

When the morning stars sang together, and all the sons of God shouted for joy?

Or who shut up the sea with doors, when it brake forth, as if it had issued out of the womb?

When I made the cloud the garment thereof, and thick darkness a swaddling band for it,

And brake up for it my decreed place, and set bars and doors,

And said, Hitherto shalt thou come, but no further: and here shall thy proud waves be stayed?

Hast thou commanded the morning since thy days; and caused the dayspring to know his place;

That it might take hold of the ends of the earth, that the wicked might be shaken out of it?

It is turned as clay to the seal; and they stand as a garment.

And from the wicked their light is withholden, and the high arm shall be broken.

Hast thou entered into the springs of the sea? or hast thou walked in the search of the depth?

Have the gates of death been opened unto thee? or hast thou seen the doors of the shadow of death?

Hast thou perceived the breadth of the earth; declare if thou knowest it all.

Where is the way where light dwelleth? and as for darkness, where is the place thereof.

That thou shouldest take it to the bound thereof,

and that thou shouldest know the paths to the house thereof?

Knowest thou it, because thou wast then born? or because the number of thy days is great?

Hast thou entered into the treasures of the snow? or hast thou seen the treasures of the hail,

Which I have reserved against the time of trouble, against the day of battle and war?

By what way is the light parted, which scattereth the east wind upon the earth?

Knowest thou the time when the wild goats of the rock bring forth? or canst thou mark when the hinds do calve?

Canst thou number the months that they fulfill? or knowest thou the time when they bring forth?

They bow themselves, they bring forth their young ones, they cast out their sorrows.

Their young ones are in good liking, they grow up with corn; they go forth, and return not unto them.

Who hath sent out the wild ass free? or who hath loosed the bands of the wild ass?

Whose house I have made the wilderness, and the barren land his dwellings.

He scorneth the multitude of the city, neither regardeth he the crying of the driver.

The range of the mountains is his pasture, and he searcheth after every green thing.

Will the unicorn be willing to serve thee, or abide by the crib?

Canst thou bind the unicorn with his band in the furrow? or will he harrow the valleys after thee?

Wilt thou trust him, because his strength is great? or wilt thou leave thy labor to him?

Wilt thou believe him, that he will bring home thy seed, and gather it into thy barn?

Gavest thou the goodly wings unto the peacocks? or wings and feathers unto the ostrich?

Which leaveth her eggs in the earth, and warmeth them in dust,

And forgetteth that the foot may crush them, or that the wild beast may break them.

She is hardened against her young ones, as though they were not hers: her labor is in vain without fear:

Because God hath deprived her of wisdom, neither hath he imparted to her understanding.

What time she lifteth up herself on high, she scorneth the horse and his rider.

Hast thou given the horse strength? hast thou clothed his neck with thunder?

Canst thou make him afraid as a grasshopper? the glory of his nostrils is terrible.

He paweth in the valley, and rejoiceth in his strength: he goeth on to meet the armed men.

He mocketh at fear, and is not affrighted; neither turneth he back from the sword.

The quiver rattleth against him, the glittering spear and the shield.

He swalloweth the ground with fierceness and rage: neither believeth he that it is the sound of the trumpet.

He saith among the trumpets, Ha, ha; and he smelleth the battle afar off, the thunder of the captains, and the shouting.

Doth the hawk fly by thy wisdom, and stretch her wings toward the south?

Doth the eagle mount up at thy command, and make her nest on high?

She dwelleth and abideth on the rock, upon the crag of the rock, and the strong place.

From thence she seeketh the prey, and her eyes behold afar off.

Her young ones also suck up blood: and where the slain are, there is she.

Out of the Whirlwind

Gird up thy loins now like a man: I will demand of thee, and declare thou unto me.

Wilt thou also disannul my judgment? wilt thou condemn me, that thou mayest be righteous?

Hast thou an arm like God? or canst thou thunder with a voice like him?

Deck thyself now with majesty and excellency; and array thyself with glory and beauty.

Cast abroad the rage of thy wrath: and behold every one that is proud, and abase him.

Look on every one that is proud, and bring him low; and tread down the wicked in their place.

Hide them in the dust together; and bind their faces in secret.

Then will I also confess unto thee that thine own right hand can save thee.

Behold now behemoth, which I made with thee; he eateth grass as an ox.

Lo now, his strength is in his loins, and his force is in the navel of his belly.

He moveth his tail like a cedar: the sinews of his stones are wrapped together.

His bones are as strong pieces of brass; his bones are like bars of iron.

He is the chief of the ways of God: he that made him can make his sword to approach unto him.

Surely the mountains bring him forth food, where all the beasts of the field play.

He lieth under the shady trees, in the covert of the reed, and fens.

The shady trees cover him with their shadow; the willows of the brook compass him about.

Behold he drinketh up a river, and hasteth not: he trusteth that he can draw up Jordan into his mouth.

He taketh it with his eyes: his nose pierceth through snares.

Canst thou draw out leviathan with an hook? or his tongue with a cord which thou lettest down?

Canst thou put an hook into his nose? or bore his jaw through with a thorn?

Will he make many supplications unto thee? will he speak soft words unto thee?

Will he make a covenant with thee? wilt thou take him for a servant for ever?

Wilt thou play with him as with a bird? or wilt thou bind him for thy maidens?

Shall the companions make a banquet of him? shall they part him among the merchants?

Canst thou fill his skin with barbed irons? or his head with fish spears?

Lay thine hand upon him, remember the battle, do no more.

Behold, the hope of him is in vain: shall not one be cast down even at the sight of him?

None is so fierce that dare stir him up: who then is able to stand before me?

Who hath prevented me, that I should repay him? whatsoever is under the whole heaven is mine.

I will not conceal his parts, nor his power, nor his comely proportion.

Who can discover the face of his garment? or who can come to him with his double bridle?

Who can open the doors of his face? his teeth are terrible round about.

His scales are his pride, shut up together as with a close seal.

One is so near to another, that no air can come between them.

They are joined one to another, they stick together, that they cannot be sundered.

By his neesings a light doth shine, and his eyes are like the eyelids of the morning.

Out of his mouth go burning lamps, and sparks of fire leap out.

Out of his nostrils goeth smoke, as out of a seething pot or caldron.

His breath kindleth coals, and a flame goeth out of his mouth.

In his neck remaineth strength and sorrow is turned into joy before him.

The flakes of his flesh are joined together: they are firm in themselves; they cannot be moved.

His heart is as firm as a stone; yea, as hard as a piece of the nether millstone.

When he raiseth up himself, the mighty are afraid; by reason of breakings they purify themselves.

The sword of him that layeth at him cannot hold: the spear, the dart, nor the habergeon.

He esteemeth iron as straw, and brass as rotten wood.

The arrow cannot make him flee: slingstones are turned with him into stubble.

Darts are counted as stubble: he laugheth at the shaking of a spear.

Sharp stones are under him: he spreadeth sharp pointed things upon the mire.

He maketh the deep to boil like a pot: he maketh the sea like a pot of ointment.

He maketh a path to shine after him; one would think the deep to be hoary.

Upon earth there is not his like, who is made without fear.

He beholdeth all high things: he is a king over all the children of pride.

ECCLESIASTES

CAST THY BREAD UPON THE WATERS

CAST thy bread upon the waters: for thou shalt find it after many days.

Give a portion to seven, and also to eight; for thou knowest not what evil shall be upon the earth.

If the clouds be full of rain, they empty themselves

upon the earth: and if the tree fall toward the south, or toward the north, in the place where the tree falleth, there it shall be.

He that observeth the wind shall not sow; and he that regardeth the clouds shall not reap.

As thou knoweſt not what is the way of the spirit, nor how the bones do grow in the womb of her that is with child: even so thou knoweſt not the works of God who maketh all.

In the morning sow thy seed, and in the evening withhold not thine hand: for thou knoweſt not whether shall prosper, either this or that, or whether they both shall be alike good.

Remember Now Thy Creator

REMEMBER now thy Creator in the days of thy youth, while the evil days come not, nor the years draw nigh, when thou shalt say, I have no pleasure in them;

While the sun, or the light, or the moon, or the ſtars, be not darkened, nor the clouds return after the rain:

In the day when the keepers of the house shall tremble, and the ſtrong men shall bow themselves, and the grinders cease because they are few, and those that look out of the windows be darkened,

And the doors shall be shut in the ſtreets, when the sound of the grinding is low, and he shall rise up at the voice of the bird, and all the daughters of music shall be brought low;

Also when they shall be afraid of that which is high, and fears shall be in the way, and the almond tree shall flourish, and the grasshopper shall be a burden, and desire shall fail; because man goeth to his long home, and the mourners go about the ſtreets:

Or ever the silver cord be loosed, or the golden bowl be broken, or the pitcher be broken at the fountain, or the wheel broken at the ciſtern.

Then shall the duſt return to the earth as it was: and the spirit shall return unto God who gave it.

Judah Ha-Levi

1085–1140

TO ZION

Art thou not hungry for thy children, Zion,—
Thy sons far-scattered through an alien world?
From earth's four corners, over land and sea,
The heavy-hearted remnant of thy flock
Now send thee greeting: "Know that as the dew
Falls daily on the ancient slopes of Hermon,
So daily on the faces of thy children
Tears of vain-longing fall." And as for me,
When I remember thee, the Desolate,
My voice is like the jackal's in the night,
A wailing and a lamentation old;
But when a dream of resurrection wakes—
A momentary glory—then my voice
Breaks like the harp's into a jubilant ringing.
Thy names are on my lips, and in my heart
Restless desire: Beth-El, Mach'nayim, P'niel—
Assemblies once of the elect—on you
The glory of His name was shed, for you
The gates were open flung, and with a light
Neither of sun, moon, stars, your beauty shone.
Where on the dearest of His chosen ones
God poured his spirit, let me pour my heart.
I will pass to Hebron, where the ancient graves
Still wait for me, and wander in the dusk
Of the forests of Carmel. I will go to Gilead
And from Gilead pass to Habarim and Hor,
And stand upon the summit of the mountains
Where once the unforgotten brothers stood
And the light of them was seen throughout the world.
There let me fall to earth and press my lips
Into the dust, and weep thy desolation
Till I am blind, and, blind, still comfort thee.
I would to God that I were turned to dust
So that the wind could scatter me upon thee.
What comfort is in life for me, since now

Thine eagles have become the prey of vultures?
What pleasure in the light of day, since now
Thy lions, dead, are less than living dogs?
Oh, I can weep no more: enough, the cup
Of bitterness is full and overflows,
O Zion, beauty and gladness of the world,
Thine is all love and grace, and unto thee
In love and grace we are for ever chained.
We who in thy happiness were happy
Are broken in thy desolation. Each
In the prison of his exile bows to earth,
And turns him toward thy gates. Scattered and loſt,
We will remember till the end of time
The cradle of our childhood, from a thousand seas
Turn back and seek again thy hills and vales.
Glory of Pathros, glory of Shinar,
Compared to the light and truth that ſtreamed from thee,
Are duſt and vanity: and in all the world
Whom shall I find to liken to thy seers,
Thy princes, thy eleſt, thy anointed ones?
The kingdoms of the heathen pass like shadows,
Thy glory and thy name endure for ever.
God made His home in thee: well for the man
Who makes God's choice his own, with thee to dwell.
And happy, happy the man who vigil keeps
Until the day break over thee again,
Until thy chosen are returned to thee,
And thy firſt youth in glory is renewed.

                                        (*Maurice Samuel*)

Chaim Nachman Bialik

                                        1873–

FROM "SONGS OF THE PEOPLE"

I

Two ſteps from my garden rail
Sleeps my well beneath its pail:
    Every sabbath comes my love
    And I let him drink thereof.

All the world is sleeping now
Like the fruit beneath the bough.
    Father, mother, both are gone
    And my heart wakes here alone.

And the pail awakes with me,
Dripping, dripping, drowsily:
    Drops of gold and crystal clear . . .
    And my love is drawing near.

Hist! I think that something stirred;
Was it he, or but a bird?
    Dearest friend, my lover dear,
    There is no one with me here.

By the trough we sit and speak,
Hand in hand and cheek to cheek;
    Hear this riddle: Can you tell
    Why the pitcher seeks the well?

That you cannot answer, nor
What the pail is weeping for?
    Morn to even, drop by drop,
    Fall its tears and cannot stop.

This then tell me, why my breast
Daylong, nightlong is oppressed.
    Spoke my mother truth in saying
    That your heart from me was straying?

And my lover answered: See,
Enemies have slandered me.
    Ere another year be gone,
    We shall marry, foolish one.

On that golden day of days
Shall the summer be ablaze.
    Fruited branches overhead
    Shall in benediction spread.

Friend and kinsman, young and old
Shall be gathered to behold,
　　And with music and with mirth
　　They shall come to lead us forth.

And the bridal canopy
In this place shall lifted be.
　　I shall slip a ring of gold
　　On this finger that I hold.

And pronounce the blessing: "Thee
God makes consecrate to me."
　　And my enemies shall there
　　Burst with envy and despair.

　　　　　　　　　　　　(*Maurice Samuel*)

THE DEAD OF THE WILDERNESS [1]

(*in part*)

YONDER great shadow—that blot on the passionate glare
　　of the desert—
'Tis not an army of lions couched in the sun with their
　　young ones,
'Tis not the pride of the forests of Bashan uprooted and
　　fallen:
Those are the Dead of the Wilderness under the sun-
　　light recumbent.
Hard by their tents are they laid, like children of Anak
　　for stature,
Stretched on the desolate sands like numberless lions
　　in slumber;
Under the might of their limbs the floor of the desert
　　is hollowed.
Armed as for battle they sleep and clad in the armor
　　of giants;
Swords like crags at their heads and spears twixt their
　　shoulders protruding,
Sound to their girdle the quiver and firm in the sand is
　　the lance thrust.

[1] The subject of this poem is derived from a Talmudic legend
which says that the Jews who left Egypt did not die in the desert,
as the Bible tells, but were cast into slumber.—(Tr.)

Deep in the earth are their heads sunk, heavy with
tangles neglected,

Matted and monstrous and vast, and uncouth as the
mane of a lion;

Matted and monstrous and vast are their beards like to
tangles of serpents.

Strong are their faces and burnished, and darkened to
bronze are their eyelids,

Targets to arrows of sunlight and rocks to the fury of
tempests.

Hard are their foreheads and grim and changeless up-
turned to the heavens,

Eyes that are cruel and terrible peer through the tangle
of eyebrows.

Cast as of lava upthrown from volcanoes and hardened
their breasts are

Lifted like anvils of iron that wait for the blow of the
hammer;

Yet though the hammer of time beats long and unceasing upon them,

Like to the stone that enfolds it the strength of their
hearts sleeps for ever.

Only, the faces unmoving, the breasts multitudinous,
naked,

Strangely are covered, like ancient memorials, with runes
of the desert

Graven by arrows and swords which the tempests have
tossed and uplifted.

And when the eagle descends in his flight to behold he
shall read there,

Graven on breast and on brow, the tale of unbroken
endurance,

How many arrows and spears these breasts have en-
countered and shattered.

Sunlight and darkness revolve and cycle succeeds unto
cycle,

Stormwinds awake and are stilled and the desert turns
back to its silence.

Far stand the crags, as amazed in beholding the first
  things created,
Clothed by the silence with splendor, the proud, the
  eternally lonely,
Limitless, limitless stretches the wilderness, lifeless and
  soundless.
Lost to the end of all time is the jubilant voice of the
  giants,
Laid into stillness for ever the tumult that followed their
  footsteps;
Where they once trod are now lifted the sandhills and
  crags of the desert.
Silence has breathed on the mighty and cast into slumber
  their fierceness.
And the hot winds of the desert eaten their strength and
  their beauty.

Fierce burns the sun on the blades gigantic and wears
  them to brightness;
Blinding arrows of sunlight shot at the heads of the
  lances
Break into myriads of sparks that are dashed on the
  breasts of the sleepers
Lying there bared to the desolate sunlight for ever and
  ever.
Dried by the withering east-wind, dust of their bodies is
  lifted,
Whirled into other lands, scattered under the footsteps
  of pygmies;
Jackals there nuzzle with unclean snouts in the ruins of
  heroes.
No one remembers among them the old generation of
  giants
Fallen and turned into voiceless stone in the sands of
  the desert. . . .
Sometimes a shadow is born alone on the face of the
  desert,
Floats on the sands till it reaches the ranks of the army
  of sleepers,

Trembles a moment above them and breaks into circles
of motion,

Suddenly chooses a body outstretched and over it stands
and is moveless;

And the body beneath it is darkened and half of its
neighbor.

Suddenly quivers the air as the pinions stupendous are
folded.

Full with his weight like a meteor descending he falls
on his victim—

One of the eagle-kings, crag-born, crooked of beak and
of talon.

Over the breast of the sleeper a granite-like talon is
lifted;

Yet but an instant and granite on granite will ring in
the stillness;

And in that instant he pauses and stands with his talon
uplifted,

Stilled and rebuked in his pride by the loftier pride of
the sleeper;

Wondering stands, then unfolds the strength of his
pinions and rises,

Beating great waves through the air and screaming in
stretches of sunlight,

Scales untiring the measureless heights and is lost in the
splendor.

Long, long after still flutters, held fast on the point of
a lancehead,

One gray feather that fell unseen and unmarked was
abandoned,

Flutters and strains at the lance-head and fluttering
earthwards is wafted.

Silence returns to the desert and peace to the sleep of
the heroes.

Sometimes when midday is hot and the desert swoons
under the sunlight,

Slides from its fastness a serpent, vast as the beam of a
weaver,

Issues to warm on the sands the glistening rings of his
 body.

Now he shrinks on himself, coils himself moveless and
 breathless,

Languid with joy in the warmth and bathing in light
 as in waters;

Now he wakes and uncoils and stretches his length in
 the sunlight,

Opens the width of his jaws and his scales are like net-
 work of lightnings,

Spangled and knitted in splendor, a lonely delight in
 the desert.

Sudden he starts from his languor, leaps into rigid attention,

Bends and unwinds on the sand, then swiftly he glides
 from his station

Over the waste till he reaches the army of sleepers and
 stands then,

Lifted one-third in the air, like a column of bright
 hieroglyphics,

Raises his crown and outstretches his neck and his eyeballs green sparkle.

Swaying he broods on the slumbering army from margin
 to margin.

Vast is the soundless encampment and countless the dead
 it encloses,

Numberless, numberless faces and foreheads exposed to
 the heavens.

Then like a flash reawakens the hatred of dead generations,

Gleams in the start of his eyes like a brand that is
 sudden uncovered.

Hatred instinctive and ancient runs through the shuddering body.

Trembling he lowers his head and darts with it hither
 and thither,

Hangs then suspended an instant and stares in the face of
 a sleeper.

Under their hoods are his eyeballs twin centers of
  hatred and fury;
Hissing he opens his jaws and the flash of his fangs
  is uncovered—
And in that instant he pauses, sinks on the coils of his
  body,
Stilled and rebuked in his rage by the bitterer rage of
  the sleeper,—
Sinks and uncircles his length and turns from the visage
  of granite,
Moves off, a rhythm of waves till his splendor is lost
  in the distance.
Silence returns to the desert and peace to the sleep of
  the heroes.

Moonlight descends on the waste and sleeps on the
  measureless broadness,
Lays on the desert a garment speckled with light and
  with shadow.
Pallid the wilderness league after league rolls from dimness to dimness.
Broad at the foot of the towering crags are their shadows
  recumbent,
Couched like dragons primeval, things from the dawn
  of creation.
Gathered in monstrous conspiracy under the cover of
  darkness—
They will arise ere the morning, return to the caverns
  they came from.
Mournful the moon from her loneliness looks on the
  mystery threefold—
Wilderness, midnight and monsters crept out from the
  dawn of creation.
Lapped is the desert in merciless dreams of its old desolation,
Wails in its dreams, and its wailing half-uttered is broken
  and stifled.

But there are moments when, tortured too long by the
   silence eternal,

Wild with unbearable sickness of æons, the desert up-
   rises,

Wakens and rages for vengeance against the inhuman
   Creator,

Raises a column of sand to ascend to the fastness of
   heaven,

Once and for ever to meet Him and shatter the throne
   of His glory,

Once for the torture eternal to loose the floods of its
   fury,

Sweep his whole world into darkness and bring back the
   kingdom of chaos. . . .

Then the Creator is stirred, and His anger envelops the
   heavens,

Like a great cover of iron, He bends them to blot out
   the desert.

Red from the blast of His breath, the flame of His anger
   outbreaking

Wraps the desert in fury and scatters its crags in a
   furnace.

Stubborn and bitter the desert responds, and new furies
   are loosened,

Rise from the bowels of Hell, and all earth is in fury
   confounded.

Seized by the madness that spins like a vehement wheel
   in the vastness

Tigers and lions, with manes uplifted and eyeballs
   aglitter,

Join in the riot infernal, and howl with the voice of the
   tempest,

Lifted and torn by the strength of the tempest like
   gossamer insects.

And in that instant—

Wakes the terrible power that slumbered in chains,

Suddenly stirs and arises the old generation of heroes,

Mighty in battle: their eyes are like lightning, like blades
   are their faces.

Then flies the hand to the sword.

Sixty myriads of voices—a thunder of heroes—awaken,

Crash through the tempest and tear asunder the rage
of the desert

Round them in wildness and blindness:

                         And they cry

"We are the mighty!

The last generation of slaves and the first generation
of freemen!

Alone our hand in its strength

Tore from the pride of our shoulders the yoke of
bondage.

We lifted our heads to the heavens and behold their
broadness was narrow in the pride of our eyes,

So we turned to the desert, we said to the Wilderness:
'Mother!'

Yea, on the tops of the crags, in the thickness of clouds,

With the eagles of heaven we drank from her fountains
of freedom.

And who is lord of us?

Even now, though the God of vengeance has shut the
desert upon us,

A song of strength and revolt has reached us, and we
arise.

To arms! To arms! Form ranks! Forward!

Forward into the heavens and the wrath thereof.

Behold us! We will ascend

With the tempest!

Though the Lord has withdrawn His hand from us,

And the Ark stands moveless in its place,

Still we will ascend—alone!

Even under the eye of His wrath, daring the lightning
of His countenance,

We will carry with storm the citadels of the hills,

And face to face in combat encounter the armed foe!

Listen!

The storm, too, calls unto us—'Courage and daring!'

To arms! To arms! Let the hills be shattered and the
mountains blasted into dust,

Or let our lifeless bodies be heaped in countless cairns.
Forward!
On to the hills!".

And in that instant the desert is wild with a fierce
     anger—
And who shall conquer it?
In the storm goes up a terrible voice, a mingling of
     cries.
It must surely
That the desert is bringing to birth a deed of evil,
A bitter thing, a cruel and a terrible. . . .

Passed is the tempest. The desert is silent, and pure is
     the silence.
Bright is the broadness of heaven, and marvelous quiet
     beneath it.
Now from their terror awaking, the caravans trapped in
     the tempest
Rise from their crouching and call on their God and
     adore Him and praise Him.
Still in the sand are the sixty myriads of heroes aslumber.
Darkened their faces, for death has brought them to
     peace with their Maker.
No man knoweth the place of their slumber. The crags
     of the desert,
Split by the strength of their rising, over them closed in
     their falling.
Stillness returns as of old. Desolate stretches the desert.

                              (*Maurice Samuel*)

Yehoash

                    (*Solomon Bloomgarden*)
                        1870–1926

AN OLD SONG
(Yiddish)

IN the blossom-land Japan
Somewhere thus an old song ran.

Said a warrior to a smith
"Hammer me a sword forthwith.
Make the blade
Light as wind on water laid.
Make it long
As the wheat at harvest song.
Supple, swift
As a snake, without rift,
Full of lightnings, thousand-eyed!
Smooth as silken cloth and thin
As the web that spiders spin.
And merciless as pain, and cold."

"On the hilt what shall be told?"

"On the sword's hilt, my good man,"
Said the warrior of Japan,
"Trace for me
A running lake, a flock of sheep
And one who sings her child to sleep."

(*Marie Syrkin*)

EGYPTIAN

From the Book of the Dead

3500 B.C., *et seq.*

Both external detail and central faith of the Egyptian religion are incorporated in the Chapters of Coming Forth by Day, commonly known as the Book of the Dead. About 3500 B.C., when the first Chapter was set down by the scribes, many of the symbols were already so ancient that the men who wrote them were ignorant of their significance. Yet all were retained, because all were holy to the traditional-minded people of the Nile. . . . This race loved life and pleasure with a fierce intensity; all the somber pomp of the ritual of the dead had as its object the prolongation of an existence too delightful to relinquish. It is erroneous to picture the early Egyptians as an austere, funereal people. . . . Their theology, their sacraments, and their conception of the after life are based on a single doctrine; eternal life manifested through eternal living forms.—ROBERT HILLYER.

THE DEAD MAN ARISETH AND SINGETH A HYMN TO THE SUN

HOMAGE to thee, O Ra, at thy tremendous rising!
Thou risest! Thou shinest! the heavens are rolled aside!
Thou art the King of Gods, thou art the All-comprising,
From thee we come, in thee are deified.

Thy priests go forth at dawn; they wash their hearts
    with laughter;
Divine winds move in music across thy golden strings.
At sunset they embrace thee, as every cloudy rafter
Flames with reflected color from thy wings.

Thou sailest over the zenith, and thy heart rejoices;
Thy Morning Boat and Evening Boat with fair winds
    meet together;

Before thy face the goddess Maat exalts her fateful
    Feather,
And at thy name the halls of Anu ring with voices.

O Thou Perfect! Thou Eternal! Thou Only One!
Great Hawk that fliest with the flying Sun!
Between the Turquoise Sycamores that risest, young for
    ever,
Thine image flashing on the bright celestial river.

Thy rays are on all faces; Thou art inscrutable.
Age after age thy life renews its eager prime.
Time whirls its dust beneath thee; thou art immutable,
Maker of Time, thyself beyond all Time.

Thou passest through the portals that close behind the
    night,
Gladdening the souls of them that lay in sorrow.
The True of Word, the Quiet Heart, arise to drink thy
    light;
Thou art To-day and Yesterday; Thou are To-morrow!

Homage to thee, O Ra, who wakest life from slumber!
Thou risest! Thou shinest! Thy radiant face appears!
Millions of years have passed,—we can not count their
    number,—
Millions of years shall come. Thou art above the years!

HE HOLDETH FAST TO THE MEMORY OF HIS
IDENTITY

In the Great House, and in the House of Fire,
On the dark night of counting all the years,
On the dark night when months and years are num-
    bered,—
O let my name be given back to me!

When the Divine One on the Eastern Stairs
Shall cause me to sit down with him in peace,
And every god proclaims his name before me,—
Let me remember then the name I bore!

HE APPROACHETH THE HALL OF JUDGMENT

O MY Heart, my Mother, my Heart, my Mother,
The seed of my being, my earthly existence,
O stay with me still in the Hall of the Princes,
In the presence of the God who keepeth the Balance.
And when thou art weighed in the scale with the feather
Of Truth, then render no judgment against me;
Let not the Lords of the Trial cry before me:
He hath wrought Evil and spoken Untruth!

And ye, divine Gods, cloud-enthroned with your
    scepters,
At the weighing of words, speak me fair to Osiris.
Lift up my cause to the Forty-two Judges,
And let me not die yet again in Amentet.
Behold, O my Heart, if there be not a parting
Between us, our name shall be one with to-morrow,
Yea, Millions-of-Years is the name we have written,
Yea, Millions-of-Years, O my Mother, my Heart!

HE IS DECLARED TRUE OF WORD

"THUS saith the great god Thoth,
The judge of Right and Truth,
Unto the Company of Gods
Who sit before Osiris.

"Now verily this heart
Was weighed, and it is pure.
No wickedness was found in him
Whose heart withstood the Balance."

And thus respond the gods
Who sit before Osiris,
"Thy words are true, let him come in
And live in peace for ever.

"Give him a house amid
The everlasting Fields.
Let not Oblivion devour
The soul that is triumphant."

Thus Horus, son of Isis,
Saith to divine Osiris,
"O Father, I have brought to thee
This vindicated spirit.

"His deeds have been adjudged,
His heart weighed in the Balance;
Grant him thy cakes and ale, and grant
Him welcome in thy presence."

Thus saith the living soul,
"Behold, O Lord of lords,
Here to thy presence am I come,
Sinless before Osiris.

"Thou art the Beautiful,
The Prince of all the World,
Thee have I loved, O favor me,
And make me thy Beloved."

HE COMETH FORTH INTO THE DAY

I am here, I have traversed the Tomb, I behold thee,
    Thou who art strong!
I have passed through the Underworld, gazed on Osiris,
    Scattered the night.

I have come, I have gazed on my Father, Osiris,
    I am his son.
I am the son who loveth his Father,
    I am beloved.

I have made me a path through the western horizon,
    Even as God.
I have followed his footsteps, and won through his magic
    Millions of years.

The Gate between Heaven and Earth ſtandeth open,
   Glad is my path.
Hail, every god! every soul! out of darkness
   Shineth my light!

Like the Hawk I went in; I come forth like the Phœnix,
   Star of the dawn.
In the beautiful world by the bright Lake of Horus,
   Riseth the Day.

HE MAKETH HIMSELF ONE WITH THE ONLY GOD, WHOSE LIMBS ARE THE MANY GODS

O EVERLASTING Kingdom of the Scepter,
O Reſting-place where Ra's bright boat is moored,
O White Crown of the Form which is divine!
I come! I am the Child! I am the Child!
My hair is Nu, my face the disk of Ra,
My eyes are Hathor, and my neck is Isis;—
Each member of my body is a god,
My flesh and bones, the names of Living Gods.
Jhoth shelters me, for always, day by day.
I come as Ra, I come as he whose name
Is yet unknown. I come as Yeſterday,
As Prophet of the million years to be
For nations and for peoples ſtill untold.
I am the Child who marcheth down the road
Of Yeſterday, To-day, and of To-morrow.
I am the One, the Only One, who goeth
Forever round his course through all horizons;
Whose moment is in your bodies, but whose forms
Reſt in their temple, secret and unveiled;
Who holdeth you in his hand, but whom no hand
Can ever hold; who knoweth your name and season,
But whom you can not know, nor any mortal;
For whom the days return in conſtant passing,
Moving in splendor toward the end of time.

Yea, I am He, and shall not die again;
Nor men, nor sainted dead, nor even gods
Shall drag me back from my immortal path!

HE WALKETH BY DAY

I am Yesterday, To-day, and To-morrow,
The Divine Hidden Soul who created the gods,
And who feedeth the blessed.

I am Lord of the Risers from Death,
Whose Forms are the lamps in the House of the Dead,
Whose shrine is the Earth.

When the sky is illumined with crystal,
Then gladden my road and broaden my path
And clothe me in light.

Keep me safe from the Sleeper in Darkness,
When eventide closeth the eyes of the god
And the door by the wall.

In the dawn I have opened the Sycamore;
My Form is the form of all women and men,
My spirit is God.

HE ESTABLISHETH HIS TRIUMPH

Hail, thou who shinest from the Moon
And walketh through the crowded night
Lifting high thy torch!

I also come, a Shining Soul
Standing firm upon my feet
Despite my shadowy foes.

Open wide the Gate of Death
For me who bear the Rod of Gold
Victorious through the Dark!

HE KNOWETH THE SOULS OF THE WEST

High on the Mountain of Sunrise where standeth the
    Temple of Sebek,
There lieth a serpent of flint and glistening plates of
    metal.

His name is The Dweller in Fire, and he is the foe of
the Morning,
He stoppeth the Boat of Ra, and wrappeth the Boatman
in slumber.
But he shall be held in reſtraint and the Boat of Ra
sail onward,
Yea, I am the Man who reſtraineth the Serpent with
mighty enchantment
And fettereth the foe of the Sunrise till Ra resume the
horizon.
I, even I, have fettered him, and greeted the Souls of
the Weſt,
The Lord of the Mountain of Sunset, and Hathor, the
Lady of Evening.

HE IS LIKE THE LOTUS

I AM the pure lotus,
Springing up in splendor
Fed by the breath of Ra.

Rising into sunlight,
Out of soil and darkness,
I blossom in the Field.

HE SINGETH IN THE UNDERWORLD

PURE is the body on the Earth,
The Spirit in the Field;
Pure are the praises from my mouth
Happy with two-fold joy.

The Serpent dieth in the place
Eſtablished by the gods.
Osiris liveth, and his throne
Is set upon the waters.

Thy beauties are a flowing stream
Reſting the traveler,
A house of festival, where all
Adore their chosen gods.

Thy beauties are a columned court
With incense burned to Ra.
Thy face is brighter than the hall
Where shineth the full moon.

Thy hair is rippling like the hair
Of women from the Eaſt,
And blacker than the doors which guard
The midnight underworld.

Thy face is azure blue, and bright
As lapis lazuli;
The rays of Ra are on thy face.
Thy garments are of gold.

Thine eyebrows are twin goddesses
Who sit enthroned in peace,
And when thy noſtrils breathe, the winds
Of heaven bend the grain.

Thine eyes look on the Mount of Dawn;
Thy hands are cryſtal pools;
Thy knees are sedges where the birds
Sing in their golden neſt.

Thy feet are on the happy path;
O thou, the favored one,
Thou batheſt in the Lake of God,
And goeſt on thy way.

THE OTHER WORLD

HERE are cakes for thy body,
Cool water for thy throat,
Sweet breezes for thy noſtrils,
And thou art satisfied.

No longer doſt thou stumble
Upon thy chosen path,
From thy mind all evil
And darkness fall away.

Here by the river,
Drink and bathe thy limbs,
Or cast thy net, and surely
It shall be filled with fish.

The holy cow of Hapi
Shall give thee of her milk,
The ale of gods triumphant
Shall be thy daily draught.

White linen is thy tunic,
Thy sandals shine with gold;
Victorious thy weapons,
That death come not again.

Now upon the whirlwind
Thou followest thy Prince,
Now thou hast refreshment
Under the leafy tree.

Take wings to climb the zenith,
Or sleep in Fields of Peace;
By day the Sun shall keep thee,
By night the rising Star.

ADORATION OF THE DISK BY KING AKHN-ATEN AND PRINCESS NEFER NEFERIU ATEN

Thy dawn, O Ra, opens the new horizon,
And every realm that thou hast made to live
Is conquered by thy love, as joyous Day
Follows thy footsteps in delightful peace.

And when thou settest, all the world is bleak;
Houses are tombs where blind men lie in death;
Only the lion and the serpent move
Through the black oven of the sightless night.

Dawn in the East again! the land's awake,
And men leap from their slumber with a song;
They bathe their bodies, clothe them with fresh garments,
And lift their hands in happy adoration.

The cattle roam again across the fields;
Birds flutter in the marsh, and lift their wings
Also in adoration, and the flocks
Run with delight through all the pleasant meadows.

Both north and south along the dazzling river
Ships raise their sails and take their course before thee;
And in the ocean, all the deep-sea fish
Swim to the surface to drink in thy light.

For thou art all that lives, the seed of men,
The son within his mother's womb who knows
The comfort of thy presence near, the babe
To whom thou givest words and growing wisdom;

The chick within the egg, whose breath is thine,
Who runneth from its shell, chirping its joy,
And dancing on its small, unsteady legs
To greet the splendor of the rising sun.

Thy heart created all, this teeming earth,
Its people, herds, creatures that go afoot,
Creatures that fly in air, both land and sea,
Thou didst create them all within thy heart.

Men and their fates are thine, in all their stations,
Their many languages, their many colors,
All thine, and we who from the midst of peoples,
Thou madest different, Master of the Choice.

And lo, I find thee also in my heart,
I, Khu en Aten, find thee and adore.
O thou, whose dawn is life, whose setting, death,
In the great dawn, then lift up me, thy son.

(*Robert Hillyer*)

GREEK

Homeric Hymns

7th century B.C. ?

HYMN TO EARTH THE MOTHER OF ALL

O UNIVERSAL Mother, who dost keep
From everlasting thy foundations deep,
Eldest of things, Great Earth, I sing of thee!
All shapes that have their dwelling in the sea,
All things that fly, or on the ground divine
Live, move, and there are nourished—these are thine;
These from thy wealth thou dost sustain; from thee
Fair babes are born, and fruits on every tree
Hang ripe and large, revered Divinity!

The life of mortal men beneath thy sway
Is held; thy power both gives and takes away!
Happy are they whom thy mild favors nourish;
All things unstinted round them grow and flourish;
For them, endures the life-sustaining field
Its load of harvest, and their cattle yield
Large increase, and their house with wealth is filled.
Such honored dwell in cities fair and free,
The homes of lovely women, prosperously;
Their sons exult in youth's new budding gladness,
And their fresh daughters free from care and sadness,
With bloom-inwoven dance and happy song,
On the soft flowers the meadow-grass among,
Leap round them sporting—such delights by thee
Are given, rich Power, revered Divinity.

Mother of gods, thou wife of starry Heaven,
Farewell! be thou propitious, and be given
A happy life for this brief melody,
Nor thou nor other songs shall unremembered be.

(*Percy Bysshe Shelley*)

Alcman

c. 680 B.C.

FRAGMENT

The mountain summits sleep, glens, cliffs, and caves
  Are silent;—all the black earth's reptile brood,
    The bees, the wild beasts of the mountain wood;
In depths beneath the dark red ocean's waves
  Its monsters rest; whilst, wrapt in bower and spray,
    Each bird is hush'd, that stretch'd its pinions to the
      day.

(Thomas Campbell)

Alcæus

610 B.C.

THE STORM

Jove descends in sleet and snow,
Howls the vexed and angry deep;
Every stream forgets to flow,
Bound in winter's icy sleep,
Ocean wave and forest hoar
To the blast responsive roar.

Drive the tempest from your door,
Blaze on blaze your hearthstone piling,
And unmeasured goblets pour
Brimful, high with nectar smiling.
Then, beneath your poet's head
Be a downy pillow spread.

(John Hermann Merivale)

Sappho

Judging even from the mutilated fragments fallen within
our reach from the broken altar of her sacrifice of song,
I for one have always agreed with all Grecian tradition
in thinking Sappho to be beyond all question and comparison the very greatest poet that ever lived.—Algernon
Charles Swinburne.

FRAGMENTS

Hesperus the Bringer

O Hesperus, thou bringest all good things—
  Home to the weary, to the hungry cheer,

To the young bird the parent's brooding wings,
    The welcome stall to the o'erlabored steer;
Whate'er of peace about our hearthstone clings,
    Whate'er our household gods protect of dear,
Are gathered round us by thy look of rest;
Thou bring'st the child too to its mother's breast.

(Lord Byron)

One Girl

1

Like the sweet apple which reddens upon
    the topmost bough,
A-top on the topmost twig,—which the
    pluckers forgot, somehow,—
Forget it not, nay, but got it not, for none
    could get it till now.

2

Like the wild hyacinch flower which on the
    hills is found,
Which the passing feet of the shepherds
    for ever tear and wound,
Until the purple blossom is trodden in the
    ground.

(D. G. Rossetti)

Mother, I Cannot Mind My Wheel

Mother, I cannot mind my wheel;
    My fingers ache, my lips are dry;
Oh! if you felt the pain I feel!
    But oh, who ever felt as I!

(Walter Savage Landor)

The Dust of Timas

This dust was Timas; and they say
That almost on her wedding day
She found her bridal home to be
The dark house of Persephone.

And many maidens, knowing then
That she would not come back again,
Unbound their curls; and all in tears,
They cut them off with sharpened shears.

(Edwin Arlington Robinson)

ROUND ABOUT ME

ROUND about me hum the winds of autumn,
Cool between the apple boughs: and slumber,
Flowing from the quivering leaves to earthward,
    Spreads as a river.

FULL MOON

OFF in the twilight hung the low full moon,
And all the women stood before it grave,
As round an altar. Thus at holy times
The Cretan damsels dance melodiously
With delicate feet about the sacrifice,
Trampling the tender bloom of the soft grass.

FOREVER DEAD

DEATH shall be death forever unto thee,
Lady, with no remembrance of thy name
Then or thereafter; for thou gatherest not
The roses of Pieria, loving gold
Above the Muses. Even in Hades' House
Wander thou shalt unmarked, flitting forlorn
Among the shadowy, averted dead.

(William Ellery Leonard)

Theognis

540 B.C.

HOPE

FOR human nature Hope remains alone
Of all the deities; the rest are flown.
Faith is departed; Truth and Honor dead;
And all the Graces too, my friends, are fled.

The scanty specimens of living worth,
Dwindled to nothing, and extinct on earth.
Yet whilst I live and view the light of heaven,
Since hope remains and never has been driven
From the distracted world— the single scope
Of my devotion is to worship Hope.
When hecatombs are slain, and altars burn,
When all the deities adored in turn,
Let Hope be present; and with Hope, my friend,
Let every sacrifice commence and end.
Yes, Insolence, Injustice, every crime,
Rapine and Wrong, may prosper for a time;
Yet shall they travel on to swift decay,
Who tread the crooked path and hollow way.

(John Hookham Frere)

POVERTY

For noble minds, the worst of miseries,
Worse than old age, or wearisome disease,
Is Poverty. From Poverty to flee,
From some tall precipice into the sea,
It were a fair escape to leap below!
In Poverty, dear Kyrnus, we forego
Freedom in word and deed, body and mind;
Action and thought are fetter'd and confin'd.
Let me then fly, dear Kyrnus, once again!
Wide as the limits of the land and main,
From these entanglements; with these in view,
Death is the lighter evil of the two.

(John Hookham Frere)

Anacreon and Anacreontics

6th century B.C. *et seq.*

THE GRASSHOPPER

Happy insect! what can be
In happiness compar'd to thee?
Fed with nourishment divine,
The dewy morning's gentle wine!

Nature waits upon thee ſtill,
And thy verdant cup does fill;
'Tis filled wherever thou doſt tread,
Nature self's thy Ganymede.
Thou doſt drink, and dance, and sing;
Happier than the happieſt king!
All the fields which thou doſt see,
All the plants belong to thee;
All that summer hours produce;
Fertile made with early juice.
Man for thee does sow and plow;
Farmer he, and landlord thou!
Thou doſt innocently joy;
Nor does thy luxury deſtroy;
The shepherd gladly heareth thee,
More harmonious than he.
Thee country-hinds with gladness hear,
Prophet of the ripen'd year!
Thee Phœbus loves, and does inspire;
Phœbus is himself thy sire.
To thee, of all things upon earth,
Life's no longer than thy mirth.
Happy inſect, happy, thou
Doſt neither age nor winter know;
But, when thou'ſt drunk, and danc'd and sung
Thy fill, the flowery leaves among,
(Voluptuous and wise withal,
Epicurean animal!)—
Sated with thy summer feaſt,
Thou retir'ſt to endless reſt.

(*Abraham Cowley*)

AGE

Oft am I by the women told,
"Poor Anacreon! thou grow'ſt old;
Look! how thy hairs are falling all;
Poor Anacrean, how they fall!"—
Whether I grow old or no,
By the effects I do not know;

But this I know, without being told,
'Tis time to live, if I grow old;
'Tis time short pleasures now to take,
Of little life the best to make,
And manage wisely the last stake.

(*Abraham Cowley*)

BEAUTY

Horns to bulls wise Nature lends;
Horses she with hoofs defends;
Hares with nimble feet relieves;
Dreadful teeth to lions gives;
Fishes learn through streams to slide;
Birds through yielding air to glide;
Men with courage she supplies;
But to women these denies.
What then gives she? Beauty, this
Both their arms and armor is:
She, that can this weapon use,
Fire and sword with ease subdues.

(*Thomas Stanley*)

THE PICTURE

Painter, by unmatch'd desert
Master of the Rhodian art,
Come, my absent mistress take,
As I shall describe her: make
First her hair, as black as bright,
And if colors so much right
Can but do her, let it too
Smell of aromatic dew;
Underneath this shade, must thou
Draw her alabaster brow;
Her dark eyebrows so dispose
That they neither part nor close,
But by a divorce so slight
Be disjoin'd, may cheat the sight:

From her kindly killing eye
Make a flash of lightning fly,
Sparkling like Minerva's, yet
Like Cythera's mildly sweet:
Roses in milk swimming seek
For the pattern of her cheek:
In her lip such moving blisses,
As from all may challenge kisses;
Round about her neck (outvying
Parian ſtone) the Graces flying;
And o'er all her limbs at laſt
A loose purple mantle caſt;
But so ordered that the eye
Some part naked may descry,
An essay by which the reſt
That lies hidden, may be guess'd.
    So, to life th' haſt come so near,
    All of her, but voice, is here.

(Thomas Stanley)

SPRING

SEE the Spring herself discloses,
And the Graces gather roses;
See how the becalmed seas
Now their swelling waves appease;
How the duck swims, how the crane
Comes from winter home again;
See how Titan's cheerful ray
Chaseth the dark clouds away;
Now in their new robes of green
Are the plowman's labors seen:
Now the luſty teeming Earth
Springs each hour with a new birth;
Now the olive blooms: the vine
Now doth with plump pendants shine;
And with leaves and blossoms now
Freshly bourgeons every bough.

(Thomas Stanley)

YOUTHFUL AGE

Young men dancing, and the old
Sporting I with joy behold;
But an old man gay and free
Dancing most I love to see;
Age and youth alike he shares,
For his heart belies his hairs.

(Thomas Stanley)

THE WISH

Niobe on Phrygian sands
Turn'd a weeping statue stands,
And the Pandionian Maid
In a swallow's wings array'd;
But a mirror I would be,
To be look'd on still by thee;
Or the gown wherein thou'rt drest,
That I might thy limbs invest;
Or a crystal spring, wherein
Thou might'st bathe thy purer skin;
Or sweet unguents, to anoint
And make supple every joint;
Or a knot, thy breast to deck;
Or a chain, to clasp thy neck;
Or thy shoe I wish to be,
That thou might'st but tread on me.

(Thomas Stanley)

ANACREON'S DOVE

"Lovely courier of the sky,
Whence and whither dost thou fly?
Scattering, as thy pinions play,
Liquid fragrance all the way.
Is it business? Is it love?
Tell me, tell me, gentle Dove."—
"Soft Anacreon's vows I bear,
Vows to Myrtale the fair;

Graced with all that charms the heart,
Blushing nature, smiling art,
Venus, courted by an ode,
On the Bard her Dove bestow'd.
Vested with a master's right,
Now Anacreon rules my flight:
As the letters that you see,
Weighty charge consign'd to me:
Think not yet my service hard,
Joyless task without reward:
Smiling at my master's gates,
Freedom my return awaits:
But the liberal grant in vain
Tempts me to be wild again.
Can a prudent Dove decline
Blissful bondage such as mine?
Over hills and fields to roam,
Fortune's guest without a home;
Under leaves to hide one's head,
Slightly shelter'd, coarsely fed;
Now my better lot bestows
Sweet repast, and soft repose;
Now the generous bowl I sip
As it leaves Anacreon's lip;
Void of care, and free from dread
From his fingers snatch his bread,
Then with luscious plenty gay
Round his chambers dance and play;
Or, from wine as courage springs,
O'er his face expand my wings;
And, when feast and frolic tire,
Drop asleep upon his lyre.
This is all; be quick and go,
More than all thou can'st not know;
Let me now my pinions ply,—
I have chatter'd like a pye."

(*Samuel Johnson*)

Simonides of Ceos

480 B.C.

THERMOPYLÆ

Go tell the Spartans, thou that passeth by,
That here, obedient to their laws, we lie.

(*William Lisle Bowles*)

Bacchylides

450 B.C.

PEACE ON EARTH

To mortal men Peace giveth these good things:
Wealth, and the flowers of honey-throated song;
  The flame that springs
On craven altars from fat sheep and kine,
Slain to the gods in heaven; and, all day long,
Games for glad youths, and flutes, and wreaths, and
    circling wine.
Then in the steely shield swart spiders weave
  Their web and dusky woof:
Rust to the pointed spear and sword doth cleave;
  The brazen trump sounds no alarms;
Nor is sleep harried from our eyes aloof,
But with sweet rest my bosom warms:
The streets are thronged with lovely men and young,
And hymns in praise of boys like flames to heaven are
  flung.

(*John Addington Symonds*)

Æschylus

525–456 B.C.

Nothing could equal the sublime emotion with which the
Trilogy inspired me, and to the last words of the
Eumenides I lived in an atmosphere so far removed from
the present day that I have never since been really able
to reconcile myself with modern literature.—RICHARD
WAGNER.

CHORUS FROM AGAMEMNON

GREAT Fortune is an hungry thing,
  And filleth no heart anywhere,

Though men with fingers menacing
   Point at the great house, none will dare,
When Fortune knocks, to bar the door
Proclaiming: "Come thou here no more!"
Lo, to this man the Gods have given
   Great Ilion in the dust to tread
And home return, emblazed of heaven;
If it is writ, he too shall go
Through blood for blood spilt long ago;
If he too, dying for the dead,
   Should crown the deaths of alien years,
   What mortal afar off, who hears,
Shall boast him Fortune's Child, and led
   Above the eternal tide of tears?

                    (Sir Gilbert Murray)

CHORUS FROM THE SEVEN AGAINST THEBES

Lament for the Two Brothers Slain by Each Other's Hand

   Now do our eyes behold
   The tidings which were told:
Twin fallen kings, twin perished hopes to mourn,
   The slayer, the slain,
   The entangled doom forlorn
   And ruinous end of twain.
  Say, is not sorrow, is not sorrow's sum
   On home and hearthstone come?
   Oh, waft with sighs the sail from shore,
   Oh, smite the bosom, cadencing the oar
 That rows beyond the rueful stream for aye
    To the far strand,
   The ship of souls, the dark,
   The unreturning bark
  Whereon light never falls nor foot of Day,
Even to the bourne of all, to the unbeholden land.

                    (A. E. Housman)

Sophocles

495–406 B.C.

Who saw life steadily, and saw it whole.—MATTHEW
ARNOLD.

CHORUS FROM ŒDIPUS COLONEUS

WHAT man is he that yearneth
   For length unmeasured of days?
Folly mine eye discerneth
   Encompassing all his ways.
For years over-running the measure
   Small change thee in evil wise:
Grief draweth nigh thee; and pleasure,
   Behold it is hid from thine eyes.
   This to their wage have they
   Which overlive their day.
And He that looseth from labor
   Doth one with other befriend,
   Whom bride nor bridesmen attend,
Song, nor sound of the tabor,
   Death, that maketh an end.

Thy portion esteem I highest,
   Who wast not ever begot;
Thine next, being born who diest
   And straightway again art not.
With follies light as the feather
   Doth Youth to man befall;
Then evils gather together,
   There wants not one of them all—
   Wrath, envy, discord, strife,
   The sword that seeketh life.
And sealing the sum of trouble
   Doth tottering Age draw nigh,
   Whom friends and kinsfolk fly,
Age, upon whom redouble
   All sorrows under the sky.

This man, as me, even so,
Have the evil days overtaken;
And like as a cape sea-shaken
With tempest at earth's last verges
And shock of all winds that blow,
His head the seas of woe,
The thunders of awful surges
Ruining overflow;
Blown from the fall of eve,
    Blown from the dayspring forth,
Blown from the noon in heaven,
    Blown from night and the North.

(A. E. Housman)

CHORUS FROM AJAX

Fair Salamis, the billow's roar
    Wanders around thee yet;
And sailors gaze upon thy shore
    Firm in the Ocean set.
Thy son is in a foreign clime
    Where Ida feeds her countless flocks,
    Far from thy dear remembered rocks,
Worn by the waste of time,—
Comfortless, nameless, hopeless,—save
In the dark prospect of the yawning grave.
    And Ajax, in his deep distress
        Allied to our disgrace,
    Hath cherished in his loneliness
        The bosom friend's embrace.
    Frenzy hath seized thy dearest son,
        Who from thy shores in glory came
        The first in valor and in fame;
    The deeds that he hath done
Seem hostile all to hostile eyes;
The sons of Atreus see them and despise.

Woe to the mother, in her close of day,
Woe to her desolate heart, and temples gray,
        When she shall hear

Her loved one's story whispered in her ear!
          "Woe, woe!" will be the cry,—
No quiet murmur like the tremulous wail
Of the lone bird, the querulous nightingale,—
          But shrieks that fly
Piercing, and wild, and loud, shall mourn the tale;
And she will beat her breast, and rend her hair,
Scattering the silver locks that Time hath left her
    there.

Oh! when the pride of Græcia's noblest race
Wanders, as now, in darkness and disgrace,
          When Reason's day
Sets rayless—joyless—quenched in cold decay,
          Better to die, and sleep
The never-waking sleep, than linger on,
And dare to live, when the soul's life is gone:
          But thou shalt weep,
Thou wretched father, for thy dearest son,
Thy best beloved, by inward Furies torn,
The deepest, bitterest curse thine ancient house hath
    borne!

                    (*Winthrop Mackworth Praed*)

Euripides

                                480–406 B.C.
Sad Electra's poet—MILTON.

CHORUS FROM ALCESTIS

THE STRENGTH OF FATE

IN heaven-high musings and many,
          Far-seeking and deep debate,
Of strong things find I not any
          That is as the strength of Fate.
Help nor healing is told
In soothsayings uttered of old,
In the Thracian runes, the verses
          Engraven of Orpheus' pen;

No balm of virtue to save
Apollo aforetime gave,
Who stayeth with tender mercies
    The plagues of the children of men.

She hath not her habitation
    In temples that hands have wrought;
Him that bringeth oblation,
    Behold, she heedeth him naught.
Be thou not wroth with us more,
O mistress, than heretofore;
For what God willeth soever,
    That thou bringest to be;
Thou breakest in sunder the brand
Far forged in the Iron Land;
Thine heart is cruel, and never
    Came pity anigh unto thee.

Thee, too, O King, hath she taken
    And bound in her tenfold chain;
    Yet faint not, neither complain:
The dead thou wilt not awaken
    For all thy weeping again.
    They perish, whom gods begot;
    The night releaseth them not.
    Beloved was she that died
    And dear shall ever abide,
For this was the queen among women, Admetus,
    that lay by thy side.

Not as the multitude lowly
    Asleep in their sepulchres,
    Not as their grave be hers,
But like as the gods held holy,
    The worship of wayfarers.
Yea, all that travel the way
Far off shall see it and say.

Lo, erst for her lord she died,
To-day she sitteth enskied;
Hail, lady, be gracious to usward; that alway
her honor abide.

(A. E. Housman)

CHORUSES FROM THE CYCLOPS

Love Song

One with eyes the fairest
  Cometh from his dwelling,
Some one loves thee, rarest,
  Bright beyond my telling.
In thy grace thou shinest
Like some nymph divinest,
  In her caverns dewy:—
All delights pursue thee,
Soon pied flowers, sweet-breathing,
Shall thy head be wreathing.

Chorus of Satyrs, Driving Their Goats

Where has he of race divine
  Wandered in the winding rocks?
Here the air is calm and fine
  For the father of the flocks;
Here the grass is soft and sweet,
And the river-eddies meet
In the trough beside the cave,
Bright as in their fountain wave.
Neither here, nor on the dew
  Of the lawny uplands feeding?
Oh, you come!—a stone at you
  Will I throw to mend your breeding;
Get along, you hornèd thing,
Wild, seditious, rambling!
An Iacchic melody
  To the golden Aphrodite

Will I lift, as erst did I
  Seeking her and her delight
With the Mænads, whose white feet
To the music glance and fleet.
Bacchus, O belovèd, where
Shaking wide thy yellow hair,
Wanderest thou alone, afar?
  To the one-eyed Cyclops we,
Who by right thy servants are,
  Minister in misery,
In these wretched goat-skins clad,
  Far from thy delights and thee.

(Percy Bysshe Shelley)

CHORUS FROM HIPPOLYTUS

O For the Wings of a Dove

Could I take me to some cavern for mine hiding,
  In the hilltops where the Sun scarce hath trod;
Or a cloud make the home of mine abiding,
  As a bird among the bird-droves of God.
Could I wing me to my rest amid the roar
Of the deep Adriatic on the shore
Where the water of Eridanus is clear,
  And Phaeton's sad sisters by his grave
  Weep into the river, and each tear
  Gleams a drop of amber, in the wave.

To the strand of the Daughters of the Sunset,
  The Apple-tree, the singing and the gold;
Where the mariner must stay him from his onset,
  And the red wave is tranquil as of old;
    Yea, beyond that pillar of the End
    That Atlas guardeth, would I wend;
Where a voice of living waters never ceaseth
  In God's quiet garden by the sea,
And Earth, the ancient life-giver, increaseth
  Joy among the meadows, like a tree.

(Sir Gilbert Murray)

Aristophanes

444–380 B.C.

The half divine humorist in whose incomparable genius the highest qualities of Rabelais were fused and harmonized with the supremest gifts of Shelley.—ALGERNON CHARLES SWINBURNE.

CHORUS OF BIRDS

COME on then, ye dwellers by Nature in darkness, and like to the leaves' generations,

That are little of might, that are molded of mire, unenduring and shadow-like nations,

Poor plumeless ephemerals, comfortless mortals, as visions of shadows fast fleeing

Lift up your mind unto us that are deathless, and dateless the date of our being;

Us, children of heaven; us, ageless for aye; us, all of whose thoughts are eternal:

That ye may from henceforth, having heard of us all things aright as to matters supernal,

Of the being of birds and beginning of Gods and of streams and the dark beyond reaching,

Trustfully knowing aright, in my name bid Prodicos pack with his preaching,

It was Chaos, and Night at the first, and the blackness of darkness, and Hell's broad border,

Earth was not, not air, neither heaven; when in depths of the womb of the dark without order

First thing, first born of the black-plumed Night, was a wind-egg hatcht in her bosom,

Whence timely with seasons revolving again sweet Love burst out as a blossom,

Gold wings glittering forth of his back, like whirlwinds gustily turning.

He, after his wedlock with Chaos, whose wings are of darkness, in Hell broad burning,

For his nestlings begat him the race of us first and upraised us to light new-lighted.

And before this was not the race of the Gods, until all
    things by Love were united:

And of kind united in kind with communion of Nature
    the sky and the sea are

Brought forth and the earth and the race of the Gods
    everlasting and blest. So that we are

Far away the most ancient of all things blest! And
    that we are of Love's generation

There are manifest manifold signs. We have wings and
    with us have the Loves habitation;

And manifold fair young folk that forswore love once,
    ere the bloom of them ended

Have the men pursued that pursued and desired them
    subdued by the help of us only befriended,

With such bait as a quail, a flamingo, a goose, or a
    cock's comb staring and splendid.

All best good things that befall men come from us birds,
    as is plain to all reason:

For first we proclaim and make known to them Spring
    and the Winter and Autumn in season;

Bid sow, when the crane starts clanging for Afric in
    shrill-voiced emigrant number

And calls to the pilot to hang up his rudder again for
    the season and slumber;

And then weave a cloak for Orestes the thief, lest he
    strip men of theirs if it freezes.

And again thereafter the kite reappearing announces a
    change in the breezes.

And that here is the season for shearing your sheep of
    their spring wool. Then does the swallow

Give you notice to sell your greatcoat and provide some-
    thing light for the heat that's to follow.

Thus are we as Ammon or Delphoi unto you, Dodona,
    nay Phoibos Apollo!

For, as first ye come all to get auguries of birds, even
    such is in all things your carriage,

Be the matter a matter of trade, or of earning your
    bread, or of any one's marriage.

And all things ye lay to the charge of a bird that belongs
    to discerning prediction.
Winged fame is a bird, as you reckon; you sneeze and
    the sign's as a bird for conviction.
All tokens are *birds* with you—sounds, too, and lackeys
    and donkeys. Then must it not follow
That we are to you all as the manifest Godhead that
    speaks in prophetic Apollo?

                (*Algernon Charles Swinburne*)

Theocritus

3rd century b.c.

That which distinguishes Theocritus from all other poets,
both Greek and Latin, and which raises him even above
Virgil in his Eclogues, is the inimitable tenderness of his
passions, and the natural expression of them in words so
becoming of a pastoral. A simplicity shines through all
he writes: he shows his art and learning by disguising
both.—JOHN DRYDEN.

IDYLL I

THE DEATH OF DAPHNIS

THYRSIS

SWEET are the whispers of yon pine that makes
Low music o'er the spring, and, Goatherd, sweet
Thy piping; second thou to Pan alone.
Is his the horned ram? then thine the goat.
Is his the goat? to thee shall fall the kid;
And toothsome is the flesh of unmilked kids.

GOATHERD

SHEPHERD, thy lay is as the noise of streams
Falling and falling aye from yon tall crag.
If for their meed the Muses claim the ewe,
Be thine the stall-fed lamb; or if they choose
The lamb, take thou the scarce less-valued ewe.

THYRSIS

PRAY by the Nymphs, pray, Goatherd, seat thee here
Against this hill-slope in the tamarisk shade,
And pipe me somewhat, while I guard thy goats.

GOATHERD

I DURST not, Shepherd, O I durst not pipe
At noontide; fearing Pan, who at that hour
Rests from the toils of hunting. Harsh is he;
Wrath at his nostrils aye sits sentinel.
But, Thyrsis, thou canst sing of Daphnis' woes;
High is thy name for woodland minstrelsy:
Then rest we in the shadow of the elm
Fronting Priapus and the Fountain-nymphs.
There, where the oaks are and the Shepherd's seat,
Sing as thou sang'st erewhile, when matched with him
Of Libya, Chromis; and I'll give thee, first,
To milk, ay thrice, a goat—she suckles twins,
Yet ne'ertheless can fill two milkpails full;—
Next, a deep drinking-cup, with sweet wax scoured,
Two-handled, newly-carven, smacking yet
O' the chisel. Ivy reaches up and climbs
About its lip, gilt here and there with sprays
Of woodbine, that enwreathed about it flaunts
Her saffron fruitage. Framed therein appears
A damsel ('tis a miracle of art)
In robe and snood: and suitors at her side
With locks fair-flowing, on her right and left,
Battle with words, that fail to reach her heart.
She, laughing, glances now on this, flings now
Her chance regards on that: they, all for love
Wearied and eye-swoln, find their labor lost.
Carven elsewhere an ancient fisher stands
On the rough rocks: thereto the old man with pains
Drags his great casting-net, as one that toils
Full stoutly: every fiber of his frame
Seems fishing: so about the gray-beard's neck
(In might a youngster yet) the sinews swell.
Hard by the wave-beat sire a vineyard bends
Beneath its graceful load of burnished grapes;
A boy sits on the rude fence watching them.
Near him two foxes: down the rows of grapes
One ranging steals the ripest; one assails

With wiles the poor lad's scrip, to leave him soon
Stranded and supperless. He plaits meanwhile
With ears of corn a right fine cricket-trap,
And fits it on a rush: for vines, for scrip,
Little he cares, enamored of his toy.
The cup is hung all round with lissom briar,
Triumph of Æolian art, a wondrous sight.
It was a ferryman's of Calydon:
A goat it cost me, and a great white cheese.
Ne'er yet my lips came near it, virgin still
It stands. And welcome to such boon art thou,
If for my sake thou'lt sing that lay of lays.
I jest not: lad, sing: no songs thou'lt own
In the dim land where all things are forgot.

THYRSIS

Begin, sweet Maids, begin the woodland song.
The voice of Thyrsis. Ætna's Thyrsis I.
Where were ye, Nymphs, oh where, while Daphnis
    pined?
In fair Peneus' or in Pindus' glens?
For great Anapus' stream was not your haunt,
Nor Ætna's cliff, nor Acis' sacred rill.
Begin, sweet Maids, begin the woodland song.
O'er him the wolves, the jackals howled o'er him;
The lion in the oak-copse mourned his death.
Begin, sweet Maids, begin the woodland song.
The kine and oxen stood around his feet,
The heifers and the calves wailed all for him.
Begin, sweet Maids, begin the woodland song.
First from the mountain Hermes came, and said,
"Daphnis, who frets thee? Lad, whom lov'st thou so?"
Begin, sweet Maids, begin the woodland song.
Came herdsmen, shepherds came, and goatherds came;
All asked what ailed the lad. Priapus came
And said, "Why pine, poor Daphnis? while the maid
Foots it round every pool and every grove,
    (*Begin, sweet Maids, begin the woodland song*)

"O lack-love and perverse, in quest of thee;
Herdsman in name, but goatherd rightlier called.
With eyes that yearn the goatherd marks his kids
Run riot, for he fain would frisk as they:
 (*Begin, sweet Maids, begin the woodland song*):
"With eyes that yearn dost thou too mark the laugh
Of maidens, for thou may'st not share their glee."
Still naught the herdsman said: he drained alone
His bitter portion, till the fatal end.
 Begin, sweet Maids, begin the woodland song.
Came Aphrodite, smiles on her sweet face,
False smiles, for heavy was her heart, and spake:
"So, Daphnis, thou must try a fall with Love!
But stalwart Love hath won the fall of thee."
 Begin, sweet Maids, begin the woodland song.
Then "Ruthless Aphrodite," Daphnis said,
"Accursed Aphrodite, foe to man!
Say'st thou mine hour is come, my sun hath set?
Dead as alive, shall Daphnis work Love woe."
 Begin, sweet Maids, begin the woodland song.
"Fly to Mount Ida, where the swain (men say)
And Aphrodite—to Anchises fly:
There are oak-forests; here but galingale,
And bees that make a music round the hives.
 Begin, sweet Maids, begin the woodland song.
"Adonis owed his bloom to tending flocks
And smiting hares, and bringing wild beasts down.
 Begin, sweet Maids, begin the woodland song.
"Face once more Diomed: tell him 'I have slain
The herdsman Daphnis! now I challenge thee.'
 Begin, sweet Maids, begin the woodland song.
"Farewell, wolf, jackal, mountain-prisoned bear!
Ye'll see no more by grove or glade or glen
Your herdsman Daphnis! Arethuse, farewell,
And the bright streams that pour down Thymbris' side.
 Begin, sweet Maids, begin the woodland song.
"I am that Daphnis, who lead here my kine,
Bring here to drink my oxen and my calves.
 Begin, sweet Maids, begin the woodland song.

"Pan, Pan, oh whether great Lyceum's crags
Thou haunt'ſt to-day, or mightier Mænalus,
Come to the Sicel isle! Abandon now
Rhium and Helice, and the mountain-cairn
(That e'en gods cherish) of Lycaon's son!
   Forget, sweet Maids, forget your woodland song.
"Come, king of song, o'er this my pipe, compaȼt
With wax and honey-breathing, arch thy lip:
For surely I am torn from life by Love.
   Forget, sweet Maids, forget your woodland song.
"From thicket now and thorn let violets spring,
Now let white lilies drape the juniper,
And pines grow figs, and nature all go wrong:
For Daphnis dies. Let deer pursue the hounds,
And mountain-owls outsing the nightingale.
   Forget, sweet Maids, forget your woodland song."

So spake he, and he never spoke again.
Fain Aphrodite would have raised his head;
But all his thread was spun. So down the ſtream
Went Daphnis: closed the waters o'er a head
Dear to the Nine, of nymphs not unbeloved.
   Now give me goat and cup; that I may milk
The one, and pour the other to the Muse.
Fare ye well, Muses, o'er and o'er farewell!
I'll sing ſtrains lovelier yet in days to be.

GOATHERD

   Thyrsis, let honey and the honeycomb
Fill thy sweet mouth, and figs of Ægilus:
For ne'er cicala trilled so sweet a song.
Here is the cup; mark, friend, how sweet it smells:
The Hours, thou'lt say, have washed it in their well.
Hither, Cissætha! Thou, go milk her! Kids,
Be ſteady, or your pranks will rouse the ram.

                              (*Charles Stuart Calverley*)

Idyll II

THE INCANTATION

Where are the bay-leaves, Thestylis, and the charms?
Fetch all; with fiery wood the caldron crown;
Let glamour win me back my false lord's heart!
Twelve days the wretch hath not come nigh to me,
Nor made enquiry if I die or live,
Nor clamored (oh unkindness!) at my door.
Sure his swift fancy wanders otherwhere,
The slave of Aphrodite and of Love.
I'm off to Timagetus' wrestling-school
At dawn, that I may see him and denounce
His doings; but I'll charm him now with charms.
So shine out fair, O moon! To thee I sing
My soft low song: to thee and Hecate
The dweller in the shades, at whose approach
E'en the dogs quake, as on she moves through blood
And darkness and the barrows of the slain.
All hail, dread Hecate: companion me
Unto the end, and work me witcheries
Potent as Circe or Medea wrought,
Or Perimede of the golden hair!
   Turn, magic wheel, draw homeward him I love.
First we ignite the grain. Nay, pile it on:
Where are thy wits flown, timorous Thestylis?
Shall I be flouted, I, by such as thou?
Pile, and still say, "This pile is of his bones."
   Turn, magic wheel, draw homeward him I love.
Delphis racks me: I burn him in these bays,
As, flame-enkindled, they lift up their voice,
Blaze once, and not a trace is left behind:
So waste his flesh to powder in yon fire!
   Turn, magic wheel, draw homeward him I love.
E'en as I melt, not uninspired, the wax,
May Mindian Delphis melt this hour with love:
And, swiftly as this brazen wheel whirls round,
May Aphrodite whirl him to my door.
   Turn, magic wheel, draw homeward him I love.

Next burn the husks. Hell's adamantine floor
And aught that else stands firm can Artemis move.
Thestylis, the hounds bay up and down the town:
The goddess stands i' the crossroads: sound the gongs.
   Turn, magic wheel, draw homeward him I love.
Hushed are the voices of the winds and seas;
But O not hushed the voice of my despair.
He burns my being up, who left me here
No wife, no maiden, in my misery.
   Turn, magic wheel, draw homeward him I love.
Thrice I pour out; speak thrice, sweet mistress, thus:
"What face soe'er hangs o'er him be forgot
Clean as, in Dia, Theseus (legends say)
Forgat his Ariadne's locks of love."
   Turn, magic wheel, draw homeward him I love.
The coltsfoot grows in Arcady, the weed
That drives the mountain-colts and swift mares wild.
Like them may Delphis rave: so, maniac-wise,
Race from his burnished brethren home to me.
   Turn, magic wheel, draw homeward him I love.
He lost this tassel from his robe; which I
Shred thus, and cast it on the raging flames.
Ah baleful Love! why, like the marsh-born leech,
Cling to my flesh, and drain my dark veins dry?
   Turn, magic wheel, draw homeward him I love.
From a crushed eft to-morrow he shall drink
Death! But now, Thestylis, take these herbs and smear
That threshold o'er, whereto at heart I cling
Still, still—albeit he thinks scorn of me—
And spit, and say, " 'Tis Delphis' bones I smear."
   Turn, magic wheel, draw homeward him I love.
Now all alone, I'll weep a love whence sprung,
When born? Who wrought my sorrow? Anaxo came,
Her basket in her hand, to Artemis' grove.
Bound for the festival, troops of forest beasts
Stood round, and in the midst a lioness.
   Bethink thee, Mistress Moon, whence came my love.
Theucharidas' slave, my Thracian nurse now dead,
Then my dear neighbor, prayed me and implored

To see the pageant: I, the poor doomed thing,
Went with her, trailing a fine silken train,
And gathering round me Clearista's robe.
  Bethink thee, Mistress Moon, whence came my love.
Now, the mid-highway reached by Lycon's farm,
Delphis and Eudamippus passed me by.
With beards as lustrous as the woodbine's gold
And breasts more sheeny than myself, O Moon,
Fresh from the wrestler's toil they came.
  Bethink thee, Mistress Moon, whence came my love.
I saw, I raved, smit (weakling) to my heart.
My beauty withered, and I cared no more
For all the pomp; and how I gained my home
I know not: some strange fever wasted me.
Ten nights and days I lay upon my bed.
  Bethink thee, Mistress Moon, whence came my love.
And wan became my flesh, as 't had been dyed,
And all my hair streamed off, and there was left
But bones and skin. Whose threshold crossed I not,
Or missed what grandam's hut who dealt in charms?
For no light thing was this, and time sped on.
  Bethink thee, Mistress Moon, whence came my love.
At last I spake the truth to that my maid:
"Seek, an thou canst, some cure for my sore pain.
Alas, I am all the Mindian's! But begone,
And watch by Timegetus' wrestling-school:
There doth he haunt, there soothly take his rest.
  Bethink thee, Mistress Moon, whence came my love.
"Find him alone: not softly: say, 'she waits';
And bring him." So I spake: she went her way,
And brought the lustrous-limbed one to my roof.
And I, the instant I beheld him step
Lightfooted o'er the threshold of my door,
  (*Bethink thee, mistress Moon, whence came my love,*)
Became all cold like snow, and from my brow
Brake the damp dewdrops: utterance I had none,
Not e'en such utterance as a babe may make

That babbles to its mother in its dreams;
But all my fair frame stiffened into wax.
   Bethink thee, Mistress Moon, whence came my love.
He bent his pitiless eyes on me; looked down,
And sate down on my couch, and sitting, said:
"Thou hast gained on me, Simætha, (e'en as I
Gained once on young Philinus in the race),
Bidding me hither ere I came unasked.
   Bethink thee, Mistress Moon, whence came my love.
"For I had come, by Eros I had come,
This night, with comrades twain or maybe more,
The fruitage of the Wine-god in my robe,
And, wound about my brow with ribands red,
The silver leaves so dear to Heracles.
   Bethink thee, Mistress Moon, whence came my love.
"Had ye said 'Enter,' well; for 'mid my peers
High is my name for goodliness and speed:
I had kissed that sweet mouth once and gone my way.
But had the door been barred, and I thrust out,
With brand and axe would we have stormed ye then.
   Bethink thee, Mistress Moon, whence came my love.
"Now be my thanks recorded, first to Love,
Next to thee, maiden, who didst pluck me out,
A half-burned helpless creature, from the flames,
And badst me hither. It is Love that lights
A fire more fierce than his of Lipara;
   Bethink thee, Mistress Moon, whence came my love.
"Scares, mischief-mad, the maiden from her bower,
The bride from her warm couch." He spake: and I,
A willing listener, sat, my hand in his,
Among the cushions, and his cheek touched mine,
Each hotter than its wont, and we discoursed
In soft low language. Need I prate to thee,
Sweet Moon, of all we said and all we did?
Till yesterday he found no fault with me,
Nor I with him. But lo, to-day there came
Philista's mother—hers who flutes to me—
With her Melampo's; just when up the sky
Gallop the ma es that chariot rose-limbed Dawn:

And divers tales she brought me, with the rest
How Delphis loved, she knew not rightly whom:
But this she knew; that of the rich wine aye
He poured "to Love"; and at the last had fled,
To line, she deemed, the fair one's hall with flowers.
Such was my visitor's tale, and it was true:
For thrice, nay four times, daily he would stroll
Hither, leave here full oft his Dorian flask:
Now—'tis a fortnight since I saw his face.
Doth he then treasure something sweet elsewhere?
Am I forgot? I'll charm him now with charms.
But let him try me more, and by the Fates
He'll soon be knocking at the gates of hell.
Spells of such power are in this chest of mine,
Learned, lady, from mine host in Palestine.

Lady, farewell: turn ocean-ward thy steeds:
As I have purposed, so shall I fulfill.
Farewell, thou bright-faced Moon! Ye stars, farewell,
That wait upon the car of noiseless Night.

(Charles Stuart Calverley)

Epigram V

A SYLVAN REVEL

What ho! my shepherds, sweet it were
To fill with song this leafy glade.
 Bring harp and flute. The gods have made
An hour for music. Daphnis there
Shall give the note with jocund blare
From out his horn. The rest will aid
 With fifes and drums, and charm the shade,
And rout the dusky wings of care.
We'll pipe to fox and wolf and bear,
We'll wake the wood with rataplan,
Fetch every beast from every lair,
Make every creature dance who can,
Set every Satyr's hoof in air,
 And tickle both the feet of Pan!

Epigram IX

CLEONICOS

Let sailors watch the waning Pleiades,
And keep the shore. This man, made over-bold
By godless pride, and too much greed of gold,
Setting his gains before his health and ease,
Ran up his sails to catch the whistling breeze:
Whose corpse, ere now, the restless waves have rolled
From deep to deep, while all his freight, unsold,
Is tost upon the tumult of the seas.
Such fate had one whose avaricious eyes
Lured him to peril in a mad emprise.
Yea, from the Syrian coast to Thasos bound,
He slipt his anchor with rich merchandise,
While the wet stars were slipping from the skies,
And with the drowning stars untimely drowned.

Epigram XVIII

THE MONUMENT OF CLEITA

Here Cleita sleeps. You ask her life and race?
Read on, and learn a simple tale and true.
A nurse she was from the far land of Thrace,
Who tended little Medëos while he grew
A healthy, happy child, and did imbue
His nascent mind with godliness and grace;
So fencing him from evil that he knew
No word of what is impious or base.
And when at length, her tale of years all told,
She came to lie in this reposeful spot,
Young Medëos, still a child, but sagely old,
Upreared this monument, that unforgot
The care beyond his recompense of gold
Might live a memory and perish not.

Epigram XXI
THE GRAVE OF HIPPONAX

Here lies a bard, Hippònax—honored name!
Sweet were the songs that won him endless praise,
And yet his life was sweeter than his lays.
Traveler, a question fronts thee: Canst thou claim
Kinship with such in conduct void of blame?
If not, forbear this precinct; go thy ways;
Lest some bright watcher of the tomb should raise
A jealous hand to cover thee with shame.
But if thy soul is free from shade of guilt,
Or, having sinned, hath been at length forgiven
To thee all rights of common kin belong;
Lay down thy weary limbs, and, if thou wilt,
Let slumber wrap them round, nor fear that Heaven
Will suffer any sprite to do thee wrong.

(Edward Cracroft Lefroy)

Idyll XI
THE CYCLOPS

And so an easier life our Cyclops drew,
   The ancient Polyphemus, who in youth
Loved Galatea while the manhood grew
   Adown his cheeks, and darkened round his mouth.
No jot he cared for apples, olives, roses;
   Love made him mad; the whole world was neglected,
The very sheep went backward to their closes
   From out the fair green pastures, self-directed.
And singing Galatea, thus, he wore
The sunrise down along the weedy shore,
   And pined alone, and felt the cruel wound
Beneath his heart, which Cypris' arrow bore,
   With a deep pang: but, so, the cure was found;
And, sitting on a lofty rock, he cast
His eyes upon the sea, and sang at last:
"O whitest Galatea, can it be
   That thou shouldst spurn me off who love thee so?

More white than curds, my girl, thou art to see,
More meek than lambs, more full of leaping glee
　　Than kids, and brighter than the early glow
On grapes that swell to ripen,—sour like thee!
Thou comeſt to me with the fragrant sleep,
　　And with the fragrant sleep thou goeſt from me;
Thou flieſt . . . flieſt as a frightened sheep
　　Flies the gray wolf!—yet love did overcome me,
So long!—I loved thee maiden, firſt of all,
　　When down the hills (my mother faſt beside thee)
I saw thee ſtray to pluck the summer-fall
　　Of hyacinth-bells, and went myself to guide thee;
And since my eyes have seen thee, they can leave thee
　　No more, from that day's light! But thou . . . by
　　　Zeus,
Thou wilt not care for *that,* to let it grieve thee!
　　I know thee, fair one, why thou springeſt loose
From my arm round thee. Why? I tell thee, dear!
　　One shaggy eyebrow draws its smudging road
Straight through my ample front, from ear to ear;
　　One eye rolls underneath; and yawning, broad,
Flat noſtrils feel the bulging lips too near.
Yet . . . ho, ho!—*I,*—whatever I appear,—
　　Do feed a thousand oxen! When I have done,
I milk the cows, and drink the milk that's beſt!
　　I lack no cheese, while summer keeps the sun;
And after, in the cold, it's ready preſt!
　　And then, I know to sing, as there is none
Of all the Cyclops can, . . . a song of thee,
Sweet apple of my soul, on love's fair tree,
And of myself who love thee . . . till the Weſt
Forgets the light, and all but I have reſt.
I feed for thee, besides, eleven fair does,
　　And all in fawn; and four tame whelps of bears.
Come to me, sweet! thou shalt have all of those
　　In change for love! I will not halve the shares.
Leave the blue sea, with pure white arms extended
　　To the dry shore; and, in my cave's recess,

Thou shalt be gladder for the noon-light ended;
  For here be laurels, spiral cypresses,
Dark ivy, and a vine whose leaves infold
Most luscious grapes; and here is water cold,
  The wooded Ætna pours down thro the trees
From the white snows, which gods were scarce too bold
  To drink in turn with nectar. Who with these
  Would choose the salt wave of the lukewarm seas?
Nay, look on me! If I am hairy and rough,
  I have an oak's heart in me; there's a fire
In these gray ashes which burns hot enough;
  And, when I burn for *thee,* I grudge the pyre
No fuel . . . not my soul, nor this one eye,—
Most precious thing I have, because thereby
I see thee, fairest! Out, alas! I wish
My mother had borne me finnèd like a fish,
That I might plunge down in the ocean near thee,
  And kiss thy glittering hand between the weeds,
If still thy face were turned; and I would bear thee
  Each lily white, and poppy fair that bleeds
Its red heart down its leaves!—one gift, for hours
  Of summer,—one for winter; since to cheer thee,
I could not bring at once all kinds of flowers.
Even now, girl, now, I fain would learn to swim,
If stranger in a ship sailed nigh, I wis
  That I may know how sweet a thing it is
To live down with you in the deep and dim!
Come up, O Galatea, from the ocean,
  And, having come, forget again to go!
As I, who sing out here my heart's emotion,
  Could sit forever. Come up from below.
Come, keep my flocks beside me, milk my kine;
  Come, press my cheese, distrain my whey and curd!
Ah, mother! she alone . . . that mother of mine . . .
  Did wrong me sore! I blame her! Not a word
Of kindly intercession did she address
Thine ear with for my sake; and ne'ertheless
She saw me wasting, wasting, day by day:
  Both head and feet were aching, I will say,

All sick for grief, as I myself was sick.
   O Cyclops, Cyclops! whither haſt thou sent
   Thy soul on fluttering wings? If thou wert bent
On turning bowls, or pulling green and thick
   The sprouts to give thy lambkins, thou wouldſt make
     thee
   A wiser Cyclops than for what we take thee.
Milk dry the present! Why pursue too quick
That future which is fugitive aright?
Thy Galatea thou shalt haply find,
Or else a maiden fairer and more kind;
For many girls do call me thro the night,
   And, as they call, do laugh out silvery.
   I, too, am something in the world, I see!"

While thus the Cyclops love and lambs did fold,
Ease came with song, he could not buy with gold.

                    (*Elizabeth Barrett Browning*)

Bion

                         3rd century B.C.

IDYLL I

LAMENT FOR ADONIS

(*in part*)

WAIL, wail, Ah for Adonis! He is loſt to us, lovely
   Adonis!
Loſt is lovely Adonis! The Loves respond with lament-
   ing.

Nay, no longer in robes of purple recline, Aphrodite:
Wake from thy sleep, sad queen, black-ſtoled, rain blows
   on thy bosom;
Cry to the listening world, *He is lost to us, lovely
   Adonis!*
   Wail, wail, Ah for Adonis! The Loves respond with
   lamenting.

Lovely Adonis is lying, sore hurt in his thigh, on the
   mountains,

Hurt in his thigh with the tusk, while grief consumes
Aphrodite:
Slowly he drops toward death, and the black blood
drips from his fair flesh,
Down from his snow-white skin; his eyes wax dull 'neath
the eyelids,
Yea and the rose hath failed his lips, and around them
the kisses

Die and wither, the kisses that Kupris will not relinquish:
Still, though he lives no longer, a kiss consoles Aphrodite;
But he knows not, Adonis, she kissed him while he was
dying.
Wail, wail, Ah for Adonis! The Loves respond with
lamenting.

Cruel, cruel the wound in the thigh that preys on
Adonis;
But in her heart Cytherea hath yet worse wounds to
afflict her.
Round him his dear hounds bay, they howl in their
grief to the heavens;
Nymphs of the woodlands wail: but she, the Queen
Aphrodite,
Loosing her locks to the air, roams far and wide through
the forest,
Drowned in grief, disheveled, unsandaled, and as she
flies onward,
Briars stab at her feet and cull the blood of the goddess.
She with shrill lamentation thro' glen and thro' glade
is carried,
Calling her Syrian lord, demanding him back, and de-
manding.
But where he lies, dark blood wells up and encircles
the navel;
Blood from the gushing thighs empurples the breast;
and the snow-white

Flank that was once so fair, is now dyed red for
    Adonis.
  Wail, wail, Ah, Cytherea! The Loves respond with
    lamenting.

She then hath loſt her lord, and with him hath loſt her
    celestial
Beauty; for fair was he, and fair, while he lived, Aphro-
    dite:
Now in his death her beauty hath died. *Ah, Ah,*
    Cytherea!
All the mountains lament, and the oaks moan, *Ah for*
    Adonis!
Streams as they murmur and flow complain of thy
    griefs, Aphrodite:
Yea and the springs on the hills, in the woods, weep
    tears for Adonis:
Flowers of the field for woe flush crimson red; and
    Cythêra,
Through the dells and the glens, shrills loud the dirge
    of her anguish:
Woe, woe, Ah, Cytherea! He is loſt to us, lovely Adonis!
Echo repeats the groan: *Loſt, loſt, is lovely Adonis!*
Kupris, who but bewailed thy pangs of a love over-
    whelming?

Lapped in his purple robes is the delicate form of
    Adonis.
Round him weeping Loves complain and moan in their
    anguish,
Clipping their locks for Adonis: and one of them treads
    on his arrows,
One of them breaks his bow, and one sets heel on the
    quiver;
One hath loosed for Adonis the latchet of sandals, and
    some bring
Water to pour in an urn; one laves the wound in his
    white thigh;

One from behind with his wings keeps fanning dainty
    Adonis.
  Wail, wail, Ah for Adonis! The Loves respond with
    lamenting.

Wail, wail, Ah, Cytherea! The Loves respond with
    lamenting.
Every torch at the doors hath been quenched by thy
    hand, Hymenæus;
Every bridal wreath has been torn to shreds and no
    longer,
Hymen, Hymen no more is the song, but a new song
    of sorrow,
Woe, woe! and *Ah for Adonis!* resounds in lieu of the
    bridesong.
This the Graces are shrilling, the son of Cinyras hymn-
    ing,
Lost is lovely Adonis! in loud antiphonal accents.
Woe, woe! sharply repeat, far more than the praises of
    Paiôn,
Woe! and *Ah for Adonis!* the Muses who wail for
    Adonis,
Chaunt their charms to Adonis.—But he lists not to
    their singing;
Not that he wills not to hear, but the Maiden doth not
    release him.
Cease from moans, Cytherea, to-day refrain from the
    death-songs:
Thou must lament him again, and again shed tears in a
    new year.

                  (John Addington Symonds)

Moschus

                    3rd century B.C.

LAMENT FOR BION

Ye mountain valleys, pitifully groan!
Rivers and Dorian springs, for Bion weep!
Ye plants drop tears; ye groves, lamenting moan!
Exhale your life, wan flowers; your blushes deep

In grief, anemones and roses, steep;
In whimpering murmurs, Hyacinth! prolong
The sad, sad woe thy lettered petals keep;
Our minstrel sings no more his friends among—
Sicilian Muses! now begin the doleful song.

Ye nightingales! that mid thick leaves set loose
The gushing gurgle of your sorrow, tell
The fountains of Sicilian Arethuse
That Bion is no more—with Bion fell
The song—the music of the Dorian shell.
Ye swans of Strymon! now your banks along
Your plaintive throats with melting dirges swell
For him, who sang like you the mournful song;
Discourse of Bion's death the Thracian nymphs among—

The Dorian Orpheus, tell them all, is dead.
His herds the song and darling herdsman miss,
And oaks, beneath whose shade he propt his head;
Oblivion's ditty now he sings for Dis;
The melancholy mountain silent is;
His pining cows no longer wish to feed,
But moan for him; Apollo wept, I wis,
For thee, sweet Bion! and in mourning weed
The brotherhood of Fauns, and all the Satyr breed.

Sicilian Muses! lead the doleful chant;
Not so much near the shore the dolphin moans;
Nor so much wails within her rocky haunt
The nightingale; nor on their mountain thrones
The swallows utter such lugubrious tones;
Nor Cëyx such for faithful Halcyon,
Whose song the blue wave, where he perished, owns;
Nor in the valley, neighbor to the sun,
The funeral birds so wail their Memnon's tomb upon—

As these moan, wail, and weep for Bion dead,
The nightingales and swallows, whom he taught,
For him their elegiac sadness shed;
And all the birds contagious sorrow caught;

The sylvan realm was all with grief distraught.
Who, bold of heart, will play on Bion's reed,
Fresh from his lip, yet with his breathing fraught?
For still among the reeds does Echo feed
On Bion's minstrelsy, Pan only may succeed

To Bion's pipe; to him I make the gift;
But, lest he second seem, e'en Pan may fear
The pipe of Bion to his mouth to lift.
For thee sweet Galatea drops the tear,
And thy dear song regrets, which sitting near
She fondly listed; ever did she flee
The Cyclops and his songs—but ah! more dear
Thy song and sight than her own native sea;
On the deserted sands the nymph without her fee

Me with thy minstrel still as proper heir—
Others thou didst endow with thine estate.
Alas! alas! when in a garden fair
Mallows, crisp dill, and parsley yield to fate,
These with another year regerminate;
But when of mortal life the bloom and crown,
The wise, the good, the valiant, and the great
Succumb to death, in hollow earth shut down,
We sleep, for ever sleep—for ever lie unknown.

(George Chapman)

THE OCEAN

When winds that move not its calm surface sweep
The azure sea, I love the land no more;
The smiles of the serene and tranquil deep
Tempt my unquiet mind.—But when the roar
Of Ocean's gray abyss resounds, and foam
Gathers upon the sea, and vast waves burst,
I turn from the drear aspect to the home
Of earth and its deep woods, where intersperst,
When winds blow loud, pines make sweet melody.
Whose house is some lone bark, whose toil the sea,
Whose prey the wondering fish, an evil lot

Has chosen.—But I my languid limbs will fling
Beneath the plane, where the brook's murmuring
Moves the calm spirit, but disturbs it not.

(*Percy Bysshe Shelley*)

"*Æsop's Fables*"

3rd century ?

THE SHEPHERD-BOY AND THE WOLF

A SHEPHERD-BOY beside a stream
"The Wolf, the Wolf," was wont to scream,
And when the Villagers appeared,
He'd laugh and call them silly-eared.
A Wolf at last came down the steep—
"The Wolf, the Wolf—my legs, my sheep!"
The creature had a jolly feast,
Quite undisturbed, on boy and beast.

For none believes the liar, forsooth,
Even when the liar speaks the truth.

THE ASS IN THE LION'S SKIN

AN Ass put on a Lion's skin and went
About the forest with much merriment,
Scaring the foolish beasts by brooks and rocks,
Till at last he tried to scare the Fox.
But Reynard, hearing from beneath the mane
That raucous voice so petulant and vain,
Remarked, 'O Ass, I too would run away,
But that I know your old familiar bray.'

That's just the way with asses, just the way.

⋋ THE SWAN AND THE GOOSE

A RICH man bought a Swan and Goose—
That for song, and this for use.
It chanced his simple-minded cook
One night the Swan for Goose mistook.

But in the dark about to chop
The Swan in two above the crop,
He heard the lyric note, and stayed
The action of the fatal blade.

(And thus we see a proper tune
Is sometimes very opportune.)

(William Ellery Leonard)

The Greek Anthology

490 B.C.–1000 A.D.

The Anthology may from some points of view be regarded as the most valuable relic of antique literature which we possess. Composed of several thousand short poems, written at different times and by a multitude of authors, it is coextensive with the whole current of Greek history, from the splendid period of the Persian war to the decadence of Christianized Byzantium. Perhaps, however, the true secret of their charm is this; that in their couplets, after listening to the choric raptures of triumphant public art, we turn aside to hear the private utterances, the harmoniously modulated whispers of a multitude of Greek poets telling us their inmost thoughts and feelings. The unique melodies of Meleager, the chaste and exquisite delicacy of Callimachus, the clear dry style of Straton, Plato's unearthly subtlety of phrase, Antipater's perfect polish, the good sense of Palladas, the fretful sweetness of Agathias, the purity of Simonides, the gravity of Poseidippus, the pointed grace of Philip, the few but mellow tones of Sappho and Erinna, the tenderness of Simmias, the biting wit of Lucillius, the sunny radiance of Theocritus—all these good things are ours in the Anthology. But beyond these perfumes of the poets known to fame is yet another. Over very many of the sweetest and the strongest of the epigrams is written the pathetic word ἀδέσποτον—"without a master." Hail to you, dead poets, unnamed, but dear to the Muses! Surely with Pindar and Anacreon, with Sappho and with Sophocles, the bed of flowers is spread for you in those "black-petalled hollows of Pieria" where you bade Euripides farewell.—JOHN ADDINGTON SYMONDS.

Agathias

NOT SUCH YOUR BURDEN

Not such your burden, happy youths, as ours—
Poor women-children nurtured daintily—

For ye have comrades when ill-fortune lours,
  To hearten you with talk and company;
And ye have games for solace, and may roam
  Along the ftreets and see the painters' shows.
But woe betide us if we ftir from home—
  And there our thoughts are dull enough, God knows!

(William M. Hardinge)

PLUTARCH

CHAERONEAN Plutarch, to thy deathless praise
Does martial Rome this grateful ftatue raise;
Because both Greece and she thy fame have shared,
(Their heroes written and their lives compared;)
But thou thyself could'ft never write thine own;
Their lives have parallels, but thine has none.

(John Dryden)

Anonymous

SPIRIT OF PLATO

EAGLE! why soareft thou above that tomb?
To what sublime and ftar-ypaven home
    Floateft thou?
I am the image of swift Plato's spirit,
Ascending heaven—Athens doth inherit
    His corpse below.

(Percy Bysshe Shelley)

DION OF TARSUS

DION of Tarsus, here I lie, who sixty years have seen.
I was not ever wed, and would my father had not been!

(Alma Strettell)

THE TOMB OF DIOGENES

'TELL me, good dog, whose tomb you guard so well.'
'The Cynic's.' 'True; but who that Cynic tell.'
'Diogenes, of fair Sinope's race.'
'What? He that in a tub was wont to dwell?'
'Yes: but the ftars are now his dwelling-place.'

(John Addington Symonds)

THE LION OVER THE TOMB OF LEONIDAS

Of beasts am I, of men was he most brave
Whose bones I guard, bestriding this his grave.

(*Walter Leaf*)

Asclepiades

EUMARES

Tumultuous sea, whose wrath and foam are spent
So nigh to Eumares' worn monument;
Spare if thou wilt and shatter if thou must,
For nothing shalt thou find but bones and dust.

(*Richard Garnett*)

Callimachus

HERACLITUS

They told me, Heraclitus, they told me you were dead,
They brought me bitter news to hear and bitter tears to
shed.
I wept as I remembered how often you and I
Had tired the sun with talking and sent him down
the sky.

And now that thou art lying, my dear old Carian guest,
A handful of gray ashes, long, long ago at rest,
Still are thy pleasant voices, thy nightingales, awake;
For Death, he taketh all away, but them he cannot take.

(*William Cory*)

TIMON'S EPITAPH

Here lie I, Timon; who, alive, all living men did hate:
Pass by, and curse thy fill; but pass and stay not here
thy gate.

(*William Shakespeare*)

HIS SON

BUT twelve short years you lived, my son,
 Just twelve short years, and then you died:
And now your life's brief course is run,
 This grave a father's hopes doth hide.

(G. B. Grundy)

Carphyllides

A HAPPY MAN

WHEN these graven lines you see,
Traveler, do not pity me;
Though I be among the dead,
Let no mournful word be said.

Children that I leave behind,
And their children, all were kind;
Near to them and to my wife,
I was happy all my life.

My three sons I married right,
And their sons I rocked at night;
Death nor sorrow ever brought
Cause for one unhappy thought.

Now, and with no need of tears,
Here they leave me, full of years,—
Leave me to my quiet rest
In the region of the blest.

(Edwin Arlington Robinson)

Glaucus

AN INSCRIPTION BY THE SEA

No dust have I to cover me,
 My grave no man may show;
My tomb is this unending sea,
 And I lie far below.

My fate, O stranger, was to drown;
And where it was the ship went down
    Is what the sea-birds know.

           (*Edwin Arlington Robinson*)

Leonidas of Alexandria

MENODOTIS

MENODOTIS's portrait here is kept;
    Most odd it is
How very like to all the world, except
    Menodotis.

           (*Richard Garnett*)

Leonidas of Tarentum

THE SPINNING WOMAN

MORNING and evening, sleep she drove away,
    Old Platthis,—warding hunger from the door,
And still to wheel and distaff hummed her lay
    Hard by the gates of Eld, and bent and hoar;
Plying her loom until the dawn was gray,
    The long course of Athene did she tread:
With withered hand by withered knee she spun
    Sufficient for the loom of goodly thread,
Till all her work and all her days were done.
    And in her eightieth year she saw the wave
Of Acheron,—old Platthis,—kind and brave.

           (*Andrew Lang*)

THE TOMB OF CRETHON

I AM the tomb of Crethon; here you read
His name; himself is number'd with the dead;
Who once had wealth not less than Gyges' gold;
Who once was rich in stable, stall, and fold;
Who once was blest above all living men—
With lands, how narrow now, how ample then!

           (*John Hermann Merivale*)

THE LAST JOURNEY

With courage seek the kingdom of the dead;
   The path before you lies,
It is not hard to find, nor tread;
No rocks to climb, no lanes to thread;
But broad, and straight, and even still,
And ever gently slopes down-hill;
You cannot miss it, though you shut your eyes.

(Charles Merivale)

Lucianus

ARTIFICIAL BEAUTY

You give your cheeks a rosy stain,
   With washes dye your hair,
But paint and washes both are vain
   To give a youthful air.

Those wrinkles mock your daily toil;
   No labor will efface them;
You wear a mask of smoothest oil,
   Yet still with ease we trace them.

An art so fruitless then forsake,
   Which though you much excel in,
You never can contrive to make
   Old Hecuba young Helen.

(William Cowper)

Marcus Argentarius

THE OLD STORY

Like many a one, when you had gold
Love met you smiling, we are told;
But now that all your gold is gone,
Love leaves you hungry and alone.

And women, who have called you more
Sweet names than ever were before,
Will ask another now to tell
What man you are and where you dwell.

Was ever anyone but you
So long in learning what is true?
Must you find only at the end
That who has nothing has no friend?

(*Edwin Arlington Robinson*)

Meleager

IN THE SPRING

Now the bright crocus flames, and now
    The slim narcissus takes the rain,
And, straying o'er the mountain's brow,
    The daffodillies bud again.
The thousand blossoms wax and wane
    On wold, and heath, and fragrant bough,
    But fairer than the flowers art thou
Than any growth of hill or plain.

Ye gardens cast your leafy crown,
    That my love's feet may tread it down,
        Like lilies on the lilies set;
My love, whose lips are softer far
Than drowsy poppy petals are,
        And sweeter than the violet!

(*Andrew Lang*)

SPRING

Now Winter's winds are banished from the sky,
Gay laughs the blushing face of flowery Spring:
Now lays the land her duskier raiment by
And dons her grass-green vest, for signal why
Young plants may choose themselves appareling.

Now drinking tender dews of generous morn,
The meadows break into their summer smile,
The rose unfolds her leaves: and glad, the while,
In far-off hills the shepherd winds his horn,
And his white brede the goatherd's heart beguile.

Now sail the sailors over billowing seas
While careless Zephyr fills the canvas fair,
And singing crowds with dances debonair
Praise Dionysus for the grapes' increase—
The berried ivy twisted in their hair.

Forth from the rotting hide now bees are come—
Deft craftsmen working well and warily—
And in the hive they settle, while they ply
Fresh-flowing waxen store, with busy hum,
And small pierced cells for their sweet industry.

Now shrilleth clear each several bird his note,
The Halcyon charms the wave that knows no gale,
About our eaves the swallow tells her tale,
Along the river banks the swan, afloat,
And down the woodland glades the nightingale.

Now tendrils curl and earth bursts forth anew—
Now shepherd's pipe and fleecy flocks are gay—
Now sailors sail, and Bacchus gets his due—
Now wild birds chirp and bees their toil pursue—
Sing, poet, thou—and sing thy best for May!

(*William M. Hardinge*)

A GARLAND FOR HELIODORA

I'll frame, my Heliodora! a garland for thy hair,
Which thou, in all thy beauty's pride, mayst not disdain
    to wear;
For I with tender myrtles white violets will twine,
White violets, but not so pure as that pure breast o'
    thine;

With laughing lilies I will twine narcissus, and the
    sweet
Crocus shall, in its yellow hue, with purple hyacinth
    meet.
And I will twine with all the reſt, and all the reſt
    above,
Queen of them all, the red red rose, the flower which
    lovers love.

(Christopher North)

Nicarchus

THE RAVEN

The gloom of death is on the raven's wing,
    The song of death is in the raven's cries:
But when Demophilus begins to sing,
    The raven dies.

(Edwin Arlington Robinson)

Nicias

THE FOUNTAIN AT THE TOMB

Stay weary traveler, ſtay!
    Beneath these boughs repose;
A ſtep out of the way
    My little fountain flows.
And never quite forget
    The monumental urn,
Which Simus here hath set
    His buried child to mourn.

(Charles Merivale)

Palladas

VANITY OF VANITIES

Naked to earth was I brought—naked to earth I descend.
Why should I labor for naught, seeing how naked the
    end?

(William M. Hardinge)

Paulus Silentiarius

NO MATTER

My name, my country, what are they to thee?
What, whether proud or base my pedigree?
Perhaps I far surpassed all other men;
Perhaps I fell below them all. What then?
Suffice it, stranger, that thou seest a tomb.
Thou knowst its use. It hides—no matter whom.

(*William Cowper*)

Plato

MORNING AND EVENING STAR

Thou wert the morning star among the living,
    Ere thy fair light had fled;
Now, having died, thou art as Hesperus, giving
    New splendor to the dead.

(*Percy Bysshe Shelley*)

ON A SEAL

Five oxen, grazing in a flowery mead,
A jasper seal, done to the life, doth hold;
The little herd away long since had fled,
Were't not enclos'd within a pale of gold.

(*Thomas Stanley*)

FAREWELL

Far from the deep roar of the Ægean main,
Here lie we in the midst of Media's plain.
Farewell, great Fatherland! Farewell to thee,
Eubœa's neighbor, Athens! Farewell, Sea!

(*Charles Whibley*)

Posidippus

DORICHA

So now the very bones of you are gone
Where they were dust and ashes long ago;
And there was the last ribbon you tied on
To bind your hair, and that is dust also;
And somewhere there is dust that was of old
A soft and scented garment that you wore—
The same that once till dawn did closely fold
You in with fair Charaxus, fair no more.

But Sappho, and the white leaves of her song,
Will make your name a word for all to learn,
And all to love thereafter, even while
It's but a name; and this will be as long
As there are distant ships that will return
Again to your Naucratis and the Nile.

(*Edwin Arlington Robinson*)

Rufinus

THE LOVER'S POSY

I SEND a garland to my love
Which with my own hands I wove:
Rose and lily here there be
Twined with cool anemone,
White narcissus, dewy wet,
And the purple violet.
Take and bind it on your brow,
Nor be proud, as you are now.
As the flowers bloom and fade,
So must you too, haughty maid.

(*W. H. D. Rouse*)

LATIN

Titus Lucretius Carus

95–52 B.C.

The distinguishing character of Lucretius (I mean of his soul and genius) is a certain kind of noble pride, and positive assertion of his opinions. . . . From this sublime and daring genius of his it must of necessity come to pass that his thoughts must be masculine, full of argumentation, and that sufficiently warm. From the same fiery temper proceeds the loftiness of his expressions, and the perpetual torrent of his verse, where the barrenness of his subject does not too much constrain the quickness of his fancy. . . . He was so much an atheist that he forgot sometimes to be a poet.—JOHN DRYDEN.

NO SINGLE THING ABIDES

Sic igitur magni quoque circum moenia mundi
Expugnata dabunt labem putresque ruinas.

I

(No single thing abides; but all things flow.
Fragment to fragment clings—the things thus grow
    Until we know and name them. By degrees
They melt, and are no more the things we know.)

II

Globed from the atoms falling slow or swift
I see the suns, I see the systems lift
    Their forms; and even the systems and the suns
Shall go back slowly to the eternal drift.

III

Thou too, oh earth—thine empires, lands, and seas—
Least, with thy stars, of all the galaxies,
    Globed from the drift like these, like these thou too
Shalt go. Thou art going, hour by hour, like these.

IV

Nothing abides. Thy seas in delicate haze
Go off; those moonéd sands forsake their place;
   And where they are, shall other seas in turn
Mow with their scythes of whiteness other bays.

V

Lo, how the terraced towers, and monſtrous round
Of league-long ramparts riſe from out the ground,
   With gardens in the clouds. Then all is gone,
And Babylon is a memory and a mound.

VI

Observe this dew-drenched rose of Tyrian grain—
A rose to-day. But you will ask in vain
   To-morrow what it is; and yeſterday
It was the duſt, the sunshine and the rain.

VII

This bowl of milk, the pitch on yonder jar,
Are ſtrange and far-bound travelers come from far.
   This is a snow-flake that was once a flame—
The flame was once the fragment of a ſtar.

VIII

Round, angular, soft, brittle, dry, cold, warm,
Things *are* their qualities: things *are* their form—
   And these in combination, even as bees,
Not singly but combined, make up the swarm:

IX

And when the qualities like bees on wing,
Having a moment cluſtered, cease to cling,
   As the thing dies without its qualities,
So die the qualities without the thing.

X

Where is the coolness when no cool winds blow?
Where is the music when the lute lies low?
   Are not the redness and the red rose one,
And the snow's whiteness one thing with the snow?

XI

Even so, now mark me, here we reach the goal
Of Science, and in little have the whole—
   Even as the redness and the rose are one,
So with the body one thing is the soul.

XII

For, as our limbs and organs all unite
To make our sum of suffering and delight,
   And without eyes and ears and touch and tongue,
Were no such things as taste and sound and sight.

XIII

So without these we all in vain shall try
To find the thing that gives them unity—
   The thing to which each whispers, "Thou art thou"—
The soul which answers each, "And I am I."

XIV

What! shall the dateless worlds in dust be blown
Back to the unremembered and unknown,
   And this frail Thou—this flame of yesterday—
Burn on, forlorn, immortal, and alone?

XV

Did Nature, in the nurseries of the night
Tend it for this—Nature whose heedless might,
   Casts, like some shipwrecked sailor, the poor babe,
Naked and bleating on the shores of light?

XVI

What is it there? A cry is all it is.
It knows not if its limbs be yours or his.
   Less than that cry the babe was yesterday.
The man to-morrow shall be less than this.

XVII

Tissue by tissue to a soul he grows,
As leaf by leaf the rose becomes the rose.
   Tissue from tissue rots; and, as the Sun
Goes from the bubbles when they burst, he goes.

XVIII

Ah, mark those pearls of Sunrise! Fast and free
Upon the waves they are dancing. Souls shall be
   Things that outlast their bodies, when each spark
Outlasts its wave, each wave outlasts the sea.

XIX

The seeds that once were we take flight and fly,
Winnowed to earth, or whirled along the sky,
   Not lost but disunited. Life lives on.
It is the lives, the lives, the lives, that die.

XX

They go beyond recapture and recall,
Lost in the all-indissoluble All:—
   Gone like the rainbow from the fountain's foam,
Gone like the spindrift shuddering down the squall.

XXI

Flakes of the water, on the waters cease!
Soul of the body, melt and sleep like these.
   Atoms to atoms—weariness to rest—
Ashes to ashes—hopes and fears to peace!

XXII

Oh Science, lift aloud thy voice that stills
The pulse of fear, and through the conscience thrills—
　　Thrills through the conscience the news of peace—
How beautiful thy feet are on the hills!

　　　　　　　　　　　　　　　(*W. H. Mallock*)

AGAINST THE FEAR OF DEATH

What has this bugbear Death to frighten man,
If souls can die, as well as bodies can?
For, as before our birth we felt no pain,
When Punic arms infested land and main,
When heaven and earth were in confusion hurl'd
For the debated empire of the world,
Which awed with dreadful expectation lay,
Soon to be slaves, uncertain who should sway:
So, when our mortal frame shall be disjoin'd,
The lifeless lump uncoupled from the mind,
From sense of grief and pain we shall be free;
We shall not feel, because we shall not be.
Though earth in seas, and seas in heaven were lost,
We should not move, we only should be toss'd.
Nay, e'en suppose when we have suffered fate
The soul should feel in her divided state,
What's that to us? for we are only we,
While souls and bodies in our frame agree.
Nay, though our atoms should revolve by chance,
And matter leap into the former dance;
Though time our life and motion could restore,
And make our bodies what they were before,
What gain to us would all this bustle bring?
The new-made man would be another thing.
When once an interrupting pause is made,
That individual being is decay'd.
We, who are dead and gone, shall bear no part
In all the pleasures, nor shall feel the smart,
Which to that other mortal shall accrue,
Whom to our matter time shall mold anew.

For backward if you look on that long space
Of ages past, and view the changing face
Of matter, toss'd and variously combin'd
In sundry shapes, 'tis easy for the mind
From thence to infer, that seeds of things have been
In the same order as they now are seen:
Which yet our dark remembrance cannot trace,
Because a pause of life, a gaping space,
Has come betwixt, where memory lies dead,
And all the wandering motions from the sense are fled.
For whosoe'er shall in misfortunes live,
Must be, when those misfortunes shall arrive;
And since the man who is not, feels not woe,
(For death exempts him, and wards off the blow,
Which we, the living, only feel and bear,)
What is there left for us in death to fear?
When once that pause of life has come between
'Tis just the same as we had never been.

(*John Dryden*)

Caius Valerius Catullus

87–57 B.C.

Tenderest of Roman poets nineteen hundred years ago.—
LORD TENNYSON.

MY SWEETEST LESBIA

MY sweetest Lesbia, let us live and love,
And though the sager sort our deeds reprove,
Let us not weigh them. Heaven's great lamps do dive
Into their west, and straight again revive,
But, soon as once set is our little light,
Then must we sleep one ever-during night.

If all would lead their lives in love like me,
Then bloody swords and armor should not be;
No drum nor trumpet peaceful sleeps should move,
Unless alarm came from the camp of Love:
But fools do live and waste their little light,
And seek with pain their ever-during night.

When timely death my life and fortune ends,
Let not my hearse be vext with mourning friends,
But let all lovers rich in triumph come
And with sweet pastimes grace my happy tomb:
And, Lesbia, close up thou my little light,
And crown with love my ever-during night.

(*Thomas Campion*)

TO CELIA

Kiss me, sweet: the wary lover
Can your favors keep, and cover,
When the common courting jay
All your bounties will betray.
Kiss again! no creature comes;
Kiss, and score up wealthy sums
On my lips, thus hardly sundered,
While you breathe. First give a hundred,
Then a thousand, then another
Hundred, then unto the other
Add a thousand, and so more;
Till you equal with the store
All the grass that Romney yields,
Or the sands in Chelsea fields,
Or the drops in silver Thames,
Or the stars that gild his streams
In the silent summer-nights,
When youths ply their stolen delights;
That the curious may not know
How to tell 'em as they flow,
And the envious when they find
What their number is, be pined.

(*Ben Jonson*)

LESBIA RAILING

Lesbia forever on me rails.
To talk of me she never fails.
Now, hang me, but for all her art,
I find that I have gained her heart.

My proof is this: I plainly see
The case is just the same with me;
I curse her every hour sincerely,
Yet, hang me, but I love her dearly.

(*Jonathan Swift*)

TRUE OR FALSE

None could ever say that she,
Lesbia! was so loved by me.
Never all the world around
Faith so true as mine was found.
If no longer it endures
(Would it did!) the fault is yours.
I can never think again
Well of you: I try in vain.
But . . . be false . . . do what you will.—
Lesbia! I must love you still.

(*Walter Savage Landor*)

SAPPHO

Like to a god he seems to me,
O more than god, if that may be,
The man who, seated next to thee,
  Gazes, and hears

Thy laugh of love that snatched away
My soul and sense: for on the day
I saw thee, lady, voice could say
  Not any word;

But tongue grew stark, and thro my frame
Fed unforeseen a subtle flame,
And rang my ears, and eyes became
  Veiled, as in night.

(*William Ellery Leonard*)

ON THE BURIAL OF HIS BROTHER

By ways remote and distant waters sped,
  Brother, to thy sad graveside am I come,

That I may give the laſt gifts to the dead,
   And vainly parley with thine ashes dumb;
Since She who now beſtows and now denies
   Hath ta'en thee, hapless brother from mine eyes.
But lo! these gifts, the heirlooms of paſt years,
   Are made sad things to grace thy coffin-shell;
Take them, all drenchèd with a brother's tears,
   And, brother, for all time, hail and farewell.

(Aubrey Beardsley)

SIRMIO

Gᴇᴍ of all iſthmuses and isles that lie,
Fresh or salt water's children, in clear lake
Or ampler ocean: with what joy do I
Approach thee, Sirmio! Oh! am I awake,
Or dream that once again my eye beholds
Thee, and has looked its laſt on Thynian wolds?
Sweeteſt of sweets to me that paſtime seems,
When the mind drops her burden: when—the pain
Of travel paſt—our own cot we regain,
And neſtle on the pillow of our dreams!
'Tis this one thought that cheers us as we roam.
Hail, O fair Sirmio! Joy, thy lord is here!
Joy too, ye waters of the Garda Mere!
And ring out, all ye laughter-peals of home.

(Charles Stuart Calverley)

LOVE AND DEATH

Fʀɪᴇɴᴅ, if the mute and shrouded dead
   Are touched at all by tears,
By love long fled and friendship sped
   And the unreturning years,

O then, to her that early died,
   O doubt not, bridegroom, to thy bride
Thy love is sweet and sweeteneth
   The very bitterness of death.

(H. W. Garrod)

THE YACHT

STRANGER, the bark you see before you says
That in old times and in her early days
She was a lively vessel that could make
The quickest voyages, and overtake
All her competitors with sail or oar;
And she defies the rude Illyrian shore,
And Rhodes with her proud harbor, and the seas
That intersect the scattered Cyclades,
And the Propontic and the Thracian coast,
(Bold as it is) to contradict her boast.
She calls to witness the dark Euxine sea
And mountains that had known her as a tree,
Before her transformation, when she stood
A native of the deep Cytorian wood,
Where all her ancestors had flourished long,
And, with their old traditionary song,
Had whispered her responses to the breeze.
And waked the chorus of her sister·trees.

Amastris, from your haven forth she went,
You witnessed her first outset and descent,
Adventuring on an unknown element.
From thence she bore her master safe and free
From danger and alarm through many a sea;
Nor ever once was known to lag behind,
Foremost on every tack, with every wind.
At last, to this fair inland lake, she says
She came to pass the remnant of her days,
Leaving no debt due to the Deities
For vows preferred in danger on the seas:
Clear of incumbrance, therefore, and all other
Contentious claims, to Castor or his brother
As a free gift and offering she devotes
Herself, as long as she survives and floats.

(John Hookham Frere)

LATIN

Publius Vergilius Maro

70–19 B.C.

Thou that singeſt wheat and woodland, tilth and vineyard, hive and horse and herd;
All the charm of all the Muses often flowering in a
lonely word.—LORD TENNYSON.

ECLOGUE IV

THE MESSIAH

SICILIAN Muse, begin a loftier ſtrain!
Tho' lowly shrubs, and trees that shade the plain,
Delight not all; Sicilian Muse, prepare
To make the vocal woods deserve a consul's care.
The laſt great age, foretold by sacred rhymes,
Renews its finished course: Saturnian times
Roll round again; and mighty years, begun
From their firſt orb, in radiant circles run.
The base degenerate iron offspring ends;
A golden progeny from heaven descends.
O chaſte Lucina, speed the mother's pains,
And haſte the glorious birth! thy own Apollo reigns!
The lovely boy, with his auspicious face,
Shall Pollio's consulship and triumph grace;
Majeſtic months set out with him to their appointed race.
The father banished virtue shall reſtore,
And crimes shall threat the guilty world no more.
The son shall lead the life of gods, and be
By gods and heroes seen, and gods and heroes see.
The jarring nations he in peace shall bind,
And with paternal virtues rule mankind.
Unbidden Earth shall wreathing ivy bring,
And fragrant herbs (the promises of spring),
As her first offerings to her infant king.
The goats with strutting dugs shall homeward speed,
And lowing herds secure from lions feed.
His cradle shall with rising flowers be crowned:
The serpent's brood shall die; the sacred ground

Shall weeds and poisonous plants refuse to bear;
Each common bush shall Syrian roses wear.
But when heroic verse his youth shall raise,
And form it to hereditary praise,
Unlabored harvests shall the fields adorn,
And clustered grapes shall blush on every thorn;
The knotted oaks shall showers of honey weep,
And thro' the matted grass the liquid gold shall creep.
Yet of old fraud some footsteps shall remain:
The merchant still shall plow the deep for gain;
Great cities shall with walls be compassed round,
And sharpened shares shall vex the fruitful ground;
Another Tiphys shall new seas explore;
Another Argo land the chiefs upon the Iberian shore;
Another Helen other wars create,
And great Achilles urge the Trojan fate.
But when to ripened manhood he shall grow,
The greedy sailor shall the seas forego;
No keel shall cut the waves for foreign ware,
For every soil shall every product bear.
The laboring hind his oxen shall disjoin;
No plow shall hurt the glebe, no pruning hook the vine;
Nor wool shall in dissembled colors shine.
But the luxurious father of the fold,
With native purple, or unborrowed gold,
Beneath his pompous fleece shall proudly sweat;
And under Tyrian robes the lamb shall bleat.
The Fates, when they this happy web have spun,
Shall bless the sacred clew, and bid it smoothly run.
Mature in years, to ready honors move,
O of celestial seed! O foster son of Jove!
See, laboring Nature calls thee to sustain
The nodding frame of heaven, and earth, and main!
See to their base restored, earth, seas, and air;
And joyful ages, from behind, in crowding ranks appear.
To sing thy praise, would Heaven my breath prolong,
Infusing spirits worthy such a song,
Not Thracian Orpheus should transcend my lays,
Nor Linus crowned with never-fading bays;

Tho' each his heavenly parent should inspire;
The Muse instruct the voice, and Phœbus tune the lyre.
Should Pan contend in verse, and thou my theme,
Arcadian judges should their god condemn.
Begin, auspicious boy, to cast about
Thy infant eyes, and, with a smile, thy mother single
out:
Thy mother well deserves that short delight,
The nauseous qualms of ten long months and travel to
requite.
Then smile: the frowning infant's doom is read;
No god shall crown the board, nor goddess bless the bed.

(John Dryden)

Quintus Horatius Flaccus

65–8 B.C.

That which will distinguish his style from all other poets
is the elegance of his words, and the numerousness of his
verse; there is nothing so delicately turned in the Roman
language. There appears in every part of his language a
kind of noble and bold purity. There is a secret happiness
attends his choice, which in Petronius is called *curiosa
felicitas*. But the most distinguishing part of all his character seems to me to be his briskness, his jollity, and his
good humor.—JOHN DRYDEN.

TO THALIARCHUS

(ODES, I, 9)

BEHOLD yon mountain's hoary height,
    Made higher with new mounts of snow;
Again behold the winter's weight
    Oppress the laboring woods below:
And streams with icy fetters bound,
Benumb'd and cramp'd to solid ground.

With well-heap'd logs dissolve the cold,
    And feed the genial hearth with fires;
Produce the wine, that makes us bold,
    And sprightly wit of love inspires.
For what hereafter shall betide,
God, if 'tis worth his care, provide.

Let him alone, with what he made,
　To toss and turn the world below:
At his command the storms invade;
　The winds by his commission blow;
Till with a nod he bids them cease,
And then the calm returns, and all is peace.

To-morrow and her works defy,
　Lay hold upon the present hour,
And snatch the pleasures passing by,
　To put them out of Fortune's power.
Nor Love, nor Love's delights, disdain;
Whate'er thou gett'st to-day is gain.

Secure those golden, early joys,
　That youth, unsour'd by sorrow, bears,
Ere withering Time the taste destroys
　With sickness and unwieldly years.
For active sports, for pleasing rest,
This is the time to be possest;
The best is but in season best.

The appointed hour of promis'd bliss,
　The pleasing whisper in the dark,
The half-unwilling, willing kiss,
　The laugh that guides thee to the mark,
When the kind nymph would coyness feign,
And hides but to be found again:
These, these are joys, the gods for youth ordain.

(John Dryden)

TO MÆCENAS

(Odes, III, 29)

Descended of an ancient line,
　That long the Tuscan scepter sway'd,
Make haste to meet the generous wine,
　Whose piercing is for thee delay'd:
　The rosy wreath is made;
And artful hands prepare
The fragrant Syrian oil, that shall perfume thy hair.

When the wine sparkles from afar,
   An the well-natur'd friend cries, come away;
Make haste and leave thy business and thy care,
   No mortal interest can be worth thy stay.
Leave, for a while, thy costly country seat;
And, to be great indeed, forget
The nauseous pleasures of the great.

   Make haste and come:
Come and forsake thy cloying store;
Thy turret that surveys from high
   The smoke, and wealth, and noise of Rome,
And all the busy pageantry
That wise men scorn, and fools adore.
Come, give thy soul a loose, and taste the pleasures of
     the poor.
Sometimes 'tis grateful for the rich to try
A short vicissitude, and fit of poverty:
   A savory dish, a homely treat,
   Where all is plain, where all is neat,
Without the stately spacious room,
The Persian carpet, or the Tyrian loom,
   Clear up the cloudy foreheads of the great.

The sun is in the Lion mounted high;
   The Syrian star barks from afar,
And with his sultry breath infects the sky;
The ground below is parch'd, the heavens above us fry.
   The shepherd drives his fainting flock
   Beneath the covert of a rock,
And seeks refreshing rivulets nigh:
The sylvans to their shades retire,
Those very shades and streams new shades and streams
     require,
And want a cooling breeze of wind to fan the raging fire.
   Thou, what befits the new Lord Mayor;
   And what the city factions dare,
   And what the Gallic arms will do,
   And what the quiver-bearing foe,
   Art anxiously inquisitive to know:

But God has wisely hid from human sight
  The dark decrees of future fate,
And sown their seeds in depths of night.
   He laughs at all the giddy turns of state.
   Where mortals search too soon, and fear too late.

Enjoy the present smiling hour,
And put it out of Fortune's power;
The tide of business, like the running stream,
  Is sometimes high and sometimes low,
  A quiet ebb or a tempestuous flow,
And always in extreme.

Now with a noiseless gentle course
  It keeps within the middle bed;
  Anon it lifts aloft its head,
And bears down all before it with impetuous force;
  And trunks of trees come rolling down,
  Sheep and their folds together drown:
Both house and homestead into seas are borne,
And rocks are from their old foundations torn,
And woods, made thin with winds, their scatter'd honors
      mourn.

Happy the man, and happy he alone,
He, who can call to-day his own:
He who secure within, can say,
To-morrow do thy worst, for I have lived to-day.
Be fair or foul, or rain or shine,
The joys I have possess'd, in spite of fate, are mine.
Not Heaven itself upon the past has power,
But what has been, has been, and I have had my hour.

Fortune that with malicious joy
  Does man, her slave, oppress,
Proud of her office to destroy,
  Is seldom pleased to bless:
Still various, and inconstant still,
But with an inclination to be ill,

Promotes, degrades, delights in strife,
And makes a lottery of life.
  I can enjoy her while she is kind;
  But when she dances in the wind,
And shakes her wings, and will not stay,
I puff the prostitute away;
  The little or the much she gave, is quietly resign'd:
Content with poverty my soul I arm,
And Virtue, though in rags, will keep me warm.

                        What is 't to me,
Who never sail in her unfaithful sea,
If storms arise, and clouds grow black;
If the mast split, and threaten wreck?
Then let the greedy merchant fear
  For his ill-gotten gain,
And pray to gods that will not hear
While the debating winds and billows bear
  His wealth unto the main.
For me, secure from Fortune's blows,
Secure of what I cannot lose,
In my small pinnace I can sail,
  Contemning all the blustering roar;
And running with a merry gale,
With friendly stars my safety seek
Within some little winding creek,
  And see the storm ashore.

                              (*John Dryden*)

THE IMMORTALITY OF VERSE

(ODES, IV, 9)

Lest you should think that verse shall die,
  Which sounds the silver Thames along,
Taught on the wings of truth to fly
  Above the reach of vulgar song;

Though daring Milton sits sublime,
  In Spenser native Muses play;

Nor yet shall Waller yield to time,
   Nor pensive Cowley's mortal lay.

Sages and chiefs long since had birth
   Ere Cæsar was, or Newton named;
These raised new empires o'er the earth,
   And those, new heavens and systems framed.
Vain was the chief's, the sage's pride!
   They had no poet, and they died.
In vain they schemed, in vain they bled!
   They had no poet, and are dead.

(Alexander Pope)

TO FUSCUS ARISTUS

(Epistles I, 10)

Health from the lover of the country, me,
Health to the lover of the city, thee.
A difference in our souls this only proves;
In all things else, we pair like married doves.
But the warm nest and crowded dove-house thou
Dost like: I loosely fly from bough to bough,
And rivers drink, and all the shining day
Upon fair trees or mossy rocks I play;
In fine, I live and reign, when I retire
From all that you equal with heaven admire;
Like one at last from the priest's service fled,
Loathing the honied cakes, I long for bread.
Would I a house for happiness erect,
Nature alone should be the architect;
She'd build it more convenient than great,
And doubtless in the country choose her seat:
Is there a place doth better helps supply
Against the wounds of winter's cruelty?
Is there an aid that gentlier does assuage
The mad celestial dog's, or lion's rage?
Is it not there that sleep (and only there)
Nor noise without, nor cares within does fear?

Does art through pipes a purer water bring
Than that which Nature strains into a spring?
Can all your tap'stries, or your pictures, show
More beauties than in herbs and flowers do grow?
Fountains and trees our wearied pride do please,
Ev'n in the midst of gilded palaces;
And in your towns that prospect gives delight
Which opens round the country to our sight.
Men to the good from which they rashly fly,
Return at last; and their wild luxury
Does but in vain with those true joys contend,
Which Nature did to mankind recommend.
The man who changes gold for burnish'd brass,
Or small right gems for larger ones of glass,
Is not at length more certain to be made
Ridiculous, and wretched by the trade,
Than he who sells a solid good to buy
The painted goods of pride and vanity.
If thou be wise, no glorious fortune choose,
Which 'tis but pain to keep, yet grief to lose;
For, when we place ev'n trifles in the heart,
With trifles, too, unwillingly we part.
An humble roof, plain bed, and homely board,
More clear untainted pleasures do afford
Than all the tumult of vain greatness brings
To kings, or to the favorites of kings.
The horned deer by Nature arm'd so well,
Did with the horse in common pasture dwell;
And when they fought, the field it always won;
Till the ambitious horse begg'd help of man,
And took the bridle, and thenceforth did reign
Bravely alone, as lord of all the plain.
But never after could he the rider get
From off his back, or from his mouth the bit.
So they, who poverty too much do fear,
T' avoid that weight, a greater burden bear;
That they might power above their equals have,
To cruel masters they themselves enslave.
For gold, their liberty exchang'd we see,

That fairest flower which crowns humanity.
And all this mischief does upon them light,
Only, because they know not how, aright,
That great, but secret, happiness to prize,
That's laid up in a little, for the wise:
That is the best and easiest estate
Which to a man sits close, but not too straight;
'Tis like a shoe, it pinches and it burns,
Too narrow; and too large, it overturns.
My dearest friend! stop thy desires at last,
And cheerfully enjoy the wealth thou hast:
And, if me seeking still for more you see,
Chide and reproach, despise and laugh at me.
Money was made, not to command our will,
But all our lawful pleasures to fulfill:
Shame! woe to us, if we our wealth obey:
The horse doth with the horseman run away.

(Abraham Cowley)

TO LICINIUS

(ODES, II, 10)

RECEIVE, dear friend, the truths I teach;
So shalt thou live beyond the reach
    Of adverse Fortune's power;
Not always tempt the distant deep,
Nor always timorously creep
    Along the treacherous shore.

He that holds fast the golden mean,
And lives contentedly between
    The little and the great,
Feels not the wants that pinch the poor,
Nor plagues that haunt the rich man's door,
    Embittering all his state.

The tallest pines feel most the power
Of wintry blasts; the loftiest tower
    Comes heaviest to the ground;

The bolts that spare the mountain's side,
His cloud-capt eminence divide,
    And spread the ruin round.

The well-inform'd philosopher
Rejoices with a wholesome fear,
    And hopes, in spite of pain;
If winter bellow from the north,
Soon the sweet spring comes dancing forth,
    And Nature laughs again.

What if thine heaven be overcast?
The dark appearance will not last;
    Expect a brighter sky.
The god, that strings the silver bow,
Awakes sometimes the Muses too,
    And lays his arrows by.

If hindrances obstruct thy way,
Thy magnanimity display,
    And let thy strength be seen;
But oh! if Fortune fill thy sail,
With more than a propitious gale,
    Take half thy canvas in.

                           (*William Cowper*)

PERSIAN FOPPERIES

(Odes, I, 38)

Boy, I hate their empty shows,
    Persian garlands I detest,
Bring not me the late-blown rose
    Lingering after all the rest:

Plainer myrtle pleases me
    Thus outstretched beneath my vine,
Myrtle more becoming thee,
    Waiting with thy master's wine.

                           (*William Cowper*)

TO PYRRHA

(Odes, I, 5)

WHAT slender youth, bedew'd with liquid odors,
Courts thee on roses in some pleasant cave,
      Pyrrha? For whom bind'st thou
      In wreaths thy golden hair,
Plain in thy neatness? O how oft shall he
Of faith and changed gods complain, and seas
      Rough with black winds, and storms
      Unwonted shall admire!
Who now enjoys thee credulous, all gold,
Who, always vacant, always amiable
      Hopes thee, of flattering gales
      Unmindful. Hapless they
To whom thou untried seem'st fair. Me, in my vow'd
Picture, the sacred wall declares to have hung,
      My dank and dropping weeds
      To the stern god of sea.

(John Milton)

TO SALLY

(Odes, I, 22)

THE man in righteousness arrayed,
  A pure and blameless liver,
Needs not the keen Toledo blade,
  Nor venom-freighted quiver.
What though he wind his toilsome way
  O'er regions wild and weary—
Through Zara's burning desert stray,
  Or Asia's jungles dreary:

What though he plow the billowy deep
  By lunar light, or solar,
Meet the resistless Simoon's sweep,
  Or iceberg circumpolar!

In bog or quagmire deep and dank
  His foot shall never settle;
He mounts the summit of Mont Blanc,
  Or Popocatapetl.

On Chimborazo's breathless height
  He treads o'er burning lava;
Or snuffs the Bohan Upas blight,
  The deathful plant of Java.
Through every peril he shall pass,
  By Virtue's shield protected;
And still by Truth's unerring glass
  His path shall be directed.

Else wherefore was it, Thursday last,
  While strolling down the valley,
Defenseless, musing as I passed
  A canzonet to Sally,
A wolf, with mouth-protruding snout,
  Forth from the thicket bounded—
I clapped my hands and raised a shout—
  He heard—and fled—confounded.

Tangier nor Tunis never bred
  An animal more crabbèd;
Nor Fez, dry-nurse of lions, fed
  A monster half so rabid;
Nor Ararat so fierce a beast
  Has seen since days of Noah;
Nor stronger, eager for a feast,
  The fell constrictor boa.

(John Quincy Adams)

THE SHIP OF STATE

(Odes, I, 14)

Oh Ship! new billows sweep thee out
Seaward. What wilt thou? Hold the port, be stout
    See'st not thy mast
How rent by stiff Southwestern blast?

Thy side, of rowers how forlorn?
Thine hull, with groaning yards, with rigging torn,
 Can ill sustain
The fierce, and ever fiercer main;

Thy gods, no more than sails entire,
From whom yet once thy need might aid require,
 Of Pontic Pine,
The first of woodland stocks is thine,

Yet race and name are but as dust.
Not painted sterns give storm-tost seamen trust;
 Unless thou dare
To be the sport of storms, beware.

O fold at best a weary weight,
A yearning care and constant strain of late,
 O shun the seas
That gird those glittering Cyclades.

       (William Ewart Gladstone)

EXTREMUM TANAIN

(ODES, III, 10)

BEFORE thy door too long of late,
O Lyce, I bewail my fate;
 Not Don's barbarian maids, I trow,
 Would treat their luckless lovers so;
Thou,—thou alone art obstinate.
Hast thou nor eyes nor ears, Ingrate!
Hark! how the NORTH WIND shakes thy gate!
 Look! how the laurels bend with snow
  Before thy doors!
Lay by thy pride,—nor hesitate,
Lest Love and I grow desperate;
 If prayers, if gifts for naught must go,
 If naught my frozen pallor show,—
Beware! . . . I shall not always wait
  Before thy doors!

       (Austin Dobson)

TO CHLOË

(Odes, I, 23)

You shun me, Chloë, wild and shy,
 As some stray fawn that seeks its mother
Through trackless woods. If spring winds sigh
 It vainly strives its fears to smother.

Its trembling knees assail each other
 When lizards stir the brambles dry;—
You shun me, Chloë, wild and shy,
 As some stray fawn that seeks its mother.

And yet no Libyan lion I,—
 No ravening thing to rend another;
Lay by your tears, your tremors dry,
 A husband's better than a brother;
Nor shun me, Chloë, wild and shy,
 As some stray fawn that seeks its mother.

(*Austin Dobson*)

TO THE FOUNTAIN OF BANDUSIA

(Odes, III, 13)

O FOUNTAIN of Bandusia!
 Whence crystal waters flow.
With garlands gay and wine I'll pay
 The sacrifice I owe;
A sportive kid with budding horns
 I have, whose crimson blood
Anon shall dye and sanctify
 Thy cool and babbling flood.

O fountain of Bandusia!
 The Dog-star's hateful spell
No evil brings into the springs
 That from thy bosom well;

Here oxen, wearied by the plow,
   The roving cattle here
Hasten in quest of certain rest,
   And quaff thy gracious cheer.

O fountain of Bandusia!
   Ennobled shalt thou be,
For I shall sing the joys that spring
   Beneath yon ilex-tree.
Yes, fountain of Bandusia,
   Posterity shall know
The cooling brooks that from thy nooks,
   Singing and dancing go.

(Eugene Field)

AD LEUCONOEN

(Odes, I, 13)

It is not right for you to know, so do not ask, Leuconoë,
How long a life the gods may give or ever we are gone
      away;
Try not to read the Final Page, the ending colophonian,
Trust not the gypsy's tea-leaves, nor the prophets Baby-
      lonian,
Better to have what is to come enshrouded in obscurity
Than to be certain of the sort and length of our futurity.
Why, even as I monologue on wisdom and longevity
How Time has flown! Spear some of it!
   The longest life is brevity.

(F. P. Adams)

AD XANTHIAM PHOCEUM

(Odes, II, 4)

Nay, Xanthias, feel unashamed
   That she you love is but a servant.
Remember, lovers far more famed
   Were just as fervent.

Achilles loved the pretty slave
  Brisëis for her fair complexion;
And to Tecmessa Ajax gave
  His young affection.

Why, Agamemnon at the height
  Of feasting, triumph, and anointment,
Left everything to keep, one night,
  A small appointment.

And are you sure the girl you love—
  This maid on whom you have your heart set
Is lowly—that she is not of
  The Roman smart set?

A maiden modest as is she,
  So full of sweetness and forbearance,
Must be all right; her folks must be
  Delightful parents.

Her arms and face I can commend,
  And, as the writer of a poem,
I fain would compliment, old friend,
  The limbs below 'em.

Nay, be not jealous. Stop your fears.
  My tendencies are far from sporty.
Besides, the number of my years
  Is over forty.

                                    (*F. P. Adams*)

INVOCATION

(ODES, I, 21)

MAIDENS young and virgins tender,
Sing Diana in her splendor;
Boys at play within the hollow,
Sing the flowing-haired Apollo.

(Ye that, moved by love and duty,
Praise Diana's holy beauty,
Shall be granted joys unceasing
And, perhaps, a mate that's pleasing.)

(And if winning words we hit on,
Phœbus may present the Briton,
Persian, Parthian and the reſt, with
All the wars and plagues *we're* blessed with.)

(*Louis Untermeyer*)

HOLIDAY

(ODES, III, 28)

WHAT celebration should there be? . . .
　　Quick, Lyde, bring a jar!
Againſt a dull sobriety
　　We'll wage a luſty war.

The feſtive sun is setting low,
　　The dusk is almoſt there;
And yet you scarcely move, as though
　　We both had time to spare!

Let's pour the wine and sing in turns
　　Of Neptune in his lair,
Of mermaids in the water-ferns,
　　And of their sea-green hair.

And you, upon your curving lyre,
　　Shall spend a tuneful hour,
Singing Dianas darts of fire
　　And her benignant power.

Hymns shall arise to Her who sends
　　Fresh laughter and delight,
Until our weary singing ends
　　In lullabies to-night.

(*Louis Untermeyer*)

Sextus Aurelius Propertius

51–? B.C.

WHEN THOU MUST HOME

WHEN thou must home to shades of underground,
And there arrived, a new admirèd guest,
The beauteous spirits do ingirt thee round,
White Iope, blithe Helen, and the rest,
To hear the stories of thy finished love
From that smooth tongue whose music hell can move;

Then wilt thou speak of banqueting delights,
Of masks and revels which sweet youth did make,
Of tourneys and great challenges of knights,
And all these triumphs for thy beauties' sake:
When thou hast told these honors done to thee,
Then tell, O tell, how thou didst murder me.

(Thomas Campion)

REVENGE TO COME

(ELEGIES, III, 25)

I WAS a joke at dinners; aye, any would-be wit
Might use me for a target, and I must stomach it.
Five years I could be loyal; but now, you'll often mourn,
Biting your nails for anguish, the faith at last outworn,
Nay, weeping will not touch me—I know that trick of
    old;
You always weep from ambush, I cannot be cajoled.
I shall depart in tears, but my wrongs will check their
    flow;
Ours was a team well sorted—you could not leave it so.
So now, my mistress' threshold, where oft my tear-drops
    fell,
And thou, the door I haunted, I bid ye both farewell.
May age afflict you, Cynthia, with ill-dissembled years,
And may you see the wrinkles your fading beauty fears.

And when your glass flings at you the ruin pictured
  there,
Go curse them, every wrinkle, and every whitening hair.
Be you in turn excluded, and suffer proud disdain,
And all you did to others be done to you again.
So fate shall soon avenge me—my page bids you give
  ear—
Your beauty waits this ending. Woman, believe—and
  fear!

(Kirby Flower Smith)

Publius Ovidius Naso

43 B.C.–18 A.D.

As the soul of Euphorbus was thought to live in Pytha-
goras, so the sweet witty soul of Ovid lives in mellifluous
and honey-tongued Shakespeare.—FRANCIS MERES.

WINTER AT TOMI

(TRISTIA)

THE snow lies deep: nor sun nor melting shower
Serves to abate the winter's icy power.
One fall has scarcely come another's there,
And stays in drifts unmelted all the year.
Fierce and tempestuous is the North-wind's sway;
It levels towers of stone and carries roofs away.

With skins and trousers men keep out the cold;
Naught but their faces can your eyes behold.
Into one mass their hair is frozen tight,
Their beards with hoary rime hang glistening white.
Nor need they jars their liquor to confine,
They do not quaff a cup, they break a bit of wine.

Water is brittle here; you use a spade;
And running streams by frost are solid made.
Even the Danube flows with waves concealed
The dark blue surface into ice congealed.

On foot we go across the unmoving tide
And horses' hoofs ring loud where once their oarsmen
  plied.

(F. A. Wright)

FROM THE METAMORPHOSES

MAGIC

YE elves of hills, brooks, standing lakes, and groves,
And ye that on the sands with printless foot
Do chase the ebbing Neptune, and do fly him
When he comes back, you demi-puppets that
By moonshine do the green sour ringlets make,
Whereof the ewe not bites; and you whose pastime
Is to make midnight mushrooms, that rejoice
To hear the solemn curfew; by whose aid,
Weak masters though ye be, I have bedimm'd
The noontide sun, call'd forth the mutinous winds,
And 'twixt the green sea and the azur'd vault
Set roaring war; to the dread rattling thunder
Have I given fire, and rifted Jove's stout oak
With his own bolt; the strong-bas'd promontory
Have I made shake, and by the spurs pluck'd up
The pine and cedar; graves at my command
Have wak'd their sleepers, op'd, and let 'em forth
By my so potent art.

(William Shakespeare)

BAUCIS AND PHILEMON

THEN Lelex rose, an old experienced man,
And thus, with sober gravity, began:
"Heaven's power is infinite: earth, air, and sea,
The manufactur'd mass, the making power obey:
By proof to clear your doubt; in Phrygian ground
Two neighboring trees, with walls encompass'd round,
Stand on a moderate rise, with wonder shown;
One a hard oak, a softer linden one:
I saw the place, and them, by Pittheus sent
To Phrygian realms, my grandsire's government.

Not far from thence is seen a lake, the haunt
Of coots, and of the fishing cormorant:
Here Jove with Hermes came; but in disguise
Of mortal men conceal'd their deities;
One laid aside his thunder, one his rod,
And many toilsome steps together trod:
For harbor at a thousand doors they knock'd;
Not one of all the thousand but was lock'd.
At last a hospitable house they found,
A homely shed; the roof, not far from ground,
Was thatch'd, with reeds and straw together bound.
There Baucis and Philemon lived, and there
Had lived long married, and a happy pair:
Now old in love, though little was their store,
Inured to want, their poverty they bore,
Nor aim'd at wealth, professing to be poor.
For master or for servant here to call
Were all alike, where only two were all.
Command was none, where equal love was paid,
Or rather both commanded, both obey'd.

   "From lofty roofs the gods repulsed before,
Now stooping, enter'd through the little door:
The man (their hearty welcome first express'd)
A common settle drew for either guest,
Inviting each his weary limbs to rest.
But ere they sat, officious Baucis lays
Two cushions stuff'd with straw, the seat to raise;
Coarse, but the best she had; then rakes the load
Of ashes from the hearth, and spreads abroad
The living coals; and, lest they should expire,
With leaves and bark she feeds her infant fire.
It smokes; and then with trembling breath she blows,
Till in a cheerful blaze the flames arose.
With brushwood and with chips she strengthens these
And adds at last the boughs of rotten trees.
The fire thus form'd, she sets the kettle on
(Like burnish'd gold the little seether shone;)
Next took the coleworts which her husband got
From his own ground (a small, well-water'd spot;)

She ſtripp'd the ſtalks of all their leaves; the beſt
She cull'd, and them with handy care she dress'd.
High o'er the hearth a chine of bacon hung;
Good old Philemon seized it with a prong,
And from the sooty rafter drew it down,
Then cut a slice, but scarce enough for one;
Yet a large portion of a little ſtore,
Which for their sakes alone he wish'd were more.
This in the pot he plunged without delay,
To tame the flesh, and drain the salt away.
The time between, before the fire they sat,
And shorten'd the delay by pleasing chat.

  "A beam there was, on which a beechen pail
Hung by the handle, on a driven nail:
This fill'd with water, gently warmed, they set
Before their gueſts; in this they bathed their feet,
And after with clean towels dried their sweat.
This done, the hoſt produced the genial bed,
Sallow the feet, the borders, and the ſtead,
Which with no coſtly coverlet they spread,
But coarse old garments; yet such robes as these
They laid alone at feaſts on holydays.
The good old housewife, tucking up her gown
The table sets; the invited gods lie down.
The trivet-table of a foot was lame,
A blot which prudent Baucis overcame,
Who thruſt beneath the limping leg a sherd;
So was the mended board exaċtly rear'd:
Then rubb'd it o'er with newly-gather'd mint,
A wholesome herb, that breathed a grateful scent.
Pallas began the feaſt, where firſt was seen
The party-color'd olive, black and green:
Autumnal cornels next in order serv'd,
In lees of wine well pickled and preserved.
A garden salad was the third supply,
Of endive, radishes, and succory:
Then curds and cream, the flower of country fare,
And new-laid eggs, which Baucis' busy care
Turn'd by a gentle fire, and roaſted rare.

All these in earthenware were served to board,
And, next in place, an earthen pitcher stored
With liquor of the best the cottage could afford.
This was the table's ornament and pride,
With figures wrought: like pages at his side
Stood beechen bowls; and these were shining clean,
Varnish'd with wax without, and lined within.
By this the boiling kettle had prepared,
And to the table sent the smoking lard;
On which with eager appetite they dine,
A sav'ry bit, that serv'd to relish wine;
The wine itself was suiting to the rest,
Still working in the must, and lately press'd.
The second course succeeds like that before,
Plums, apples, nuts; and of their wintry store
Dry figs, and grapes, and wrinkled dates were set
In canisters, to enlarge the little treat:
All these a milkwhite honey-comb surround,
Which in the midst a country banquet crown'd:
But the kind hosts their entertainment grace
With hearty welcome, and an open face:
In all they did, you might discern with ease
A willing mind, and a desire to please.

    "Meanwhile the beechen bowls went round, and still,
Though often emptied, were observed to fill:
Fill'd without hands, and, of their own accord,
Ran without feet, and danced about the board.
Devotion seiz'd the pair, to see the feast
With wine, and of no common grape, increased;
And up they held their hands, and fell to pray'r,
Excusing, as they could, their country fare.

    "One goose they had ('twas all they could allow,)
A wakeful sentry, and on duty now,
Whom to the gods for sacrifice they vow:
Her with malicious zeal the couple view'd;
She ran for life, and limping they pursued:
Full well the fowl perceived their bad intent,
And would not make her master's compliment;
But persecuted, to the powers she flies,

And close between the legs of Jove she lies:
He with a gracious ear the suppliant heard,
And saved her life; then what he was declared,
And own'd the god. 'The neighborhood,' said he,
'Shall justly perish for impiety:
You stand alone exempted: but obey
With speed, and follow where we lead the way:
Leave these accursed, and to the mountain's height
Ascend, nor once look backward in your flight.'
 "They haste, and what their tardy feet denied,
Their trusty staff (their better leg) supplied.
An arrow's flight they wanted to the top,
And there secure, but spent with travel, stop;
They turn their now no more forbidden eyes;
Lost in a lake the floated level lies:
A watery desert covers all the plains,
Their cot alone, as in an isle, remains.
Wondering, with weeping eyes, while they deplore
Their neighbor's fate, and country now no more;
Their little shed, scarce large enough for two,
Seems, from the ground increased, in height and bulk to
      grow.
A stately temple shoots within the skies,
The crotches of their cot in columns rise;
The pavement polish'd marble they behold,
The gates with sculpture graced, the spires and tiles of
      gold.
 "Then thus the sire of gods, with looks serene:
'Speak thy desire, thou only just of men;
And thou, O woman, only worthy found
To be with such a man in marriage bound.'
 "Awhile they whisper; then, to Jove address'd,
Philemon thus prefers their joint request:
'We crave to serve before your sacred shrine,
And offer at your altar rites divine:
And since not any action of our life
Has been polluted with domestic strife,
We beg one hour of death, that neither she
With widow's tears may live to bury me,

Nor weeping I, with wither'd arms, may bear
My breathless Baucis to the sepulchre.'
The godheads sign their suit. They run their race,
In the same tenor, all the appointed space:
Then, when their hour was come, while they relate
These past adventures at the temple gate,
Old Baucis is by old Philemon seen
Sprouting with sudden leaves of sprightly green:
Old Baucis look'd where old Philemon stood,
And saw his lengthen'd arms a sprouting wood:
New roots their fasten'd feet begin to bind,
Their bodies stiffen in a rising rind:
Then, ere the bark above their shoulders grew,
They give and take at once their last adieu.
'At once farewell, O faithful spouse,' they said;
At once the encroaching rinds their closing lips invade.
E'en yet, an ancient Tyanæan shows
A spreading oak, that near a linden grows;
The neighborhood confirm the prodigy,
Grave men, not vain of tongue, or like to lie.
I saw myself the garlands of their boughs,
And tablets hung for gifts of granted vows;
And offering fresher up, with pious prayer,
'The good,' said I, 'are God's peculiar care,
And such as honor Heaven, shall heavenly honor share.' "

(John Dryden)

Phaedrus

1st century

ÆSOP AT PLAY

As Æsop was with boys at play,
And had his nuts as well as they,
A grave Athenian, passing by,
Cast on the sage a scornful eye,
As on a dotard quite bereaved:
Which, when the moralist perceived,
(Rather himself a wit professed
Than the poor subject of a jest)

Into the public way he flung
A bow that he had just unstrung:
"There solve, thou conjurer," he cries,
"The problem, that before thee lies."
The people throng; he racks his brain,
Nor can the thing enjoined explain.
At last he give it up—the seer
Thus then in triumph made it clear:
"As the tough bow exerts its spring,
A constant tension breaks the string;
But if 'tis let at seasons loose,
You may depend upon its use."

Thus recreative sports and play
Are good upon a holiday,
And with more spirit they'll pursue
The studies which they shall renew.

(*Christopher Smart*)

THE DOG IN THE RIVER

THE churl that wants another's fare
Deserves at least to lose his share.

As through the stream a Dog conveyed
A piece of meat, he spied his shade
In the clear mirror of the flood,
And thinking it was flesh and blood,
Snapped to deprive him of the treat:—
But mark the glutton's self-defeat,
Missed both another's and his own,
Both shade and substance, beef and bone.

(*Christopher Smart*)

Petronius Arbiter

1st century

ENCOURAGEMENT TO EXILE

LEAVE thine own home, O youth, seek distant shores!
For thee a larger order somewhere shines—
Fear not thy fate! For thee through unknown pines
Under the cold north-wind the Danube pours;

For thee in Egypt the untroubled lands
Wait, and strange men behold the setting sun
Fall down and rise. Greatly be thou as one
Who disembarks, fearless, on alien sands.

(Howard Mumford Jones)

Marcus Valerius Martialis

40–104

Not altogether a pleasant period, those evil days of
Domitian. But after dwelling in the gloom of Tacitus,
after being dazzled by the lightning of Juvenal's rhetoric,
it is well for us that we can see that age in the broad
sunlight of Martial's genius, that we can use the keen
and penetrating yet just and kindly eyes of one who saw
it as it really was. As he himself said, "his page has the
true relish of human life."—KIRBY FLOWER SMITH.

NON AMO TE

I DO not love thee, Dr. Fell,
The reason why I cannot tell;
But this alone I know full well,
I do not love thee, Dr. Fell.

(Tom Brown)

PROCRASTINATION

To-MORROW you will live, you always cry;
In what far country does this morrow lie,
That 'tis so mighty long ere it arrive?
Beyond the Indies does this morrow live?
'Tis so far fetched, this morrow, that I fear
'Twill be both very old and very dear.
To-morrow I will live, the fool does say;
To-day itself's too late: the wise lived yesterday.

(Abraham Cowley)

INVITING A FRIEND TO SUPPER

To-NIGHT, grave sir, both my poor house and I
Do equally desire your company.
Not that we think us worthy such a guest,
But that your worth will dignify our feast,

With those that come; whose grace may make that seem
Something, which else could hope for no esteem.
It is the fair acceptance, sir, creates
The entertainment perfect, not the cates.
Yet shall you have, to rectify your palate,
An olive, capers, or some better salad
Ushering the mutton, with a short-legged hen
If we can get her, full of eggs, and then
Lemons, and wine for sauce; to these, a coney
Is not to be despaired of for our money;
And though fowl now be scarce, yet there are clerks,
The sky not falling, think we may have larks.
I'll tell you of more, and lie, so you will come:
Of partridge, pheasant, woodcock, of which some
May yet be there; and godwit if we can,
Knat, rail, and ruff too. Howsoe'er, my man
Shall read a piece of Virgil, Tacitus,
Livy, or of some better book to us,
Of which we'll speak our minds, amidst our meat;
And I'll profess no verses to repeat:
To this if aught appear, which I not know of,
That will the pastry, not my paper, show of.
Digestive cheese and fruit there sure will be,
But that which most doth take my Muse and me,
Is a pure cup of rich Canary wine,
Which is the Mermaid's now, but shall be mine:
Of which had Horace or Anacreon tasted,
Their lives, as do their lines, till now had lasted.
Tobacco, nectar, or the Thespian spring,
Are all but Luther's beer, to this I sing.
Of this we will sup free, but moderately,
And we will have no Pooly or Parrot by;
Nor shall our cups make any guilty men,
But, at our parting, we will be as when
We innocently met. No simple word
That shall be uttered at our mirthful board,
Shall make us sad next morning; or affright
The liberty that we'll enjoy to-night.

(*Ben Jonson*)

POST-OBITS AND THE POETS

He unto whom thou art so partial,
Oh, reader! is the well-known Martial,
The Epigrammatist: while living,
Give him the fame thou wouldst be giving;
So shall he hear, and feel, and know it—
  Post-obits rarely reach a poet.

(*Lord Byron*)

BOUGHT LOCKS

The golden hair that Gulla wears
  Is hers: who would have thought it?
She swears 'tis hers, and true she swears,
  For I know where she bought it.

(*Sir John Harington*)

TEMPERAMENT

In all thy humors, whether grave or mellow,
Thou'rt such a touchy, testy, pleasant fellow,
Hast so much wit and mirth and spleen about thee,
There is no living with thee nor without thee.

(*Joseph Addison*)

A HINTED WISH

You told me, Maro, whilst you live
You'd not a single penny give,
But that, whene'er you chanct to die,
You'd leave a handsome legacy:
You must be mad beyond redress,
If my next wish you cannot guess!

(*Samuel Johnson*)

WHAT MAKES A HAPPY LIFE

What makes a happy life, dear friend,
If thou wouldst briefly learn, attend—
An income left, not earned by toil;
Some acres of a kindly soil;

The pot unfailing on the fire;
No lawsuits, seldom town attire;
Health; strength with grace; a peaceful mind;
Shrewdness with honesty combined;
Plain living; equal friends and free;
Evenings of temperate gayety;
A wife discreet yet blithe and bright;
Sound slumber that lends wings to night.
With all thy heart embrace thy lot,
Wish not for death, and fear it not.

(Goldwin Smith)

ON THE DEATH OF A YOUNG AND FAVORITE SLAVE

DEAR youth, too early lost, who now art laid
Beneath the turf in green Labicum's glade,
O'er thee no storied urn, no labored bust
I rear to crumble with the crumbling dust;
But tapering box and shadowy vine shall wave,
And grass, with tears bedewed, shall clothe thy grave.
These gifts my sorrowing love to thee shall bring,
Gifts ever fresh and deathless as the Spring.
O when to me the fatal hour shall come,
Mine be as lowly and as green a tomb!

(Goldwin Smith)

EROTION

DEAR father and dear mother: Let me crave
Your loving kindness there beyond the grave
For my Erotion, the pretty maid
Who bears these lines. Don't let her be afraid!
She's such a little lassie—only six—
To toddle down that pathway to the Styx
All by herself! Black shadows haunt those steeps
And Cerberus the Dread who never sleeps.
May she be comforted, and may she play
About you merry as the livelong day,

And in her childish prattle often tell
Of that old master whom she loved so well.
Oh earth, bear lightly on her! 'Tis her due;
The little girl so lightly bore on you.

(*Kirby Flower Smith*)

Decimus Junius Juvenalis

60–140

CELESTIAL WISDOM

(From the Tenth Satire)

Must hapless man, in ignorance sedate,
Roll darkling down the torrent of his fate?
Must no dislike alarm, no wishes rise,
No cries invoke the mercies of the skies?
Inquirer, cease: petitions yet remain,
Which Heaven may hear: nor deem religion vain.
Still raise for good the supplicating voice,
But leave to Heaven the measure and the choice.
Safe in his power, whose eyes discern afar
The secret ambush of a specious prayer,
Implore his aid, in his decisions rest,
Secure, whate'er he gives, he gives the best.
Yet when the sense of sacred presence fires,
And strong devotion to the skies aspires,
Pour forth thy fervors for a healthful mind,
Obedient passions, and a will resigned;
For love, which scarce collective man can fill;
For patience, sovereign o'er transmuted ill;
For faith, that, panting for a happier seat,
Counts death kind Nature's signal of retreat.
These goods for man the laws of Heaven ordain,
These goods he grants, who grants the power to gain;
With these celestial Wisdom calms the mind,
And makes the happiness she does not find.

(*Samuel Johnson*)

The Emperor Hadrian

76–138

THE DYING CHRISTIAN TO HIS SOUL

Vital spark of heavenly flame!
Quit, oh quit this mortal frame:
   Trembling, hoping, lingering, flying,
   Oh the pain, the bliss of dying!
Cease, fond Nature, cease thy strife,
And let me languish into life.

Hark! they whisper; Angels say,
Sister Spirit, come away.
   What is this absorbs me quite?
   Steals my senses, shuts my sight,
Drowns my spirits, draws my breath?
Tell me, my Soul, can this be Death?
The world recedes: it disappears!
Heaven opens on my eyes! my ears
   With sounds seraphic ring:
Lend, lend your wings! I mount! I fly!
O Grave! where is thy Victory?
   O Death! where is thy Sting.

(Alexander Pope)

Decimus Magnus Ausonius

310–395

TO HIS WIFE

Be life what it has been, and let us hold,
Dear wife, the names we each gave each of old;
And let not time work change upon us two,
I still your boy, and still my sweetheart you.
What though I outlive Nestor? and what though
You in your turn a Sibyl's years should know?
Ne'er let us know old age or late or soon;
Count not the years, but take of each its boon.

(Terrot Reaveley Glover)

Claudius Claudianus

c. 400

THE OLD MAN OF VERONA

HAPPY the man, who his whole time doth bound
Within th' inclosure of his little ground,
Happy the man whom the same humble place,
The hereditary cottage of his race,
From his first rising infancy has known,
And by degrees sees gently bending down,
With natural propension, to that earth
Which both preserved his life, and gave him birth.
Him no false distant lights, by fortune set,
Could ever into foolish wanderings get.
He never dangers either saw or feared:
The dreadful storms at sea he never heard.
He never heard the shrill alarms of war,
Or the worse noises of the lawyers' bar.
No change of consuls marks to him the year;
The change of seasons is his calendar.
The cold and heat, winter and summer shows;
Autumn by fruits, and spring by flowers, he knows.
He measures time by landmarks, and has found
For the whole day the dial of his ground.
A neighboring wood, born with himself, he sees,
And loves his old contemporary trees.
He has only heard of near Verona's name,
And knows it, like the Indies, but by fame.
Does with a like concernment notice take
Of the Red sea, and of Benacus' lake.
Thus health and strength he to a third age enjoys,
And sees a long posterity of boys.
About the spacious world let others roam,
The voyage, life, is longest made at home.

(Abraham Cowley)

THE LONELY ISLE

DEEP in a distant bay, and deeply hidden
There is an island far away from me

Which lulls the tumbling waves to dreamy quiet;
And there steep cliffs against the water's riot
Stand up, and to their shelter ships are bidden,
Where those curved arms shut in a tranquil sea.

(*Howard Mumford Jones*)

Medieval Latin Students' Songs

12th–13th centuries

A SONG OF THE OPEN ROAD

We in our wandering,
Blithesome and squandering,
    Tara, tantara, teino!

Eat to satiety,
Drink with propriety;
    Tara, tantara, teino!

Laugh till our sides we split,
Rags on our hides we fit;
    Tara, tantara, teino!

Jesting eternally,
Quaffing infernally:
    Tara, tantara, teino!

Craft's in the bone of us,
Fear 'tis unknown of us:
    Tara, tantara, teino!

When we're in neediness,
Thieve we with greediness:
    Tara, tantara, teino!

Brother catholical,
Man apostolical,
    Tara, tantara, teino!

Say what you will have done,
What you ask 'twill be done!
    Tara, tantara, teino!

Folk, fear the toss of the
Horns of philosophy!
    Tara, tantara, teino!

Here comes a quadruple
Spoiler and prodigal!
    Tara, tantara, teino!

License and vanity
Pamper insanity:
    Tara, tantara, teino!

As the Pope bade us do,
Brother to brother's true:
    Tara, tantara, teino!

Brother, best friend, adieu!
Now, I must part from you!
    Tara, tantara, teino!

When will our meeting be?
Glad shall our greeting be!
    Tara, tantara, teino!

Vows valedictory
Now have the victory;
    Tara, tantara, teino!

Clasped on each other's breast,
Brother to brother pressed,
    Tara, tantara, teino!

(John Addington Symonds)

A PASTORAL

THERE went out in the dawning light,
    A little rustic maiden;
Her flock so white, her crook so slight,
    With fleecy new wool laden.

Small is the flock, and there you'll see
    The she-ass and the wether;
This goat's a he, and that's a she,
    The bull-calf and the heifer.

She looked upon the green sward, where
    A student lay at leisure:
"What do you there, young sir, so fair?"
    "Come, play with me, my treasure!"

(John Addington Symonds)

Latin Hymns

VENI CREATOR SPIRITUS

CREATOR SPIRIT, by whose aid
The world's foundations first were laid,
Come visit ev'ry pious mind;
Come pour thy joys on humankind;
From sin and sorrow set us free,
And make thy temples worthy thee.
    O source of uncreated light,
The Father's promis'd Paraclite!
Thrice holy fount, thrice holy fire,
Our hearts with heav'nly love inspire,
Come, and thy sacred unction bring
To sanctify us, while we sing!
    Plenteous of grace, descend from high,
Rich in thy sev'nfold energy,
Thou strength of his almighty hand,
Whose pow'r does heav'n and earth command!
Proceeding Spirit, our defense,
Who dost the gifts of tongues dispense,
And crown'st thy gift with eloquence!
    Refine and purge our earthy parts;
But, O, inflame and fire our hearts!
Our frailties help, our vice control,
Submit the senses to the soul;
And when rebellious they are grown,

Then lay thy hand, and hold 'em down.
  Chase from our minds th' infernal foe,
And peace, the fruit of love, bestow;
And lest our feet should step astray,
Protect and guide us in the way.
  Make us eternal truths receive,
And practice all that we believe:
Give us thyself, that we may see
The Father and the Son, by thee.
  Immortal honor, endless fame,
Attend th' Almighty Father's name:
The Savior Son be glorified,
Who for lost man's redemption died;
And equal adoration be,
Eternal Paraclete, to thee.

(John Dryden)

THE TE DEUM

Thee, Sovereign God, our grateful accents praise;
We own thee Lord, and bless thy wondrus ways;
To thee, Eternal Father, earth's whole frame,
With loudest trumpets, sound immortal fame.
Lord God of Hosts! for thee the heavenly powers
With sounding anthems fill the vaulted towers.
Thy Cherubims thrice, Holy, Holy, Holy, cry;
Thrice, Holy, all the Seraphims reply,
And thrice returning echoes endless songs supply.
Both heaven and earth thy majesty display;
They owe their beauty to thy glorious ray.
Thy praises fill the loud apostles' choir;
The train of prophets in the song conspire.
Legions of martyrs in the chorus shine,
And vocal blood with vocal music join.
By these thy church, inspir'd by heavenly art,
Around the world maintains a second part;
And tunes her sweetest notes, O God, to thee,
The Father of unbounded majesty;
The Son, ador'd copartner of thy seat,

And equal everlasting Paraclete.
Thou King of Glory, Christ, of the most high,
Thou coeternal filial Deity;
Thou who, to save the world's impending doom,
Vouchsaf'dst to dwell within a Virgin's womb;
Old tyrant Death disarm'd, before thee flew
The bolts of heaven, and back the foldings drew,
To give access, and make thy faithful way;
From God's right hand thy filial beams display.
Thou art to judge the living and the dead;
Then spare those souls for whom thy veins have bled.
O take us up amongst thy blest above,
To share with them thy everlasting love.
Preserve, O Lord, thy people, and enhance
Thy blessing on thine own inheritance.
For ever raise their hearts, and rule their ways;
Each day we bless thee, and proclaim thy praise:
No age shall fail to celebrate thy name,
No hour neglect thy everlasting fame.
Preserve our souls, O Lord, this day from ill;
Have mercy on us, Lord, have mercy still:
As we have hop'd, do thou reward our pain;
We've hop'd in thee—let not our hope be vain.

(John Dryden ?)

ITALIAN

Saint Francis of *Assisi*

CANTICA

Our Lord Christ: of order

Set Love in order, thou that lovest Me.
   Never was virtue out of order found;
And though I fill thy heart desirously,
   By thine own virtue I must keep My ground:
When to My love thou dost bring charity,
   Even she must come with order girt and gown'd.
      Look how the trees are bound
      To order, bearing fruit;
      And by one thing compute,
In all things earthly, order's grace or gain.

All earthly things I had the making of
   Were numbered and were measured then by Me;
And each was ordered to its end by Love,
   Each kept, through order, clean for ministry.
Charity most of all, when known enough,
   Is of her very nature orderly.
      Lo, now! what heat in thee,
      Soul, can have bred this rout?
      Thou putt'st all order out.
Even this love's heat must be its curb and rein.

                      (D. G. Rossetti)

Guido Guinicelli

13th century

SONNET

Of Moderation and Tolerance

He that has grown to wisdom hurries not,
   But thinks and weighs what Reason bids him do

And after thinking he retains his thought
    Until as he conceived the fact ensue.
Let no man to o'erweening pride be wrought,
    But count his state as Fortune's gift and due.
He is a fool who deems that none has sought
    The truth, save he alone, or knows it true.
Many strange birds are on the air abroad,
    Nor all are of one flight or of one force,
    But each after his kind dissimilar:
To each was portioned of the breath of God,
    Who gave them divers instincts from one source.
    Then judge not thou thy fellows what they are.

                           (*D. G. Rossetti*)

CANZONE

He perceives his Rashness in Love, but has no choice

I HOLD him, verily of mean emprise,
    Whose rashness tempts a strength too great to bear;
As I have done, alas! who turned mine eyes
    Upon those perilous eyes of the most fair.
        Unto her eyes I bow'd;
No need her other beauties in that hour
    Should aid them, cold and proud:
As when the vassals of a mighty lord,
    What time he needs his power,
Are all girt round him to make strong his sword.

With such exceeding force the stroke was dealt
    That by mine eyes its path might not be stay'd;
But deep into the heart it pierced, which felt
    The pang of the sharp wound, and waxed afraid;
        Then rested in strange wise,
As when some creature utterly outworn
    Sinks into bed and lies.
And she the while doth in no manner care,
    But she goes her way in scorn,
Beholding herself alway proud and fair.

And she may be as proud as she shall please,
  For she is still the fairest woman found:
A sun she seems among the rest; and these
  Have all their beauties in her splendor drown'd.
      In her is every grace,—
  Simplicity of wisdom, noble speech,
    Accomplished loveliness;
All earthly beauty is her diadem,
    This truth my song would teach,—
My lady is of ladies chosen gem.

Love to my lady's service yieldeth me,—
  Will I, or will I not, the thing is so,—
Nor other reason can I say or see,
  Except that where it lists the wind doth blow.
     He rules and gives no sign;
Nor once from her did show of love upbuoy
    This passion which is mine.
It is because her virtue's strength and stir
    So fill her full of joy
That I am glad to die for love of her.

                                (D. G. Rossetti)

Jacopo la Lentino

                             13th century

SONNET

Of his Lady in Heaven

I HAVE it in my heart to serve God so
  That into Paradise I shall repair,—
  The holy place through the which everywhere
I have heard say that joy and solace flow.
Without my lady I were loath to go,—
  She who has the bright face and the bright hair;
  Because if she were absent, I being there,
My pleasure would be less than nought, I know.
Look you, I say not this to such intent
  As that I there would deal in any sin:

I only would behold her gracious mien,
And beautiful soft eyes, and lovely face,
That so it should be my complete content
To see my lady joyful in her place.

(*D. G. Rossetti*)

Giacomino Pugliesi

13th century

CANZONE

Of his Dead Lady

DEATH, why hast thou made life so hard to bear,
  Taking my lady hence? Hast thou no whit
Of shame? The youngest flower and the most fair
  Thou hast plucked away, and the world wanteth it.
O leaden Death, hast thou no pitying?
Our warm love's very spring
  Thou stopp'st, and endest what was holy and meet;
And of my gladdening
Mak'st a most woeful thing,
And in my heart dost bid the bird not sing
  That sang so sweet.

Once the great joy and solace that I had
  Was more than is with other gentlemen:—
Now is my love gone hence, who made me glad.
  With her that hope I lived in she hath ta'en
And left me nothing but these sighs and tears,—
Nothing of the old years
  That come not back again,
Wherein I was so happy, being hers.
Now to mine eyes her face no more appears,
Nor doth her voice make music in mine ears,
  As it did then.

O God, why hast thou made my grief so deep?
  Why set me in the dark to grope and pine?
Why parted me from her companionship,
  And crushed the hope which was gift of thine?

To think, dear, that I never any more
Can see thee as before!
  Who is it shuts thee in?
Who hides that smile for which my heart is sore,
And drowns those words that I am longing for,
  Lady of mine?

Where is my lady, and the lovely face
  She had, and the sweet motion when she walk'd?—
Her chaste, mild flavor—her so delicate grace—
  Her eyes, her mouth, and the dear way she talk'd?—
Her courteous bending—her most noble air—
The soft fall of her hair? . . .
My lady—she to whom my soul
  A gladness brought!
Now I do never see her anywhere,
And may not, looking in her eyes, gain there
  The blessing which I sought.

So if I had the realm of Hungary,
  With Greece, and all the Almayn even to France,
Or Saint Sophia's treasure-hoard, you see
  All could not give me back her countenance.
For since the day when my dear lady died
From us, (with God being born and glorified,)
  No more pleasaunce
Her image bringeth, seated at my side,
But only tears. Ay me! the strength and pride
  Which it brought once.

Had I my will, beloved, I would say
  To God, unto whose bidding all things bow,
That we were still together night and day:
  Yet be it done as His behests allow.
I do remember that while she remain'd
With me, she often called me her sweet friend;
  But does not now,
Because God drew her towards Him, in the end.
Lady, that peace which none but He can send
  Be thine. Even so.

                            (*D. G. Rossetti*)

Folgore da San Geminiano

13th century

SONNET

Of Virtue

THE flower of Virtue is the heart's content;
　　And fame is Virtue's fruit that she doth bear;
　　And Virtue's vase is fair without and fair
Within; and Virtue's mirror brooks no taint;
And Virtue by her names is sage and saint;
　　And Virtue hath a steadfast front and clear;
　　And Love is Virtue's constant minister;
And Virtue's gift of gifts is pure descent.
And Virtue dwells with knowledge, and therein
　　Her cherished home of rest is real love;
　　And Virtue's strength is in a suffering will;
And Virtue's work is life exempt from sin,
　　With arms that aid; and in the sum hereof,
　　All Virtue is to render good for ill.

(*D. G. Rossetti*)

ON KNIGHTHOOD

I

THIS morn a young squire shall be made a knight;
　　Whereof he fain would be right worthy found,
　　And therefore pledgeth lands and castles round
To furnish all that fits a man of might.
Meat, bread, and wine he gives to many a wight;
　　Capons and pheasants on his board abound,
　　Where serving men and pages march around.
Choice chambers, torches, and wax candle light.
Barbed steeds, a multitude, are in his thought,
　　Mailed men at arms and noble company,
　　Spears, pennants, housing cloths, bells richly
　　　　wrought;
Musicians following with great barony
　　And jesters through the land his state have brought,
　　With dames and damsels whereso rideth he.

II

Comes Blithesomeness with mirth and merriment,
  All decked in flowers, she seemeth a rose-tree;
  Of linen, silk, cloth, fur, now beareth she
  To the new knight a rich habiliment;
Head-gear and cap and garland flower-besprent,
  So brave they were May-bloom he seemed to be;
  With such a rout, so many and such glee,
  That the floor shook. Then to her work she went;
And stood him on his feet in hose and shoon;
  And purse and gilded girdle neath the fur
  That drapes his goodly limbs, she buckles on;
Then bids the singers and sweet music stir,
  And showeth him to ladies for a boon
  And all who in that following went with her.

(John Addington Symonds)

Pier Moronelli di Fiorenza

13th century

CANZONETTA

A Bitter Song to his Lady

O LADY amorous,
Merciless lady,
Full blithely play'd ye
These your beguilings.
So with an urchin
A man makes merry,—
In mirth grows clamorous,
Laughs and rejoices,—
But when his choice is
To fall aweary,
Cheats him with silence.
This is Love's portion:—
In much wayfaring
With many burdens
He loads his servants,
But at the sharing,

The underservice
And overservice
Are alike barren.

As my disaster
Your jest I cherish,
And well may perish.
Even so a falcon
Is sometimes taken
And scantly cautell'd;
Till when his master
At length to loose him,
To train and use him,
Is after all gone,—
The creature's throttled
And will not waken.
Wherefore, my lady,
If you will own me,
O look upon me!
If I'm not thought on,
At least perceive me!
O do not leave me
So much forgotten!

If, lady, truly
You wish my profit,
What follows of it
Though still you say so?—
For all your well-wishes
I still am waiting.
I grow unruly,
And deem at last I'm
Only your pastime.
A child will play so,
Who greatly relishes
Sporting and petting
With a little wild bird:
Unaware he kills it,—
Then turns it, feels it,

Calls it with a mild word,
Is angry after,—
Then again in laughter
Loud is the child heard.

O my delightful
My own, my lady,
Upon the Mayday
Which brought me to you
Was all my haſte then
But a fool's venture?
To have my sight full
Of you propitious
Truly my wish was,
And to pursue you
And let love chaſten
My heart to the center.
But warming, lady,
May end in burning.
Of all this yearning
What comes, I beg you?
In all your glances
What is't a man sees?—
Fever and ague.

(*D. G. Rossetti*)

Ruſtico di Filippo

1200?–1270

SONNET

Of the Making of Maſter Messerin

WHEN God had finished Maſter Messerin,
  He really thought it something to have done:
  Bird, man, and beaſt had got a chance in one,
And each felt flattered, it was hoped, therein.
For he is like a goose i' the windpipe thin,
  And like a cameleopard high i' the loins;
  To which, for manhood, you'll be told, he joins

Some kinds of flesh-hues and a callow chin.
As to his singing he affects the crow;
   As to his learning, beasts in general;
     And sets all square by dressing like a man.
God made him, having nothing else to do;
   And proved there is not anything at all
     He cannot make, if that's a thing He can.

(D. G. Rossetti)

Guido Cavalcanti

1250–1301

SONNET

To his Lady Joan, of Florence

FLOWERS hast thou in thyself, and foliage
   And what is good, and what is glad to see;
The sun is not so bright as thy visàge;
   All is stark naught when one hath looked on thee;
There is not such a beautiful personage
   Anywhere on the green earth verily;
If one fear love, thy bearing sweet and sage
   Comforteth him, and no more fear hath he.
Thy lady friends and maidens ministering
   Are all, for love of thee, much to my taste:
And much I pray them that in everything
   They honor thee even as thou meritest,
And have thee in their gentle harboring:
   Because among them all thou art the best.

(D. G. Rossetti)

TO DANTE

RETURNING from its daily quest, my Spirit
   Changed thoughts and vile in thee doth weep to find:
   It grieves me that thy mild and gentle mind
Those ample virtues which it did inherit,
Has lost. Once thou didst loathe the multitude
   Of blind and maddening men: I then loved thee—
I loved thy lofty songs, and that sweet mood
   When thou wert faithful to thyself and men.

I dare not now, through thy degraded state,
  Own the delight thy strains inspire—in vain
I seek what once thou wert—we cannot meet
  As we were wont. Again and yet again
Ponder my words: so the false Spirit shall fly,
  And leave to thee thy true integrity.

(Percy Bysshe Shelley)

SONNET

Of an ill-favored Lady

Just look, Manetto, at that wry-mouth'd minx;
  Merely take notice what a wretch it is;
  How well contrived in her deformities,
How beastly favored when she scowls and blinks.
Why, with a hood on (if one only thinks)
  Or muffle of prim veils and scapularies,—
  And set together, on a day like this
Some pretty lady with the odious sphinx;—
Why, then thy sins could hardly have such weight,
  Nor thou be so subdued from Love's attack,
    Nor so possessed in Melancholy's sway,
But that perforce thy peril must be great
  Of laughing till the very heart-strings crack:
    Either thou'dst die, or thou must run away.

(D. G. Rossetti)

BALLATA

In Exile at Sarzana

Because I think not ever to return,
      Ballad, to Tuscany,—
      Go therefore thou for me
      Straight to my lady's face,
      Who, of her noble grace,
      Shall show thee courtesy.

Thou seekest her in charge of many sighs,
  Full of much grief and of exceeding fear.
But have good heed thou come not to the eyes
  Of such as are sworn foes to gentle cheer:

For, certes, if this thing should chance,—from her
   Thou then couldſt only look
   For scorn, and such rebuke
   As needs muſt bring me pain;—
   Yea, after death again
   Tears and fresh agony.

Surely thou knoweſt, Ballad, how that Death
 Assails me, till my life is almoſt sped:
Thou knoweſt how my heart ſtill travaileth
 Though the sore pangs which in my soul are bred:—
 My body being now so nearly dead,
   It cannot suffer more.
   Then, going, I implore
   That this my soul thou take
   (Nay, do so for my sake,)
   When my heart sets it free.

Ah! Ballad, undo thy dear offices
 I do commend my soul, thus trembling;
That thou mayſt lead it, for pure piteousness,
 Even to that lady's presence whom I sing.
 Ah! Ballad, say thou to her, sorrowing,
   Whereso thou meet her then:
   'This thy poor handmaiden
   Is come, nor will be gone,
   Being parted now from one
   Who served Love painfully.'

Thou also, thou bewildered voice and weak,
 That goeſt forth in tears from my grieved heart,
Shall, with my soul and with this ballad, speak
 Of my dead mind, when thou doſt hence depart,
 Unto that lady (piteous as thou art!)
   Who is so calm and bright,
   It shall be deep delight
   To feel her presence there.
   And thou, Soul, worship her
   Still in her purity.

          (D. G. Rossetti)

Francesco da Barberino

1264–1348

OF CAUTION

Say, wouldst thou guard thy son,
That sorrow he may shun?
Begin at the beginning
And let him keep from sinning.

Wouldst guard thy house? One door
Make to it, and no more.
Wouldst guard thine orchard-wall?
Be free of fruit to all.

(D. G. Rossetti)

Dante Alighieri

1265–1321

FROM LA VITA NUOVA

The narrative of the New Life is quaint, embroidered
with conceits, deficient in artistic completeness, but it
has the simplicity of youth, the charm of sincerity, the
freedom of personal confidence; and so long as there are
lovers in the world, and so long as lovers are poets, this
first and tenderest love-story of modern literature will be
read with appreciation and responsive sympathy.—
Charles Eliot Norton.

2

All ye that pass along Love's trodden way,
Pause ye awhile and say
　If there be any grief like unto mine:
I pray you that you hearken a short space
Patiently, if my case
　Be not a piteous marvel and a sign.
Love (never, certes, for my worthless part,
But of his own great heart),
　Vouchsafed to me a life so calm and sweet
That oft I heard folk question as I went
What such great gladness meant:—
　They spoke of it behind me in the street.

But now that fearless bearing is all gone
  Which with Love's hoarded wealth was given me;
  Till I am grown to be
So poor that I have dread to think thereon.

And thus it is that I, being like as one
  Who is ashamed and hides his poverty,
  Without seem full of glee,
And let my heart within travail and moan.

3

DEATH, always cruel, Pity's foe in chief,
Mother who brought forth grief,
  Merciless judgment and without appeal!
  Since thou alone haſt made my heart to feel
  This sadness and unweal,
My tongue upbraideth thee without relief.

And now (for I muſt rid thy name of ruth)
Behoves me speak the truth
  Touching thy cruelty and wickedness:
  Not that they be not known; but ne'ertheless
  I would give hate more ſtress
With them that feed on love in very sooth.

Out of this world thou haſt driven courtesy,
  And virtue, dearly prized in womanhood;
  And out of youth's gay mood
The lovely lightness is quite gone through thee.

Whom now I mourn, no man shall learn from me
  Save by the measure of these praises given.
  Whoso deserves not Heaven
May never hope to have her company.

8

THE thoughts are broken in my memory,
  Thou lovely joy, whene'er I see thy face;

When thou art near me, Love fills up the space,
Often repeating, "If death irk thee, fly."
My face shows my heart's color, verily,
  Which, fainting, seeks for any leaning-place;
  Till, in the drunken terror of disgrace,
  The very stones seem to be shrieking, "Die!"
It were a grievous sin, if one should not

  Strive then to comfort my bewildered mind
    (Though merely with a simple pitying)
  For the great anguish which thy scorn has wrought
  In the dead sight o' the eyes grown nearly blind,
    Which look for death as for a blessed thing.

9

At whiles (yea oftentimes) I muse over
  The quality of anguish that is mine
  Through Love: then pity makes my voice to pine,
Saying, "Is any else thus, anywhere?"
Love smiteth me, whose strength is ill to bear;
  So that of all my life is left no sign
  Except one thought; and that, because 'tis thine,
Leaves not the body but abideth there.
And then if I, whom other aid forsook,
  Would aid myself, and innocent of art
    Would fain have sight of thee as a last hope,
No sooner do I lift mine eyes to look
  Than the blood seems as shaken from my heart,
    And all my pulses beat at once and stop.

12

My lady carries love within her eyes;
  All that she looks on is made pleasanter;
  Upon her path men turn to gaze at her;
He whom she greeteth feels his heart to rise,
And droops his troubled visage, full of sighs,
  And of his evil heart is then aware:
  Hate loves, and pride becomes a worshiper.

O women, help to praise her in somewise.
Humbleness, and the hope that hopeth well,
  By speech of hers into the mind are brought,
    And who beholds is blessèd oftenwhiles,
    The look she hath when she a little smiles
  Cannot be said, nor holden in the thought;
'Tis such a new and gracious miracle.

14

A VERY pitiful lady, very young,
  Exceeding rich in human sympathies,
    Stood by, what time I clamor'd upon Death
And at the wild words wandering on my tongue
  And at the piteous look within mine eyes
    She was affrighted, that sobs choked her breath.
    So by her weeping where I lay beneath,
Some other gentle ladies came to know
My state, and made her go:
Afterward, bending themselves over me,
One said, "Awaken thee!"
    And one, "What thing thy sleep disquieteth?"
With that, my soul woke up from its eclipse,
The while my lady's name rose to my lips:

But utter'd in a voice so sob-broken,
  So feeble with the agony of tears,
    That I alone might hear it in my heart;
And though that look was on my visage then
  Which he who is ashamed so plainly wears,
    Love made that I through shame held not apart,
    But gazed upon them. And my hue was such
That they look'd at each other and thought of death;
Saying under their breath
Most tenderly, "O let us comfort him:"
Then unto me: "What dream
    Was thine, that it hath shaken thee so much?"
And when I was a little comforted,
"This, ladies, was the dream I dreamt," I said.

"I was a-thinking how life fails with us
 Suddenly after such a little while;
  When Love sobb'd in my heart, which is his home.
Whereby my spirit wax'd so dolorous
 That in myself I said, with sick recoil:
  'Yea, to my lady too this Death muſt come.'
  And therewithal such a bewilderment
Possess'd me, that I shut mine eyes for peace;
And in my brain did cease
Order of thought, and every healthful thing.
Afterwards, wandering
 Amid a swarm of doubts that came and went,
Some certain women's faces hurried by,
And shrieked to me, 'Thou too shalt die, shalt die!'

"Then saw I many broken hinted sights
 In the uncertain ſtate I ſtepp'd into.
  Meseem'd to be I know not in what place,
Where ladies through the ſtreets, like mournful lights,
 Ran with loose hair, and eyes that frighten'd you,
  By their own terror, and a pale amaze:
  The while, little by little, as I thought,
The sun ceased, and the ſtars began to gather,
And each wept at the other;
And birds dropp'd in mid-flight out of the sky;
And earth shook suddenly;
 And I was 'ware of one, hoarse and tired out,
Who ask'd of me: 'Haſt thou not heard it said? . . .
Thy lady, she that was so fair, is dead.'

"Then lifting up mine eyes, as the tears came,
 I saw the Angels, like a rain of manna,
  In a long flight flying back Heavenward;
Having a little cloud in front of them,
 After the which they went and said, 'Hosanna';
  And if they had said more, you should have heard.
  Then love said, 'Now shall all things be made
   clear:
Come and behold our lady where she lies.'

These 'wildering phantasies.
Then carried me to see my lady dead.
Even as I there was led,
  Her ladies with a veil were covering her;
And with her was such very humbleness
That she appeared to say, 'I am at peace.'

15

I FELT a spirit of love begin to stir
  Within my heart, long time unfelt till then;
  And saw Love coming towards me fair and fain,
(That I scarce knew him for his joyful cheer),
Saying, "Be now indeed my worshiper!"
  And in his speech he laugh'd and laugh'd again.
  Then, while it was his pleasure to remain,
I chanced to look the way he had drawn near
And saw the Ladies Joan and Beatrice
  Approach me, this the other following,
    One and a second marvel instantly.
And even as now my memory speaketh this,
  Love spake it then: "The first is christen'd Spring;
    The second Love, she is so like to me."

16

My lady looks so gentle and so pure
  When yielding salutation by the way,
  That the tongue trembles and has nought to say,
And the eyes, which fain would see, may not endure.
And still, amid the praise she hears secure
  She walks with humbleness for her array;
  Seeming a creature sent from Heaven to stay
On earth, and show a miracle made sure.
She is so pleasant in the eyes of men
That through the sight the inmost heart doth gain
  A sweetness which needs proof to know it by:
And from between her lips there seems to move
A soothing essence that is full of love,
  Saying for ever to the spirit, "Sigh!"

21

WHATEVER while the thought comes over me
  That I may not again
    Behold that lady whom I mourn for now,
About my heart my mind brings constantly
  So much of extreme pain
    That I say, Soul of mine, why stayest thou?
    Truly the anguish, soul, that we must bow
Beneath, until we win out of this life,
  Gives me full oft a fear that trembleth:
  So that I call on Death
Even as on Sleep one calleth after strife,
Saying, Come unto me. Life showeth grim
And bare; and if one dies, I envy him,

For ever, among all my sighs which burn,
  There is a piteous speech
    That clamors upon death continually:
Yea, unto him doth my whole spirit turn
  Since first his hand did reach
    My lady's life with most foul cruelty.
    But from the height of woman's fairness, she,
Going up from us with the joy we had,
  Grew perfectly and spiritually fair;
  That so she treads even there
A light of Love which makes the Angels glad,
And even unto their subtle minds can bring
A certain awe of profound marveling.

24

LOVE's pallor and the semblance of deep ruth
  Were never yet shown forth so perfectly
    In any lady's face, chancing to see
Grief's miserable countenance uncouth,
As in thine, lady, they have sprung to soothe,
  When in mine anguish thou hast looked on me;
    Until sometimes it seems as if, through thee,
My heart might almost wander from its truth.

Yet so it is, I cannot hold mine eyes
   From gazing very often upon thine
      In the sore hope to shed those tears they keep;
And at such time, thou mak'ſt the pent tears rise
   Even to the brim, till the eyes waſte and pine;
      Yet cannot they, while thou art present, weep.

26

A GENTLE thought there is will often ſtart,
   Within my secret self, to speech of thee:
   Also of Love it speaks so tenderly
That much in me consents and takes its part.
'And what is this,' the soul saith to the heart,
   'That cometh thus to comfort thee and me,
   And thence where it would dwell, thus potently
Can drive all other thoughts by its ſtrange art?'
And the heart answers: 'Be no more at ſtrife
   'Twixt doubt and doubt: this is Love's messenger
      And speaketh but his words, from him received;
And all the ſtrength it owns and all the life
   It draweth from the gentle eyes of her
      Who, looking on our grief, hath often grieved.'

28

YE pilgrim-folk, advancing pensively
   As if in thought of diſtant things, I pray,
   Is your own land indeed so far away—
As by your aspeɕt it would seem to be—
That this our heavy sorrow leaves you free
   Though passing through the mournful town midway;
   Like unto men that underſtand to-day
Nothing at all of her great misery?
Yet if ye will but ſtay, whom I accoſt,
   And liſten to my words a little space,
      At going ye shall mourn with a loud voice.
It is her Beatrice that she hath loſt;
   Of whom the leaſt word spoken holds such grace
      That men weep hearing it, and have no choice.

29

Beyond the sphere which spreads to widest space
　　Now soars the sigh that my heart sends above;
　　A new perception born of grieving Love
Guideth it upward the untrodden ways.
When it hath reached unto the end, and stays,
　It sees a lady round whom splendors move
　In homage; till, by the great light thereof
Abashed, the pilgrim spirit stands at gaze.
It sees her such, that when it tells me this
　　Which it hath seen, I understand it not,
　　It hath a speech so subtile and so fine.
And yet I know its voice within my thought
Often remembereth me of Beatrice:
　　So that I understand it, ladies mine.

(D. G. Rossetti)

Sonnet

TO GUIDO CAVALCANTI

Guido, I would that Lapo, thou, and I,
　　Led by some strong enchantment, might ascend
　　A magic ship, whose charmèd sails should fly
With winds at will, where'er our thoughts might
　　wend,
And that no change, nor any evil chance,
　Should mar our joyous voyage; but it might be
　That even satiety should still enhance
　Between our hearts their strict community,
And that the bounteous wizard then would place
　　Vanna and Bice and my gentle love,
　　Companions of our wandering, and would grace
With passionate talk, wherever we might rove,
　　Our time, and each were as content and free
　　As I believe that thou and I should be.

(Percy Bysshe Shelley)

SONNET

Of Beatrice d' Portinari, on All Saints' Day

Last All Saints' holy-day, even now gone by,
  I met a gathering of damozels:
    She that came first, as one doth who excels,
Had Love with her, bearing her company:
A flame burned forward through her steadfast eye,
  As when in living fire spirit dwells:
    So, gazing with the boldness which prevails
O'er doubt, I knew an angel visibly.
As she passed on, she bowed her mild approof
  And salutation to all men of worth
Lifting the soul to solemn thoughts aloof.
  In Heaven itself that lady had her birth,
I think, and is with us for our behoof:
  Blessed are they who meet her on the earth.

(*D. G. Rossetti*)

BALLATA

He will gaze upon Beatrice

Because mine eyes can never have their fill
Of looking at my lady's lovely face,
  I will so fix my gaze
That I may become blessed beholding her.
Even as an angel, up at his great height
Standing amid the light,
  Becometh blessed by only seeing God:—
So, though I be a simple earthly wight,
Yet none the less I might,
  Beholding her who is my heart's dear load,
Be blessed, and in the spirit soar abroad.
Such power abideth in that gracious one;
Albeit felt of none
  Save of him who, desiring, honors her.

(*D. G. Rossetti*)

SONNET

Of Beauty and Duty

Two ladies to the summit of my mind
  Have clomb, to hold an argument of love.
  The one has wisdom with her from above,
For every noblest virtue well designed:
The other, beauty's tempting power refined
  And the high charm of perfect grace approve:
  And I, as my sweet Master's will doth move,
At feet of both their favors am reclined.
Beauty and Duty in my soul keep strife,
  At question if the heart such course can take
    And 'twixt the two ladies hold its love complete.
    The fount of gentle speech yields answer meet,
  That Beauty may be loved for gladness sake,
And Duty in the lofty ends of life.

(D. G. Rossetti)

SESTINA

Of the Lady Pietra degli Scrovigni

To the dim light and the large circle of shade
I have clomb, and to the whitening of the hills,
There where we see no color in the grass.
Natheless my longing loses not its green,
It has so taken root in the hard stone
Which talks and hears as though it were a lady.

Utterly frozen is this youthful lady,
Even as the snow that lies within the shade;
For she is no more moved than is the stone
By the sweet season which makes warm the hills
And alters from afresh from white to green
Covering their sides again with flowers and grass.

When on her hair she sets a crown of grass
The thought has no more room for other lady,
Because she weaves the yellow with the green
So well that Love sits down there in the shade,—

Love who has shut me in among low hills
Faster than between walls of granite-stone.

She is more bright than is a precious stone;
The wound she gives may not be healed with grass:
I therefore have fled far o'er plains and hills
For refuge from so dangerous a lady;
But from her sunshine nothing can give shade,—
Not any hill, nor wall, nor summer-green.

A while ago, I saw her dressed in green,—
So fair, she might have wakened in a stone
This love which I do feel even for her shade;
And therefore, as one woos a graceful lady,
I wooed her in a field that was all grass
Girdled about with very lofty hills.

Yet shall the streams turn back and climb the hills
Before Love's flame in this damp wood and green
Burn, as it burns within a youthful lady,
For my sake, who would sleep away in stone
My life, or feed like beasts upon the grass,
Only to see her garments cast a shade.

How dark so'er the hills throw out their shade,
Under her summer-green the beautiful lady
Covers it, like a stone cover'd in grass.

(D. G. Rossetti)

Cino da Pistoia

1270–1336

MADRIGAL

*To his Lady Selvaggia Vergiolesi; likening his Love to
a search for Gold*

I am all bent to glean the golden ore
    Little by little from the river-bed;
        Hoping the day to see
When Crœsus shall be conquered in my store.
    Therefore, still sifting where the sands are spread,
        I labor patiently:

Till, thus intent on this thing and no more,—
  If to a vein of silver I were led,
      It scarce could gladden me.
And, seeing that no joy's so warm i' the core
  As this whereby the heart is comforted
      And the desire set free,—
Therefore, thy bitter love is still my scope,
  Lady, from whom it is my life's sore theme
More painfully to sift the grains of hope
  Than gold out of that stream.

(D. G. Rossetti)

SONNET

Of the Grave of Selvaggia, on the Monte della Sambuca

I was upon the high and blessed mound,
  And kissed, long worshipping, the stones and grass,
  There on the hard stones prostrate, where, alas!
That pure one laid her forehead in the ground.
Then were the springs of gladness sealed and bound,
  The day that unto Death's most bitter pass
  My sick heart's lady turned her feet, who was
Already in her gracious life renown'd.

So in that place I spake to Love, and cried:
  'O sweet my god, I am one whom Death may claim
    Hence to be his; for lo! my heart lies here.'
    Anon, because my Master lent no ear,
  Departing, still I called Selvaggia's name.
So with my moan I left the mountain-side.

(D. G. Rossetti)

CANZONE

His Lament for Selvaggia

Ay me, alas! the beautiful bright hair
  That shed reflected gold
    O'er the green growths on either side of the way:
Ay me! the lovely look, open and fair,
  Which my heart's core doth hold

With all else of that best remembered day;
   Ay me! the face made gay
With joy that Love confers;
Ay me! that smile of hers
   Where whiteness as of snow was visible
Among the roses at all seasons red!
      Ay me! and was this well,
O Death, to let me live when she is dead?

(D. G. Rossetti)

Cecco Angiolieri, da Siena

c. 1300

SONNET

Of Becchina in a Rage

WHEN I behold Becchina in a rage,
   Just like a little lad I trembling stand
   Whose master tells him to hold out his hand.
Had I a lion's heart, the sight would wage
Such a war against it, that in that sad stage
   I'd wish my birth might never have been plann'd,
   And curse the day and hour that I was bann'd
With such a plague for my life's heritage.
Yet even if I should sell me to the Fiend,
   I must so manage matters in some way
      That for her rage I may not care a fig;
Or else from death I cannot long be screen'd.
   So I'll not blink the fact, but plainly say
      It's time I got my valor to grow big.

(D. G. Rossetti)

SONNET

In absence from Becchina

MY heart's so heavy with a hundred things
   That I feel dead a hundred times a-day;
Yet death would be the least of sufferings,
   For life's all suffering save what's slept away;

Though even in sleep there is no dream but brings
  From dream-land such dull torture as it may.
And yet one moment would pluck out these stings,
  If for one moment she were mine to-day
Who gives my heart the anguish that it has.
  Each thought that seeks my heart for its abode
  Becomes a wan and sorrow-stricken guest:
Sorrow has brought me to so sad a pass
  That men look sad to meet me on the road;
  Nor any road is mine that leads to rest.

(D. G. Rossetti)

SONNET

He rails against Dante, who has censured his homage to Becchina

Dante Alighieri in Becchina's praise
  Won't have me sing and bears him like my lord.
  He's but a pinchbeck florin, on my word;
Sugar he seems, but salt's in all his ways;
He looks like wheaten bread, who's bread of maize;
  He's but a sty, though like a tower in height;
  A falcon, till you find that he's a kite;
Call him a cock!—a hen's more like his case.
Go now to Florence, Sonnet of my own,
  And there with dames and maids hold pretty parles,
  And say that all he is doth only seem.
And I meanwhile will make him better known
  Unto the Court of Provence, good King Charles;
  And in this way we'll singe his skin for him.

(D. G. Rossetti)

SONNET

Of all he would do

If I were fire, I'd burn the world away;
  If I were wind, I'd turn my storms thereon;
  If I were water, I'd soon let it drown;
If I were God, I'd sink it from the day;
If I were Pope, I'd never feel quite gay

Until there was no peace beneath the sun;
　　If I were Emperor, what would I have done?
I'd lop men's heads all around in my own way.
If I were Death, I'd look my father up;
　　If I were life, I'd run away from him;
　　　　And treat my mother to like calls and runs.
If I were Cecco (and that's all my hope),
　　I'd pick the nicest girls to suit my whim,
　　　　And other folk should get the ugly ones.

(*D. G. Rossetti*)

Francesco Petrarca

1304-1374

What he had achieved for the modern world was not merely to bequeath to his Italian imitators masterpieces of lyrical art unrivalled for perfection of workmanship, but also, and far more, to open out for Europe a new sphere of mental activity. Standing within the threshold of the middle ages, he surveyed the kingdom of the modern spirit, and, by his own inexhaustible industry in the field of scholarship, he determined what we call the revival of learning.—J. A. SYMONDS

VISIONS

I

BEING one day at my window all alone,
　　So manie strange things happened me to see,
As much it grieveth me to thinke thereon.
　　At my right hand a hynde appear'd to mee,
So faire as mote the greatest god delite;
　　Two eager dogs did her pursue in chace,
Of which the one was blacke, the other white:
　　With deadly force so in their cruell race
They pincht the haunches of that gentle beast,
　　That at the last, and in short time, I spide,
Under a rocke, where she alas, opprest,
　　Fell to the ground, and there untimely dide.
Cruell death vanquishing so noble beautie
Oft makes me wayle so hard a destenie.

II

After, at sea a tall ship did appeare,
   Made all of heben and white yvorie;
The sailes of golde, of silke the tackle were:
   Milde was the winde, calme seem'd the sea to bee,
The skie eachwhere did show full bright and faire:
   With rich treasures this gay ship fraighted was:
But sudden storme did so turmoyle the aire,
   And tumbled up the sea, that she (alas)
Strake on a rock, that under water lay,
   And perished past all recoverie.
O! how great ruth, and sorrowfull assay,
   Doth vex my spirite with perplexitie,
Thus in a moment to see lost, and drown'd,
So great riches, as like cannot be found.

III

The heavenly branches did I see arise
   Out of the fresh and lustie lawrell tree,
Amidst the young greene wood of paradise;
   Some noble plant I thought my selfe to see:
Such store of birds therein yshrowded were,
   Chaunting in shade their sundrie melodie,
That with their sweetnes I was ravisht nere.
   While on this lawrell fixed was mine eie,
The skie gan everie where to overcast,
   And darkened was the welkin all about,
When sudden flash of heavens fire out brast,
   And rent this royall tree quite by the roote;
Which makes me much and ever to complaine;
For no such shadow shal be had againe.

VI

At last so faire a ladie did I spie,
   That thinking yet on her I burne and quake;
On hearbs and flowres she walked pensively,
   Milde, but yet love she proudly did forsake;

White seem'd her robes, yet woven so they were,
  As snow and golde together had been wrought:
Above the waſt a darke clowde shrouded her,
  A ſtinging serpent by the heele her caught;
Wherewith she languisht as the gathered floure;
  And, well assur'd, she mounted up to ioy.
Alas, on earth so nothing doth endure,
  But bitter griefe and sorrowfull annoy:
Which makes their life wretched and miserable,
Tossed with ſtormes of fortune variable.

VII

When I beheld this fickle truſtles ſtate
  Of vaine worlds glorie, flitting too and fro,
And mortall men tossed by troublous fate
  In reſtles seas of wretchedness and woe;
I wish I might this wearie life forgoe,
  And shortly turne unto my happie reſt,
Where my free spirite might not anie moe
  Be vexed with sights, that doo her peace moleſt.
And ye, faire ladie, in whose bounteous breſt
  All heavenly grace and vertue shrined is,
When ye these rythmes doo read, and vew the reſt,
  Loath this base world, and thinke of heavens blis:
And though ye be the faireſt of Gods creatures,
Yet thinke, that Death shall spoyle your godly features.

                              (*Edmund Spenser*)

SUMMER IS COME

The soote season, that bud and bloom forth brings
With green hath clad the hill, and eke the vale.
The nightingale with feathers new she sings;
The turtle to her mate hath told her tale.
Summer is come, for every spray now springs;
The hart has hung his old head on the pale;
The buck in brake his winter coat he flings;
The fishes flete with new repairèd scale;

The adder all her slough away she slings;
The swift swallow pursueth the flies smale;
The busy bee her honey now she mings.
Winter is worn that was the flowers' bale,
And thus I see among these pleasant things
Each care decays, and yet my sorrow springs!

(*The Earl of Surrey*)

LOVE'S FIDELITY

Set me whereas the sun doth parch the green,
   Or where his beams do not dissolve the ice:
   In temperate heat, where he is felt and seen;
   In presence prest of people mad or wise;
Set me in high, or yet in low degree;
   In longest night, or in the shortest day;
   In clearest sky, or where the clouds thickest be;
   In lusty youth, or when my hairs are gray:
Set me in heaven, in earth, or else in hell,
   In hill or dale, or in the foaming flood;
   Thrall, or at large, alive whereso I dwell,
Sick or in health, in evil frame or good,
   Hers will I be; and only with this thought
   Content myself although my chance be nought.

(*The Earl of Surrey*)

LOVE'S INCONSISTENCY

I find no peace, and all my war is done;
   I fear and hope, I burn and freeze likewise;
   I fly above the wind, yet cannot rise;
   And nought I have, yet all the world I seize on;
That looseth, nor locketh, holdeth me in prison,
   And holds me not, yet can I 'scape no wise;
   Nor lets me live, nor die, at my devise,
   And yet of death it giveth none occasion.
Without eyes I see, and without tongue I plain;
   I wish to perish, yet I ask for health;
   I love another, and yet I hate myself;
I feed in sorrow, and laugh in all my pain;

Lo, thus displeaseth me both death and life,
And my delight is causer of my grief.

(Sir Thomas Wyatt)

SIGNS OF LOVE

IF amorous faith, a heart of guileless ways,
    Soft languors, courteously controlled desire,
    And virtuous will, kindled with noble fire,
And lengthened wanderings in a lightless maze;
If thoughts, which evermore the brow displays,
    Or words that faint and brokenly suspire,
    Still checked with fear and shame; if hues no
        higher
Than the pale violet hath, or love displays;
If holding some one than one's self more dear,
    If sorrowing and sighing evermore,
    If chewing grief, and rage, and many a cross,
If burning far away, and freezing near,
    Are signs that Love consumes me to the core,
    Yours, lady, is the fault and mine the loss.

(C. B. Cayley)

IF IT BE DESTINED

IF it be destined that my Life, from thine
    Divided, yet with thine shall linger on
Till, in the later twilight of Decline,
    I may behold those Eyes, their luster gone;
When the gold tresses that enrich thy brow
    Shall all be faded into silver-gray,
From which the wreaths that well bedeck them now
    For many a Summer shall have fall'n away;
Then should I dare to whisper in your ears
    The pent-up Passion of so long ago,
That Love which hath survived the wreck of years
    Hath little else to pray for, or bestow,
Thou wilt not to the broken heart deny
The boon of one too-late relenting Sigh.

(Edward FitzGerald)

Giovanni Boccaccio

1313-1375

SONNETS

Inscription for a Portrait of Dante

DANTE ALIGHIERI, a dark oracle,
  Of wisdom and of art, I am; whose mind
  Has to my country such great gifts assign'd
That men account my powers a miracle.
My lofty fancy passed as low as Hell,
  As high as Heaven, secure and unconfin'd;
  And in my noble book doth every kind
Of earthly lore and heavenly doctrine dwell.
Renownéd Florence was my mother,—nay,
  Stepmother unto me her piteous son,
    Through sin of cursed slander's tongue and tooth.
Ravenna sheltered me so cast away;
  My body is with her,—my soul with One
    For whom no envy can make dim the truth.

Of his last sight of Fiammetta

ROUND her red garland and her golden hair
  I saw a fire about Fiammetta's head;
  Thence to a little cloud I watched it fade,
Than silver or than gold more brightly fair;
And like a pearl that a gold ring doth bear,
  Even so an angel sat therein, who sped
  Alone and glorious throughout heaven, array'd
In sapphires and in gold that lit the air.
Then I rejoiced as hoping happy things,
  Who rather should have then discerned how God
    Had haste to make my lady all His own,
Even as it came to pass. And with these stings
  Of sorrow, and with life's most weary load
    I dwell, who fain would be where she is gone.

Of Three Girls and of their Talk

By a clear well, within a little field
  Full of green grass and flowers of every hue,
  Sat three young girls, relating (as I knew)
Their loves. And each had twined a bough to shield
Her lovely face; and the green leaves did yield
  The golden hair their shadow; while the two
  Sweet colors mingled, both blown lightly through
With a soft wind for ever stirred and still'd.
After a little while one of them said,
  (I heard her,) "Think! If, ere the next hour struck,
  Each of our lovers should come here to-day,
Think you that we should fly or feel afraid?"
  To whom the others answered, "From such luck
  A girl would be a fool to run away."

                        (*D. G. Rossetti*)

Fazio degli Uberti

                  1326–1360

OF ENGLAND, AND OF ITS MARVELS

Now to Great Britain we must make our way,
Unto which kingdom Brutus gave its name
What time he won it from the giants' rule.
'Tis thought at first its name was Albion,
And Anglia, from a damsel, afterwards.
The island is so great and rich and fair,
It conquers others that in Europe be,
Even as the sun surpasses other stars,
Many and great sheep-pastures bountifully
Nature has set there, and herein more bless'd,
That they can hold themselves secure from wolves.
Black amber also doth the land enrich,
(Whose properties my guide Solinus here
Told me, and how its color comes to it;)

And pearls are found in great abundance too.
The people are as white and comely-faced

As they of Ethiop land are black and foul.
Many hot springs and limpid fountain-heads
We found about this land, and spacious plains,
And divers beasts that dwell within thick woods.
Plentiful orchards too and fertile fields
It has, and castle-forts, and cities fair
With palaces and girth of lofty walls.
And proud wide rivers without any fords
We saw, and flesh, and fish, and crops enough.
Justice is strong throughout those provinces.

Now this I saw not; but so strange a thing
It was to hear, and by all men confirm'd,
That it is fit to note it as I heard;—
To wit, there is a certain islet here
Among the rest, where folk are born with tails,
Short, as are found in stags and such-like beasts.
For this I vouch,—that when a child is freed
From swaddling bands, the mother without stay
Passes elsewhere, and 'scapes the care of it.
I put no faith herein; but it is said
Among them, how such marvelous trees are there
That they grow birds, and this is their sole fruit.

Forty times eighty is the circuit ta'en,
With ten times fifteen, if I do not err,
By our miles reckoning its circumference.
Here every metal may be dug; and here
I found the people to be given to God,
Steadfast, and strong, and restive to constraint.
Nor is this strange, when one considereth;
For courage, beauty, and large-heartedness,
Were there, as it is said, in ancient days.

North Wales, and Orkney, and the bankes of Thames,
Land's End and Stonehenge and Northumberland,
I chose with my companion to behold.
We went to London, and I saw the Tower
Where Guenevere her honor did defend,

With the Thames river which runs close to it.
I saw the castle which by force was ta'en
With the three shields by gallant Lancelot,
The second year that he did deeds of arms.
I beheld Camelot despoiled and waste;
And was where one and the other had her birth,
The maids of Corbonek and Astolat.
Also I saw the castle where Geraint
Lay with his Enid; likewise Merlin's stone,
Which for another's love I joyed to see.
I found the tract where is the pine-tree well,
And where of old the knight of the black shield
With weeping and with laughter kept the pass,
What time the pitiless and bitter dwarf
Before Sir Gawaine's eyes discourteously
With many heavy stripes led him away.
I saw the valley which Sir Tristram won
When having slain the giant hand to hand
He set the stranger knights from prison free.
And last I viewed the field, at Salisbury,
Of that great martyrdom which left the world
Empty of honor, valor, and delight.

So, compassing that Island round and round,
I saw and hearkened many things and more
Which might be fair to tell but which I hide.

(D. G. Rossetti)

Franco Sacchetti

1335–1400?

CATCH

On a Wet Day

As I walk'd thinking through a little grove,
   Some girls that gathered flowers came passing me,
   Saying, "Look here! look there!" delightedly.
"Oh, here it is!" "What's that?" "A lily, love."
"And there are violets!"

"Further for roses! Oh, the lovely pets—
The darling beauties! Oh, the nasty thorn!
Look here, my hand's all torn!"
"What's that that jumps!" "Oh, don't! it's a grass-
  hopper!"
"Come run, come run,
Here's bluebells!" "Oh, what fun!"
"Not that way! Stop her!"
"Yes, this way!" "Pluck them, then!"
"Oh, I've found mushrooms! Oh, look here!" "Oh, I'm
Quite sure that further on we'll get wild thyme."

"Oh, we shall stay too long, it's going to rain!
There's lightning, oh there's thunder!"
"Oh, shan't we hear the vesper bell, I wonder?"
"Why, it's not nones, you silly little thing;
And don't you hear the nightingales that sing
Fly away O die away?"
"Oh, I hear something! Hush!"
"Why, where? what is it, then?" "Ah! in that bush!"
So every girl here knocks it, shakes and shocks it,
Till with the stir they make
Out skurries a great snake.
"O Lord! O me! Alack! Ah me! alack!"
They scream, and then all run and scream again,
And then in heavy drops down comes the rain.

Each running at the other in a fright,
Each trying to get before the other, and crying,
And flying, stumbling, tumbling, wrong or right;
One sets her knee
There where her foot should be;
One has her hands and dress
All smothered up with mud in a fine mess;
And one gets trampled on by two or three.
What's gathered is let fall
About the wood and not picked up at all.
The wreaths of flowers are scattered on the ground;
And still as screaming hustling without rest

They run this way and that and round and round,
She thinks herself in luck who runs the best.

I stood quite still to have a perfect view,
And never noticed till I got wet through.
(*D. G. Rossetti*)

Lorenzo de' Medici

1448–1492

A LYRIC

I

How can I sing light-souled and fancy-free,
When my loved lord no longer smiles on me?

Dances and songs and merry wakes I leave
   To lovers fair, more fortunate and gay;
Since to my heart so many sorrows cleave
   That only doleful tears are mine for aye:
   Who hath heart's ease, may carol, dance, and play;
While I am fain to weep continually.

How can I sing light-souled and fancy-free,
When my loved lord no longer smiles on me?

I too had heart's ease once, for so Love willed,
   When my lord loved me with love strong and great:
But envious fortune my life's music stilled,
   And turned to sadness all my gleeful state.
   Ah me! Death surely were less desolate
Than thus to live and love-neglected be!

How can I sing light-souled and fancy-free,
When my loved lord no longer smiles on me?

One only comfort soothes my heart's despair,
   And mid this sorrow lends my soul some cheer;
Unto my lord I ever yielded fair
   Service of faith untainted pure and clear;
   If then I die thus guiltless, on my bier
It may be she will shed one tear for me.

How can I sing light-souled and fancy-free,
When my loved lord no longer smiles on me?

(John Addington Symonds)

Niccolo Machiavelli

1469–1527

OPPORTUNITY

"But who art thou, with curious beauty graced,
O woman, stamped with some bright heavenly seal?
Why go thy feet on wings, and in such haste?"

"I am that maid whose secret few may steal,
Called Opportunity. I hasten by
Because my feet are treading on a wheel,

"Being more swift to run than birds to fly.
And rightly on my feet my wings I wear,
To blind the sight of those who track and spy;

"Rightly in front I hold my scattered hair
To veil my face, and down my breast to fall,
Lest men should know my name when I am there;

"And leave behind my back no wisp at all
For eager folk to clutch, what time I glide
So near, and turn, and pass beyond recall."

"Tell me; who is that Figure at thy side?"
"Penitence. Mark this well that by degrees
Who lets me go must keep her for his bride.

"And thou hast spent much time in talk with me
Busied with thoughts and fancies vainly grand,
Nor hast remarked, O fool, neither dost see
How lightly I have fled beneath thy hand."

(James Elroy Flecker)

Michelangelo Buonarroti

1475–1564

THE DOOM OF BEAUTY

Choice soul, in whom, as in a glass, we see,
  Mirrored in thy pure form and delicate,
  What beauties heaven and nature can create,
  The paragon of all their works to be!
Fair soul, in whom love, pity, piety,
  Have found a home, as from thy outward state
  We clearly read, and are so rare and great
  That they adorn none other like to thee!
Love takes me captive; beauty binds my soul;
  Pity and mercy with their gentle eyes
  Wake in my heart a hope that cannot cheat.
What law, what destiny, what fell control,
  What cruelty, or late or soon, denies
  That death should spare perfection so complete?

(*John Addington Symonds*)

CELESTIAL LOVE

No mortal thing enthralled these longing eyes
  When perfect peace in thy fair face I found;
  But far within, where all is holy ground,
  My soul felt Love, her comrade of the skies:
For she was born with God in Paradise;
  Nor all the shows of beauty shed around
  This fair false world her wings to earth have bound:
  Unto the Love of Loves aloft she flies.
Nay, things that suffer death, quench not the fire
  Of deathless spirits; nor eternity
  Serves sordid Time, that withers all things rare.
Not love but lawless impulse is desire:
  That slays the soul; our love makes still more fair
  Our friends on earth, fairer in death on high.

(*John Addington Symonds*)

ON THE BRINK OF DEATH

Now hath my life across a stormy sea
   Like a frail bark reached that wide port where all
   Are bidden, ere the final reckoning fall
   Of good and evil for eternity.
Now know I well how that fond phantasy
   Which made my soul the worshiper and thrall
   Of earthly art, is vain; how criminal
   Is that which all men seek unwillingly.
Those amorous thoughts which were so lightly dressed,
   What are they when the double death is nigh?
   The one I know for sure, the other dread.
Painting nor sculpture now can lull to rest
   My soul that turns to His great love on high,
   Whose arms to clasp us on the cross were spread.

(John Addington Symonds)

JOY MAY KILL

Too much good luck no less than misery
   May kill a man condemned to mortal pain,
   If, lost to hope and chilled in every vein,
   A sudden pardon comes to set him free.
Thus thy unwonted kindness shown to me
   Amid the gloom where only sad thoughts reign,
   With too much rapture bringing light again,
   Threatens my life more than that agony.
Good news and bad may bear the self-same knife;
   And death may follow both upon their flight;
   For hearts that shrink or swell, alike will break.
Let then thy beauty, to preserve my life,
   Temper the source of this supreme delight,
   Lest joy so poignant slay a soul so weak.

(John Addington Symonds)

LOVE'S JUSTIFICATION

Yes! hope may with my strong desire keep pace,
And I be undeluded, unbetrayed;

For if of our affections none find grace
In sight of Heaven, then wherefore hath God made
The world which we inhabit? Better plea
Love cannot have, than that in loving thee
Glory to that eternal peace is paid,
Who such divinity to thee imparts
As hallows and makes pure all gentle hearts.
His hope is treacherous only whose love dies
With beauty, which is varying every hour;
But, in chaste hearts uninfluenced by the power
Of outward change, there blooms a deathless flower,
That breathes on earth the air of paradise.

(William Wordsworth)

TO THE SUPREME BEING

The prayers I make will then be sweet indeed,
If Thou the spirit give by which I pray:
My unassisted heart is barren clay,
Which of its native self can nothing feed:
Of good and pious works Thou art the seed,
Which quickens only where Thou say'st it may;
Unless Thou show to us Thine own true way,
No man can find it: Father! Thou must lead.
Do Thou, then, breathe those thoughts into my mind
By which such virtue may in me be bred
That in Thy holy footsteps I may tread;
The fetters of my tongue do Thou unbind,
That I may have the power to sing of Thee,
And sound Thy praises everlastingly.

(William Wordsworth)

TO VITTORIA COLONNA

When the prime mover of my many sighs
  Heaven took through death from out her earthly
    place,
  Nature, that never made so fair a face,
  Remained ashamed, and tears were in all eyes.

O fate, unheeding my impassioned cries!
 O hopes fallacious! O thou spirit of grace,
  Where art thou now? Earth holds in its embrace
 Thy lovely limbs, thy holy thoughts the skies.
Vainly did cruel death attempt to stay
 The rumor of thy virtuous renown,
  That Lethe's waters could not wash away!
A thousand leaves, since he hath stricken thee down,
 Speak of thee, not to thee could Heaven convey,
  Except through death, a refuge and a crown.

        (*H. W. Longfellow*)

DANTE

WHAT should be said of him cannot be said;
 By too great splendor is his name attended;
  To blame is easier than those who him offended,
 Than reach the faintest glory round him shed.
This man descended to the doomed and dead
 For our instruction; then to God ascended;
  Heaven opened wide to him its portals splendid,
 Who from his country's, closed against him, fled.
Ungrateful land! To its own prejudice
 Nurse of his fortunes; and this showeth well
  That the most perfect most of grief shall see.
Among a thousand proofs let one suffice,
 That as his exile hath no parallel,
  Ne'er walked the earth a greater man than he.

        (*H. W. Longfellow*)

POEMS

3

Ravished by all that to the eyes is fair,
Yet hungry for the joys that truly bless,
My soul can find no stair
To mount to heaven, save earth's loveliness.
For from the stars above
Descends a glorious light
That lifts our longing to their highest height

And bears the name of love.
Nor is there aught can move
A gentle heart, or purge or make it wise,
But beauty and the starlight of her eyes.

(George Santayana)

Giovanni della Casa

1503–1556

TO SLEEP

O SLEEP, O tranquil son of noiseless Night,
  Of humid, shadowy Night; O dear repose
  For wearied men, forgetfulness of woes
  Grievous enough the bloom of life to blight!
Succor this heart that hath outworn delight,
  And knows no rest; these tired limbs compose;
  Fly to me, Sleep; thy dusky vans disclose
  Over my languid eyes, then cease thy flight.
Where, where is Silence, that avoids the day?
  Where the light dreams, that with a wavering tread
  And unsubstantial footing follow thee?
Alas! in vain I call thee; and these gray,
  These frigid shades flatter in vain. O bed,
  How rough with thorns! O nights, how harsh to me!

(John Addington Symonds)

Giovanni Battista Guarini

1537–1612

SPRING

O SPRING, thou youthful beauty of the year,
Mother of flowers, bringer of warbling quires,
Of all sweet new green things and new desires,
Thou, Spring, returnest; but, alas! with thee
No more return to me
The calm and happy days these eyes were used to see.
Thou, thou returnest, thou,
But with these returns now
Nought else but dread remembrance of the pleasure
I took in my lost treasure.

Thou ſtill, thou ſtill, art the same blithe, sweet thing
Thou ever waſt, O Spring;
But I, in whose weak orbs these tears arise,
And what I was no more, dear to another's eyes.

(*Leigh Hunt*)

Torquato Tasso

1544–1595

TO HIS MISTRESS IN ABSENCE

FAR from thy deareſt self, the scope
   Of all my aims,
   I waſte in secret flames;
And only live because I hope.

O when will Fate reſtore
   The joys, in whose bright fire
   My expeƈtation shall expire,
That I may live because I hope no more!

(*Thomas Stanley*)

Giordano Bruno

1548–1600

THE PHILOSOPHIC FLIGHT

Now that these wings to speed my wish ascend,
   The more I feel vaſt air beneath my feet,
   The more toward boundless air on pinions fleet,
   Spurning the earth, soaring to heaven, I tend:
Nor makes them ſtoop their flight the direful end
   Of Dædal's son; but upward ſtill them beat.
   What life the while with this death could compete,
   If dead to earth at laſt I muſt descend?
My own heart's voice in the void air I hear.
   Where wilt thou bear me, O rash man! Recall
   Thy daring will! This boldness waits on fear!
Dread not, I answer, that tremendous fall:
   Strike through the clouds, and smile when death is
     near,
   If death so glorious be our doom at all!

(*John Addington Symonds*)

Gabriello Chiabrera

1562–1637

EPITAPHS

I

WEEP not, beloved friends! nor let the air
For me with sighs be troubled. Not from life
Have I been taken; this is genuine life,
And this alone,—the life which now I live
In peace eternal; where desire and joy
Together move in fellowship without end.—
Francesco Ceni after death enjoined
That thus his tomb should speak for him. And surely
Small cause there is for that fond wish of ours
Long to continue in this world,—a world
That keeps not faith, nor yet can point a hope
To good, whereof itself is destitute.

III

O THOU who movest onward with a mind
Intent upon thy way, pause, though in haste!
'T will be no fruitless moment. I was born
Within Savona's walls, of gentle blood.
On Tiber's banks my youth was dedicate
To sacred studies; and the Roman Shepherd
Gave to my charge Urbino's numerous flock.
Well did I watch, much labored, nor had power
To escape from many and strange indignities;
Was smitten by the great ones of the world,
But did not fall; for Virtue braves all shocks,
Upon herself resting immovably.
Me did a kindlier fortune then invite
To serve the glorious Henry, king of France,
And in his hands I saw a high reward
Stretched out for my acceptance: but Death came.
Now, reader, learn from this my fate, how false,

How treacherous to her promise, is the world,
And truſt in God,—to whose eternal doom
Muſt bend the sceptered potentates of earth.

IV

THERE never breathed a man, who, when his life
Was closing, might not of that life relate
Toils long and hard. The warrior will report
Of wounds, and bright swords flashing in the field,
And blaſt of trumpets. He who hath been doomed
To bow his forehead in the courts of kings
Will tell of fraud and never-ceasing hate,
Envy and heart-inquietude, derived
From intricate cabals of treacherous friends.
I, who on shipboard lived from earlieſt youth,
Could represent the countenance horrible
Of the vexed waters, and the indignant rage
Of Auster and Boötes. Fifty years
Over the well ſteered galleys did I rule.
From huge Pelorus to the Atlantic Pillars,
Rises no mountain to mine eyes unknown;
And the broad gulfs I traversed oft—and—oft.
Of every cloud which in the heavens might ſtir
I knew the force; and hence the rough sea's pride
Availed not to my vessel's overthrow.
What noble pomp, and frequent, have not I
On regal decks beheld! yet in the end
I learned that one poor moment can suffice
To equalize the lofty and the low.
We sail the sea of life,—a calm one finds,
And one a tempeſt,—and, the voyage o'er,
Death is the quiet haven of us all.
If more of my condition ye would know,
Savona was my birth-place, and I sprang
Of noble parents: seventy years and three
Lived I,—then yielded to a slow disease.

VI

DESTINED to war from very infancy
Was I, Roberto Dati, and I took
In Malta the white symbol of the Cross.
Nor in life's vigorous season did I shun
Hazard or toil; among the sands was seen
Of Libya, and not seldom, on the banks
Of wide Hungarian Danube, 't was my lot
To hear the sanguinary trumpet sounded.
So lived I, and repined not at such fate:
This only grieves me, for it seems a wrong,
That ftripped of arms I to my end am brought
On the soft down of my paternal home.
Yet haply Arno shall be spared all cause
To blush for me. Thou, loiter not nor halt
In thy appointed way, and bear in mind
How fleeting and how frail is human life!

VIII

NOT without heavy grief of heart did he
On whom the duty fell (for at that time
The father sojourned in a diftant land)
Deposit in the hollow of this tomb
A brother's child, moft tenderly beloved!
Francesco was the name the youth had borne,—
Possobonnelli his illuftrious house;
And when beneath this ftone the corse was laid,
The eyes of all Savona ftreamed with tears.
Alas! the twentieth April of his life
Had scarcely flowered: and at this early time,
By genuine virtue he inspired a hope
That greatly cheered his country; to his kin
He promised comfort; and the flattering thoughts
His friends had in their fondness entertained
He suffered not to languish or decay.
Now is there not good reason to break forth
Into a passionate lament? O soul!
Short while a pilgrim in our nether world,

Do thou enjoy the calm empyreal air;
And round this earthly tomb let roses rise,—
An everlasting spring!—in memory
Of that delightful fragrance which was once
From thy mild manners quietly exalted.

(William Wordsworth)

Tomasso Campanella

1568–1639

THE PEOPLE

The people is a beast of muddy brain
  That knows not its own force, and therefore stands
  Loaded with wood and stone; the powerless hands
  Of a mere child guide it with bit and rein:
One kick would be enough to break the chain;
  But the beast fears, and what the child demands,
  It does; nor its own terror understands,
  Confused and stupefied by bugbears vain.
Most wonderful! with its own hand it ties
  And gags itself—gives itself death and war
  For pence doled out by kings from its own store.
Its own are all things between earth and heaven;
  But this it knows not; and if one arise
  To tell this truth, it kills him unforgiven.

(John Addington Symonds)

Vittorio Alfieri

1749–1803

TO DANTE

"Great father Alighier, if from the skies
This thy disciple prostrate thou dost see
Before thy gravestone, shaken with deep sighs,
O turn thou not in wrathfulness from me!
O of thy kindness, favoring pure desires,
Illuminate me with a ray of thine;
Must who to pristine, deathless fame aspires
Take arms 'gainst envy and each fell design?"

"I did so, son, to my great sorrow, for
Thereby the names of men too vile to tread
Under my feet are heard for evermore.
If thou doſt truſt in me, why droop thy head?
Go thunder, triumph, and if thou shouldſt chance
To meet with such, pass by nor deign a glance."

(*Lorna De' Lucchi*)

Jacopo Vittorelli

1749–1835

ON A NUN

OF two fair virgins, modeſt, though admired,
  Heaven made us happy; and now, wretched sires,
  Heaven for a nobler doom their worth desires,
And gazing upon *either, both* required.
Mine, while the torch of Hymen newly fired
  Becomes extinguish'd, soon—too soon—expires:
  But thine, within the closing gate retired,
Eternal captive, to her God aspires.
But *thou,* at leaſt, from out the jealous door,
  Which shuts between your never-meeting eyes,
  May'ſt hear her sweet and pious voice once more:
I to the marble, where *my* daughter lies,
  Rush,—the swoln flood of bitterness I pour,
  And knock, and knock, and knock—but none replies.

(*Lord Byron*)

Giacomo Leopardi

1798–1837

A SÈ STESSO

Now reſt for evermore, my weary heart!
Perished the laſt illusion I believed
Eternal, perished! Truly I can tell
How of our cherished dreams
The hope is quenched and the desire as well.
Now reſt for evermore!
Enough of ſtrife!

There's nothing worth one throb of thine; this earth
Deserveth not a sigh! Bitter is life
And wearisome, nought else;
The world's defiled!
Despair for the laſt time and then be ſtill!
Fate made us at our birth no gift save death;
Scorn nature now, and brutal deſtiny
Who ruleth hidden for the common ill,
And of all things the infinite vanity!

(Lorna De' Lucchi)

L'INFINITO

I ALWAYS loved this solitary hill,
This hedge as well, which takes so large a share
Of the far-flung horizon from my view;
But seated here, in contemplation loſt,
My thought discovers vaſter space beyond
Supernal silence and unfathomed peace;
Almoſt I am afraid; then, since I hear
The murmur of the wind among the leaves,
I match that infinite calm unto this sound
And with my mind embrace eternity,
The vivid, speaking present and dead paſt;
In such immensity my spirit drowns,
And sweet to me is shipwreck in this sea.

(Lorna De' Lucchi)

Giosuè Carducci

1836–1907

SNOWFALL

SILENTLY, slowly falls the snow from an ashen sky,
Cries, and sounds of life from the city rise no more,

No more the hawker's shout and the sound of running
  wheels,
No more the joyous song of love and youth arise.

Raucously from the somber spire through the leaden air
The hours moan, like sighs of a world removed from
time.

Wandering birds insistent knock on the glowing panes.
My ghostly friends return, and gaze, and call to me.

Soon, my dear ones, soon—be still, O dauntless heart—
Down to the silence I come, in the shadow I will rest.

(*Romilda Rendel*)

PRIMO VERE

BEHOLD from sluggish winter's arm
    Spring lifts herself again:
Naked before the steel-cold air
    She shivers as in pain;
Look, Lalage, is that a tear
    In the sun's eye which yet shines clear?

From beds of snow the flowers awake
    Lifting in deep amaze
To heaven their eager eyes: but yet
    More in that wistful gaze
Than wonder lies: sure trembles there,
    O Lalage, some memory fair,

Some dream which 'neath the coverlet white
    Of winter snow they dreamed,
Some sleeping sight of dewy dawns
    And summer suns that gleamed,
And thy bright eyes, O Lalage;
    Was not the dream a prophecy?

To-day my spirit sleeps and dreams;
    Where do my far thoughts fly?
Close to thy beauty's face we stand
    And smile, the spring and I;—
Yet, Lalage, whence come these tears?
    Has spring, too, felt the doom of years?

(*John Bailey*)

Popular Songs of Tuscany

1

"Sleeping or waking, thou sweet face,
Lift up thy fair and tender brow:
Liſt to thy love in this ſtill place;
He calls thee to thy window now:
But bids thee not the house to quit,
Since in the night this were not meet.
Come to thy window, ſtay within;
I ſtand without, and sing and sing:
Come to thy window, ſtay at home;
I ſtand without, and make my moan."

2

"It was the morning of the first of May,
In the close I went to pluck a flower;
And there I found a bird of woodland gay,
Who whiled with songs of love the silent hour.
O bird, who flieſt from fair Florence, how
Dear love begins, I prithee teach me now!—
Love it begins with music and with song,
And ends with sorrow and with sighs ere long."

3

"Passing across the billowy sea,
I let, alas, my poor heart fall;
I bade the sailors bring it me;
They said they had not seen it fall.

I asked the sailors, one and two;
They said that I had given it you.
I asked the sailors, two and three;
They said that I had given it thee."

4

"Strew me with blossoms when I die,
Nor lay me 'neath the earth below;
Beyond those walls, there let me lie,
Where oftentimes we used to go.
There lay me to the wind and rain;
Dying for you, I feel no pain:
There lay me to the sun above;
Dying for you, I die of love."

(*John Addington Symonds*)

SPANISH

Juan II of Castile

1405–1454

CANCION

O LOVE, I never, never thought
  Thy power had been so great,
   That thou couldst change my fate
By changes in another wrought,
Till now, alas! I know it.

I thought I knew thee well,
  For I had known thee long;
   But though I felt thee strong,
I felt not all thy spell.

Nor ever, ever had I thought
  Thy power had been so great,
   That thou couldst change my fate
By changes in another wrought
Till now, alas! I know it.

(George Ticknor)

Diego de Saldaña

15th century

EYES SO TRISTFUL

EYES so tristful, eyes so tristful,
Heart so full of care and cumber,
I was lapped in rest and slumber,
Ye have made me wakeful, wistful!
In this life of labor endless
Who shall comfort my distresses?
Querulous my soul and friendless
In its sorrow shuns caresses.

Ye have made me, ye have made me
Querulous of you, that care not,
Eyes so tristful, yet I dare not
Say to what ye have betrayed me.

(*H. W. Longfellow*)

Anonymous

15th century

VILLANCICO

THREE dark maids,—I loved them when
In Jaën,—
Axa, Fatima, Marien.

Three dark maids who went together
Picking olives in clear weather,
My, but they were in fine feather
In Jaën,—
Axa, Fatima, Marien!—

There the harvests they collected,
Turning home with hearts dejected,
Haggard where the sun reflected
In Jaën,—
Axa, Fatima, Marien—

Three dark Moors so lovely, they—
Three dark Moors so lovely, they
Plucked the apples on the day
Near Jaën,—
Axa, Fatima, Marien.

(*Thomas Walsh*) [1]

Cristobal de Castillejo

1490–1550

SOME DAY, SOME DAY

SOME day, some day
O troubled breast,

[1] Courtesy of the Hispanic Society of America.

Shalt thou find reſt.
If Love in thee
To grief give birth,
Six feet of earth
Can more than he;
There calm and free
And unoppressed
Shalt thou find reſt.
The unattained
In life at laſt,
When life is passed
Shall all be gained;
And no more pained,
No more diſtressed,
Shalt thou find reſt.

(*H. W. Longfellow*)

Anonymous

16th century ?

THE SIESTA

Airs! that wander and murmur round,
  Bearing delight where'er ye blow,—
Make in the elms a lulling sound,
  While my lady sleeps in the shade below.

Lighten and lengthen her noonday reſt,
  Till the heat of the noonday sun is o'er:
Sweet be her slumbers,—though in my breaſt
  The pain she has waked may slumber no more!
Breathing soft from the blue profound,
  Bearing delight where'er ye blow,
Make in the elms a lulling sound,
  While my lady sleeps in the shade below.

Airs! that over the bending boughs,
  And under the shadows of the leaves,
Murmur soft, like my timid vows,
  Or the secret sighs my bosom heaves,—

Gently sweeping the grassy ground,
   Bearing delight where'er ye blow,
Make in the elms a lulling sound,
   While my lady sleeps in the shade below.

(William Cullen Bryant)

Old Spanish Ballads

16th century ?

GENTLE RIVER, GENTLE RIVER

Gentle river, gentle river,
Lo, thy streams are stained with gore.
Many a brave and noble captain
Floats along thy willowed shore.

All beside thy limpid waters,
All beside thy sands so bright,
Moorish chiefs and Christian warriors
Joined in fierce and mortal fight.

Lords and dukes and noble princes
On thy fatal banks were slain;
Fatal banks that gave to slaughter
All the pride and flower of Spain.

There the hero, brave Alonso,
Full of wounds and glory died;
There the fearless Urdiales
Fell a victim by his side.

Lo! where yonder, Don Saavedra
Through their squadrons slow retires;
Proud Seville, his native city,
Proud Seville his worth admires.

Close behind a renegado
Loudly shouts with taunting cry:
"Yield thee, yield thee, Don Saavedra.
Dost thou from the battle fly?

"Well I know thy aged parents,
Well thy blooming bride I know;
Seven years I was thy captive,
Seven years of pain and woe.

"May our Prophet grant my wishes,
Haughty chief, thou shalt be mine;
Thou shalt drink that cup of sorrow
Which I drank when I was thine."

Like a lion turns the warrior,
Back he sends an angry glare;
Whizzing came the Moorish javelin,
Vainly whizzing through the air.

Back the hero full of fury
Sent a deep and mortal wound;
Instant sank the renegado
Mute and lifeless on the ground.

With a thousand Moors surrounded,
Brave Saavedra stands at bay;
Wearied out but never daunted,
Cold at length the warrior lay.

Near him, fighting, great Alonso
Stout resists the Paynim bands;
From his slaughtered steed dismounted
Firm entrenched behind him stands.

Furious press the hostile squadrons
Furious he repels their rage;
Loss of blood at length enfeebles;
Who can war with thousands wage?

Where yon rock the plain o'shadows
Close behind its foot retired,
Fainting sank the bleeding hero,
And without a groan expired.

(*Thomas Percy*)

THE LAMENTATION FOR CELIN

At the gate of old Granada, when all its bolts are barred,
At twilight, at the Vega-gate, there is a trampling
　　heard;
There is a trampling heard, as of horses treading slow,
And a weeping voice of women, and a heavy sound of
　　woe!—
"What tower is fallen? what star is set; what chief
　　come these bewailing?"
"A tower is fallen! a star is set!—Alas! alas for Celin!"

Three times they knock, three times they cry,—and
　　wide the doors they throw;
Dejectedly they enter, and mournfully they go;
In gloomy lines they mustering stand beneath the hollow
　　porch,
Each horseman grasping in his hand a black and flam-
　　ing torch;
Wet is each eye as they go by, and all around is wail-
　　ing,—
For all have heard the misery,—"Alas! alas for Celin!"

Him yesterday a Moor did slay, of Bencerrage's blood,—
'Twas at the solemn jousting,—around the nobles stood;
The nobles of the land were by, and ladies bright and
　　fair
Looked from their latticed windows, the haughty sight
　　to share:
But now the nobles all lament,—the ladies are bewail-
　　ing,—
For he was Granada's darling knight,—"Alas! alas for
　　Celin!"

Before him ride his vassals, in order two by two,
With ashes on their turbans spread, most pitiful to view;
Behind him his four sisters, each wrapped in sable veil,
Between the tambour's dismal strokes take up their dole-
　　ful tale;

When stops the muffled drum, ye hear their brotherless
    bewailing,
And all the people, far and near, cry,—"Alas! alas for
    Celin!"

O, lovely lies he on the bier, above the purple pall,
The flower of all Granada's youth, the loveliest of them
    all!
His dark, dark eyes are closed, his rosy lip is pale,
The crust of blood lies black and dim upon his bur-
    nished mail;
And evermore the hoarse tambour breaks in upon their
    wailing,—
Its sound is like no earthly sound,—"Alas! alas for
    Celin!"

The Moorish maid at the lattice stands,—the Moor
    stands at his door;
One maid is wringing of her hands, and one is weeping
    sore;
Down to the dust men bow their heads, and ashes black
    they strew
Upon their broidered garments, of crimson, green, and
    blue;
Before each gate the bier stands still,—then bursts the
    loud bewailing,
From door and lattice, high and low,—"Alas! alas for
    Celin!"

An old, old woman cometh forth, when she hears the
    people cry,—
Her hair is white as silver, like horn her glazed eye;
'Twas she that nursed him at her breast,—that nursed
    him long ago:
She knows not whom they all lament, but soon she well
    shall know!
With one deep shriek, she through doth break, when
    her ears receive their wailing,—
"Let me kiss my Celin, ere I die!—Alas! alas for Celin!"

                               (John Gibson Lockhart)

Gil Vicente

16th century

SONG

IF thou art sleeping, maiden,
　　Awake and open thy door.
'Tis the break of day, and we muſt away
　　O'er meadow, and mount, and moor.

Wait not to find thy slippers,
　　But come with thy naked feet;
We shall have to pass through the dewy grass
　　And waters wide and fleet.

(*H. W. Longfellow*)

Sister Marcela de Carpio de San Felix

16th century

AMOR MYSTICUS

LET them say to my lover
That here I lie!
The thing of His pleasure,—
His slave am I.

Say that I seek Him
Only for love,
And welcome are tortures
My passion to prove.

Love giving gifts
Is suspicious and cold;
I have all, my Beloved
When thee I hold.

Hope and devotion
The good may gain;
I am but worthy
Of passion and pain.

So noble a Lord
None serves in vain,
For the pay of my love
Is my love's sweet pain.

I love Thee, to love Thee,—
No more I desire;
By faith is nourished
My love's ſtrong fire.

I kiss Thy hands
When I feel their blows;
In the place of caresses
Thou giveſt me woes.

But in Thy chaſtising
Is joy and peace.
O Maſter and Love
Let Thy blows not cease.

Thy beauty, Beloved,
With scorn is rife,
But I know that Thou loveſt me
Better than life.

And because Thou loveſt me,
Lover of mine,
Death can but make me
Utterly Thine.

I die with longing
Thy face to see;
Oh! sweet is the anguish
Of death to me!

(*John Hay*)

Saint Teresa

1515–1582

IF, LORD, THY LOVE FOR ME IS STRONG

Iꜰ, Lord, Thy love for me is ſtrong
As this which binds me unto Thee,

What holds me from Thee, Lord, so long,
What holds Thee, Lord, so long from me?

O soul, what then desirest thou?
—Lord, I would see Thee, who thus choose Thee.
What fears can yet assail thee now?
—All that I fear is but to lose Thee.

Love's whole possession I entreat,
Lord, make my soul Thine own abode,
And I will build a nest so sweet
It may not be too poor for God.

O soul in God hidden from sin,
What more desires for thee remain,
Save but to love, and love again,
And, all on flame with love within,
Love on, and turn to love again?

(Arthur Symons)

LET MINE EYES SEE THEE

Let mine eyes see Thee,
Sweet Jesus of Nazareth,
Let mine eyes see Thee,
And then see death.

Let them see that care
Roses and jessamine;
Seeing Thy face most fair
All blossoms are therein,
Flower of seraphim,
Sweet Jesus of Nazareth
Let mine eyes see Thee,
And then see death.

Nothing I require
Where my Jesus is;
Anguish all desire,
Saving only this;

All my help is His,
He only succoreth.
Let mine eyes see Thee,
Sweet Jesus of Nazareth,
Let mine eyes see Thee,
And then see death.

(Arthur Symons)

Luis Vaz de Camoëns

1524–1580

ON THE DEATH OF CATARINA DE ATTAYDA

THOSE charming eyes within whose starry sphere
Love whilom sat, and smiled the hours away,—
Those braids of light, that shamed the beams of day,—
That hand benignant, and that heart sincere,—
Those virgin cheeks, which did so late appear
Like snow-banks scattered with the blooms of May,
Turned to a little cold and worthless clay,
Are gone, forever gone, and perished here,—

But not unbathed by Memory's warmest tear!
Death thou hast torn, in one unpitying hour,
That fragrant plant, to which, while scarce a flower,
The mellower fruitage of its prime was given;
Love saw the deed,—and as he lingered near
Sighed o'er the ruin, and returned to heaven!

(R. F. Burton)

SONNET

LEAVE me, all sweet refrains my lip hath made;
　　Leave me, all instruments attuned for song;
　　Leave me, all fountains pleasant meads among;
Leave me, all charms of garden and of glade;
Leave me all melodies the pipe hath played;
　　Leave me, all rural feast and sportive throng;
　　Leave me, all flocks the reed beguiles along;
Leave me, all shepherds happy in the shade.

Sun, moon and stars, for me no longer glow;
　　Night would I have, to wail for vanished peace;
Let me from pole to pole no pleasure know;
　　Let all that I have loved and cherished cease;
But see that thou forsake me not, my Woe,
　　Who wilt, by killing, finally release.

(Richard Garnett)

Luis de Góngora

1561–1627

LET ME GO WARM

Let me go warm and merry still;
And let the world laugh, an' it will.

Let others muse on earthly things,—
The fall of thrones, the fate of kings,
　　And those whose fame the world doth fill;
Whilst muffins sit enthroned in trays
And orange-punch in winter sways
The merry scepter of my days;—
　　And let the world laugh, an' it will.

He that the royal purple wears
From golden plate a thousand cares
　　Doth swallow as a gilded pill:
On feasts like these I turn my back,
Whilst puddings in my roasting-jack
Beside the chimney hiss and crack;—
　　And let the world laugh, an' it will.

And when the wintry tempest blows,
And January's sleets and snows
　　Are spread o'er every vale and hill,
With one to tell a merry tale
O'er roasted nuts and humming ale,
I sit, and care not for the gale;—
　　And let the world laugh, an' it will.

Let merchants traverse seas and lands,
For silver mines and golden sands;
  Whilſt I beside some shadowy rill,
Juſt where its bubbling fountain swells,
Do sit and gather ſtones and shells,
And hear the tale the blackbird tells;—
  And let the world laugh, an' it will.

For Hero's sake the Grecian lover
The ſtormy Hellespont swam over:
  I cross, without the fear of ill,
The wooden bridge that slow beſtrides
The Madrigal's enchanting sides,
Or barefoot wade through Yepes' tides;—
  And let the world laugh, an' it will.

But since the Fates so cruel prove,
That Pyramus should die of love,
  And love should gentle Thisbe kill;
My Thisbe be an apple-tart,
The sword I plunge into her heart
The tooth that bites the cruſt apart;—
  And let the world laugh, an' it will.

(H. W. Longfellow)

Lope de Vega

1562–1635

A SONG OF THE VIRGIN MOTHER

From Los Paſtores de Belen

As ye go through these palm-trees
O holy angels;
Sith sleepeth my child here
Still ye the branches.

O Bethlehem palm-trees
That move to the anger
Of winds in their fury,
Tempeſtuous voices,

Make ye no clamor,
Run ye less swiftly,
Sith sleepeth the child here
Still ye your branches.

He the divine child
Is here a-wearied
Of weeping the earth-pain,
Here for his rest would he
Cease from his mourning,
Only a little while,
Sith sleepeth this child here
Stay ye the branches.

Cold be the fierce winds,
Treacherous round him.
Ye see that I have not
Wherewith to guard him,
O angels, divine ones
That pass us a-flying,
Sith sleepeth my child here
Stay ye the branches.

(Ezra Pound)

Francisco de Quevedo y Villegas
1580–1645

SONNET: DEATH WARNINGS

I saw the ramparts of my native land,
   One time so strong, now dropping in decay,
   Their strength destroyed by this new age's way
That has worn out and rotted what was grand.
   I went into the fields; there I could see
   The sun drink up the waters newly thawed;
   And on the hills the moaning cattle pawed,
Their miseries robbed the light of day for me.

I went into my house; I saw how spotted,
   Decaying things made that old home their prize;
   My withered walking-staff had come to bend.

I felt the age had won; my sword was rotted;
  And there was nothing on which to set my eyes
    That was not a reminder of the end.

(John Masefield)

Pedro Calderon de la Barca

1600–1681

He exceeds all modern dramatists, with the exception of Shakespeare, whom he resembles, however, in the depth of thought and subtlety of imagination of his writings, and in the rare power of interweaving delicate and powerful comic traits with the most tragical situations.—PERCY BYSSHE SHELLEY.

THE DREAM CALLED LIFE

A DREAM it was in which I found myself.
And you that hail me now, then hailed me king,
In a brave palace that was all my own,
Within, and all without it, mine; until,
Drunk with excess of majesty and pride,
Methought I towered so big and swelled so wide
That of myself I burst the glittering bubble
Which my ambition had about me blown
And all again was darkness. Such a dream
As this, in which I may be walking now,
Dispensing solemn justice to you shadows,
Who make believe to listen; but anon
Kings, princes, captains, warriors, plume and steel,
Ay, even with all your airy theater,
May flit into the air you seem to rend
With acclamations, leaving me to wake
In the dark tower; or dreaming that I wake
From this that waking is; or this and that,
Both waking and both dreaming; such a doubt
Confounds and clouds our mortal life about.
But whether wake or dreaming, this I know
How dreamwise human glories come and go;
Whose momentary tenure not to break,
Walking as one who knows he soon may wake,
So fairly carry the full cup, so well

Disordered insolence and passion quell,
That there be nothing after to upbraid
Dreamer or doer in the part he played;
Whether to-morrow's dawn shall break the spell,
Or the laſt trumpet of the Eternal Day,
When dreaming, with the night, shall pass away.

(*Edward FitzGerald*)

FROM "LIFE IS A DREAM"

WE live, while we see the sun,
Where life and dreams are as one;
And living has taught me this,
Man dreams the life that is his,
Until his living is done.
The king dreams he is king, and he lives
In the deceit of a king,
Commanding and governing;
And all the praise he receives
Is written in wind, and leaves
A little duſt on the way
When death ends all with a breath.
Where then is the gain of a throne,
That shall perish and not be known
In the other dream that is death?
Dreams the rich man of riches and fears,
The fears that his riches breed;
The poor man dreams of his need,
And all his sorrows and tears;
Dreams he that prospers with years
Dreams he that feigns and foregoes,
Dreams he that rails on his foes;
And in all the world, I see,
Man dreams whatever he be,
And his own dream no man knows.
And I too dream and behold,
I dream and I am bound with chains,
And I dreamed that these present pains
Were fortunate ways of old.
What is life? a tale that is told;

What is life? a frenzy extreme,
A shadow of things that seem;
And the greatest good is but small,
That all life is a dream to all,
And that dreams themselves are a dream.

(*Arthur Symons*)

Gustavo Adolfo Becquer

1836–1870

THEY CLOSED HER EYES

THEY closed her eyes
That were still open;
They hid her face
With a white linen,
And, some sobbing,
Others in silence,
From the sad bedroom
All came away.

The nightlight in a dish
Burned on the floor;
It threw on the wall
The bed's shadow,
And in the shadow
One saw sometime
Drawn in sharp line
The body's shape.

The dawn appeared.
At its first whiteness
With its thousand noises
The town awoke.
Before that contrast
Of light and darkness,
Of life and strangeness
I thought a moment.
*My God, how lonely
The dead are!*

On the shoulders of men
To church they bore her,
And in a chapel
They left her bier.
Here they surrounded
Her pale body
With yellow candles
And black stuffs.

At the laſt ſtroke
Of the ringing for the Souls,
An old crone finished
Her laſt prayers.
She crossed the narrow nave,
The doors moaned,
And the holy place
Remained deserted.

From a clock one heard
The measured ticking,
And from a candle
The guttering.
All things there
Were so dark and mournful,
So cold and rigid,
That I thought a moment;
My God, how lonely
The dead are!

From the high belfry
The tongue of iron
Clanged, giving out
A laſt farewell.
Crape on their clothes,
Her friends and kindred
Passed in a line
In homage to her.

In the laſt vault
Dark and narrow,

The pickaxe opened
A niche at one end;
They laid her away there.
Soon they bricked the place up,
And with a gesture
Bade grief farewell.

Pickaxe on shoulder
The gravedigger,
Singing between his teeth,
Passed out of sight.
The night came down,
It was all silent.
Alone in the darkness
I thought a moment,—
My God, how lonely
The dead are!

In the dark nights
Of bitter winter,
When the wind makes
The rafter creak,
When the violent rain
Lashes the windows,
Lonely I remember
That poor girl.

There falls the rain
With its noise eternal,
There the northwind
Fights with the rain.
Stretched in the hollow
Of the damp bricks,
Perhaps her bones
Freeze with the cold.

Does the dust return to dust?
Does the soul fly to heaven?
Or is all the vile matter,
Rottenness, filthiness?

I know not, but
There is something—something—
Something which gives me
Loathing, terror,—
To leave the dead
So alone, so wretched.

(*John Masefield*)

Antonio Machado

1879–

POEMS

1

A FRAIL sound of a tunic trailing
across the infertile earth,
and the sonorous weeping
of the old bells.

The dying embers
of the horizon smoke.
White ancestral ghosts
go lighting the stars.

—Open the balcony-window. The hour
of illusion draws near. . . .
The afternoon has gone to sleep
and the bells dream.

2

FIGURES in the fields against the sky!
Two slow oxen plow
on a hillside early in autumn,
and between the black heads bent down
under the weight of the yoke,
hangs and sways a basket of reeds,
a child's cradle;
And behind the yoke stride
a man who leans towards the earth

and a woman who, into the open furrows,
throws the seed.
Under a cloud of carmine and flame,
in the liquid green gold of the setting,
their shadows grow monstrous.

(John Dos Passos)

Spanish Folk Songs

I

LET the rich man fill his belly;
    Let him fast that has no bread;
And he may sleep in the moon light
    That cannot find a bed.

*   *   *

If the sea were one great ink-pot
    And the sky of paper made,
The evil that's in women
    Could not all be said.

*   *   *

If the sea were one great ink-pot
    And of paper all the sky,
It were not enough for telling,
    How deeply men can lie.

*   *   *

To love with no return
    Is a sad thing to befall;
But a sadder, to come to die
    Before having loved at all.

(Havelock Ellis)

FRENCH

From The Provençal

Dance, and Provençal song, and sun-burnt mirth!—JOHN KEATES.

Marcabrun

12th century

AT THE FOUNTAIN

A FOUNT there is, doth overfling
Green turf and garden walks; in spring
A glory of white blossoming
Shines underneath its guardian tree;
And new-come birds old music sing;
And there, alone and sorrowing,
I found a maid I could not cheer,—

Of beauty meet to be adored,
The daughter of the castle's lord;
Methought the melody outpour'd
By all the birds unceasingly,
The season sweet, the verdant sward,
Might gladden her, and eke my word
Her grief dismiss, would she but hear.

Her tears into the fountain fell;
With sorry sighs her heart did swell;
"O Jesus, King Invisible!"
She cried,—"of thee is my distress!
Through thy deep wrong bereft I dwell:
Earth's blest have bidden us farewell,
On thee at thine own shrine to wait.

"And my true Love is also gone,
The free, fair, gentle, valiant One;

264

So what can I but make my moan,
And how the sad desire suppress
That Louis' name were here unknown,
The prayers, the mandates, all undone
Whereby I am made desolate?"

Soon as I heard this plaintive cry,
Moving the limpid wave anigh,
"Weep not, fair maid; so piteously,
Nor waſte thy roses!" thus I cried,—
"Neither despair, for He is by
Who brought this leafy greenery,
And He will give thee joy one day."

"Seigneur! I well believe," she said,—
"Of God I shall be comforted
In yonder world when I am dead;
And many a sinful soul beside;—
But now hath He prohibited
My chief delight. I bow my head,—
But heaven is very far away."

(Harriet Waters Preston)

Arnaut Daniel

BEL M'ES QUAN LO VENS M'ALENA

Softly sighs the April air,
  Ere the coming of the May;
Of the tranquil night aware,
  Murmur nightingale and jay;
Then, when dewy dawn doth rise,
  Every bird in his own tongue
Wakes his mate with happy cries;
  All their joy abroad is flung.

Gladness, lo! is everywhere
  When the firſt leaf sees the day;

And shall I alone despair,
  Turning from sweet love away?
Something to my heart replies,
  Thou too waſt for rapture ſtrung;
Wherefore else the dreams that rise
  Round thee when the year is young?

One, than Helen yet more fair,
  Lovelieſt blossom of the May,
Rose-tints hath and sunny hair,
  And a gracious mien and gay;
Heart that scorneth all disguise,
  Lips where pearls of truth are hung,—
God, who gives all sovereignties,
  Knows her like was never sung.

Though she lead through long despair,
  I would never say her nay,
If one kiss—reward how rare!—
  Each new trial might repay.
Swift returns I'd then devise,
  Many labors, but not long.
Following so fair a prize
  I could nevermore go wrong.

                              (*Harriet Waters Preston*)

Peire Vidal

12th century

SONG OF BREATH

Breathing do I draw that air to me
Which I feel coming from Provença,
All that is thence so pleasureth me
That whenever I heard good speech of it
I liſten a-laughing and ſtraightway
Demand for each word an hundred more,
So fair to me is the hearing.

No man hath known such sweet repair
'Twixt Rhone's swift ſtream and Vensa,

From the shut sea to Durensa,
Nor any place with joys so rare
As among the French folk where
I left my heart a-laughing in her care,
Who turns the veriest sullen unto laughter.

(Ezra Pound)

ℳarie de France

13th century

SONG FROM CHARTIVEL

HATH any loved you well, down there,
  Summer or winter through?
Down there, have you found any fair
  Laid in the grave with you?
Is death's long kiss a richer kiss
  Than mine was wont to be—
Or have you gone to some far bliss
  And quite forgotten me?

What soft enamoring of sleep
  Hath you in some soft way?
What charmed death holdeth you with deep
  Strange lure by night and day?
A little space below the grass,
  Out of the sun and shade;
But worlds away from me, alas,
  Down there where you are laid.

My brightest waved and wasted gold,
  What is it now to thee—
Whether the rose-red life I hold
  Or white death holdeth me?
Down there you love the grave's own green,
  And evermore you rave
Of some sweet seraph you have seen
  Or dreamt of in the grave.

There you shall lie as you have lain,
  Though in the world above,

Another live your life again,
　　Loving again your love:
Is it not sweet beneath the palm?
　　Is it not warm day rife
With some long mystic golden calm
　　Better than love and life?

The broad quaint odorous leaves like hands
　　Weaving the fair day through,
Weave sleep no burnished bird withstands,
　　While death weaves sleep for you;
And many a strange rich breathing sound
　　Ravishes morn and noon:
And in that place you must have found
　　Death a delicious swoon—

Hold me no longer for a word
　　I used to say or sing:
Ah, long ago you must have heard
　　So many a sweeter thing:
For rich earth must have reached your heart
　　And turned the faith to flowers;
And warm wind stolen, part by part,
　　Your soul through faithless hours.

And many a soft seed must have won
　　Soil of some yielding thought,
To bring a bloom up to the sun
　　That else had ne'er been brought;
And, doubtless, many a passionate hue
　　Hath made that place more fair,
Making some passionate part of you
　　Faithless to me down there.

(Arthur O'Shaughnessy)

WOULD I MIGHT GO FAR OVER SEA

WOULD I might go far over sea,
My Love, or high above the air,

And come to land or heaven with thee,
Where no law is, and none shall be.
Against beholding the most rare
Strange beauty that thou hast for me.

Alas, for, in this bitter land,
Full many a written curse doth stand
Against the kiss thy lips should bear;
Against the sweet gift of thy hands;
Against the knowing that thou art fair,
And too fond loving of thy hair.

(*Arthur O'Shaughnessy*)

Charles d'Orleans

1391–1465

SPRING

THE year has changed his mantle cold
  Of wind, of rain, of bitter air;
And he goes clad in cloth of gold,
  Of laughing suns and season fair;
No bird or beast of wood or wold
  But doth with cry or song declare
The year lays down his mantle cold.
All founts, all rivers, seaward rolled,
  The pleasant summer livery wear,
  With silver studs on broidered vair;
The world puts off its raiment old,
The year lays down his mantle cold.

(*Andrew Lang*)

ALONS AU BOIS LE MAY CUEILLIR

WE'LL to the woods and gather may
Fresh from the footprints of the rain;
  We'll to the woods, at every vein
To drink the spirit of the day.
The winds of the spring are out at play,
  The needs of spring in heart and brain.
We'll to the woods and gather may
  Fresh from the footprints of the rain.

The world's too near her end, you say?—
 Hark to the blackbird's mad refrain.
 It waits for her, the vaſt Inane?—
Then, girls, to help her on the way
We'll to the woods and gather may.

(W. E. Henley)

Anonymous

JOHN OF TOURS

JOHN of Tours is back with peace,
But he comes home ill at ease.

"Good-morrow, mother." "Good-morrow, son,
Your wife has borne you a little one."

"Go now, mother, go before,
Make me a bed upon the floor.

"Very low your feet muſt fall,
That my wife hear not at all."

As it neared the midnight toll,
John of Tours gives up his soul.

"Tell me now, my mother dear,
What's the crying that I hear?"

"Daughter, it's the children wake
Crying with their teeth that ache."

"Tell me, though, my mother dear,
What's the knocking that I hear?"

"Daughter, it's the carpenter
Mending planks upon the ſtair."

"Tell me, too, my mother dear,
'What is the singing that I hear?"

"Daughter, it's the priests in rows
Going round about our house."

"Tell me then, my mother, my dear,
What's the dress that I should wear?"

"Daughter, any reds or blues,
But the black is most in use."

"Nay, but say, my mother, my dear,
Why do you fall weeping here?"

"Oh, the truth must be said,—
It's that John of Tours is dead."

"Mother, let the sexton know
That the grave must be for two;

"Aye, and still have room to spare,
For you must shut the baby there."

(D. G. Rossetti)

BALLADE DE MARGUERITE

I AM weary of lying within the chase
When the knights are meeting in the market-place.

Nay, go not thou to the red-roofed town
Lest the hoofs of the war-horse tread thee down.

But I would not go where the Squires ride,
I would only walk by my Lady's side.

Alack, and alack, thou art overbold,
A Forester's son may not eat of gold.

Will she love me the less that my Father is seen
Each Martinmas day in a doublet green?

Perchance she is sewing at tapestrie;
Spindle and loom are not meet for thee.

Ah, if she is working the arras bright
I might ravel the threads by the fire-light.

Perchance she is hunting of the deer,
How could you follow o'er hill and mere?

Ah, if she is riding with the court,
I might run beside her and wind the morte.

Perchance she is kneeling in St. Denis,
(On her soul may our Lady have gramercy).

Ah, if she is praying in lone chapelle,
I might swing the censer and ring the bell.

Come in, my son, for you look sae pale,
The father shall fill thee a stoup of ale.

But who are these knights in bright array?
Is it a pageant the rich folks play?

'Tis the king of England from over sea,
Who has come unto visit our fair countrie.

But why does the curfew toll sae low?
And why do the mourners walk a-row?

O 'tis Hugh of Amiens, my sister's son,
Who is lying stark, for his day is done.

Nay, nay, for I see white lilies clear;
It is no strong man who lies on the bier.

O 'tis old Dame Jeannette that kept the hall,
I knew she would die at the autumn fall.

Dame Jeannette has not that gold-brown hair,
Old Jeannette was not a maiden fair.

O 'tis none of our kith and none of our kin,
(Her soul may our Lady assoil from sin).

But I hear the boy's voice chaunting sweet,
"Elle est morte, la Marguerite."

Come in, my son, and lie on the bed,
And let the dead folk bury their dead.

O mother, you know I loved her true:
O mother, hath one grave room for two?

(Oscar Wilde)

MEDIEVAL NORMAN SONGS

I

FAIR is her body, bright her eye,
With smiles her mouth is kind to me;
Then, think no evil, this is she
Whom God hath made my only joy.

Between the earth and heaven high
There is no maid so fair as she;
The beauty of her sweet body
Doth ever fill my heart with joy.

He is a knave, nor do I lie,
Who loveth her not heartily;
The grace that shines from her **body**
Giveth to lovers all great joy.

II

Sad, lost in thought, and mute I go:
  The cause, ah me! you know full well:
  But see that nought thereof you tell,
For men will only laugh at woe—
For men will only laugh at woe.

V

I found at daybreak yeſter morn,
Close by the nest where she was born,
  A tender turtle dove:
    Oha! ohé! ohesa, hesa, hé!

She fluttered, but she could not fly;
I heard, but would not heed her cry:
  She had not learned to love:
    Oha! ohé! ohesa, hesa, hé!

Now she is quiet on my breaſt,
And from her new and living neſt
  She doth not seek to rove:
    Oha! ohé! ohesa, hesa, hé!

VIII

O Love, my love, and perfeᴄt bliss!
God in his goodness grant me this—
  I see thee soon again.
Nought else I need to take away
The grief that for thy sake alway
  Doth keep me in great pain.

Alas, I know not what to do,
Nor how to get good news and true:
  Dear God, I pray to Thee;
If else Thou canſt not comfort me,
Of Thy great mercy make that he
  Send speedy news to me.

Within my father's garden walls
There is a tree—when April falls
  It blossometh alway.
There wend I oft in winter drear,
Yes, and in spring, the winds to hear,
  The sweet winds at their play.

XII

My love for him shall be
    Fair love and true:
      For he loves me, I know,
And I love him, pardie!

And for I know that he
    Doth love me so,
      I should be all untrue
To love but him, pardie!

XIII

Beneath the branch of the green may
   My merry heart sleeps happily,
     Waiting for him who promised me
To meet me here again this day.

And what is that I would not do
   To please my love so dear to me?
He loves me with leal heart and true,
   And I love him no less, pardie.

Perchance I see him but a day;
   Yet maketh he my heart so free—
     His beauty so rejoiceth me—
That month thereafter I am gay.

XIV

They have said evil of my dear;
Therefore my heart is vexed and drear:
   But what is it to them
If he be fair or foul to see,
Since he is perfect joy to me.

He loves me well: the like do I:
I do not look with half an eye,
   But seek to pleasure him.

From all the rest I choose him here;
I want no other for my dear:
   How then should he displease
Those who may leave him if they please?
   God keep him from all fear.

XVII

Maid Marjory sits at the castle gate:
   With groans and sighs
   She weeps and cries:
Her grief it is great.
Her father asks, "Daughter, what is your woe?
Seek you a husband or lord I trow?"
   "Let husbands be.
   Give my love to me,
Who pines in the dungeon dark below."

"I' faith, my daughter, thou'll long want him;
For he hangs to-morrow when dawn is dim."

"Then bury my corpse at the gallows' feet;
And men will say they were true lovers sweet."

(John Addington Symonds)

BALLADS

LE PÈRE SÉVÈRE

KING LOUIS on his bridge is he,
He holds his daughter on his knee.

She asks a husband at his hand
That is not worth a rood of land.

"Give up your lover speedily,
Or you within the tower must lie."

"Although I must the prison dree,
I will not change my love for thee.

"I will not change my lover fair,
Not for the mother that me bare.

"I will not change my true lover
For friends or for my father dear."

"Now where are all my pages keen,
And where are all my serving men?

"My daughter muſt lie in the tower alway,
Where she shall never see the day."

.   .   .   .

Seven long years are paſt and gone
And there has seen her never one.

At ending of the seventh year.
Her father goes to visit her.

"My child, my child, how may you be?"
"O father, it fares ill with me.

"My feet are wasted in the mold,
The worms they gnaw my side so cold."

"My child, change your love speedily
Or you muſt ſtill in prison lie."

" 'Tis better far the cold to dree
Than give my true love up for thee."

(Andrew Lang)

Lost for a Rose's Sake

I LAVED my hands,
    By the water side;
With the willow leaves
    My hands I dried.

The nightingale sung
    On the bough of the tree;
Sing, sweet nightingale,
    It is well with thee.

Thou haſt heart's delight,
    I have sad heart's sorrow
For a false, false maid
    That will wed to-morrow.

'Tis all for a rose,
    That I gave her not,
And I would that it grew
    In the garden plot.

And I would the rose-tree
    Were ſtill to set,
That my love Marie
    Might love me yet.

(Andrew Lang)

François Villon

1431–1489

No one has ever more skilfully communicated his own disenchantments; no one ever blown a more ear-piercing note of sadness. It is in death that he finds his trueſt inspiration; in the swift and sorrowful change that over-takes beauty; in the ſtrange revolution by which great fortunes and renowns are diminished to a handful of churchyard duſt; and in the utter passing away of what was once lovable and mighty.—ROBERT LOUIS STEVENSON.

BALLAD OF THE GIBBET

An Epitaph in the form of a ballad that François Villon wrote of himself and his company, they expecting shortly to be hanged.

BROTHERS and men that shall after us be,
    Let not your hearts be hard to us:
For pitying this our misery
    Ye shall find God the more piteous.
    Look on us six that are hanging thus,
And for the flesh that so much we cherished
How it is eaten of birds and perished,
    And ashes and duſt fill our bones' place,
Mock not at us that so feeble be,
    But pray God pardon us out of His grace.

Liſten we pray you, and look not in scorn,
   Though juſtly, in sooth, we are caſt to die;
Ye wot no man so wise is born
   That keeps his wisdom conſtantly.
   Be ye then merciful, and cry
To Mary's Son that is piteous,
That his mercy take no ſtain from us,
   Saving us out of the fiery place.
We are but dead, let no soul deny
   To pray God succor us of His grace.

The rain out of heaven has washed us clean,
   The sun has scorched us black and bare,
Ravens and rooks have pecked at our eyne,
   And feathered their neſts with our beards
      and hair.
   Round are we tossed, and here and there,
This way and that, at the wild wind's will,
Never a moment my body is ſtill;
   Birds they are busy about my face.
Live not as we, not fare as we fare;
   Pray God pardon us out of His grace.

L'envoy

Prince Jesus, Maſter of all, to thee
We pray Hell gain no maſtery,
   That we come never anear that place;
And ye men, make no mockery,
   Pray God, pardon us out of His grace.
               (*Andrew Lang*)

RONDEL

Good-by, the tears are in my eyes;
   Farewell, farewell, my prettieſt;
   Farewell, of women born the beſt;
Good-by, the saddeſt of good-bys.
Farewell, with many vows and sighs
   My sad heart leaves you to your reſt;

Farewell, the tears are in my eyes;
Farewell, from you my miseries
  Are more than now may be confessed,
  And most by thee have I been blessed,
Yea, and for thee have wasted sighs;
Good-by, the last of my good-bys.

(Andrew Lang)

NO, I AM NOT AS OTHERS ARE

No, I am not, as others are,
Child of the angels, with a wreath
Of planets or of any star.
My father's dead, and lies beneath
The churchyard stone: God rest his breath!
I know that my poor old mother
(And she too knows) must come to death,
And that her son must follow her.

I know that rich and poor and all,
Foolish and wise, and priest and lay,
Mean folk and noble, great and small,
High and low, fair and foul, and they
That wore rich clothing on the way,
Being of whatever stock or stem,
And are coiffed newly every day,
Death shall take every one of them.

Paris and Helen are both dead.
Whoever dies, dies with much pain;
For when his wind and breath are sped
His gall breaks on his heart, and then
He sweats, God knows that sweat of men!
Then shall he pray against his doom
Child, brother, sister, all in vain:
None will be surety in his room.

Death makes him tremble and turn pale,
His veins stretch and his nose fall in,
His flesh grow moist and his neck swell,
Joints and nerves lengthen and wax thin;

Body of woman, that hath been
Soft, tender, precious, smooth and even,
Muſt thou be spoiled in bone and skin?
Yes, or else go alive to heaven.

(*Arthur Symons*)

THE BALAD OF DEAD LADIES

TELL me now in what hidden way is
  Lady Flora the lovely Roman?
Where's Hipparchia, and where is Thais,
  Neither of them the fairer woman?
  Where is Echo, beheld of no man,
Only heard on river and mere,—
  She whose beauty was more than human? . . .
But where are the snows of yeſter-year?

Where's Héloise, the learned nun,
  For whose sake Abeillard, I ween,
Loſt manhood and put prieſthood on?
  (From Love he won such dule and teen!)
  And where, I pray you, is the Queen
Who willed that Buridan should ſteer
  Sewed in a sack's mouth down the Seine? . . .
But where are the snows of yeſter-year?

White Queen Blanche, like a queen of lilies,
  With a voice like any mermaiden,—
Bertha Broadfoot, Beatrice, Alice,
  And Ermengarde the lady of Maine,—
  And that good Joan whom Englishmen
At Rouen doomed and burned her there,—
  Mother of God, where are they then? . . .
But where are the snows of yeſter-year?

Nay, never ask this week, fair lord,
  Where they are gone, nor yet this year,
Save with this much for an overword,—
  But where are the snows of yeſter-year?

(*D. G. Rossetti*)

BALLAD OF THE LORDS OF OLD TIME

(After the former argument)

WHAT more? Where is the third Calixt,
　Laſt of that name now dead and gone,
Who held four years the Papaliſt?
　Alfonso king of Aragon,
　The gracious lord, duke of Bourbon,
And Arthur, duke of old Britaine?
　And Charles the Seventh, that worthy one?
Even with the good knight Charlemain.

The Scot too, king of the mount and miſt,
　With half his face vermilion,
Men tell us, like an amethyſt
　From brow to chin that blazed and shone;
　The Cypriote king of old renown,
Alas! and that good king of Spain,
　Whose name I cannot think upon?
Even with the good knight Charlemain.

No more to say of them I liſt;
　'Tis all but vain, all dead and done:
For death may no man born resiſt,
　Nor make appeal when death comes on.
　I make yet one more queſtion;
Where's Lancelot, king of far Bohain?
　Where's he whose grandson called him son?
Even with the good knight Charlemain.

Where is Guesclin, the good Breton?
　The lord of the eaſtern mountain-chain,
And the good late duke of Alençon?
　Even with the good knight Charlemain.

(Algernon Charles Swinburne)

BALLAD OF THE WOMEN OF PARIS

ALBEIT the Venice girls get praise
　For their sweet speech and tender air,
And though the old women have wise ways
　Of chaffering for amorous ware,

Yet at my peril dare I swear,
Search Rome, where God's grace mainly tarries,
  Florence and Savoy, everywhere,
There's no good girl's lip out of Paris.

The Naples women, as folk prattle,
  Are sweetly spoken and subtle enough;
German girls are good at tattle,
  And Prussians make their boast thereof;
  Take Egypt for the next remove,
Or that waste land the Tartar harries,
  Spain or Greece, for the matter of love,
There's no good girl's lip out of Paris.

Breton and Swiss know nought of the matter,
  Gascony girls or girls of Toulouse;
Two fishwomen with a half-hour's chatter
  Would shut them up by threes and twos;
  Calais, Lorraine, and all their crews,
(Names enow the mad song marries,)
  England and Picardy, search them and choose,
There's no good girl's lip out of Paris.

Prince, give praise to our French ladies
  For the sweet sound their speaking carries;
'Twixt Rome and Cadiz many a maid is,
  But no good girl's lip out of Paris.

(Algernon Charles Swinburne)

Clement Marot

1495–1544

THE POSY RING

This on thy posy-ring I've writ:
  "True Love and Faith"
For, failing Love, Faith droops her head,
And lacking faith, why, love is dead
  And's but a wraith.
But Death is stingless where they've lit
And stayed, whose names hereon I've writ.

(Ford Madox Ford)

A LOVE-LESSON

A sweet "No! no!" with sweet smile beneath
Becomes an honest girl,—I'd have you learn it;
As for plain, "Yes!" it may be said, i' faith,
Too plainly and too soft,—pray, well discern it!

Not that I'd have my pleasure incomplete,
Or lose the kiss for which my lips beset you;
But that in suffering me to take it, sweet!
I'd have you say—"No! no! I will not let you!"

(Leigh Hunt)

MADAME D'ALBERT'S LAUGH

Yes! that fair neck, too beautiful by half,
Those eyes, that voice, that bloom, all do her honor;
Yet, after all, that little giddy laugh
Is what, in my mind, sits the best upon her.

Good God! 'twould make the very streets and ways,
Through which she passes, burst into a pleasure!
Did melancholy come to mar my days
And kill me in the lap of too much leisure,
No spell were wanting, from the dead to raise me,
But only that sweet laugh wherewith she slays me.

(Leigh Hunt)

Pierre de Ronsard

1524–1585

FRAGMENT OF A SONNET

Nature withheld Cassandra in the skies,
For more adornment, a full thousand years;
She took their cream of Beauty, fairest dies,
And shaped and tinted her above all Peers:
Meanwhile Love kept her dearly with his wings,
And underneath their shadow filled her eyes
With such a richness that the cloudy Kings
Of high Olympus uttered slavish sighs.
When from the Heavens I saw her first descend,
My heart took fire, and only burning pains,

They were my pleasures—they my Life's sad end;
Love poured her beauty into my warm veins.

(*John Keats*)

ROSES

I SEND you here a wreath of blossoms blown,
  And woven flowers at sunset gathered,
  Another dawn had seen them ruined, and shed
Loose leaves upon the grass at random ſtrown.
By this, their sure example, be it known,
  That all your beauties, now in perfeĉt flower,
  Shall fade as these, and wither in an hour.
Flowerlike, and brief of days, as the flower sown.

Ah, time is flying, lady,—time is flying;
  Nay, 'tis not time that flies but we that go,
Who in short space shall be in churchyard, lying,
  And of our loving parley none shall know,
Nor any man consider what we were;
Be therefore kind, my love, whilſt thou art fair.

(*Andrew Lang*)

THE ROSE

SEE, Mignonne, hath not the Rose,
That this morning did unclose
  Her purple mantle to the light,
Loſt before the day be dead,
The glory of her raiment red,
  Her color, bright as yours is bright?

Ah, Mignonne, in how few hours
The petals of her purple flowers
  All have faded, fallen, died;
Sad Nature, mother ruinous,
That seeſt thy fair child perish thus
  'Twixt matin song and even-tide.

Hear me, my darling, speaking sooth,
Gather the fleet flower of your youth,
  Take ye your pleasure at the beſt;

Be merry ere your beauty flit,
For length of days will tarnish it
Like roses that were loveliest.

(*Andrew Lang*)

OF HIS LADY'S OLD AGE

When you are very old, at evening
   You'll sit and spin beside the fire, and say,
Humming my songs, "Ah, well, ah well-a-day.
When I was young, of me did Ronsard sing."
None of your maidens that doth hear the thing,
   Albeit with her weary task foredone,
   But wakens at my name, and calls you one
Blest, to be held in long remembering.

I shall be low beneath the earth, and laid
On sleep, a phantom in the myrtle shade,
   While you beside the fire, a grandame gray,
My love, your pride, remember and regret;
Ah, love me, love, we may be happy yet,
   And gather roses, while 'tis called to-day.

(*Andrew Lang*)

HIS LADY'S TOMB

As in the gardens, all through May, the rose,
Lovely, and young, and fair appareled,
   Makes sunrise jealous of her rosy red,
When dawn upon the dew of dawning glows;
Graces and Loves within her breast repose,
   The woods are faint with the sweet odor shed,
   Till rains and heavy suns have smitten dead
The languid flower, and the loose leaves unclose,—

So this, the perfect beauty of our days,
When earth and heaven were vocal of her praise,
   The fates have slain, and her sweet soul reposes;
And tears I bring, and sighs, and on her tomb
Pour milk, and scatter buds of many a bloom,
   That dead, as living, she may be with roses.

(*Andrew Lang*)

THE PARADOX OF TIME

(*A variation on Ronsard*)

Le temps s'en va, le temps s'en va, madame!
Las! le temps non: mais "NOUS nous en allons!"

TIME goes, you say? Ah, no!
Alas, Time stays, *we* go;
  Or else, were this not so,
What need to chain the hours,
For Youth were always ours?
  Time goes, you say?—ah, no!

Ours is the eyes' deceit
Of men whose flying feet
  Lead through some landscape low;
We pass, and think we see
The earth's fixed surface flee;—
  Alas, Time stays,—we go!

Once in the days of old,
Your locks were curling gold,
  And mine had shamed the crow.
Now, in the self-same stage,
We've reached the silver age;
  Time goes, you say?—ah, no!

Once, when my voice was strong,
I filled the woods with song
  To praise your "rose" and "snow";
My bird, that sang, is dead;
Where are your roses fled?
  Alas, Time stays,—we go!

See, in what traversed ways,
What backward Fate delays
  The hopes we used to know;
Where are your old desires?—
Ah, where those vanished fires?
  Time goes, you say?—ah, no!

How far, how far, O Sweet,
The past behind our feet
　Lies in the even-glow!
Now on the forward way,
Let us fold hands, and pray;
　Alas, Time stays,—*we* go.

　　　　　　　　　　(*Austin Dobson*)

Joachim du Bellay

1525–1560

TO HIS FRIEND IN ELYSIUM

So long you wandered on the dusky plain,
Where flit the shadows with their endless cry,
You reach the shore where all the world goes by,
You leave the strife, the slavery, the pain;
But we, but we, the mortals that remain
　In vain stretch hands; for Charon sullenly
Drives us afar, we may not come anigh
Till that last mystic obolus we gain.
But you are happy in the quiet place,
And with the learned lovers of old days,
　And with your love, you wander evermore
In the dim woods, and drink forgetfulness
Of us your friends, a weary crowd that press
　About the gate, or labor at the oar.

　　　　　　　　　　(*Andrew Lang*)

A SONNET TO HEAVENLY BEAUTY

If this our little life is but a day
In the Eternal,—if the years in vain
Toil after hours that never come again,—
If everything that hath been must decay,
Why dreamest thou of joys that pass away,
　My soul, that my sad body doth restrain?
　Why of the moment's pleasure art thou fain?
Nay, thou hast wings,—nay, seek another stay.

There is the joy where to each soul aspires,
And there the reſt that all the world desires,
　　And there is love, and peace, and gracious mirth;
And there in the moſt higheſt heavens shalt thou
Behold the Very Beauty, whereof now
　　Thou worshipeſt the shadow upon earth.

(*Andrew Lang*)

ROME

O THOU newcomer who seek'ſt Rome in Rome
And find'ſt in Rome no thing thou canſt call Roman;
Arches worn old and palaces made common,
Rome's name alone within these walls keeps home.

Behold how pride and ruin can befall
One who hath set the whole world 'neath her laws,
All-conquering, now conquered, because
She is Time's prey and Time consumeth all.

Rome that are Rome's one sole laſt monument,
Rome that alone haſt conquered Rome the town,
Tiber alone, transient and seaward bent,
Remains of Rome. O world, thou unconſtant mine.
That which ſtands firm in thee Time batters down,
And that which fleeteth doth outrun swift time.

(*Ezra Pound*)

Jean de la Fontaine

1621–1695

La Fontaine is the one French poet who speaks to all the
world. No one is more truly and variously human than
he. We love him, and laugh with him, even at him
sometimes, and should like some day to come across him
in the Elysian fields.—JOHN BAILEY.

THE COCK AND THE FOX

UPON a tree there mounted guard
　　A veteran cock, adroit and cunning;

When to the roots a fox up running
 Spoke thus, in tones of kind regard:—
"Our quarrel, brother, 's at an end;
 Henceforth I hope to live your friend;
  For peace now reigns
  Throughout the animal domains.
I bear the news. Come down, I pray,
And give me the embrace fraternal;
 And please, my brother, don't delay:
So much the tidings do concern all,
 That I muſt spread them far to-day.
Now you and yours can take your walks
Without a fear or thought of hawks;
And should you clash with them or others,
In us you'll find the beſt of brothers;—
 For which you may, this joyful night,
 Your merry bonfires light.
  But, firſt, let's seal the bliss
  With one fraternal kiss."
"Good friend," the cock replied, "upon my word,
A better thing I never heard;
  And doubly I rejoice
  To hear it from your voice:
And, really, there muſt be something in it,
 For yonder come two greyhounds, which, I flatter
 Myself, are couriers on this very matter:
They come so faſt, they'll be here in a minute.
 I'll down, and all of us will seal the blessing
 With general kissing and caressing."
  "Adieu," said Fox, "my errand's pressing;
  I'll hurry on my way,
  And we'll rejoice some other day."
So off the fellow scampered, quick and light,
To gain the fox-holes of a neighboring height,—
Less happy in his ſtratagem than flight.
 The cock laughed sweetly in his sleeve;—
 'Tis doubly sweet deceiver to deceive.

         (*Elizur Wright*)

THE CROW AND THE FOX

A Crow sat perched upon an oak,
And in his beak he held a cheese.
A Fox snuffed up the savory breeze,
And thus in honeyed accent spoke:
"O Prince of Crows, such grace of mien
Has never in these parts been seen.
If but your song be half as good,
You are the Phœnix of the wood!"
The Crow, beside himself with pleasure,
And eager to display his voice,
Opened his beak, and dropped his treasure.
The Fox was on it in a trice.
"Learn, sir," said he, "that flatterers live
On those who swallow what they say.
A cheese is not too much to give
For such a piece of sound advice."
The Crow, ashamed to have been such easy prey
Swore, but too late, he shouldn't catch him twice.

(*Edward Marsh*)

Jean-Baptiste Poquelin Molière

1622–1673

TO MONSIEUR DE LA MOTHE LE VAYER

(*Upon the death of his son*)

Let thy tears, Le Vayer, let them flow;
None of scant cause thy sorrowing can accuse,
Since, losing that which thou for aye doſt lose,
E'en the moſt wise might find a ground for woe.

Vainly we ſtrive with precepts to forego
The drops of pity that are Pity's dues;
And Nature's self, indignant, doth refuse
To count for fortitude that heartless show.

No grief, alas! can now bring back again
The son too dear, by Death untimely ta'en;

Yet, not the less, his loss is hard to bear,
Graced as he was by all the world reveres,
Large heart, keen wit, a lofty soul and rare,
—Surely these claim eternity of tears!

(Austin Dobson)

André Chénier

(1760–1794)

ELEGIES

EVERY man has his sorrows; yet each still
Hides under a calm forehead his own will.
Each pities but himself. Each in his grief
Envies his neighbor; he too seeks relief;
For one man's pain is of no other known:
They hide their sorrows as he hides his own;
And each, with tears and aching heart, can sigh:
All other men are happy, but not I.
They are unhappy all. They, desolate,
Cry against heaven and bid heaven change their fate.
Their fate is changed; they soon, with fresh tears, know
They have but changed one for another woe.

2

A white nymph wandering in the woods by night
Spies a swift satyr, and pretends a flight;
She runs, and running, feigns to call him back!
The goat-foot, following on her flying track,
Falls down and flounders in the stagnant pool:
Whereat they, while he whimpers, mock the fool.

(Arthur Symons)

Pierre Jeane de Beranger

1780–1857

THE KING OF YVETOT

THERE flourished once a potentate,
Whom history doesn't name;

He rose at ten, retired at eight,
 And snored unknown to fame!
A night-cap for his crown he wore,
 A common cotton thing,
Which Jeanette to his bedside bore,
 This jolly little king!
Ho, ho, ho, ho! Ha, ha, ha, ha!
 This jolly little king!

With four diurnal banquets he
 His appetite allayed,
And on a jackass leisurely
 His royal progress made.
No cumbrous state his steps would clog,
 Fear to the winds he'd fling;
His single escort was a dog,
 This jolly little king!
Ho, ho, ho, ho! Ha, ha, ha, ha!
 This jolly little king!

He owned to only one excess,—
 He doted on his glass,—
But when a king gives happiness,
 Why that, you see, will pass!
On every bottle, small or great,
 For which he used to ring,
He laid a tax inordinate,
 This jolly little king!
Ho, ho, ho, ho! Ha, ha, ha, ha!
 This jolly little king!

Such crowds of pretty girls he found
 Occasion to admire,
It gave his subjects double ground
 For greeting him as Sire!
To shoot for cocoanuts he manned
 His army every spring,
But all conscription sternly banned
 This jolly little king!

Ho, ho, ho, ho! Ha, ha, ha, ha!
   This jolly little king!

He eyed no neighboring domain
   With envy or with greed,
And, like a pattern sovereign,
   Took Pleasure for his creed!
Yet, it was not, if aright I ween,
   Until his life took wing,
His subjects saw that he had been
   A jolly little king.
Ho, ho, ho, ho! Ha, ha, ha, ha!
   This jolly little king!

This worthy monarch, readers mine,
   You even now may see
Embellishing a tavern-sign
   Well known to you and me!
There, when the fête-day bottle flows,
   Their bumpers they will bring,
And toast beneath his very nose
   This jolly little king!
Ho, ho, ho, ho! Ha, ha, ha, ha!
   This jolly little king!

                  (*William Toynbee*)

Alphonse Marie Louis de Lamartine
1792–1869

THE CEDARS OF LEBANON

Eagles, that wheel above our crests,
Say to the storms that round us blow,
They can not harm our gnarled breasts,
Firm-rooted as we are below.
Their utmost efforts we defy.
They lift the sea-waves to the sky;
But when they wrestle with our arms
Nervous and gaunt, or lift our hair,
Balanced within its cradle fair
The tiniest bird has no alarms.

Sons of the rock, no mortal hand
Here planted us: God-sown we grew.
We are the diadem green and grand
On Eden's summit that He threw.
When waters in a deluge rose,
Our hollow flanks could well enclose
Awhile the whole of Adam's race;
And children of the Patriarch
Within our forest built the Ark
Of Covenant, foreshadowing grace.

We saw the Tribes as captives led.
We saw them back return anon;
As rafters have our branches dead
Cover'd the porch of Solomon;
And later, when the Word, made man,
Came down in God's salvation-plan
To pay for sin the ransom-price,
The beams that form'd the Cross we gave:
These, red in blood of power to save,
Were altars of that Sacrifice.

In memory of such great events,
Men come to worship our remains;
Kneel down in prayer within our tents,
And kiss our old trunks' weather-stains.
The saint, the poet, and the sage,
Hear and shall hear from age to age
Sounds in our foliage like the voice
Of many waters; in these shades
Their burning words are forged like blades,
While their uplifted souls rejoice.

(Toru Dutt)

Alfred de Vigny

1797–1863

THE SOUND OF THE HORN

I LOVE the sound of the horn in the deep, dim woodland,
  Whether it wail with the doe that is nigh to death,

Or cry the hunter's farewell on the echoes waning,
    From leaf to leaf borne on by the north wind's breath.

How often alone, in the shadow at midnight straying,
    I have smiled to hear it, how often have wept still
        more!
For I seemed to hear the rumor of things foreboding
    The death of the Paladin knights that lived of yore.

O azure Mountain! O land that my heart is fain of!
    Franzona fells, and summits of Marboré,
Fountains that fall with the drifted snows for a burden
    Torrents and brooks of the Pyrenees' chill spray,

Mountains frozen or fertile, throning the seasons,
    Who have ice for crown and the meadows about your
        feet,
'Tis there would I dwell, 'tis there would I wait to
        hearken
    The far-borne sound of the horn blow sad and sweet.

A traveler strayed mayhap when the air is stilly,
    Lifts up this brazen voice that the night repeats;
With the sound of his cadenced songs for a while is
        blending
    The tiny bell of the tethered lamb that bleats.

A doe that heareth the sound flies not but rather
    Stands still as a stone on the hill-top, while waters
        chime
In vast uproar with the music for ever calling
    From the old romance of the immemorial time.

Souls of the Paladins, say, do your ghosts still haunt us?
    Is it you who speaks to us still in the blare of the
        horn?
Roncevaux! Roncevaux! deep in thy somber valley
    The shades of the noble Roland is still forlorn!

                                        (*Wilfrid Thorley*)

NATURE

I AM the stage, impassive, mute and cold,
    That thrills not where the actor's foot hath trod.
My alabaster halls, my emerald
    Stairs, and my tones were sculptured by a god:
Your voice of crying I know not, no, nor see
The passing of the human comedy
    That looks to heaven to find its period.

I roll, and to my deep disdain I thrust
    The seed of ants and human populations;
Their tenements I know not from their dust,
    Their names I know not—I that bear the nations;
Mother in name, in deed a very room
For death; my winter takes its hecatomb,
    My spring is careless of your adorations.

Before you, always essenced, always fair,
    I shook my locks abroad the winds of heaven,
And trod my customary path in air,
    While the divine hands held the balance even.
And onward, to that void where all things roll
I shall be carried silently and sole,
    And by my breast and brows the air be riven.

                    (Margaret Jourdain)

Victor Hugo

1802–1885

A SUNSET

(From "Feuilles d'Automne")

I LOVE the evenings, passionless and fair, I love the evens,
Whether old manor-fronts their ray with golden fulgence
      leavens,
  In numerous leafage bosomed close;
Whether the mist in reefs of fire extend its reaches sheer,
Or a hundred sunbeams splinter in an azure atmosphere
  On cloudy archipelagos.

Oh, gaze ye on the firmament! a hundred clouds in
    motion,
Up-piled in the immense sublime beneath the winds'
    commotion,
    Their unimagined shapes accord:
Under their waves at intervals flame a pale levin through,
As if some giant of the air amid the vapors drew
    A sudden elemental sword.

The sun at bay with splendid thrusts still keeps the
    sullen fold;
And momently at distance sets, as a cupola of gold,
    The thatched roof of a cot a-glance;
Or on the blurred horizon joins his battle with the haze;
Or pools the blooming fields about with inter-isolate
    blaze,
    Great moveless meres of radiance.

Then mark you how there hangs athwart the firma-
    ment's swept track,
Yonder, a mighty crocodile with vast irradiant back,
    A triple row of pointed teeth?
Under its burnished belly slips a ray of eventide,
The flickerings of a hundred glowing clouds in tene-
    brous side
    With scales of golden mail ensheathe.

Then mounts a palace, then the air vibrates—the vision
    flees.
Confounded to its base, the fearful cloudy edifice
    Ruins immense in mounded wrack;
Afar the fragments strew the sky, and each envermeiled
    cone
Hangeth, peak downward, overhead, like mountains
    overthrown
    When the earthquake heaves its hugy back.

These vapors, with their leaden, golden, iron, bronzèd
    glows,
Where the hurricane, the waterspout, thunder, and hell
    repose,

Muttering hoarse dreams of destined harms,—
'Tis God who hangs their multitude amid the skiey deep,
As a warrior that suspendeth from the roof-tree of his
     keep
  His dreadful and resounding arms!

All vanishes! The Sun, from topmost heaven precipi-
     tated,
Like a globe of iron which is tossed back fiery red
  Into the furnace stirred to fume,
Shocking the cloudy surges, plashed from its impetuous
     ire,
Even to the zenith spattereth in a flecking scud of fire
  The vaporous and inflamèd spaume.

O contemplate the heavens! Whenas the vein-drawn day
     dies pale,
In every season, every place, gaze through their every
     veil?
  With love that has not speech for need!
Beneath their solemn beauty is a mystery infinite:
If winter hue them like a pall, or if the summer night
  Fantasy them starry brede.

                      (Francis Thompson)

THE GRAVE AND THE ROSE

The Grave said to the Rose,
  "What of the dews of dawn,
Love's flower, what end is theirs?"
  "And what of spirits flown,
The souls whereon doth close
  The tomb's mouth unawares?"
The Rose said to the Grave.

The Rose said, "In the shade
  From the dawn's tears is made
A perfume faint and strange,
  Amber and honey sweet."
  "And all the spirits fleet

Do suffer a sky-change,
  More strangely than the dew,
  To God's own angels new,"
The Grave said to the Rose.

(Andrew Lang)

THE GENESIS OF BUTTERFLIES

THE dawn is smiling on the dew that covers
The tearful roses; lo, the little lovers
That kiss the buds, and all the flutterings
In jasmine bloom, and privet, of white wings,
That go and come, and fly, and peep and hide,
With muffled music, murmured far and wide.
Ah, the Spring time, when we think of all the lays
That dreamy lovers send to dreamy mays,
Of the fond hearts within a billet bound,
Of all the soft silk paper that pens wound,
The messages of love that mortals write
Filled with intoxication of delight,
Written in April and before the May time
Shredded and flown, playthings for the wind's playtime,
We dream that all white butterflies above,
Who seek through clouds or waters souls to love,
And leave their lady mistress in despair,
To flit to flowers, as kinder and more fair,
Are but torn love-letters, that through the skies
Flutter, and float, and change to butterflies.

(Andrew Lang)

MORE STRONG THAN TIME

SINCE I have set my lips to your full cup, my sweet,
Since I my pallid face between your hands have laid,
Since I have known your soul, and all the bloom of it,
And all the perfume rare, now buried in the shade;

Since it was given to me to hear one happy while,
The words wherein your heart spoke all its mysteries,
Since I have seen you weep, and since I have seen you
      smile,
Your lips upon my lips, and your eyes upon my eyes;

Since I have known above my forehead glance and
    gleam,
A ray, a single ray, of your star, veiled always,
Since I have felt the fall, upon my lifetime's stream,
Of one rose petal plucked from the roses of your days;

I now am bold to say to the swift changing hours,
Pass, pass upon your way, for I grow never old,
Fleet to the dark abysm with all your fading flowers,
One rose that none may pluck, within my heart I hold.

Your flying wings may smite, but they can never spill
The cup fulfilled of love, from which my lips are wet;
My heart has far more fire than you can frost to chill,
My soul more love than you can make my soul forget.

                          (Andrew Lang)

THE POOR CHILDREN

TAKE heed of this small child of earth;
    He is great; he hath in him God most high.
Children before their fleshly birth
    Are lights alive in the blue sky.

In our light bitter world of wrong
    They come; God gives us them awhile.
His speech is in their stammering tongue,
    And his forgiveness in their smile.

Their sweet light rests upon our eyes.
    Alas! their right to joy is plain.
If they are hungry Paradise
    Weeps, and, if cold, Heaven thrills with pain.

The want that saps their sinless flower
    Speaks judgment on sin's ministers.
Man holds an angel in his power.
    Ah! deep in Heaven what thunder stirs,

When God seeks out these tender things
    Whom in the shadow where we sleep

He sends us clothed about with wings,
   And finds them ragged babes that weep!

(Algernon Charles Swinburne)

Gérard de Nerval

1808–1855

AN OLD TUNE

THERE is an air for which I would disown
   Mozart's, Rossini's, Weber's melodies,—
A sweet sad air that languishes and sighs,
   And keeps its secret charm for me alone.

Whene'er I hear that music vague and old,
   Two hundred years are mist that rolls away;
The thirteenth Louis reigns, and I behold
   A green land golden in the dying day.

An old red castle, strong with stony towers,
   The windows gay with many colored glass;
Wide plains, and rivers flowing among flowers,
   That bathe the castle basement as they pass.

In antique weed, with dark eyes and gold hair,
   A lady looks forth from her window high;
It may be that I knew and found her fair,
   In some forgotten life, long time gone by.

(Andrew Lang)

Alfred de Musset

1810–1857

JUANA

AGAIN I see you, ah my queen,
Of all my old loves that have been,
   The first love, and the tenderest;
Do you remember or forget—
Ah me, for I remember yet—
   How the last summer days were blest?

Ah lady, when we think of this,
The foolish hours of youth and bliss,
   How fleet, how sweet, how hard to hold.
How old we are, ere spring be green.
You touch the limit of eighteen
   And I am twenty winters old.

My rose, that mid the red roses,
Was brightest, ah, how pale she is.
   Yet keeps the beauty of her prime;
Child, never Spanish lady's face
Was lovely with so wild a grace;
   Remember the dead summertime.

Think of our loves, our feuds of old,
And how you gave your chain of gold
   To me for a peace offering;
And how all night I lay awake
To touch and kiss it for your sake,—
   To touch and kiss the lifeless thing.

Lady, beware for all we say,
This love shall live another day,
   Awakened from his deathly sleep;
The heart that once has been your shrine
For other loves is too divine;
   A home, my dear, too wide and deep.

What did I say,—why do I dream?
Why should I struggle with the stream
   Whose waves return not any day?
Close heart, and eyes, and arms from me;
Farewell, farewell, so must it be,
   So runs, so runs, the world away.

The season bears upon its wing
The swallows and the songs of spring,
   And days that were, and days that flit;

The loved lost hours are far away;
And hope and fame are scattered spray
For me, that gave you love a day
For you that not remember it.

(Andrew Lang)

Théophile Gautier

1811–1872

ART

ALL things are doubly fair
If patience fashion them
    And care—
Verse, enamel, marble, gem

No idle chains endure:
Yet, Muse, to walk aright
    Lave tight
Thy buskin proud and sure.

Fie on facile measure,
A shoe where every lout
    At pleasure
Slip his foot in and out!

Sculptor lay by the day
On which thy nerveless finger
    May linger,
Thy thoughts flown far away.

Keep to Carrara rare,
Struggle with Paros cold,
    That hold
The subtle line and fair.

Lest haply nature lose
That proud, that perfect line,
    Make thine
The bronze of Syracuse.

And with a tender dread
Upon an agate's face
    Retrace
Apollo's golden head.

Despise a watery hue
And tints that soon expire.
    With fire
Burn thine enamel true.

Twine, twine in artful wise
The blue-green mermaid's arms,
    Mid charms
Of thousand heraldries.

Show in their triple lobe
Virgin and Child, that hold
    Their globe,
Cross crowned and aureoled.

—All things return to dust
Save beauties fashioned well;
    The bust
Outlasts the citadel.

Oft doth the plowman's heel,
Breaking an ancient clod,
    Reveal
A Cæsar or a god.

The gods, too, die, alas!
But deathless and more strong
    Than brass
Remains the sovereign song.

Chisel and carve and file,
Till thy vague dream imprint
    Its smile
On the unyielding flint.

(George Santayana)

CLARIMONDE

With elbow buried in the downy pillow
  I've lain and read,
All through the night, a volume strangely written
  In tongues long dead.

For at my bedside lie no dainty slippers;
  And, save my own,
Under the paling lamp I hear no breathing:—
  I am alone!

But there are yellow bruises on my body
  And violet stains;
Though no white vampire came with lips blood-crim-
   soned
  To suck my veins!

Now I bethink me of a sweet weird story,
  That in the dark
Our dead loves thus with seal of chilly kisses
  Our bodies mark.

Gliding beneath the coverings of our couches
  They share our rest,
And with their dead lips sign their loving visit
  On arm and breast.

Darksome and cold the bed where now she slumbers,
  I loved in vain,
With sweet eyelids closed, to be reopened
  Never again.

Dead sweetheart, can it be that thou hast lifted
  With thy frail hand
Thy coffin-lid, to come to me again
  From shadowland?

Thou who, one joyous night, didst, pale and speechless,
  Pass from us all,
Dropping thy silken mask and gift of flowers
  Amidst the ball?

Oh, fondest of my loves, from that far heaven
    Where thou must be,
Hast thou returned to pay the debt of kisses
    Thou owest to me?

               (*Lafcadio Hearn*)

Charles Baudelaire

1821–1867

In the poetry of Baudelaire there is a deliberate science of sensual and sexual perversity which has something curious in its accentuation of vice with horror, in its passionate devotion to passions. Baudelaire lived and died solitary, secret, a confessor of sins who had never told the whole truth, an ascetic of passion, a hermit of the Brothel.—ARTHUR SYMONS.

LES HIBOUX

UNDER the yew-tree's heavy weight
The owls stand in their sullen fashions,
Like Pagan gods of Pagan passions
They dart their eyes and meditate.
Unmoving they stare ,with living flame
Until the end of the melancholy
Hour sees the oblique sun set in folly,
And darkness falls in shades of shame.
Their aspect to the wise man teaches
All that he needs, all he beseeches,
Tumult and change and discontent;
The man drunk of a shadow that passes
Keeps always the imperishable scent
That makes the wind change and the grasses.

               (*Arthur Symons*)

SOIS SAGE O MA DOULEUR

PEACE, be at peace, O thou my heaviness,
Thou callest for the evening, lo! 'tis here,
The City wears a somber atmosphere
That brings repose to some, to some distress.

Now while the heedless throng make haste to press
Where pleasure drives them, ruthless charioteer,
To pluck the fruits of sick remorse and fear,
Come thou with me, and leave their fretfulness.

See how they hang from heaven's high balconies,
The old lost years in faded garments dressed,
And see Regret with faintly smiling mouth;
And while the dying sun sinks in the west,
Hear how, far off, Night walks with velvet tread,
And her long robe trails all about the south.

(Lord Alfred Douglas)

LA BEAUTÉ

FAIR am I, mortals, as a stone-carved dream,
And all men wound themselves against my breast,
The poet's last desire, the loveliest.
Voiceless, eternal as the world I seem,
In the blue air, strange sphinx, I brood supreme
With heart of snow whiter than swan's white crest,
No movement mars the plastic line—I rest
With lips untaught to laugh or eyes to stream.

Singers who see, in trancèd interludes,
My splendor set with all superb design,
Consume their days, in toilful ecstasy.
To these revealed, the starry amplitudes
Of my great eyes which make all things divine
Are crystal mirrors of eternity.

(Lord Alfred Douglas)

HARMONIE DU SOIR

Now is the hour when, swinging in the breeze,
Each flower, like a censer, sheds its sweet.
The air is full of scents and melodies,
O languorous waltz! O swoon of dancing feet!

Each flower, like a censer, sheds its sweet,
The violins are like sad souls that cry,

O languorous waltz! O swoon of dancing feet!
A shrine of Death and Beauty is the sky.

The violins are like sad souls that cry,
Poor souls that hate the vast black night of Death;
A shrine of Death and Beauty is the sky.
Drowned in red blood, the Sun gives up his breath.

This soul that hates the vast black night of Death
Takes all the luminous past back tenderly,
Drowned in red blood, the Sun gives up his breath.
Thine image like a monstrance shines in me.

(Lord Alfred Douglas)

Frédéric Mistral

1830–1914

THE COCOONING

(From the Mirèio)

When the crop is fair in the olive-yard,
    And the earthen jars are ready
For the golden oil from the barrels poured,
    And the big cart rocks unsteady
With its tower of gathered sheaves, and strains
And groans on its way through fields and lanes:

When brawny and bare as an old athlete
    Comes Bacchus the dance a-leading,
And the laborers all, with juice-dyed feet,
    The vintage of Crau are treading,
And the good wine pours from the brimful presses,
And the ruby foam in the vats increases;

When under the leaves of the Spanish broom
    The clear silk-worms are holden,
An artist each, in a tiny loom,
    Weaving a web of golden,
Fine, frail cells out of sunlight spun,
Where they creep and sleep by the million.—

Glad is Provence on a day like that,
  'Tis the time of jeſt and laughter:
The Ferigouet and the Baume Muscat
  They quaff, and they sing thereafter.
And lads and lasses, their toils between,
Dance to the tinkling tambourine.

(Harriet Waters Preston)

THE LEAF-PICKING

Sing, magnarello, merrily,
  As the green leaves you gather!
In their third sleep the silk-worms lie,
  And lovely is the weather.
Like brown bees that in open glades
  From rosemary gather honey,
The mulberry-trees swarm full of maids,
  Glad as the air is sunny!

Sing, magnarello, merrily,
  The green leaves are piling!
Two comely children sit on high,
  Amid the foliage, smiling.
Sing, magnarello, loud and oft:
  Your merry labor haſten.
The guileless pair who laugh aloft
  Are learning love's firſt lesson.

Sing, magnarello, merrily,
  As the green leaves you gather!
The sun of May is riding higher,
  And ardent is the weather.

Sing, magnarello, heap your leaves,
  While sunny is the weather!
He comes to aid her when she grieves:
  The two are now together.

(Harriet Waters Preston)

Catulle Mendès

1841-1909

I GO BY ROAD

I go by road, I go by street—
    Lira, la, la!
O white high roads, ye know my feet!
A loaf I carry and, all told,
Three broad bits of lucky gold—
    Lira, la, la!
And oh, within my flowering heart
(Sing, dear nightingale!) is my Sweet.

A poor man met me and begged for bread—
    Lira, la, la!
"Brother, take all the loaf," I said,
I shall but go with lighter cheer—
    Lira, la, la!
And oh, within my flowering heart
(Sing, sweet nightingale!) is my Dear.

A thief I met on the lonely way—
    Lira, la, la!
He took my gold; I cried to him, "Stay!
And take my pocket and make an end."
    Lira, la, la!
And oh, within my flowering heart
(Sing, soft nightingale!) is my Friend.

Now on the plain I have met with death—
    Lira, la, la!
My bread is gone, my gold, my breath.
But oh, this heart is not afraid—
    Lira, la, la!
For oh, within this lonely heart
(Sing, sad nightingale!) is my Maid.

(Alice Meynell)

Stéphane Mallarmé

1842–1898

SIGH

My soul, calm sister, towards thy brow, whereon scarce
    grieves
An autumn strewn already with its russet leaves,
And towards the wandering sky of thine angelic eyes,
Mounts, as in melancholy gardens may arise
Some faithful fountain sighing whitely towards the blue!
Towards the blue, pale and pure, that sad October knew,
When, in those depths, it mirrored languors infinite,
And agonizing leaves upon the waters white,
Windily drifting, traced a furrow cold and dun,
Where, in one long last ray, lingered the yellow sun.

(*Arthur Symons*)

SEA-WIND

The flesh is sad, alas! and all the books are read.
Flight, only flight! I feel that birds are wild to tread
The floor of unknown foam, and to attain the skies!
Nought, neither ancient gardens mirrored in the eyes,
Shall hold this heart that bathes in waters its delight,
O nights! nor yet my waking lamp, whose lonely light
Shadows the vacant paper, whiteness profits best,
Nor the young wife who rocks her baby on her breast.
I will depart! O steamer, swaying rope and spar,
Lift anchor for exotic lands that lie afar!
A weariness, outworn by cruel hopes, still clings
To the last farewell handkerchief's last beckonings!
And are not these, the masts inviting storms, not these
That an awakening wind bends over wrecking seas,
Lost, not a sail, a sail, a flowering isle, ere long?
But, O my heart, hear thou, hear thou, the sailors' song!

(*Arthur Symons*)

José-Maria de Heredia

1842–1905

THE LABORER

HERE is the yoke, with arrow and share near by,
The goad, the scythe that in a day hath mown
Swathes that would make the wide barn-flooring groan,
And here the fork the brown haymakers ply.
Too heavy tools! He hath vowed them utterly
   Unto immortal Rhea, who alone
   Brings seed to blossom from hard tilth. His own
Labor is done and he not loth to die.

Fourscore long years, sun-blistered, poor, he drave
   The coulter, without mirth, through stubborn soil,
Who now goes grimly onward to the grave.
   Yet he bewails the labor too long borne,
   And dreads to find more fallow for his toil
   In sunless fields of Erebus forlorn.

(Wilfrid Thorley)

Paul Verlaine

1844–1896

He was the purest lyrical singer that France had ever
known. He strikes a discreet and troubling note that
leaves its vibrations in the heart and in the nerves forever.—LUDWIG LEWISOHN.

IL PLEUT DOUCEMENT SUR LA VILLE

TEARS fall within mine heart,
As rain upon the town:
Whence does this languor start,
Possessing all mine heart?

O sweet fall of the rain
Upon the earth and roof,
Unto an heart in pain,
O music of the rain.

Tears that have no reason
Fall in my sorry heart:
What, there was no treason?
This grief hath no reason.

Nay, the more desolate,
Because, I know not why,
(Neither for love nor hate)
Mine heart is desolate.

(Ernest Dowson)

SPLEEN

AROUND were all the roses red,
The ivy all around was black.

Dear, so thou only move thine head,
Shall all mine old despairs awake.

Too blue, too tender was the sky,
The air too soft, too green the sea.

Always I fear, I know not why,
Some lamentable flight from thee.

I am so tired of holly-sprays
And weary of the bright box-tree,

Of all the endless country ways;
Of everything, alas, save thee.

(Ernest Dowson)

THE SKY IS UP ABOVE THE ROOF

THE sky is up above the roof
   So blue, so soft.
A tree there, up above the roof,
   Swayeth aloft.

A bell within that sky we see,
   Chimes low and faint;
A bird upon that tree we see,
   Maketh complaint.

Dear God, is not the life up there
  Simple and sweet?
How peacefully are borne up there
  Sounds of the street.

What hast thou done, who comest here,
  To weep alway?
Where hast thou laid, who comest here,
  Thy youth away?

                                      (Ernest Dowson)

A CLYMENE

MYSTICAL strains unheard,
A song without a word,
Dearest, because thine eyes,
Pale as the skies,

Because thy voice, remote
As the far clouds that float
Veiling for me the whole
Heaven of the soul,

Because the stately scent
Of thy swan's whiteness, blent
With the white lily's bloom
Of thy perfume,

Ah, because thy dear love,
The music breathed above
By angels halo-crowned,
Odor and sound,

Hath, in my subtle heart,
With some mysterious art
Transposed thy harmony,
So let it be.

                                      (Arthur Symons)

PANTOMIME

PIERROT, no sentimental swain,
Washes a pâté down again
   With furtive flagons, white and red.

Cassandre, to chasten his content,
Greets with a tear of sentiment
   His nephew disinherited.

That blackguard of a Harlequin
Pirouettes, and plots to win
   His Colombine that flits and flies.

Colombine dreams, and starts to find
A sad heart sighing in the wind,
   And in her heart a voice that sighs.

                    (*Arthur Symons*)

MANDOLINE

(*Fêtes Galantes*)

THE singers of serenades
   Whisper their faded vows
Unto fair listening maids
   Under the singing boughs.

Tircis, Aminte, are there,
   Clitandre has waited long,
And Damis for many a fair
   Tyrant makes many a song.

Their short vests, silken and bright,
   Their long pale silken trains,
Their elegance of delight,
   Twine soft blue silken chains.

And the madolines and they,
   Faintlier breathing, swoon
Into the rose and gray
   Ecstasy of the moon.

                    (*Arthur Symons*)

CHANSONS D'AUTOMNE

(From Poèmes Saturniens)

WHEN a sighing begins
In the violins
Of the autumn-song,

My heart is drowned
In the slow sound
Languorous and long.

Pale as with pain,
Breath fails me when
The hour tolls deep.
My thoughts recover
The days that are over,
And I weep.

And I go
Where the winds know,
Broken and brief,
To and fro,
As the winds blow
A dead leaf.

(Arthur Symons)

FEMME ET CHATTE

(From Poèmes Saturniens)

THEY were at play, she and her cat,
And it was marvelous to mark
The white paw and the white hand pat
Each other in the deepening dark.

The stealthy little lady hid
Under her mittens' silken sheath
Her deadly agate nails that thrid
The silk-like dagger-points of death.

The cat purred primly and drew in
Her claws that were of steel filed thin:
The devil was in it all the same.
The devil was in it all the same.

And in the boudoir, while a shout
Of laughter in the air rang out,
Four sparks of phosphor shone like flame.

(*Arthur Symons*)

FROM SAGESSE

SLUMBER dark and deep
Falls across my life;
I will put to sleep
Hope, desire and strife.

All things pass away,
Good and evil seem
To my soul to-day
Nothing but a dream;

I a cradle laid
In a hollow cave,
By a great hand swayed:
Silence, like the grave.

(*Arthur Symons*)

Arthur Rimbaud

1854–1891

SENSATION

ON summer evenings blue, pricked by the wheat
On rustic paths the thin grass I shall tread,
And feel its freshness underneath my feet,
And, dreaming, let the wind bathe my bare head.

I shall not speak, nor think, but, walking slow
Through Nature, I shall rove with Love my guide,
As gypsies wander, where, they do not know,
Happy as one walks by a woman's side.

(*Jethro Bithell*)

THE SLEEPER OF THE VALLEY

THERE's a green hollow where a river sings
Silvering the torn grass in its glittering flight,
And where the sun from the proud mountain flings
Fire—and the little valley brims with light.

A soldier young, with open mouth, bare head,
Sleeps with his neck in dewy water cress,
Under the sky and on the grass his bed,
Pale in the deep green and the light's excess.

He sleeps amid the iris and his smile
Is like a sick child's slumbering for a while.
Nature, in thy warm lap his chilled limbs hide!

The perfume does not thrill him from his rest.
He sleeps in sunshine, hand upon his breast,
Tranquil—with two red holes in his right side.

(Ludwig Lewisohn)

SONG OF THE HIGHEST TOWER

MAY they come, may they come,
The days which enchant us.

I have been so long resigned
That I forgot it all.
Fears and sufferings
To the skies are gone,
And the unclean thirst
Darkens my veins.

May they come, may they come,
The days which enchant us.

Like the meadows
Left to ruin,
Spreading and overgrown
With flowers and weeds,
In the angry humming
Of filthy flies.

May they come, may they come
The days which enchant us.

(Edgell Rickword)

Emile Verhaeren

1855–1916

THE POOR

WITH hearts of poor men it is so:
That they are full of tears that flow,
That they are pale as head-stones white
In the moon light.

And so with poor men's backs it is—
More bent with heavy miseries
Than sagging roofs of brown huts be
Beside the sea.

And it is so with poor men's hands,
Like leaves along autumnal lands,
Leaves that lie sere and dead and late
Beside the gate.

And it is so with poor men's eyes,
Humble and in all sorrow wise,
And like the cattle's, sad and dumb,
When the storms come.

Oh, it is so with the poor folk
That under misery's iron yoke
Have gestures weary and resigned
On earth's far plains of sun and wind.

(Ludwig Lewisohn)

FROM SUMMER HOURS

FLOWER petals fall.
    Dull flares the torch's mane;
    Mine eyes to weep were fain,
Mine eyes possess thee all.

Yielded beyond recall,
  Heart, naught shall heal thee again,
  O clay molded into pain . . .
Flower petals fall.

The roses all are dying . . .
I am saying nothing, thou hearest
Under thy motionless hair.

Love is heavy. My soul is sighing . . .
What wing brushes both of us, dearest,
In the sick and soundless air?

(*Jethro Bithell*)

Maurice Maeterlinck

1862–

SONG

THREE little maidens they have slain,
To find out what their hearts contain.

The first of them was brimmed with bliss,
  And everywhere her blood was shed,
For full three years three serpents hiss.

The second full of kindness sweet,
  And everywhere her blood was shed,
Three lambs three years have grass to eat.

The third was full of pain and rue,
  And everywhere her blood was shed,
Three seraphim watch three years through.

(*Jethro Bithell*)

THE LAST WORDS

AND if he ever should come back,
  What am I to say?
—Tell him that I watch'd for him
  All my life away.

And if he should ask me more,
  Nor know my face again?
—Speak gently as a sister speaks,
  He may be in pain.

If he ask me where you are,
  How shall I reply?
—Then give him my golden ring,
  Very silently.

And if he should want to know
  Why the hall stands bare?
—Then show him the burn-out lamp
  And the door ajar.

And if he should ask me then
  How you fell asleep?
—Tell him that I smiled and died.
  Do not let him weep.

                    (*Frederick York Powell*)

Henri de Regnier

                              1864–

NIGHT

An odorous shade lingers the fair day's ghost,
  And the frail moon now by no wind is tost,
And shadow-laden scents of tree and grass
  Build up again a world our eyes have lost.

Now all the wood is but a murmured light
  Where leaf on leaf falls softly from the height;
The hidden freshness of the river seems
  A breath that mingles with the breath of night.

And time and shade and silence seem to say,
  Close now your eyes nor fear to die with day;
For if the daylight win to earth again,
  Will not its beauty also find a way?

And flower and ſtream and foreſt, will they not
  Bring back to-morrow, as to-day they brought,
This shadow-hidden scent—this odorous shade?
  Yea, and with more abiding memories fraught.
                        (*Seumas O'Sullivan*)

JE NE VEUX DE PERSONNE AUPRES DE MA TRISTESSE

SAY, sweet, my grief and I, we may not brook
Even your light footfall, even your shy look,
Even your light hand that touches carelessly
The faded ribbon in the closed-up book.

Let be; my door is closed for this one day,
Nor may morn's freshness through my window ſtray;
My heart is a gueſt-chamber, and awaits
Sorrow, a sweet shy gueſt from far away.

Shyly it comes from its far diſtant home,
O keep a silence leſt its voice be dumb;
For every man that lives and laughs and loves
Muſt hear that whisper when his hour has come.
                        (*Seumas O'Sullivan*)

André Spire

1868–

LONELY

THEY pity me.
"Look at him, see.
Taking his walking ſtick, and going out. So lonely.
He flees us. Look at his ſtrange eyes.
Not even a book does he take with him. Only
His ſtick. What does he mean to do?
Is he intent on evil? In revolt? Or fever-sick?"

Alone, O beautiful white road,
Between your ditches full of grass and flowers,
Over your pebbles telling tales of old,

Alone, O forest, with the blue bark of your pines;
And with your wind that parleys with your trees;
And with your ants processioning that drag
Bodies of little beetles on their backs.

Alone, with you, you sun-drenched fields,
All full of cries, and noises, and heads raised alert,
Alone with you, flies, merlins, buzzards, kites,
Rocks, brambles, sources, crevices,
Fogs, clouds, mists, cones, peaks, precipices,
Heat, odor, order, chaos, and disorder,
Among the dialogues your rival mouths
Exchange for ever!
Alone with my stick, alone with my fatigue,
My dust, my throbbing temples, and my dizziness,
And the proud sweat glued to my skin.

(Jethro Bithell)

Francis Jammes

1868–

AMSTERDAM

THE pointed houses lean so you would swear
That they were falling. Tangled vessel masts
Like leafless branches lean against the sky
Amid a mass of green, and red, and rust,
Red herrings, sheepskins, coal along the quays.

Robinson Crusoe passed through Amsterdam,
(At least I think he did), when he returned
From the green isle shaded with cocoa-trees.

What were the feeling of his heart before
These heavy knockers and these mighty doors! . . .

Did he look through the window-panes and watch
The clerks who write in ledgers all day long?
Did tears come in his eyes when he remembered
His parrot, and the heavy parasol
Which shaded him in the sad and clement isle?

"Glory to thee, good Lord," he would exclaim,
Looking at chests with tulip-painted lids.
But, saddened by the joy of the return,
He must have mourned his kid left in the vines
Alone, and haply on the island dead.

I have imagined this before the shops
Which make you think of Jews who handle scales,
With bony fingers knotted with green rings.
See! Amsterdam under a shroud of snow
Sleeps in a scent of fog and bitter coal.

Last night the white globes of the lighted inns,
Whence issue heavy women's whistled calls,
Were hanging down like fruits resembling gourds.
Posters blue, red, and green shone on their walls.
The bitter pricking of their sugared beer
Rasped on my tongue and gave my nose the itch.

And in the Jewry where detritus lies,
You smell the raw, cold reek of fresh-caught fish.
The slippery flags are strown with orange-peel.
Some swollen face would open staring eyes,
A wrangling arm moved onions to and fro.

Rebecca, from your little tables you
Were selling sticky sweets, a scanty show. . . .
The sky seemed pouring, like a filthy sea,
A tide of vapor into the canals.
Smoke that one does not see, commercial calm
Rose from the husked roofs and rich table-cloths,
And from the houses' comfort India breathed.

Fain had I been one of those merchant princes,
Who sailed in olden days from Amsterdam
To China, handing over their estate
And home affairs to trusty mandatories.
Like Robinson before a notary
I would have signed my pompous procuration.

Then honesty had piled from day to day
My riches more, and flowered them like a moon-beam
Upon my laden ships' imposing prows.
And in my house the nabobs of Bombay
Would have been tempted by my florid spouse.

The Mogul would have sent a gold-ringed negro
To traffic, with a smiling row of teeth,
Under his spreading parasol. And he
Would have enchanted with his savage tales
My eldest girl, to whom he would have given
A robe of rubies cut by cunning slaves.

I should have had my family portrayed
By some poor wretch whose paintings lived and breathed:
My plump and sumptuous wife with rosy face,
My sons, whose beauty would have charmed the town,
My daughters, with their pure and different grace.

And so to-day, instead of being myself,
I should have been another, visiting
A pompous mansion of old Amsterdam,
Launching my soul before the plain devise,
Under a gable: Here lived Francis Jammes.

(Jethro Bithell)

PRAYER TO GO TO PARADISE WITH THE ASSES

O God, when You send for me, let it be
Upon some festal day of dusty roads.
I wish, as I did ever here-below
By any road that pleases me, to go
To Paradise, where stars shine all day long.
Taking my stick out on the great highway,
To my dear friends the asses I shall say:
I am Francis Jammes going to Paradise,
For there is no hell where the Lord God dwells.
Come with me, my sweet friends of azure skies,
You poor, dear beasts who whisk off with your ears
Mosquitoes, peevish blows, and buzzing bees . . .

Let me appear before You with these beasts,
Whom I so love because they bow their head
Sweetly, and halting join their little feet
So gently that it makes you pity them.
Let me come followed by their million ears,
By those that carried panniers on their flanks,
And those that dragged the cars of acrobats,
Those that had battered cans upon their backs,
She-asses limping, full as leather-bottles,
And those too that they breech because of blue
And oozing wounds round which the stubborn flies
Gather in swarms. God, let me come to You
With all these asses into Paradise.
Let angels lead us where your rivers soothe
Their tufted banks, and cherries tremble, smooth
As is the laughing flesh of tender maids.
And let me, where Your perfect peace pervades,
Be like Your asses, bending down above
The heavenly waters through eternity,
To mirror their sweet, humble poverty
In the clear waters of eternal love.

(Jethro Bithell)

THE CHILD READS AN ALMANAC

The child reads on; her basket of eggs stands by.
She sees the weather signs, the Saints with awe,
And watches the fair houses of the sky:
The *Goat,* the *Bull,* the *Ram,* et cetera.

And so the little peasant maiden knows
That in the constellations we behold,
Are markets like the one to which she goes
Where goats and bulls and rams are bought and sold.

She reads about the market in the sky.
She turns a page and sees the *Scales* and then
Says that in Heaven, as at the grocery,
They weigh salt, coffee and the souls of men.

(Ludwig Lewisohn)

Paul Fort

1872–

BALLADE

THE pretty maid she died, she died, in love-bed as she
lay;
They took her to the churchyard, all at the break of
day;
They laid her all alone there, all in her white array;
They laid her all alone there, a-coffined in the clay;
And they came back so merrily, all at the dawn of day;
A-singing, all so merrily, *"The dog must have his day!"*
The pretty maid is dead, is dead, in love-bed as she lay;
And they went off a-field to work, as they do every day.

(*Frederick York Powell*)

Paul Valéry

1872–

HELEN, THE SAD QUEEN

AZURE, I come! from the caves of death withdrawn
To hear the waves break rhythmic on the shores,
To see swift galleys clear, across the dawn,
Lifting from darkness on the blades of golden oars.

My lonely hands now summon forth the kings
Whose salt-gray beards amuse my chaste fingers. . . .
I wept. . . . And each his gloomy triumph sings
And behind the stern of his bark the furrow lingers.

I hear sonorous conchs and clarion calls
Marking the lift of the oars and their even falls.
The clear chant of the undulant oarsmen charms
The tumult; and the gods! heroic at the prow,
With their olden smile and the spray hurled at their
brow,
Stretch toward me their indulgent, graven arms.

(*Joseph T. Shipley*)

Charles Vildrac

1882–

AFTER MIDNIGHT

It is at morning, twilight they expire;
Death takes in hand, when midnight sounds,
Millions of bodies in their beds,
And scarcely anybody thinks of it. . . .

O men and women, you
About to die at break of day,
I see your hands' uneasy multitude,
Which now the blood deserts for ever!

White people in the throes of death,
Wrestling in all the world to-night,
And whom the weeping dawn will silence,
Fearful I hear your gasping breath!
How many of you there are dying!
How can so many other folks be lying
Asleep upon the shore of your death-rattles!

. . . Here is noise in the house;
I am not the only one who hears you:
Some one has stepped about a room,
Some one has risen to watch over you.

But no! It is a little song I hear.
If some one stepped about a room,
It was to go and rock a little child,
Who has been born this evening in the house.

(*Jethro Bithell*)

Jules Romains

1885–

ANOTHER SPIRIT ADVANCES

What is it so transforms the boulevard?
The lure of the passersby is not of the flesh;

There are no movements; there are flowing rhythms
And I have no need of eyes to see them there.
The air I breathe is fresh with spirit-savor.
Men are ideas that a mind sends forth.
From them to me all flows, yet is internal;
Cheek to cheek we lie across the distance,
Space in communion binds us in one thought.

(*Joseph T. Shipley*)

GERMAN

From the Minnesingers

It is a bright, animated, eventful age which we find reflected in the literature of the Minnesingers; not trivial, for the stern premonition of coming struggle is felt; frank, artless, and natural; original, because reaped on fresh fields, by fresh hands; and with a direct impress of Nature, which we find for the first time in any literature.—BAYARD TAYLOR.

Sir Heinrich von Rugge
12th century

HE THAT LOVES A ROSY CHEEK

Ask not overmuch for fair
Form and face: let women be
Good: beauty is but a snare:
Gladly woo, if good is she.

After the strewn leaves of roses
Richer the rich mind uncloses.
Boorish is he, and unwise,
Who judges women by the eyes.

(*Jethro Bithell*)

Sir Reinmar von Hagenau
12th century

A CHILDISH GAME

Long as I can call to mind,
Never was so much of ill.
In the world you shall not find
One who does attain his will.
So it was, and is alas!
Grief did ever hearts harass.
Joy and sorrow both shall pass.
He whose passion is misprized

Vainly suffers agony.
Where's the gain, to be despised?—
Only sorrow's usury.
This is all that I have got.
She I loved so well hath not
Deigned assuage my cruel lot.
　　"Constancy is lovers' aid."—
This is but a juggler's tale.
Since on her my eyes first strayed,
Never did my service fail.
From that service I depart.—
No, I cannot rend my heart.—
Love, a childish game thou art!

　　　　　　　　　　　　　(*Jethro Bithell*)

Sir Walther von der Vogelweide

13th century

AWAKE!

AWAKE! The day is coming now
That brings the sweat of anguish to the brow
Of Christians, Jews, and Pagans all!
Many a token in the sky
And on the earth shows it is nigh:
Foretold in Holy Writ withal.
The sun no longer shows
His face; and treason sows
His secret seeds that no man can detect;
Fathers by their children are undone;
The brother would the brother cheat;
And the cowled monk is a deceit,
Who should the way to Heaven direct;
Might is right, and justice there is none.
Arise! we slept, nor of the peril recked.

　　　　　　　　　　　　　(*Jethro Bithell*)

WITH A ROD NO MAN ALIVE

WITH a rod no man alive
Goodness in a child can drive:

Whom you may to honor bring
As a blow a word will sting.
As a blow a word will sting
Whom you may to honor bring:
Goodness in a child can drive
With a rod no man alive.

Have a good care of your tongue,
Guarded speech beseems the young;
Shoot the bolt the door behind,
Lock within the words unkind.
Lock within the words unkind,
Shoot the bolt the door behind;
Guarded speech beseems the young,
Have a good care of your tongue.

Have a good care of your eyes,
They were never meant for spies:
Noble manners let them mind,
Be they to ignoble blind.
Be they to ignoble blind,
Noble manners let them mind:
They were never meant for spies,
Have a good care of your eyes.

Have a good care of your ears,
Foolish is who all things hears:
Evil speech if they admit,
You will be defiled by it.
You will be defiled by it,
Evil speech if they admit;
Foolish is who all things hears,
Have a good care of your ears.

Have good care of all the three,
They are often all too free:
Tongue and eyes and ears are bent
On delight and devilment.
On delight and devilment.
Tongue and eyes and ears are bent:
They are often all too free,
Have good care of all the three.

(Jethro Bithell)

Sir Wolfram von Eschenbach

13th century

HIS OWN TRUE WIFE

HIDDEN lovers' woes
Thou wast wont to sing ere dawn arose:
Bitter parting after raptured meetings.
Whosoever love and lady's greeting
So received that he was torn
From her breast by fear of men,
Thou wouldst sing him counsel, when
Shone the star of morn.
Warder, sing it now no more, lay by thy bugle-horn!
  He to whom is given
Not to be from love by morning riven—
Whom the watchers think not to beleaguer,
Hath no need to be alert and eager
To avert the peril rife
In the day: his rest is pure,
Not a warder makes secure
His unhappy life.
Love so sweet bestows in all men's sight his own true
       wife!

                                        (*Jethro Bithell*)

Sir Neidhart von Reuental

13th century

ON THE MOUNTAIN

  ON the mountain, in the valley,
Singing birds again do rally;
Now is seen
Clover green;
Winter, take away thy teen!
  Trees that erst were gray to view
Now their verdant robes renew;
In their shade
Nests are made;
Thence the toll of May is paid.

Fought an aged wife for breath
Day and night, and baffled death;
Now she rushes
Like a ram about, and pushes
All the young ones into the bushes.

(Jethro Bithell)

Sir Ulrich von Liechtenstein

13th century

LOVE, WHOSE MONTH WAS EVER MAY

WHEN with May the air is sweet
When the forest fair is clad,
All that have a love to meet
Pair in pleasure, lass and lad.
Merrily arm in arm they go,
For the time will have it so.
   Love and love, when linked together,
Love goes with to keep them gay:
All the three, this sunshine weather,
They are making holiday.
Sorrow cannot come between
Hearts where Love and May are seen.
   Where to love sweet love is plighted,
Constant and with all the soul,
And the pair are so united
That their love is sound and whole:
God shall make them man and wife
For the bliss of all their life.
   He that finds a constant heart,
Constant love, and constant mind,
All his sorrows shall depart.
Love, when constant, is so kind
That it makes a constant breast
Evermore content and blest.
   Could I find affection true,
So sincere should be mine own:
We should conquer, being two,
Care I cannot kill alone.

Conſtant love is all my care:
Love inconſtant I forbear.

(Jethro Bithell)

Anonymous

16th century

WESTPHALIAN SONG

WHEN thou to my true-love com'ſt
  Greet her from me kindly;
When she asks thee how I fare?
  Say, folks in Heaven fare finely.

When she asks, "What! Is he sick?"
  Say, dead!—and when for sorrow
She begins to sob and cry,
  Say, I come to-morrow.

(Samuel Taylor Coleridge)

Johann Gottfried von Herder

1744–1803

SIR OLAF

SIR OLAF he rideth weſt and eaſt
To bid the folk to his bridal feaſt.

On the wold are dancing an elvish band,
An Erl-king's daughter proffers her hand.

"Now welcome, Sir Olaf: what haſte's with thee?
Step into our circle and dance with me."

"To dance I neither will nor may,
To-morrow's dawn is my bridal-day."

"Nay, ſtay, Sir Olaf, and dance with me,
And golden spurs will I give to thee."

"To dance I neither will nor may,
To-morrow's dawn is my bridal-day."

"Nay, stay, Sir Olaf, and dance with me,
A heap of gold will I give to thee."

"For all thy gold I will not stay,
And dance I neither will nor may."

"If thou wilt not dance, Sir Olaf, with me,
Then Pest and Sickness shall follow thee."

She touched Sir Olaf upon the heart—
Ne'er in his life had he felt such smart.

She lifted him up on his steed that tide,
"Ride home! ride fast to thy troth-plight bride!"

And when he came to his castle-door,
His mother stood there, and trembled sore.

"Now say, sweet son, right speedilie
Why art thou wan, and white of blee?"

"Well may my face be wan and white.
I was in Erl-king's realm last night."

"Now tell me, my son so true and tried,
What thing shall I say to thy plighted bride?"

"Say that I hunt in the good greenwood,
With hound and horse as a good knight should."

When scarce the dawn in heaven shone red,
Came the train with the bride Sir Olaf should wed.

They sat at meat, they sat at wine;
"Now where is Sir Olaf, bridegroom of mine?"

"Sir Olaf rode out to the greenwood free,
With horse and hound to the hunt rode he."

The bride she lifted a cloth of red:
Beneath, Sir Olaf was lying dead.

(Elizabeth Craigmyle)

ESTHONIAN BRIDAL SONG

Deck thyself, maiden,
With the hood of thy mother;
Put on the ribands
Which thy mother once wore:
On thy head the band of duty,
On thy forehead the band of care.
Sit in the seat of thy mother,
And walk in thy mother's footsteps.
And weep not, weep not, maiden:
If thou weepest in thy bridal attire,
Thou wilt weep all thy life.

(W. Taylor)

Ludwig Heinrich Christoph Hölty
1748–1776

HARVEST SONG

Sickles sound;
On the ground
Fast the ripe ears fall;
Every maiden's bonnet
Has blue blossoms on it;
Joy is over all.

Sickles ring,
Maidens sing
To the sickle's sound;
Till the moon is beaming,
And the stubble gleaming,
Harvest songs go round.

All are springing,
All are singing,
Every lisping thing.
Man and master meet;
From one dish they eat;
Each is now a king.

Hans and Michael
Whet the sickle,
Piping merrily.
Now they mow; each maiden
Soon with sheaves is laden,
Busy as a bee.

Now the blisses,
And the kisses!
Now the wit doth flow
Till the beer is out;
Then, with song and shout,
Home they go, yo ho!

(Charles T. Brooks)

Johann Wolfgang von Goethe
1749–1832

Perennial, as a possession for ever, Goethe's History and
Writings abide there; a thousand-voiced "Melody of
Wisdom" which he that has ears may hear.—THOMAS
CARLYLE.

THE ERL-KING

O WHO rides by night thro the woodland so wild?
It is the fond father embracing his child;
And close the boy nestles within his loved arm.
To hold himself fast, and to keep himself warm.

"O father, see yonder! see yonder!" he says;
"My boy, upon what dost thou fearfully gaze?"
"O, 'tis the Erl-King with his crown and his shroud."
"No, my son, it is but a dark wreath of the cloud."

(*The Erl-King speaks*)
"O come and go with me, thou loveliest child;
By many a gay sport shall thy time be beguiled;
My mother keeps for thee full many a fair toy,
And many a fine flower shall she pluck for my boy."

"O father, my father, and did you not hear
The Erl-King whisper so low in my ear?"
"Be still, my heart's darling—my child, be at ease;
It was but the wild blast as it sung thro' the trees."

Erl-King

"O wilt thou go with me, thou loveliest boy?
My daughter shall tend thee with care and with joy;
She shall bear thee so lightly thro' wet and thro' wild,
And press thee, and kiss thee, and sing to my child."

"O father, my father, and saw you not plain
The Erl-King's pale daughter glide past thro' the rain?"
"O yes, my loved treasure, I knew it full soon;
It was the gray willow that danced to the moon."

Erl-King

"O come and go with me, no longer delay,
Or else, silly child, I will drag thee away."
"O father, O father! now, now, keep your hold,
The Erl-King has seized me—his grasp is so cold!"

Sore trembled the father; he spurr'd thro' the wild,
Clasping close to his bosom his shuddering child;
He reaches his dwelling in doubt and in dread,
But, clasp'd to his bosom, the infant was dead.

(Sir Walter Scott)

WANDERER'S NIGHT-SONGS

I

Thou that from the heavens art,
Every pain and sorrow stillest,
And the doubly wretched heart
Doubly with refreshment fillest,

I am weary with contending!
Why this rapture and unrest?
Peace descending
Come, ah, come into my breast!

II

O'er all the hill-tops
Is quiet now,
In all the tree-tops
Hearest thou
Hardly a breath;
The birds are asleep in the trees:
Wait; soon like these
Thou too shalt rest.

(H. W. Longfellow)

THE ROSE

Once a boy beheld a bright
  Rose in dingle growing;
Far, far off it pleased his sight;
Near he viewed it with delight:
  Soft it seemed and glowing.
Lo! the rose, the rose so bright,
  Rose so brightly blowing!

Spake the boy, "I'll pluck thee, grand
  Rose all wildly blowing."
Spake the rose, "I'll wound thy hand,
Thus the scheme thy wit hath planned
  Deftly overthrowing."
O! the rose, the rose so grand,
  Rose so grandly glowing.

But the stripling plucked the red
  Rose in glory growing,
And the thorn his flesh hath bled,
And the rose's pride is fled,
  And her beauty's going.
Woe! the rose, the rose once red
  Rose once redly glowing.

(James Clarence Mangan)

THE KING OF THULÉ

Oh! true was his heart while he breathèd
   That King over Thulé of old,
So she that adored him bequeathèd
   Him, dying, a beaker of gold.

At banquet and supper for years has
   He brimmingly filled it up,
His eyes overflowing with tears as
   He drank from that beaker-cup.

When Death came to wither his pleasures
   He parceled his cities wide,
His castles, his lands, and his treasures,
   But the beaker he laid aside.

They drank the red wine from the chalice.
   His barons and marshals brave;
The monarch sat in his rock-palace
   Above the white foam of the wave.

And now, growing weaker and weaker
   He quaffed his last Welcome to Death,
And hurled the golden beaker
   Down into the flood beneath.

He saw it winking and sinking,
   And drinking the foam so hoar;
The light from his eyes was shrinking,
   Nor drop did he ever drink more.

                 (James Clarence Mangan)

A VOICE FROM THE INVISIBLE WORLD

High o'er his moldering castle walls
   The warrior's phantom glides,
And loudly to the skiff it calls
   That on the billow rides—

"Behold! these arms once vaunted might,
 This heart beat wild and bold—
Behold! these ducal veins ran bright
 With wine-red blood of old.

"The noon in ſtorm, the eve in reſt,
 So sped my life's brief day.
What then? *Young bark on Ocean's breaſt,*
 Cleave thou thy deſtined way!"

(James Clarence Mangan)

PROMETHEUS

BLACKEN thy heavens, Jove,
With thunder-clouds,
And exercise thee, like a boy
Who thiſtles crops,
With smiting oaks and mountain-tops!
Yet muſt leave me ſtanding
My own firm Earth;
Muſt leave my cottage, which thou didſt not build,
And my warm hearth,
Whose cheerful glow
Thou envieſt me.

I know naught more pitiful
Under the sun than you, Gods!
Ye nourish scantily,
With altar-taxes
And with cold lip-service,
This your majeſty;—
Would perish, were not
Children and beggars
Credulous fools.

When I was a child,
And knew not whence or whither,
I would turn my wildered eye
To the sun, as if up yonder were

An ear to hear to my complaining,—
A heart, like mine,
On the oppressed to feel compassion.

Who helped me,
When I braved the Titans' insolence?
Who rescued me from death,
From slavery?
Hast thou not all thyself accomplished,
Holy-glowing heart?
And, glowing young and good,
Most ignorantly thanked
The slumberer above there?

I honor thee? For what?
Hast thou the miseries lightened
Of the down-trodden?
Hast thou the tears ever banished
From the afflicted?
Have I not to manhood been molded
By omnipotent Time,
And by Fate everlasting,—
My lords and thine?

Dreamedst thou ever
I should grow weary of living,
And fly to the desert,
Since not all our
Pretty dream-buds ripen?
Here sit I, fashion men
In mine own image,—
A race to be like me,
To weep and to suffer,
To be happy and to enjoy themselves,—
All careless of *thee* too,
As I!

(*John S. Dwight*)

TO THE PARTED ONE

AND thou art now no longer near!
　From me, O fairest, thou hast flown!
Nor rings in my accustomed ear
　A single word—a single tone.

As when, at morn, the wanderer's eye
　Pierces the air in vain to see
Where, hidden in the deep-blue sky,
　High up the lark goes singing free,—

So wanders anxiously my gaze
　Piercing the field, the bush, the grove;
On thee still call my frequent lays:
　O, come to me again, dear love.

(Christopher Pearse Cranch)

TO A GOLDEN HEART, WORN ROUND HIS NECK

REMEMBRANCER of joys long passed away,
　Relic, from which as yet I cannot part,
O, hast thou power to lengthen love's short day?
　Stronger thy chain than that which bound the heart?
Lili, I fly!—yet still thy fetters press me
　In distant valley, or far lonely wood.
Still with a struggling sigh of pain confess thee
　The mistress of my soul in every mood.

The bird may burst the silken chain that bound him,
　Flying to the green home, which fits him best;
But, ah! he bears the prisoner's badge around him,
　Still by the piece about his neck distressed.
He ne'er can breathe his free wild notes again;
They're stifled by the pressure of his chain.

(Margaret Fuller Ossoli)

MIGNON

KNOWEST thou the land where bloom the lemon trees,
And darkly gleam the golden oranges?

A gentle wind blows down from that blue sky;
Calm ſtands the myrtle and the laurel high.
Knoweſt thou the land? So far and fair!
Thou, whom I love, and I will wander there.

Knoweſt thou the house with all its rooms aglow,
And shining hall and columned portico?
The marble ſtatues ſtand and look at me.
Alas, poor child, what have they done to thee?
Knoweſt thou the land? So far and fair.
My Guardian, thou and I will wander there.

Knoweſt thou the mountain with its bridge of cloud?
The mule plods warily: the white miſts crowd.
Coiled in their caves the brood of dragons sleep;
The torrent hurls the rock from ſteep to ſteep.
Knoweſt thou the land? So far and fair.
Father, away! Our road is over there!

(James Elroy Flecker)

THE SHEPHERD'S LAMENT

Up yonder on the mountain
  A thousand times I ſtand,
Leant on my crook, and gazing
  Down on the valley-land.

I follow the flock to the paſture;
  My little dog watches them ſtill.
I have come below, but I know not
  How I descended the hill.

The beautiful meadow is covered
  With blossoms of every hue;
I pluck them, alas! without knowing
  Whom I shall give them to.

I seek, in the rain and the tempeſt,
  A refuge under the tree:
Yonder the doors are faſtened,
  And all is a dream to me.

Right over the roof of the dwelling
I see a rainbow stand;
But she has departed forever,
And gone far out in the land.

Far out in the land, and farther,—
Perhaps to an alien shore:
Go forward, ye sheep! go forward,—
The heart of the shepherd is sore.

(*Bayard Taylor*)

FROM FAUST

Prologue in Heaven

Raphæl

The sun makes music as of old
Amid the rival spheres of Heaven,
On its predestined circle rolled
With thunder speed: the Angels even
Draw strength from gazing on its glance,
Though none its meaning fathom may;
The world's unwithered countenance
Is bright as at creation's day.

Gabriel

And swift and swift, with rapid lightness,
The adorned Earth spins silently,
Alternating Elysian brightness
With deep and dreadful night; the sea
Foams in broad billows from the deep
Up to the rocks, and rocks and ocean,
Onward, with spheres which never sleep,
Are hurried in eternal motion.

Michael

And tempests in contention roar
From land to sea, from sea to land;
And, raging, weave a chain of power,
Which girds the earth, as with a band.

A flashing desolation there
   Flames before the thunder's way;
But thy servants, Lord, revere
   The gentle changes of thy day.

Chorus of the Three

The Angels draw strength from thy glance,
   Though no one comprehend thee may;
Thy world's unwithered countenance
   Is bright as on creation's day.

(Percy Bysshe Shelley)

THE THOUGHT ETERNAL

Whether day my spirit's yearning
Unto far, blue hills has led,
Or the night lit all the burning
Constellations at my head—
Hours of light or hours nocturnal
Do I praise our mortal fate:
If man think the thought eternal
He is ever fair and great.

(Ludwig Lewisohn)

Friedrich von Schiller

1759–1805

THEKLA'S SONG

From The Piccolomini

The cloud doth gather, the green wood roar,
The damsel paces along the shore;
The billows they tumble with might, with might;
And she flings out her voice to the darksome night;
   Her bosom is swelling with sorrow;

The world it is empty, the heart will die,
There's nothing to wish for beneath the sky:
Thou Holy One, call thy child away!
I've lived and loved, and that was to-day—
   Make ready my grave-clothes to-morrow.

(Samuel Taylor Coleridge)

THE MAID OF ORLEANS

At thee *the Mocker* sneers in cold derision,
  Through thee he seeks to desecrate and dim
Glory for which he hath no soul or vision,
  For "God" and "Angel" are but sounds with him.
He makes the jewels of the heart his booty,
And scoffs at Man's Belief and Woman's Beauty.

Yet thou—a lowly shepherdess!—descended
  Not from a kingly but a godly race,
Are crowned by Poësy! Amid the splendid
  Of Heaven's high ſtars she builds thy dwellingplace,
Garlands thy temples with a wreath of glory,
And swathes thy memory in eternal Story.

The Base of this weak world exult at seeing
  The Fair defaced, the Lofty in the duſt;
Yet grieve not! There are godlike hearts in being
  Which worship ſtill the Beautiful and Juſt.
Let Momus and his mummers please the crowd,
Of nobleness alone a noble mind is proud.

(James Clarence Mangan)

Johann Gaudenz von Salis
1762–1834

SONG OF THE SILENT LAND

Into the Silent Land!
  Ah! who shall lead us thither?
Clouds in the evening sky more darkly gather,
  And shattered wrecks lie thicker on the ſtrand.
  Who leads us with a gentle hand
    Thither, O, thither,
  Into the Silent Land?

Into the Silent Land!
  To you, ye boundless regions
Of all perfeᴄtion! Tender morning-visions

Of beauteous souls! The Future's pledge and band!
　　Who in Life's battle firm doth stand
　　　Shall bear Hope's tender blossoms
　　　　Into the Silent Land!

　　　　O Land! O Land!
　　　For all the broken-hearted
The mildest herald by our fate allotted
　Beckons, and with inverted torch doth stand
　　To lead us with a gentle hand
Into the land of the great departed,
　　　Into the Silent Land!

(*H. W. Longfellow*)

Justinus Kerner

1786–1862

HOME-SICKNESS

THERE calleth me ever a marvelous Horn,
　　"Come away! Come away!"
Is it earthly music faring astray,
　　Or is it air-born?
Oh, whether it be a spirit-wile
　　Or a forest voice,
It biddeth mine ailing heart rejoice,
　　Yet sorrow the while!

In the greenwood glades—o'er the garlanded bowl—
　　Night, Noontide, and Morn,
The summoning call of that marvelous Horn
　　Tones home to my soul!
In vain have I sought for it east and west,
　　But I darkly feel
That so soon as its music shall cease to peal
　　I go to my rest!

(*James Clarence Mangan*)

Ludwig Uhland

1787–1862

DURAND OF BLONDEN

Tow'RDS the lofty walls of Balbi, lo! Durand of Blonden
hies;
Thousand songs are in his bosom; Love and Pleasure
light his eyes.
There, he dreams, his own true maiden, beauteous as the
evening-star,
Leaning o'er her turret-lattice, waits to hear her knight's
guitar.

In the lindenshaded courtyard soon Durand begins his
lay.
But his eyes glance vainly upwards; there they meet no
answering ray.
Flowers are blooming in the lattice, rich of odor, fair to
see.
But the fairest flower of any, Lady Blanca, where is she?

Ah! while yet he chants the ditty, draws a mourner near
and speaks—
"She is dead, is dead forever, whom Durand of Blonden
seeks!"
And the knight replies not, breathes not: darkness
gathers round his brain:
He is dead, is dead forever, and the mourners weep the
twain.

In the darkened castle-chapel burn a many tapers bright:
There the lifeless maiden lies, with whitest wreaths and
ribands dight.
There . . . But lo! a mighty marvel! she hath oped her
eyes of blue!
All are lost in joy and wonder! Lady Blanca lives anew!

Dreams and visions flit before her, as she asks of those
anear,
"Heard I not my lover singing?—Is Durand of Blonden
here?"

Yes, O Lady, thou haſt heard him; he has died for thy
    dear sake!
He could wake his trancèd miſtress: him shall none for
    ever wake!

He is in a realm of glory, but as yet he weets not where;
He but seeks the Lady Blanca: dwells she not already
    there?
Till he finds her muſt he wander to and fro, as one
    bereaven,
Ever calling, "Blanca! Blanca!" through the desert halls
    of Heaven.

(James Clarence Mangan)

THE CASTLE BY THE SEA

"Haſt thou seen that lordly caſtle,
    That caſtle by the sea?
Golden and red above it
    The clouds float gorgeously.

"And fain it would ſtoop downward
    To the mirrored wave below;
And fain it would soar upward
    In the evening's crimson glow."

"Well have I ſeen that caſtle,
    That caſtle by the sea,
And the moon above it ſtanding,
    And the miſt rise solemnly."

"The winds and the waves of ocean,
    Had they a merry chime?
Didſt thou hear, from those lofty chambers,
    The harp and the minſtrel's rhyme?"

"The winds and the waves of ocean,
    They reſted quietly;
But I heard on the gale a sound of wail,
    And tears came to mine eye."

"And sawest thou on the turrets
 The king and his royal bride,
And the wave of their crimson mantles,
 And the golden crown of pride?

"Led they not forth, in rapture,
 A beauteous maiden there,
Resplendent as the morning sun,
 Beaming with golden hair?"

"Well saw I the ancient parents,
 Without the crown of pride;
They were moving slow, in weeds of woe;
 No maiden was by her side!"

(H. W. Longfellow)

IN A LOVELY GARDEN WALKING

In a lovely garden walking
 Two lovers went hand in hand;
Two wan, worn figures, talking
 They sat in the flowery land.

On the cheek they kissed one another,
 On the mouth with sweet refrain;
Fast held they each the other.
 And were young and well again.

Two little bells rang shrilly—
 The dream went with the hour:
She lay in the cloister stilly,
 He far in the dungeon-tower!

(George MacDonald)

A LEAF

A LEAF falls softly at my feet,
Sated with rain and summer heat;
What time this leaf was green and new,
I still had parents dear and true.

A leaf—how soon it fades away!
Child of the spring, the autumn's prey;
Yet has this leaf outlived, I see,
So much that was moſt dear to me.

(*John S. Dwight*)

THE HOSTESS' DAUGHTER

THREE fellows were marching over the Rhine,
They ſtopped where they saw the hoſtess' sign.

"Dear Hoſtess, have you good beer and wine?
Where have you your daughter so fair and fine?"

"My beer is good, my wine is clear,
My daughter is lying upon the bier."

Now into the chamber she led the way,
There in a black coffin the maiden lay.

The firſt man drew the veil aside,
And full of sorrow the maid espied.

"Ah, beautiful maiden, if thou couldſt live!
To thee alone my love I would give!"

The second laid back the veil again,
And turned away and wept in pain.

"Oh, why muſt thou lie upon the bier!
Alas, I have loved thee for many a year."

The third man lifted again the veil,
And kissed her upon the lips so pale:

"I loved thee always, I love thee to-day,
And I will love thee forever, and aye."

(*Margarete Münsterberg*)

Friedrich Rueckert

1789–1866

THE RIDE ROUND THE PARAPET

SHE said, "I was not born to mope at home in loneliness,"—
      The Lady Eleanora von Alleyne,
She said, "I was not born to mope at home in loneliness,
When the heart is throbbing soreſt there is balsam in the
forest,
      There is balsam in the foreſt for its pain,"
        Said the Lady Eleanora,
      Said the Lady Eleanora von Alleyne.

She doffed her silks and pearls, and donned inſtead her
hunting-gear,
      The Lady Eleanora von Alleyne.
She doffed her silks and pearls, and donned inſtead her
hunting-gear,
And, till Summertime was over, as a huntress and a
rover
      Did she couch upon the mountain and the
plain,
        She, the Lady Eleanora,
      Noble Lady Eleanora von Alleyne.

Returning home agen, she viewed with scorn the tourna-
ments—
      The Lady Eleanora von Alleyne.
Returning home agen, she viewed with scorn the tourna-
ments;
She saw the morions cloven and the crowning chaplets
woven,
      And the sight awakened only the disdain
        Of the Lady Eleanora,
      Of the Lady Eleanora von Alleyne.

"My feeling towards Man is one of utter scornfulness,"
      Said Lady Eleanora von Alleyne.

"My feeling towards Man is one of utter scornfulness,"
And he that would o'ercome it, let him ride around the
　　summit
　　　　　　Of my battlemented Castle by the Maine,"
　　　　　　　　Said the Lady Eleanora,
　　　　　　Said the Lady Eleanora von Alleyne.

So came a knight anon to ride around the parapet,
　　　　　　For Lady Eleanora von Alleyne.
So came a knight anon to ride around the parapet,
Man and horse were hurled together o'er the crags that
　　beetled nether.
　　　　　　Said the Lady, "There, I fancy, they'll re-
　　　　　　main!"
　　　　　　　　Said the Lady Eleanora,
　　　　　　Queenly Lady Eleanora von Alleyne!

Then came another knight to ride around the parapet,
　　　　　　For Lady Eleanora von Alleyne.
Then came another knight to ride around the parapet,
Man and horse fell down, asunder, o'er the crags that
　　beetled under.
　　　　　　Said the Lady, "They'll not leap the leap
　　　　　　again!"
　　　　　　　　Said the Lady Eleanora,
　　　　　　Lovely Lady Eleanora von Alleyne!

Came other knights anon to ride around the parapet,
　　　　　　For Lady Eleanora von Alleyne.
Came other knights anon to ride around the parapet,
Till six and thirty corses of both mangled men and
　　horses
　　　　　　Had been sacrificed as victims at the fane
　　　　　　Of the Lady Eleanora,
　　　　　　Stately Lady Eleanora von Alleyne!

That woeful year was by, and Ritter none came after-
　　wards
　　　　　　To Lady Eleanora von Alleyne.

That woeful year was by, and Ritter none came afterwards;
The Castle's lonely basscourt looked a wild o'ergrown-
with-grass court.
> 'Twas abandoned by the Ritters and their train
> To the Lady Eleanora,
> Haughty Lady Eleanora von Alleyne!

She clomb the silent wall, she gazed around her sovran-
like;
> The Lady Eleanora von Alleyne!
She clomb the silent wall, she gazed around her sovran-
like;
"And wherefore have departed all the Brave, the lion-
hearted,
> Who have left me here to play the Castellain?"
> Said the Lady Eleanora,
> Said the Lady Eleanora von Alleyne.

"And is it fled for aye, the palmy time of Chivalry?"
> Cried Lady Eleanora von Alleyne.
"And is it fled for aye, the palmy time of Chivalry?
Shame light upon the cravens! May their corpses gorge
the ravens,
> Since they tremble thus to wear a woman's
> chain!"
> Said the Lady Eleanora,
> Said the Lady Eleanora von Alleyne.

The story reached at Gratz the gallant Margrave Gondibert
> Of Lady Eleanora von Alleyne.
The story reached at Gratz the gallant Margrave Gondibert.
Quoth he, "I trow the woman must be more or less than
human;
> She is worth a little peaceable campaign,
> Is the Lady Eleanora,
> Is the Lady Eleanora von Alleyne!"

He trained a horse to pace round narrow stones laid
 merlonwise,
   For Lady Eleanora von Alleyne.
He trained a horse to pace round narrow stones laid
 merlonwise,
"Good Gray! do thou thy duty, and this rocky-bosomed
 beauty
   Shall be taught that all the vauntings are in
   vain
    Of the Lady Eleanora,
  Of the Lady Eleanora von Alleyne!"

He left his castle-halls, he came to Lady Eleanora's,
   The Lady Eleanora von Alleyne.
He left his castle-halls, he came to Lady Eleanora's.
"O, lady, best and fairest, here am I,—and, if thou
 carest,
   I will gallop round the parapet amain,
    Noble Lady Eleanora,
  Noble Lady Eleanora von Alleyne!"

She saw him spring to horse, that gallant Margrave Gon-
 dibert,
   The Lady Eleanora von Alleyne.
She saw him spring to horse, that gallant Margrave Gon-
 dibert.
"O, bitter, bitter sorrow! I shall weep for this to-morrow!
   It were better that in battle he were slain,"
    Said the Lady Eleanora,
  Said the Lady Eleanora von Alleyne.

Then rode he round and round the battlemented parapet,
   For Lady Eleanora von Alleyne.
Then rode he round and round the battlemented parapet:
The Lady wept and trembled, and her paly face re-
 sembled,
   As she looked away, a lily wet with rain;
    Hapless Lady Eleanora!
  Hapless Lady Eleanora von Alleyne!

So rode he round and round the battlemented parapet,
  For Lady Eleanora von Alleyne!
So rode he round and round the battlemented parapet;
"Accurſt be my ambition! He but rideth to perdition,
  He but rideth to perdition without rein!"
   Wept the Lady Eleanora,
  Wept the Lady Eleanora von Alleyne.

Yet rode he round and round the battlemented parapet,
  For Lady Eleanora von Alleyne.
Yet rode he round and round the battlemented parapet.
Meanwhile her terror shook her—yea, her breath well
  nigh forsook her.
   Fire was burning in the bosom and the brain
    Of the Lady Eleanora,
   Of the Lady Eleanora von Alleyne!

Then rode he round and off the battlemented parapet
   To Lady Eleanora von Alleyne.
Then rode he round and off the battlemented parapet.
"Now bleſt be God for ever! This is marvelous! I never
   Cherished hope of laying eyes on thee agayne,"
    Cried the Lady Eleanora,
   Joyous Lady Eleanora von Alleyne!

"The Man of Men thou art, for thou haſt fairly con-
  quered me,
   The Lady Eleanora von Alleyne!
"The Man of Men thou art, for thou haſt fairly con-
  quered me.
I greet thee as my lover, and, ere many days be over,
   Thou shalt wed me and be Lord of my do-
   main,"
    Said the Lady Eleanora,
   Said the Lady Eleanora von Alleyne.

Then bowed the graceful knight, the gallant Margrave
  Gondibert,
   To Lady Eleanora von Alleyne.

Then bowed that graceful knight, the gallant Margrave
      Gondibert,
And thus he answered coldly, "There be many who as
    boldly
          Will adventure an achievement they disdain,
            For the Lady Eleanora,
          For the Lady Eleanora von Alleyne.

"Mayeſt bide until they come, O ſtately Lady Eleanora!
      O, Lady Eleanora von Alleyne!
Mayeſt bide until they come, O ſtately Lady Eleanora!
And thou and they may marry, but, for me, I muſt not
    tarry,
          I have won a wife already out of Spain,
            Virgin Lady Eleanora,
          Virgin Lady Eleanora von Alleyne!"

Thereon he rode away, the gallant Margrave Gondibert,
      From Lady Eleanora von Alleyne.
Thereon he rode away, the gallant Margrave Gondibert.
And long in shame and anguish did that haughty Lady
    languish,
          Did she languish without pity for her pain,
            She the Lady Eleanora,
          She the Lady Eleanora von Alleyne.

And year went after year, and ſtill in barren maiden
    hood
          Lived Lady Eleanora von Alleyne.
And wrinkled Eld crept on, and ſtill her lot was maiden-
    hood,
And, woe! her end was tragic; she was changed, at
    length, by magic,
          To an ugly wooden image, they maintain;
            She, the Lady Eleanora,
          She, the Lady Eleanora von Alleyne!

And now, before the gate, in sight of all, transmogrified,
      Stands Lady Eleanora von Alleyne.
Before her caſtle-gate, in sight of all, transmogrified,

And he that won't salute her muſt be fined in foaming
    pewter,
        If a boor—but, if a burgher, in champagne,
            For the Lady Eleanora,
        Wooden Lady Eleanora von Alleyne!

(James Clarence Mangan)

Heinrich Heine

1799–1856

The comfort of coming to a man of genius, who finds in
verse his freeſt and moſt perfeᏨ expression, whose voyage
over the deep of poetry deſtiny makes smooth! The magic
of Heine's poetical form is incomparable; he employs this
form with the moſt exquisite lightness and ease, and yet
it has at the same time the inborn fulness, pathos, and
old-world charm of all true forms of popular poetry.
Thus in Heine's poetry, too, one perpetually blends the
impression of French modernism and clearness with that
of German sentiment and fulness.—MATTHEW ARNOLD.

AD FINEM

THE years they come and go,
    The races drop in the grave,
Yet never the love doth so
    Which here in my heart I have.

Could I see thee but once, one day,
    And sink down so on my knee,
And die in thy sight while I say,
    "Lady, I love but thee!"

(Elizabeth Barrett Browning)

MEIN KIND, WIR WAREN KINDER

MY child, we were two children,
Small, merry by childhood's law;
We used to creep to the henhouse,
And hide ourselves in the ſtraw.

We crowed like cocks, and whenever
The passers near us drew—

"Cock-a-doodle!" they thought
'Twas a real cock that crew.

The boxes about our courtyard
We carpeted to our mind,
And lived there both together—
Kept house in a noble kind.

The neighbor's old cat often
Came to pay us a visit;
(We have made the very same speeches
Each with a compliment in it.)

After her health we asked,
Our care and regard to evince—
(We have made the very same speeches
To many an old cat since).

We also sat and wisely
Discoursed, as old folks do,
Complaining how all went better
In those good old times we knew;—

How love, and truth, and believing
Had left the world to itself,
And how so dear was the coffee,
And how so rare was the pelf.

The children's games are over,
The rest is over with youth—
The world, the good games, the good times,
The belief, and the love, and the truth.

                    (*Elizabeth Barrett Browning*)

THE SEA HATH ITS PEARLS

THE sea hath its pearls,
    The heaven hath its stars;
But my heart, my heart,
    My heart hath its love.

Great are the sea, and the heaven;
   Yet greater is my heart,
And fairer than pearls or stars
   Flashes and beams my love.

Thou little, youthful maiden,
   Come unto my great heart;
My heart, and the sea and the heaven
   Are melting away with love!

(H. W. Longfellow)

SAG' MIR WER EINST DIE UHREN ERFUND

Who was it, tell me, that first of men reckon'd
Time by the hour and the minute and second?
A soulless man, without heart or light,
He sat and he mused in the long winter's night,
And counted the pittering steps of the mouse,
And the pick of the woodworm that gnawed at the
   house.

Kisses, now tell me, who first did discover?
It was the warm happy mouth of a lover;
He kiss'd without ceasing, he kiss'd without care,
He kiss'd his first kiss in the May-season fair;
The flowers from their emerald cradle upsprang,
The sun brightly beam'd, the birds sweetly sang.

(Richard Garnett)

WARUM SIND DENN DIE ROSEN SO BLASS

O dearest, canst thou tell me why
   The rose should be so pale?
And why the azure violet
   Should wither in the vale?

And why the lark should in the cloud
   So sorrowfully sing?
And why from loveliest balsam-buds
   A scent of death should spring?

And why the sun upon the mead
  So chillingly should frown?
And why the earth should, like a grave,
  Be moldering and brown?

And why it is that I myself
  So languishing should be?
And why it is, my heart of hearts,
  That thou forsakest me?

(Richard Garnett)

ES FÄLLT EIN STERN HERUNTER

See yonder, where a gem of night
Falls helpless from its heavenly height!
It is the bright star of Love
That thus forsakes the realms above.

And one by one the wind bereaves
The apple-tree of silvery leaves;
The breezes, in their reckless play,
Spurn them with dancing feet away.

And round and round swims on the pool
The tuneful swan so beautiful,
And ever singing sweet and slow
He sinks into his grave below.

It is so dreary and so dread!
The leaf is wholly witherèd,
The fallen star has flamed away,
The swan has sung his dying lay.

(Richard Garnett)

DIE ROSE, DIE LILIE, DIE TAUBE, DIE SONNE

The rose and the lily, the moon and the dove,
  Once loved I them all with a perfect love.
I love them no longer, I love alone
  The Lovely, the Graceful, the Pure, the One

Who twines in one wreath all their beauty and love,
And rose is, and lily, and moon and dove.

(*Richard Garnett*)

MEIN LIEBCHEN, WIR SASSEN ZUSAMMEN

My darling, we sat together,
  We two, in our frail boat;
The night was calm o'er the wide sea
  Whereon we were afloat.

The Specter-Island, the lovely,
  Lay dim in the moon's mild glance;
There sounded sweetest music,
  There waved the shadowy dance.

It sounded sweeter and sweeter,
  It waved there to and fro;
But we slid past forlornly
  Upon the great sea-flow.

(*James Thomson*)

✗ES STEHEN UNBEWEGLICH

For many thousand ages
  The steadfast stars above
Have gazed upon each other
  With ever mournful love.

They speak a certain language,
  So beautiful, so grand,
Which none of the philologians
  Could ever understand.

But I have learned it, learned it,
  For ever, by the grace
Of studying one grammar,
  My heart's own darling's face.

(*James Thomson*)

EIN FICHTENBAUM STEHT EINSAM

A PINE-TREE standeth lonely
  In the North on an upland bare;
It standeth whitely shrouded
  With snow, and sleepeth there.

It dreameth of a Palm Tree
  Which far in the East alone,
In mournful silence standeth
  On its ridge of burning stone.

(James Thomson)

MIR TRÄUMTE WIEDER DER ALTE TRAUM

THE old dream comes again to me:
  With May-night stars above,
We two sat under the linden-tree
  And swore eternal love.

Again and again we plighted troth,
  We chattered, and laughed, and kissed;
To make me well remember my oath
  You gave me a bite in the wrist.

O darling with the eyes serene,
  And with the teeth so white!
The vows were proper to the scene,
  Superfluous was the bite.

(James Thomson)

DU BIST WIE EINE BLUME

E'EN as a lovely flower,
  So fair, so pure thou art;
I gaze on thee, and sadness
  Comes stealing o'er my heart.

My hands I fain had folded
  Upon thy soft brown hair,
Praying that God may keep thee
  So lovely, pure and fair.

(Kate Freiligrath Kroeker)

THE MESSAGE

Up, boy! arise, and saddle quick,
And mount your swiftest steed,
And to King Duncan's castle ride
O'er bush and brake with speed.

There slip into the stable soft,
Till one shall see you hide,
Then ask him: Which of Duncan's girls
Is she that is a bride?

And if he say, The dark-haired one,
Then give your mare the spur;
But if he say, The fair-haired one,
You need not hurry here.

You only need, if that's the case,
Buy me a hempen cord,
Ride slowly back and give it me,
But never speak a word.

(*Kate Freiligrath Kroeker*)

TO MY MOTHER

I've kept a haughty heart thro' grief and mirth,
And borne my head perchance a thought too high;
If even a king should look me in the eye
I would not bend it humbly to the earth:
Yet, dearest mother, such the gentle worth
Of thy benignant presence, angel-mild,
It ever hath my proudest moods beguiled,
And given to softer, humbler feelings birth.
Was it thy mind's calm penetrative power,
Thy purer mind, that secretly came o'er me,
And unto Heaven's clearer light upbore me;
Or did remembrance sting me in that hour,
With thought of words and deeds which pierced un-
    kindly
That gentle heart, loving me still so blindly.

(*Matilda Dickson*)

MÄDCHEN MIT DEM ROTHEN MÜNDCHEN

LASSIE, with the lips sae rosy,
  With the eyne sae saft and bricht,
Dear wee lassie, I keep thinkin',
  Thinkin' on thee day and nicht.

Winter nichts are lang and eerie;
  Oh, gin I were with thee, dear,
Arms about thee, cracking couthly,
  With nae mortal by to hear!

With my kisses I would smother
  Thy white hand sae jimp and sma',
And my tears for very rapture
  On that wee white hand should fa'.

(*Sir Theodore Martin*)

ANNO 1829

I CRAVE an ampler, worthier sphere:
  I'd liefer bleed at every vein
Than stifle 'mid these hucksters here,
  These lying slaves of paltry gain.

They eat, they drink; they're every whit
  As happy as their type, the mole;
Large are their bounties—as the slit
  Through which they drop the poor man's dole.

With pipe in mouth they go their way,
  With hands in pockets; they are blest
With grand digestions: only *they*
  Are such hard morsels to digest!

The hand that's red with some dark deed,
  Some giant crime, were white as wool
Compared with these sleek saints, whose creed
  Is paying all their debts in full.

Ye clouds that sail to far-off lands,
  O waft me to what clime ye will!

To Lapland's snows, to Lybia's sands,
  To the world's end—but onward still!

Take me, O clouds! They ne'er look down;
  But (proof of a discerning mind)
One moment hung o'er Hamburg town,
  The next they leave it leagues behind.

                (*Charles Stuart Calverley*)

THE AZRA

    Daily walked the fair and lovely
    Sultan's daughter in the twilight,—
    In the twilight by the fountain,
    Where the sparkling waters plash.

    Daily stood the young slave silent
    In the twilight by the fountain
    Where the plashing waters sparkle,
    Pale and paler every day.

    Once by twilight came the princess
    Up to him with rapid questions:
    "I would know thy name, thy nation,
    Whence thou comest, who thou art."

    And the young slave said, "My name is
    Mahomet, I come from Yemmen.
    I am of the sons of Azra,
    Men who perish if they love."

                    (*John Hay*)

I'M BLACK AND BLUE

I'm black and blue from their worrying,
  They've tortured me early and late,
Some with their love—God help me!
  The others with their hate.

They've poisoned the wine on my table,
  They've poisoned the bread on my plate,

Some with their love—God help me!
    The others with their hate.

But she who moſt has worried,
    And tortured and troubled—she
Has never either loved me,
    Or even hated me.

               (John Todhunter)

FRESCO-SONNETS TO CHRISTIAN SETHE

I

I LAUGH at each dull bore, taſte's parasite
    Who ſtares upon me with his goatish eyes;
    And those raw freshmen, lean as hungry flies,
    Who gape and sniff at me in petty spite.
I laugh, too, at those apes, whose learning trite
    Puffs them with pride to pose as critics wise;
    And at those daſtard rogues, my enemies,
    'Gainſt poisoned weapons daring me to fight.
Yet when Joy's nosegay of delightful things
    Is shattered for us by the hand of Fate,
    And at our feet flung withered, without scent,
And when the heart within the breaſt is rent,
    Rent, and ſtabbcd through, sore-wounded, desperate—
    What's left us but that laugh that shrilly rings?

2

Give me a mask, I'll join the masquerade,
    Playing the knave that charlatans I see,
    Flaunting in gaudy robes of dignity,
    May count me not a craftsman of their trade.
Come vulgar words and manners to my aid,
    In popular art I'll take my base degree,
    All those rare sparks of genius banned shall be,
    Wherewith ſtale rogues of late fine tricks have played.
And thus will I dance at the grand masqued-ball,
    'Mid German knights, monks, kings in motley crew,
    Capped to by Harlequin, known to but few,

With their blunt swords of lath cudgelled by all.
  That is their sport. Should I unmask, beware!
  I should dumbfounder every jail-bird there.

(John Todhunter)

A MAIDEN LIES IN HER CHAMBER

A MAIDEN lies in her chamber
  Lit by a trembling moon;
Outside there rises and echoes
  A waltz's giddy tune.

"I wonder who breaks my slumber;
  I'll go to the window and see—"
And lo, a skeleton stands there;
  He fiddles and sings with glee:

"A dance you swore to give me,
  And you have broken your vow;
Tonight there's a ball in the churchyard;
  Come out and dance with me now!"

The maid, as though moved by magic,
  Obeys, and leaves the house;
The skeleton, fiddling and singing,
  Goes on with its wild carouse.

It fiddles and leaps and dances
  And rattles its bones to the tune;
Its skull keeps nodding and nodding
  Crazily under the moon.

(Louis Untermeyer)

OH LOVELY FISHERMAIDEN

OH lovely fishermaiden,
  Come, bring your boat to land;
And we will sit together
  And whisper, hand in hand.

O rest upon my bosom,
  And fear no harm from me.
You give your body daily,
  Unfearing to the sea. . . .

My heart is like the ocean
   With storm and ebb and flow—
And many a pearly treasure
   Burns in the depths below.

(Louis Untermeyer)

TWILIGHT

WE sat at the hut of the fisher
   And idly watched the sea,
While in the hush of evening
   The mists rose silently.

The yellow lights in the lighthouse
   Shone like a burnished bell,
And in the hazy distance
   One ship still rose and fell.

We spoke of storm and shipwreck,
   Of sailors and their life.
Pulled between sky and water,
   Fierce joy and lusty strife.

We gossiped of distant places,
   Of North and South we spoke,
Of wild and curious customs,
   And wild and curious folk.

Of how the Ganges sparkles;
   Of great exotic trees;
Of folk who worship the lotus
   Silently, on their knees.

Of Lapland; its slovenly people,
   Flat-headed, broad-featured and small,
That do little else but bake fishes
   And squat by the fire and squall. . . .

The girls all listened breathless;
   Then silence, like a spell . . .
The ship could be seen no longer—
   Swiftly the darkness fell.

(Louis Untermeyer)

THE COFFIN

THE songs, so old and bitter,
 The dreams so wild and drear,
Let's bury them together—
 What ho! A coffin here!

I have so much to bury
 It never will be done,
Unless the coffin's larger
 Than Heidelberg's great Tun.

And bring a bier to match it
 Of stoutest oaks and pines;
It must be even longer
 Than the long bridge at Mainz.

And also bring twelve giants
 Of mightier brawn and bone
Than Christopher, the sainted,
 Whose shrine is in Cologne.

And in the great sea sink it
 Beneath the proudest wave;
For such a mighty coffin
 Should have a mighty grave . . .

You know what makes my coffin
 So great, so hard to bear?
It holds my love within it,
 And my too heavy care.

       (*Louis Untermeyer*)

THE STORM

A HOWLING storm is brewing,
 The wind and rain are wild;
And what can my love be doing,
 That pale and frightened child?

There at the window dreaming,
    I see her, worn and white;
With eyes no longer beaming,
    She stares into the night.

                    (*Louis Untermeyer*)

MY SONGS ARE POISONED

My songs, they say, are poisoned.
    How else, love, could it be?
Thou hast, with deadly magic,
    Poured poison into me.

My songs, they say, are poisoned.
    How else, then could it be?
I carry a thousand serpents
    And, love, among them—thee!

                    (*Louis Untermeyer*)

WHEN TWO ARE PARTED

When two who love are parted,
    They talk, as friend to friend,
Clasp hands and weep a little,
    And sigh without an end.

We did not weep, my darling,
    Not sigh "Why must this be . . ."
The tears, the sighs, the anguish
    Came later—and to me.

                    (*Louis Untermeyer*)

FROM THE NORTH SEA

Evening Twilight

On the wan sea-strand
Lonely I lay, and in sorrowful brooding.
The sun sank lower and lower, and flung
His red rays, glowing, on the water,
And I watched the far white billows,
In the grip of the flood,

Foaming and roaring, nigher and nigher—
Strange medley of sounds! a whispering and wailing,
A laughing and murmuring, sobbing and sighing,
Low voices, the while, a strange lullaby singing.
Methought I heard long-forgotten legends,
World-old adorable folk-tales,
That long since in boyhood
From neighbors' children I learnt;
When, of a summer evening,
On the steps of stone by the house-door,
We squatted for quiet story-telling,
With small hearts eagerly listening
And young eyes keen for wonders;
While the fair grown-up maidens
Sat, 'mid balm-breathing pots of flowers,
At a window over the way there,
With rosy faces,
Smiling and lit by the moon.

(John Todhunter)

Epilog

Like the ears of wheat in a wheat-field growing,
So a thousand thoughts spring and tremble
In the minds of men.
But the tender fancies of love
Are like the happy colors that leap among them;
Red and blue flowers.
Red and blue flowers!
The sullen reaper destroys you as worthless;
Block-headed fools will scornfully thresh you;
Even the penniless wayfarer
Who is charmed and cheered by your faces,
Shakes his poor head,
And calls you pretty weeds!
But the young girl from the village,
Twining her garland,
Honors and gathers you.
And with you she brightens her lovely tresses.
And thus adorned, she hurries to the dancing,

Where fiddles and flutes are sweetly sounding;
Or runs to the sheltering beech-tree,
Where the voice of her lover sounds even sweeter
Than fiddles and flutes.

(Louis Untermeyer)

Eduard Möricke

1804–1875

BEAUTY ROHTRAUT

WHAT is the name of King Ringang's daughter?
  Rohtraut, Beauty Rohtraut!
And what does she do the livelong day,
Since she dare not knit and spin alway?
O hunting and fishing is ever her play!
And, heigh! that her huntsman I might be!
I'd hunt and fish right merrily!
  Be silent, heart!

And it chanced that, after this some time,
  Rohtraut, Beauty Rohtraut!
The boy in the Castle has gained access,
And a horse he has got and a huntsman's dress,
To hunt and to fish with the merry Princess;
And, O! that a king's son I might be!
Beauty Rohtraut I love so tenderly.
  Hush! hush! my heart.

Under a gray old oak they sat,
  Beauty, Beauty Rohtraut!
She laughs: "Why look you so slyly at me?
If you have heart enough, come, kiss me."
Cried the breathless boy, "Kiss thee?"
But he thinks kind fortune has favored my youth;
And thrice he has kissed Beauty Rohtraut's mouth.
  Down! down! mad heart.

Then slowly and silently they rode home,—
  Rohtraut, Beauty Rohtraut!
The boy was lost in his delight:
"And, wert thou Empress this very night,

I would not heed or feel the blight;
Ye thousand leaves of the wild wood wiſt
How Beauty Rohtraut's mouth I kiss'd.
    Hush! hush! wild heart."

(George Meredith)

Detlev von Liliencron

1844–1909

AUTUMN

A FLOCK of crows high from the Northland flies,
On their dark wings the evening sunshine plays.
Below the Ursulines' calm convent lies
And an old man dreams in its garden ways.
From the cool chapel float the harmonies
Upward in rapture deep of peace and grace
And fall and fade . . . All sound of living dies
While the old man unto Our Lady prays.

(Ludwig Lewisohn)

Gustav Falke

1853–1916

GOD'S HARP

THE wind, ſtirring in the dark foliage, brings
Songs to me of the wakeful nightingale;
At intervals a ſtranger music rings.
Whence are these voices that now light,
Now deeply echo from the night   .
And now of their own beauty fail?

The apple bough of white
That at my open window rocks and sways,
Againſt the pane its dewy blossom lays,
Shines magically in the blanchèd light,
A sabbath radiance covers all the ways;
My vision waxes vaſt and wide:

Oh, there arises now a solemn tide
For those who live in dreams, the delicate

Souls that to every subtle tone vibrate
Which from God's harp rings forth and prophesies
That he forever
His busy hand in ancient music plies,
And will not end the song of His delight.

Thus ends it never—
Hark, what a tone of love passed through the night.

(Ludwig Lewisohn)

Richard Dehmel

1863–1920

BEFORE THE STORM

THE sky grew darker with each minute
Outside my room, I felt within it
The clouds, disconsolate and gray.
The ash-tree yonder moved its crown
With heavy creaking up and down,
The dead leaves whirled across the way.

Then ticked, through the close room, unhurried,
As in still vaults where men are buried
The woodworm gnaws, and ticks my watch.
And through the open door close by,
Wailed the piano, thin and shy,
Beneath her touch.

Slate-like upon us weighed the heaven,
Her playing grew more sorrow-riven,
I saw her form.
Sharp gusts upon the ash-tree beat,
The air, aflame with dust and heat,
Sighed for the storm.

Pale through the walls the sounds came sobbing,
Her blind, tear-wasted hands passed throbbing
Across the keys.
Crouching she sang that song of May
That once had sung my heart away,
She panted lest the song should cease.

In the dull clouds no shadow shivered,
The aching music moaned and quivered
Like dull knives in me, stroke on stroke—
And in that song of love was blent
Two children's voices' loud lament—
Then first the lightning broke.

(Ludwig Lewisohn)

VIGIL

THE crimson roses burn and glow,
Softly the dark leaves stir and shake,
And I am in the grass awake,
Oh, wert thou here . . .
For soon the mid of night will break!

Into the lake the moonbeams flow,
The garden-gate hides her from view,
The moveless willows stand arow,
My burning forehead seeks the dew;
Oh, I have never loved thee so!

Oh, I have never so deeply known
As often as our close embrace
Made each the other, why thy face
Grew pallid and thy heart made moan
When all my being sought thy grace.

And now—oh, hadst thou seen how there
Two little fire-flies crept alow,
I never more from thee will fare,
Oh, wert thou here,
Or still the crimson roses glow.

(Ludwig Lewisohn)

HARVEST SONG

A FIELD of golden wheat there grows,
Even to the world's end it goes.
Grind, O mill, keep grinding!

The wind falters in all the land,
The mills on the horizon stand.
Grind, O mill, keep grinding!

The evening sky turns somber red;
Many poor people cry for bread.
Grind, O mill, keep grinding!

The night's womb holds a storm within;
To-morrow shall the task begin.
Grind, O mill, keep grinding!

The storm shall sweep the fields of earth
Until no man cries out for dearth!
Grind, O mill, keep grinding!

(Ludwig Lewisohn)

THE SILENT TOWN

A TOWN lies in the valley,
A pale day fades and dies;
And it will not be long before
Neither moon nor starlight,
Night only fills the skies.

From all the mountain ridges
Creeps mist, and swathes the town;
No farm, no house, no wet red roof
Can pierce the thickly woven woof,
And scarce even spires and bridges.

But as the wanderer shudders,
Deep down a streak of light rejoices
His heart; and, through the smoke and haze,
Children's voices
Begin a gentle hymn of praise.

(Jethro Bithell)

THE LABORER

WE have a bed, and a baby too,
My wife!

We have work besides, we have work for two,
And we have the sun, and the wind, and the rain,
And we only need one little thing more,
To be as free as the birds that soar:
Only time.

When we go through the fields on the Sunday morn,
My child,
And far and away o'er the bending corn,
We see the swarming swallows flash,
Then we only need a bit of a dress,
To have the birds' bright loveliness:
Only time.

The storm is gathering black as jet,
Feel the poor.
Only a little eternity yet;
We need nothing else, my wife, my child,
Except all things through us that thrive,
To be bold as the birds through the air that drive:
Only time!

(Jethro Bithell)

VOICE IN THE DARKNESS

There's moaning somewhere in the dark.
I want to know what it may be.
The wind is angry with the night—

Yet the wind's moan sounds not so near.
The wind will always moan at night.
'Tis in my ear my blood that moans—
My blood, forsooth.

Yet not so strangely moans my blood.
My blood is tranquil like the night.
I think a heart must moan somewhere.

(Margarete Münsterberg)

Cäsar Flaischlen

1864–1920

MOST QUIETLY AT TIMES

Most quietly at times and like a dream
In thee re-echoes a far distant song . . .
Thou knowest not whence suddenly it came,
Thou knowest not what it would have of thee . . .
And like a dream most peacefully and still
It dies in distant music, even as it came . . .

As suddenly as in the crowded street,
And in the very winter's frozen heart,
An odor of roses will around thee breathe,
Or as a picture unawares will rise
From far-forgotten happy childhood's days,
And gaze at thee with eyes inquisitive . . .

Most quietly, and lightly as a dream . . .
Thou knowest not whence suddenly it came,
Thou knowest not what it would have of thee,
And like a dream most peacefully and still
It pales and passes, fading when it came.

(Jethro Bithell)

Otto Julius Bierbaum

1865–1910

KINDLY VISION

Not in sleep I saw it, but in daylight,
Clear and beautiful by day before me:
Saw a meadow overgrown with daisies,
Round a cottage white in green embowered;
Statues of the gods gleam in the arbor.
And the lady that I walk with loves me,
With a quiet spirit in the coolness
And the peacefulness of this white dwelling,
Full of beauty waiting till we enter.

(Jethro Bithell)

BLACKSMITH PAIN

Pain is a blacksmith,
Hard is his hammer;
With flying flames
His hearth is hot;
A ſtraining ſtorm
Of forces ferocious
Blows his bellows.
He hammers hearts
And tinkers them,
With blows tremendous,
Till hard they hold.—
Well, well forges Pain.—
No ſtorm deſtroys,
No froſt consumes,
No ruſt corrodes,
What Pain has forged.

(Jethro Bithell)

OFT IN THE SILENT NIGHT

Oft in the silent night
When faint our breathing grows
And sickle-bright the moon
In the dark heaven glows,

When all is quieted
And no desires command,
Then my soul leadeth me
Into my childhood's land.

Then I see how infirm
My little feet did go,
And see my childish eye
And my small hands also,

And hear how then my mouth
Spoke ever pure and plain
And sink my head and of
My life take thought again:

Didſt thou, didſt thou always
Tread paths as white and sweet
As thou didſt walk upon
With little childish feet?

Haſt thou, haſt thou always
Spoken as clear and true
As long ago thy voice
Faltering was wont to do?

And haſt thou ever looked
So ſtraight into the face
Of the great sun as once
With childhood's fearless grace?

My glance, O Moon, I lift
Unto thy splendor white;
Deep, deep am I made sad
Oft in the silent night.

(*Ludwig Lewisohn*)

Stefan George

1868–

STANZAS CONCERNING LOVE

I

A NOVICE when I came beneath thy gaze,
There was no wonder in mine eyes before
And no desire till I beheld thy grace.
Be thou benign to young hands folded where
I pray to be thy servant evermore.
And with long-suffering compassion spare
The feet ſtill faltering on alien ways.

II

Now that my lips are very ſtill and burn
Do I behold whither have gone my feet:
Into a splendid realm for others meet.
Ah, yet perchance it was the hour to turn,
When thro' the lofty gateway seemed to shine
The eyes whose light my bended knees entreat
Seeking my own and giving me a sign.

III

Dead forever is my world of old.
Sense and spirit for thy presence reaches,
Interchange of unimagined speeches,
Grace, withdrawal, service manifold.
Only thee would I in dreams behold,
And I mourn the visions fugitive
With the golden dark wherein they live,
When the cloudless morning rises cold.

(Ludwig Lewisohn)

RAPTURE

I

I FEEL a breath from other planets blowing
And pallid through the darkness wax the faces
That even now so kind and near were glowing.

Gray and more gray are tree and path and meadow
So that I scarcely know familiar places,
And thou, dear summoner of my pain, bright shadow,

Too far in deeper glow dissolved hast floated
To deem me, after this wild tumult's mazes,
To any earthly love or awe devoted.

Melted I am in music, circling, driven,
In boundless gratitude and nameless praises
Will and desireless to the eternal given.

II

A tempest wafts me and I am elated
In passionate madness of the women grieving
Who deep in dust their prayers have consecrated.

Then I behold the milky mists dislimning,
A noble clearness filled with sunshine leaving
Wherein the farthest mountain peaks are swimming.

The ground beneath me, white and soft, is shaken . . .
By monstrous chasms I mount high and higher
Above the last cloud's silver edge to waken,

In seas of crystal radiance to dip under—
I am a spark of the eternal fire,
And of the eternal voice I am the thunder!

(Ludwig Lewisohn)

THE LORD OF THE ISLE

FISHERMEN will relate that in the South
Upon an island rich in spice and oil
And precious stones that glitter in the sand,
There dwelt a bird who, standing upon earth,
Could tear the crowns of lofty trees asunder
With his strong beak; who, lifting up his wings
Dyed as with ichor of the Tyrian snail,
Unto his low and heavy flight, had been
A shadow in seeming, like a somber cloud.
By day he vanished in the olive groves,
But evening ever brought him to the shore
Where in the coolness of the salt sea-breeze
He raised up his sweet voice and dolphins came,
Who are the friends of song, across the sea
With golden feathers filled and golden sparks.
Thus lived he since the making of the world
And only ship-wrecked sailors saw his form.
But when for the first time the snowy sails
Of man, guided by fortunate winds had turned
Unto his island—to its topmost hill
He rose surveying that beloved place,
And spreading out his mighty pinions
Departed with a muffled cry of pain.

(Ludwig Lewisohn)

Alfred Mombert

1872–

SLEEPING THEY BEAR ME

SLEEPING they bear me
Into my homeland.
From far away I come,
Hither over peaks and chasms

Over a dark ocean
Into my homeland.

Now that I have quelled the strongest
  of the giants,
Out of the darkest land
Won my way home,
Led by a white fairy hand—

Echo heavy the bells.
And I stagger through the streets
Sleep-bound.

(Jethro Bithell)

IDYL

AND my young sweetheart sat at board with me.
I ate and drank and cried most bitterly.
Delicate linen on the board she laid.
And of her own small shift that cloth was made.
She gave to me a little silvern cup.
And it was her own blood that filled it up.
She took a loaf and gave me bread thereof.
And that was her young body warm with love.

Then, as of some strange mystery aware,
She smiled, and put a rose into her hair.

(Ludwig Lewisohn)

Carl Busse

1872–

THE QUIET KINGDOM

THERE is a quiet kingdom's strand,
Like to no other earthly land,
The clouds and winds divide us—
Ah me, and who shall guide us?

It will be found, I say to thee,
By one who yearneth deep as we.

(Ludwig Lewisohn)

Hugo von Hofmannsthal

1874–

THE TWO

Her hand a goblet bore for him—
Her chin and mouth curved like its rim—
So gentle yet so sure her tread,
No drop was from the goblet shed.

So gentle and so firm his hand:
A tameless steed allured his daring
And with a gesture swift, uncaring
He forced its trembling form to stand.

But when at last from her pale hand
He was to take the cup of gold,
Too heavy for them both it was:
For they so trembled like the grass,
That neither hand the other found
And on the ground the dark wine rolled.

(*Ludwig Lewisohn*)

A VENETIAN NIGHT

All thro' the breathing night there seemed to flow,
Thro' the blue night, strange voices to and fro.
There was no sleep in Nature anywhere.
With dewy lips and deep intake of breath
She lay and listened in the vastness darkling
Of all the web of secret things aware.
And streaming, raining, fell the star-light sparkling
Upon the vigil of the garden there.
And ichor of all heavy fruits was swelling
Under the yellow moon and upward welling
Bubbled the glimmering fountains under trees.
And there awakened heavy harmonies.
And where in haste the clouds' dark shadows glided,
A sound of soft and naked steps abided . . .
Softly I rose—by all the magic drawn—
Then floated through the night a sweet intoning

As of the poignant flute's impassioned moaning
Which in his marble hand in thoughtful wise
By the dark laurel holds the dreamy faun,
Yonder where the deep bed of violets lies.
I saw him in his still, marmoreal gleaming,
With rays of blue and silver o'er him streaming;
And where pomegranates open to the night
I heard the murmur of the bees in flight,
And saw them suck, upon the scarlet sunken,
With ripeness and nocturnal passion drunken.
And when the darkness with low breathing now
Brought all the garden fragrance to my brow,
Over the grass I seemed to hear the trailing
Of long and billowy garments thro' the land,
And feel the warm touch of a gentle hand.
In silken whiteness of moonlight were sailing
Impassioned midges in a maddened dance,
And on the lake lay softest radiance
Swaying in silver of its watery path.
I know not whether swans were plashing there
Or the white limbs of Naiads in their bath,
But lovely odor as of woman's hair
Blended with budding aloes everywhere . . .
And all that splendor met in me and I
Was by excess of beauty overcome
That makes words empty and the senses dumb.

BALLAD OF THE OUTER LIFE

AND deep-eyed children cannot long be children,
Knowing of nothing they grow up and die,
And all men go their ways upon the earth.

And bitter fruits are sweetened by and by,
And fall at night like dead birds to the floor,
And in a few days rot even where they lie.

And ever blows the wind, and evermore
A multitude of words we speak and hear,
And now are happy, and now tired and sore.

And roads run through the grass, and towns uprear
Their torch-filled toils, some menacingly live,
And some cadaverously dry and drear.

Why are these built aloft? And ever ſtrive,
So countless many, not to be the same?
And tears drive laughter out till death arrive?

What profits man this ever-changing game?
Full-grown are we, yet ſtill like chartless ships,
And wandering never follow any aim.

What profit hath he who the furtheſt roams?
And yet he sayeth much who "evening" saith,
A word from which deep melancholy drips

Like heavy honey out of hollow combs.

(Jethro Bithell)

MANY INDEED MUST PERISH IN THE KEEL

MANY indeed muſt perish in the keel,
Chained where the heavy oars of vessels smite,
Others direct the rudder on the bridge,
And know the flight of birds and charted ſtars.

Others with weary limbs lie evermore
By the inextricable roots of life,
For others chairs are with the sibyls set,
The Queens, in whose abode they dwell at home,
With brain untaxed and soft unhampered hands.

But from those lives a shadow falls athwart
On these the lighter, and as to earth and air
The light is with the hard life bound in one.

I cannot free my eyelids from fatigues
Of nations long-forgotten, no, nor guard
My soul in terror from the soundless fall
Of ſtars remote in deeps of cosmic dark.

Existence plies her shuttle through the woof
Of many fates indissolubly one,
And my own portion of this common life
Is more than taper flame or slender lyre.

(Jethro Bithell)

Arno Holz

1863–

A LEAVE-TAKING

His friend the watchman was still awake,
The Town-hall roof one silver flake,
And the moon hung over it.

He scarcely knew what grief he bore,
At every step his heart beat sore,
And his knapsack weighed him down.

The street it was so long, so long,
And he heard a voice singing a song:
When the breeze of the May is blowing!

Now elder boughs o'er the hedgerow nod,
And he sees the marble Mother of God
Standing white at the Minster door.

Here he stood for a moment still,
And heard what the jackdaw whistled shrill
Up above on the steeple cross.

Then the landlord of the Lion Hotel
Put out his lights, and slowly the bell
Of the Minster clock pealed ten.

Everything was, as it used to be,
The nightingale sang on the linden-tree,
And the fountain dreamily ran.

Out of his coat the rose he dashed,
The flower with his stick on the flags he thrashed,
Till the sparks flew, then he went.

The lamp o'er the gateway flickered red,
And the wood into which his pathway led
Stood black in the moonlight there . . .

And where the path the Saints' Stone reaches,
Just where it bends around the beeches,
It all came back to him.

The leaves rustled, he stood and stood:
He stared down where, beneath the wood,
The roofs were glistening.

He saw the house in the garden gleaming,
And this was the end, was the end of the dreaming,
And—the roofs were glistening!

His heart beat wild with piteous pain!
When I come, when I come, when I come back again!

But he never came back any more.

(Jethro Bithell)

PHANTASUS

Its roof among the stars projected,
The courtyard throbbed with factory roar,
The common human hive erected,
With hurdy-gurdies at the door.
The dark rat scurried in the basement,
A shop served brandy, grog, and beer,
And to the top-floor's broken casement
Man's wretchedness was native here.

There by his lamp he sat in fever—
Wild scorn of men, speak not at all!
And wrote his songs to last forever,
A dreamer and a prodigal.
Into his garret could be taken
Table and bed—just room for breath·
He was as poor and as forsaken,
As once that God from Nazareth.

And tho' the world, a venal harlot,
Her old taunt: "Crazed and useless!" hissed
A radiant spirit girth with scarlet
His forehead and his eyes had kissed.
And when in lonely awe he wondered
The verse beneath his hand to see,
Forever more from him were sundered
The world in its banality.

His only coat was ripped and tattered,
Dry bread a neighbor's hand would share,
He sighed: O Muse! and nothing mattered,
Of want and misery unaware.
Thus by his lamp he sat in fever,
When day had fled and night would fall,
And wrote his songs to last forever,
A dreamer and a prodigal.

(Ludwig Lewisohn)

Karl Bulcke

1875–

THERE IS AN OLD CITY

An old town lies afar
From where the great towns be;
The storm roars over the town;
Beside it thunders the sea.

There is an ancient house
Long locked the gate has been.
On its gray walls the trembling
Blades of the grass are green.

There is a lonely heart,
Strange, full of fears,
That town and that house and that heart
Shut in my boyhood's years. . . .

(Ludwig Lewisohn)

Rainer Maria Rilke

1875–1926

FOR, LORD, THE CROWDED CITIES BE . . .

For, Lord, the crowded cities be
Desolate and divided places,
Flight as from flames upon their ways is,
And comfortless of any graces
Their little time fades utterly.
And men who dwell there heavy and humbly move
About dark rooms with dread in all their bearing,
Less than the spring-time flocks in fire and daring;
And somewhere breathes and watches earth for faring,
But they are here and do not know thereof.
And children grow up where the shadows falling
From wall and window have the light exiled,
And know not that without the flowers are calling
Unto a day of distance, wind and wild—
And every child must be a saddened child.
There blossom virgins to the unknown turning
And for their childhood's faded rest are fain
And do not find for what their soul is burning,
And trembling, close their timid buds again.
And bear in chambers shadowed and unsleeping
The days of disappointed motherhood,
And the long night's involuntary weeping,
And the cold years devoid of glow or good.
In utter darkness stand their deathbeds lowly,
For which thro' gradual years the gray heart pants;
And die as tho' in chains, and dying slowly
Go forth from life in guise of mendicants.

(Ludwig Lewisohn)

THE YOUTH DREAMS

Oh, I should love to be like one of those
Who thro' the night on tameless horses ride,
With torches like disheveled tresses wide

Which the great wind of gallop streaming blows.
And I would stand as on a shallop's prow,
Slender and tall and like a banner rolled.
Dark but for helmeting of ruddy gold
That glints and gleams. Behind me in a row
Ten men who from the equal darkness glow
With helmets of the changeful gold designed,
Now clear as glass, now dark and old and blind.
And one by me blows me a vision of space
Upon a trumpet glittering that cries,
Or makes a solitary blackness rise
Thro' which as in a rapid dream we race:
The houses slant behind us to their knees,
The crooked streets to meet us bend and strain,
The squares flee from us: but we grapple these,
And still our horses rustle like the rain.

(Ludwig Lewisohn)

PRESAGING

I AM like a flag unfurled in space,
I scent the oncoming winds and must bend with them,
While the things beneath are not yet stirring,
While the doors close gently and there is silence in the
  chimneys
And the windows do not yet tremble and the dust is still
  heavy—
Then I feel the storm and am vibrant like the sea
And expand and withdraw into myself
And thrust myself forth and am alone in the great storm.

(Jessie Lemont)

Hermann Hesse

1877–

SPRING SONG

THE storm cries every night,
Its great, moist wing falters and sweeps,
In dreamy flight the plover falls;
Now nothing sleeps

And through the land stirs new delight,
For the Spring calls.

Oh in these nights I cannot sleep
Youth stirs my heart!
From the blue wells of memory start
The ardent glories of that dawn
And look at me with eyes so deep,
And tremble, and are gone.

Be still, my heart, give o'er!
Though in the heavy blood holds sway
The passionate sweet pain
And lead thee the old paths again—
Unto youth's land no more
Forever goes thy way.

(*Ludwig Lewisohn*)

NIGHT

OFTEN this thought wakens me unawares,
That through the chill of night a vessel fares
Seeking an ocean, touching on a shore
For which my soul must yearn forevermore;
That in still places which no sailor knows
A crimson, undiscovered Northlight glows,
That an unknown and lovely lady's arm
Pulses amid the pillows white and warm;
That one long destined to become my friend
Finds in an alien sea a somber end,
And that my mother, strange and far apart,
Speaks at this hour my name within her heart.

(*Ludwig Lewisohn*)

SCANDINAVIAN

OLD NORSE

From the Elder Edda

c. 1000

The Poetic Edda is the original storehouse of Germanic mythology. It is, indeed, in many ways the greatest literary monument preserved to us out of the antiquity of the kindred races which we call Germanic. The mythological poems include, in the Voluspo, one of the vastest conceptions of the creation and ultimate destruction of the world ever crystallized in literary form.—HENRY ADAMS BELLOWS.

THE FIRST LAY OF GUDRUN

For this is the Great Story of the North, which should be to all our race what the Tale of Troy was to the Greeks.—WILLIAM MORRIS.

GUDRUN of old days
Drew near to dying
As she sat in sorrow
Over Sigurd;
Yet she sighed not
Nor smote hand on hand,
Nor wailed she aught
As other women.

Then went earls to her,
Full of all wisdom,
Fain help to deal
To her dreadful heart:
Hushed was Gudrun
Of wail, or greeting,
But with a heavy woe
Was her heart a-breaking.

Bright and fair
Sat the great earls' brides,
Gold arrayed
Before Gudrun;
Each told the tale
Of her great trouble,
The bitterest bale
She erst abode.

Then spake Giaflaug,
Giuki's sister:
"Lo upon earth
I live most loveless
Who of five mates
Must see the ending,
Of daughters twain
And three sisters,
Of brethren eight,
And abide behind lonely."

Naught gat Gudrun
Of wail and greeting,
So heavy was she
For her dead husband,
So dreadful-hearted
For the King laid dead there.

Then spake Herborg
Queen of Hunland—
"Crueler tale
Have I to tell of,
Of my seven sons
Down in the Southlands,
And the eighth man, my mate,
Felled in the death-mead.

"Father and mother,
And four brothers,
On the wide sea

The winds and death played with;
The billows beat
On the bulwark boards.

"Alone muſt I sing o'er them,
Alone muſt I array them,
Alone muſt my hands deal with
Their departing;
And all this was
In one season's wearing,
And none was left
For love or solace.

"Then was I bound
A prey of the battle,
When that same season
Wore to its ending;
As a tiring may
Muſt I bind the shoon
Of the duke's high dame,
Every day at dawning.

"From her jealous hate
Gat I heavy mocking,
Cruel lashes
She laid upon me,
Never met I
Better maſter
Or miſtress worser
In all the wide world."

Naught gat Gudrun
Of wail or greeting,
So heavy was she
For her dead husband,
So dreadful-hearted
For the King laid dead there.

Then spake Gullrond,
Giuki's daughter—

"O foster-mother,
Wise as thou mayst be,
Naught canst thou better
The young wife's bale."
And she bade uncover
The dead King's corpse.

She swept the sheet
Away from Sigurd,
And turned his cheek
Towards his wife's knees—
Look on thy loved one,
Lay lips to his lips,
E'en as thou wert clinging
To thy king alive yet!"

Once looked Gudrun—
One look only,
And saw her lord's locks
Lying all bloody,
The great man's eyes
Glazed and deadly,
And his heart's bulwark
Broken by sword-edge.

Back then sank Gudrun,
Back on the bolster,
Loosed was her head array,
Red did her cheeks grow,
And the rain-drops ran
Down over her knees.

Then wept Gudrun,
Giuki's daughter,
So that the tears flowed
Through the pillow;
As the geese withal
That were in the homefield,
The fair fowls the may owned,
Fell a-screaming.

Then spake Gullrond,
Giuki's daughter—
"Surely knew I
No love like your love
Among all men,
On the mold abiding;
Naught wouldst thou joy in
Without or within doors,
O my sister,
Save beside Sigurd."

Then spake Gudrun,
Giuki's daughter—
"Such was my Sigurd
Among the sons of Giuki,
As is the king leek
O'er the low grass waxing,
Or a bright stone
Strung on band,
Or a pearl of price
On a prince's brow.
"Once was I counted
By the king's warriors
Higher than any
Of Herjan's mays;
Now am I as little
As the leaf may be,
Amid wind-swept wood
Now when dead he lieth.

"I miss from my seat,
I miss from my bed,
My darling of sweet speech.
Wrought the sons of Giuki,
Wrought the sons of Giuki,
This sore sorrow,
Yea, for their sister,
Most sore sorrow.

"So may your lands
Lie waste on all sides,
As ye have broken
Your bounden oaths!
Ne'er shalt thou, Gunnar,
The gold have joy of,
The dear-bought rings
Shall drag thee to death,
Whereon thou swarest
Oath unto Sigurd.

"Ah, in the days by-gone
Great mirth in the homefield
When my Sigurd
Set saddle on Grani,
And they went their ways
For the wooing of Brynhild!
An ill day, an ill woman,
And most ill hap!"

Then spake Brynhild,
Budli's daughter—
"May the woman lack
Both love and children,
Who gained greeting
For thee, O Gudrun!
Who gave thee this morning
Many words!"

Then spake Gullrond,
Giuki's daughter—
"Hold peace of such words
Thou hated of all folk!
The bane of brave men
Hast thou been ever,
All waves of ill
Wash over thy mind,
To seven great kings
Hast thou been a sore sorrow,

And the death of good will
To wives and women."

Then spake Brynhild,
Budli's daughter—
"None but Atli
Brought bale upon us,
My very brother
Born of Budli.

"When we saw in the hall
Of the Hunnish people
The gold a-gleaming
On the kingly Giukings:
I have paid for that faring
Oft and full,
And for the sight
That then I saw."

By a pillar she stood
And strained its wood to her;
From the eyes of Brynhild,
Budli's daughter,
Flashed out fire,
And she snorted forth venom,
As the sore wounds she gazed on
Of the dead-slain Sigurd.

(*William Morris and Eirikr Magnusson*)

DANISH

Anonymous

14th–16th centuries

BALLADS

THE ELECTED KNIGHT

SIR OLUF he rideth over the plain,
  Full seven miles broad and seven miles wide;

But never, ah! never, can meet with the man
  A tilt with him dare ride.

He saw under the hill-side
  A knight full well equipped;
His steel was black, his helm was barred;
  He was riding at full speed.

He wore upon his spurs
  Twelve little golden birds;
Anon in eddies the wild wind blew,
  And there sat all the birds and sang.

He wore upon his mail
  Twelve little golden wheels;
Anon in eddies the wild wind blew,
  And round and round the wheels they flew.

He wore before his breast
  A lance that was poised in rest,
And it was sharper than diamond-stone;
  It made Sir Oluf's heart to groan.

He wore upon his helm
  A wreath of ruddy gold;
And that gave him the Maidens Three,
  The youngest was fair to behold.

Sir Oluf questioned the knight eftsoon
  If he were come from heaven down;
"Art thou Christ of Heaven?" quoth he,
  "So will I yield me unto thee."

"I am not Christ the Great,
  Thou shalt not yield thee yet;
I am an Unknown Knight,
  Three modest Maidens have me bedight."

"Art thou a knight elected?
  And have three maidens thee bedight?
So shalt thou ride a tilt this day,
  For all the maidens' honor!"

The firſt tilt they together rode,
  They put their ſteeds to the teſt;
The second tilt they together rode,
  They proved their manhood beſt.

The third tilt they together rode,
  Neither of them would yield;
The fourth tilt they together rode,
  They both fell on the field.

Now lie the lords upon the plain,
  And their blood runs unto death;
Now sit the Maidens in the high tower,
  The youngeſt sorrows till death.

(H. W. Longfellow)

THE MER-MAN, AND MARSTIG'S DAUGHTER

"Now rede me, dear mither, a sonsy rede;
  A sonsy rede swythe rede to me,
How Marstig's daughter I may fa',
  My love and lemman gay to be."

She's made him a ſteed o' the clear water;
  A saddle and bridle o' sand made she;
She's shap'd him into a knight sae fair,
  Syne into Mary's kirk-yard rade he.

He's tied his ſteed to the kirk-ſtile,
  Syne wrang-gates round the kirk gaed he;
When the Mer-man entered the kirk-door,
  Awa the sma' images turned their ee'.

The prieſt afore the altar ſtood:
  "O, what for a gude knight may this be?"
The may leugh till hersell, and said,
  "God gif that gude knight were for me!"

The Mer-man he ſtept o'er ae deas,
  And he has ſteppit over three:
"O maiden, pledge me faith and troth!
  O Marstig's daughter, gang wi' me!"

And she raught out her lily hand,
    And pledg'd it to the knight sae free:
"Hae; there's my faith and troth, Sir Knight,
    And willingly I'll gang wi' thee."

Out frae the kirk gaed the bridal train,
    And on they danc'd wi' fearless glee;
And down they danc'd unto the strand,
    Till twasome now alane they be:
"O Marstig's daughter, haud my steed,
    And the bonniest ship I'll bigg for thee!"

And whan they came to the white sand,
    To shore the sma' boats turning came;
And whan they came to the deep water,
    The maiden sank in the saut sea faem.

The shriek she shriek'd amang the waves
    Was heard far up upo' the land:
"I rede gude ladies, ane an a',
    They dance wi' nae sic unco man."

(Robert Jamieson)

Johannes Evald

1743–1781

KING CHRISTIAN

King Christian stood by the lofty mast
    In mist and smoke;
His sword was hammering so fast
Through Gothic helm and brain it passed;
Then sank each hostile hulk and mast
    In mist and smoke.
"Fly!" shouted they, "fly, he who can!
Who braves of Denmark's Christian
    The stroke?"

Nils Juel gave heed to the tempest's roar;
    Now is the hour!
He hoisted his blood-red flag once more,

And smote upon the foe full sore,
And shouted loud, through the tempest's roar,
 "Now is the hour!"
"Fly!" shouted they, "for shelter fly!
Of Denmark's Juel who can defy
 The power?"

North Sea! a glimpse of Wessel rent
 Thy murky sky!
Then champions to thine arms were sent;
Terror and Death glared where he went;
From the waves was heard a wail that rent
 Thy murky sky!
From Denmark thunders Tordenskiol';
Let each to Heaven commend his soul,
 And fly!

Path of the Dane to fame and might!
 Dark-rolling wave!
Receive thy friend, who, scorning flight,
Goes to meet danger with despite,
Proudly as thou the tempest's might,
 Dark-rolling wave!
And, amid pleasures and alarms,
And war and victory, be thine arms
 My grave!

       (*H. W. Longfellow*)

Jens Baggesen

        1764–1826

CHILDHOOD

THERE was a time when I was very small,
 When my whole frame was but an ell in height;
Sweetly, as I recall it, tears do fall,
 And therefore I recall it with delight.

I sported in my tender mother's arms,
 And rode a-horse-back on best father's knee;
Alike were sorrows, passions, and alarms,
 And gold, and Greek, and love, unknown to me.

Then seemed to me this world far less in size,
   Likewise it seemed to me less wicked far;
Like points in heaven, I saw the stars arise,
   And longed for wings that I might catch a star.

I saw the moon behind the island fade,
   And thought, "O, were I on that island there,
I could find out of what the moon is made,
   Find out how large it is, how round, how fair!"

Wondering, I saw God's sun, through western skies,
   Sink in the ocean's golden lap at night,
And yet upon the morrow early rise,
   And paint the eastern heaven with crimson light;

And thought of God, the gracious Heavenly Father,
   Who made me, and that lovely sun on high,
And all those pearls of heaven thick-strung together,
   Dropped, clustering, from his hand o'er all the sky.

With childish reverence, my young lips did say
   The prayer my pious mother taught to me:
"O gentle God! O, let me strive alway
   Still to be wise, and good, and follow thee!"

So prayed I for my father and my mother,
   And for my sister, and for all the town;
The king I knew not, and the beggar-brother,
   Who, bent with age, went, sighing, up and down.

They perished, the blithe days of boyhood perished,
   And all the gladness, all the peace I knew!
Now have I but their memory, fondly cherished;—
   God! may I never, never lose that too!

(H. W. Longfellow)

NORWEGIAN

Henrik Arnold Thaulov Wergeland
1808–1845

THE WALL-FLOWER

O WALL-FLOWER! or ever thy bright leaves fade,
My limbs will be that of which all are made,
Before ever thou losest thy crown of gold,
    My flesh will be mold.

And yet open the casement! till I am dead
Let my last look rest on thy golden head!
My soul would kiss thee before it flies
    To the open skies.

Twice I am kissing thy fragrant mouth,
And the first kiss wholly is thine, in truth;
But the second remember, dear Love! to close
    On my fair white Rose.

I shall not be living its Spring to see;
But bring it my greeting when that shall be,
And say that I wish'd that upon my grave
    It should bloom and wave.

Yes, say that I wish'd that against my breast
The Rose should lie that thy lips caress'd;
And, Wall-flower! do thou into Death's dark porch
    Be its bridal torch!

                (*Sir Edmund Gosse*)

Henrik Ibsen

1828–1906

IN THE ORCHARD

IN the sunny orchard closes,
  While the warblers sing and swing,

Care not whether blustering Autumn
   Break the promises of Spring!
Rose and white, the apple blossom
   Hides you from the sultry sky—
Let it flutter, blown and scatter'd,
   On the meadows by-and-by!

Will you ask about the fruitage
   In the season of the flowers?
Will you murmur, will you question,
   Count the run of weary hours?
Will you let the scarecrow clapping
   Drown all happy sounds and words?
Brothers! there is better music
   In the singing of the birds.

From your heavy-laden garden
   Will you hunt the mellow thrush;
He will play you for protection
   With his crown-song's liquid rush.
O but you will win the bargain,
   Though your fruit be spare and late,
For remember Time is flying
   And will shut the garden gate.

With my living, with my singing,
   I will tear the hedges down.
Sweep the grass and heap the blossom!
   Let it shrivel, pale and brown!
Swing the wicket! Sheep and cattle,
   Let them graze among the best!
I broke off the flowers; what matter
   Who may revel with the rest?

                        (Sir Edmund Gosse)

Björnsterne Björnson

1832–1910

THE BOY AND THE FLUTE

THROUGH the forest the boy wends all day long:
For there he has heard such a wonderful song.
He carved him a flute of the willow-tree,
And tried what the tune within it might be.
The tune came out of it sad and gay;
But while he listen'd it pass' away.
He fell asleep, and once more it sung,
And over his forehead it lovingly hung.

He thought he would catch it, and wildly woke;
And the tune in the pale night faded and broke.
"O God! my God! take me up to Thee!
For the tune Thou hast made is consuming me."
And the Lord God said: "'Tis a friend divine,
Though never one hour shalt thou hold it thine.
Yet all other music is poor and thin
By the side of this which thou never shalt win!"

(*Sir Edmund Gosse*)

SWEDISH

Gustav Rosenhane

1619–1684

SONNETS

I

DEEP in a vale where rocks on every side
  Shut out the winds, and scarcely let the sun
  Between them dart his rays down one by one,
Where all was still and cool in summer-tide,
And softly, with her whispering waves that sighed,
  A little river, that had scarce begun
  Her silver course, made bold to fleet and run

Down leafy falls to woodlands dense and wide,
There stood a tiny plain, just large enow
    To give small mountain-folk right room to dance,
    With oaks and limes and maples ringed around;
Hither I came, and viewed its turf askance,
    Its solitude with beauty seemed a-glow,—
    My Love had walked there and 'twas holy ground!

II

AND then I sat me down, and gave the rein
    To my wild thoughts, till many a song that rang
    From boughs around where hidden warblers sang
Recalled me from myself; then "Oh! in vain"
I said, "do these outpour the tender strain?
    Can these sweet birds that with such airs harangue
    Their feathered loves, like me, feel sorrow's pang?
Ah! would that I, like them, had pinions twain!
Straight would I fly to her whom I love best,
    Nor vainly warbling in the woodland sing,
But chirp my prayer, and preen my plumèd crest,
    And to this spot once more her beauty bring,
    And flutter round her flight with supple wing,
And lead her to my secret leafy nest."

                                        (*Sir Edmund Gosse*)

Olof Wexionius
                                        1656–1690

ON THE DEATH OF A PIOUS LADY

THE earthly roses at God's call have made
    Way, lady, for a dress of heavenly white,
    In which thou walk'st with other figures bright,
Once loved on earth, who now, like thee arrayed,
Feast on two-fold ambrosia, wine and bread;
    They lead thee up by sinuous paths of light
    Through lilied fields that sparkle in God's sight,
And crown thee with delights that never fade.
O thou thrice-sainted mother, in that bliss,

Forget not thy two daughters, whom a kiss
  At parting left as sad as thou art glad;
In thy deep joy think how for thee they weep,
Or conjure through the shifting glass of sleep
  The saint heaven hath, the mother once they had.

                       (*Sir Edmund Gosse*)

Esaias Tegner

                           1782–1846

Frithiof's Farewell

"No more shall I see
    In its upward motion
The smoke of the Northland. Man is a slave;
    The Fates decree
      On the waste of the ocean,
There is my fatherland, there is my grave.

"Go not to the strand,
    Ring, with thy bride,
After the stars spread their light through the sky.
    Perhaps in the sand,
      Washed up by the tide,
The bones of the outlawed Viking may lie.

"Then quoth the king,
    ' 'T is mournful to hear
A man like a whimpering maiden cry,
    The death-song they sing
      Even now in mine ear.
What avails it? He who is born must die.' "

                       (*H. W. Longfellow*)

RUSSIAN

Folk Songs

THE PLAINT OF THE WIFE

THE WIFE

FAIN would I be sleeping, dreaming:
Heavy lies my head upon the pillow.
Up and down the passage goes my husband's father,
Angrily about it keeps he pacing.

CHORUS

Thumping, scolding, thumping, scolding,—
Never lets his daughter sleep.

FATHER-IN-LAW

Up, up, up, thou sloven there!
Up, up, up, thou sluggard there!
Slovenly, slatternly, sluggardish slut!

THE WIFE

Fain would I be sleeping, dreaming:
Heavy lies my head upon the pillow.
Up and down the passage goes my husband's mother,
Angrily about it keeps she pacing.

CHORUS

Thumping, scolding, thumping, scolding,—
Never lets her daughter sleep.

MOTHER-IN-LAW

Up, up, up, thou sloven there!
Up, up, up, thou sluggard there!
Slovenly, slatternly, sluggardish slut!

THE WIFE

Fain would I be sleeping, dreaming:
Heavy lies my head upon the pillow.
Up and down the passage steals my well-beloved One,—
All so lightly, softly, keeps he whispering.

THE LOVER

Sleep, sleep, sleep, my darling One!
Sleep, sleep, sleep, my precious One!
Driven out, thrown away, married too soon!

(W. R. S. Ralston)

Ivan Andreevich Kriloff

1768–1844

THE PEASANT AND THE SHEEP

A PEASANT haled a sheep to court,
    And pressed against her there a serious objection.
A fox, as judge, is ready for a fault's detection,
Hears plaintiff first and, then, defendant in retort;
    Taking in turn each point, and cool, though others
        stammer,
      He seeks the cause of all the clamor.
    The peasant says:—"My lord! when visiting my yard,
      I found two chickens missing; 'twas in early morn-
        ing;
    Only their bones and feathers served me as a warning;
      This sheep alone was there on guard!"
The sheep replies:—"No strange event my slumbers
      marred;
      Prithee, the evidence of neighbors don't discard;
    Against me ne'er was brought a charge of thieving
        Or other crime
        At any time;
      As to my tasting flesh, 'tis notion past conceiving."
Here are the fox's judgments from their earliest weav-
      ing:—

"I noway can accept the pleadings of this sheep,
    Because all rogues are skilled to keep
        Their wicked purposes from others.
'Tis clear from plaintiff's words that, on the given
            night,
    Defendant held the fowl-house well in sight;
    Now, who can think she smothers
An inborn wish for viands choice?
So I decide, by conscience' sacred voice,
        She cannot have admitted
        Hens were for her unfitted!
Her guilt is clear and lets the peasant win;
    The carcase comes to me, and he will get the skin."

                                    (*C. Fillingham Coxwell*)

Alexander Sergeyevich Pushkin

1799–1837

He is placed in the company of Dante, Shakespeare, and
Goethe by his compatriots. The intensity of his passionate
nature was governed by a wide intelligence, a capacity
for detachment, and above all by a sense of measure and
harmony.—Babette Deutsch and Avraham Yarmolinsky.

MESSAGE TO SIBERIA

Deep in the Siberian mine,
Keep your patience proud;
The bitter toil shall not be lost,
The rebel thought unbowed.

The sister of misfortune, Hope,
In the under-darkness dumb
Speaks joyful courage to your heart:
The day desired will come.

And love and friendship pour to you
Across the darkened doors,
Even as round your galley-beds
My free music pours.

The heavy-hanging chains will fall,
The walls will crumble at a word;
And Freedom greet you in the light,
And brothers give you back the sword.

(Max Eastman)

WORK

HERE is the long-bided hour: the labor of years is accomplished.

Why should this sadness unplumbed secretly weigh on my heart?

Is it, my work being done, I stand like a laborer, useless,

One who has taken his pay, a stranger to tasks that are new?

Is it the work I regret, the silent companion of midnight,

Friend of the golden-haired Dawn, friend of the gods of the hearth?

(Babette Deutsch and Avraham Yarmolinsky)

THE PROPHET

ATHIRST in spirit, through the gloom
Of an unpeopled waste I blundered,
And saw a six-winged Seraph loom
Where the two pathways met and sundered.
He laid his fingers on my eyes:
His touch lay soft as slumber lies,—
And like an eagle's, his crag shaken,
Did my prophetic eyes awaken.
Upon my ears his fingers fell
And sound rose,—stormy swell on swell:
I heard the spheres revolving, chiming,
The angels in their soaring sweep,
The monsters moving in the deep,
The green vine in the valley climbing.
And from my mouth the Seraph wrung
Forth by its roots my sinful tongue;
The evil things and vain it babbled

His hand drew forth and so effaced,
And the wise serpent's tongue he placed
Between my lips with hand blood-dabbled;
And with a sword he clove my breast,
Plucked out the heart he made beat higher,
And in my stricken bosom pressed
Instead a coal of living fire.
Upon the wastes, a lifeless clod,
I lay, and heard the voice of God:
"Arise, oh, prophet, watch and hearken,
And with my Will thy soul engird,
Roam the gray seas, the roads that darken,
And burn men's hearts with this, my Word."

(Babette Deutsch and Avraham Yarmolinsky)

Mikhail Yuryevich Lermontov

1814–1841

This brilliant bully and egotistic rake was, after his own fashion, a knight of the Grail and a poetic genius such as rarely graces any language.—BABETTE DEUTSCH and AVRAHAM YARMOLINSKY.

DAGGER

I LOVE you well, my steel-white dagger,
Comrade luminous and cold;
Forged by a Georgian dreaming vengeance,
Whetted by Circassians bold.

A tender hand, in grace of parting,
Gave you to mark a meeting brief;
For blood there glimmered on your metal
A shining tear—the pearl of grief.

And black eyes, clinging to my glances,
Filled deep with liquid sorrow seemed;
Like your clear blade where flame is trembling,
They darkened quickly and they gleamed.

You were to be my long companion.
Give me your counsel to the end!

I will be hard of soul and faithful,
Like you, my iron-hearted friend!

(Max Eastman)

A SAIL

WHITE is the sail and lonely
　On the misty infinite blue;
Flying from what in the homeland?
　Seeking for what in the new?

The waves romp, and the winds whistle,
　And the mast leans and creaks;
Alas! He flies not from fortune,
　And no good fortune he seeks.

Beneath him the stream, luminous, azure,
　Above him the sun's golden breast;
But he, a rebel, invites the storms,
　As though in the storms were rest.

(Max Eastman)

THE MOUNTAIN

A GOLDEN cloud slept for her pleasure
All night on the gaunt hill's breast;
Light-heart to her play-ground of azure,
How early she sped from the nest.

But the soft moist trace of her sleeping
Lay in the folds of the hill.
He pondered; his tears are creeping
Down to the desert still.

(Max Eastman)

THE REED

THERE sat a happy fisherman
Upon a river bank.
Before him on the wind's wings
Tall reeds swayed rank on rank.

He cut him down a dry reed,
He pierced it through and through,
Then pinched one end together,
And in the other blew.

As if to life awaking,
The reed to speak began.
Was it the wind's voice calling
Or was it voice of man?

The reed sang slow and sadly—
"Oh let me, let me be,
Oh happy, happy fisherman,
For you are killing me.

"I was a comely maiden
With life and joy aglow.
In my ſtep-mother's house
I flowered long ago.

"And many tears and bitter
I innocently shed,
And often in the darkness
I wished that I was dead.

"She had a son beloved
Of her and none besides,
Who frightened honeſt people
And ravished girlish brides.

"And once we went at evening
Upon the ſteep high shore
To look upon the sunset
And hear the waters roar.

"He gave me gold and silver—
I would not take his gold.
He asked me for my true love—
My heart grew sad and cold.

"Then in my soft young bosom
His heavy knife-blade sank,
And here my corpse he buried
Upon the river bank.

"Out of my ſtricken bosom
A great dry reed uprose,
And in it live my dolor,
My pain and all my woes.

"Oh happy, happy fisherman,
Pray let me, let me be,
Or have you never suffered
And taſted misery?"

(J. J. Robbins)

Ivan Savvich Nikitin

1824–1861

A NIGHT IN A VILLAGE

Sultry air, the smoke of shavings,
  Dirt spread over all,
Feet and benches dirty; cobwebs
  To adorn the wall:
Smoke-begrimed each cottage chamber;
  Bread and water ſtale;
Spinners coughing, children crying—
  Want and woe prevail.
Hand to mouth lifelong they labor,
  Then a pauper's grave—
Ah! what need to learn the lesson—
  "Trust, my soul, be brave!"

(P. E. Matheson)

Fyodor Sologub

1863–

THE AMPHORA

In a gay jar upon his shoulder
The slave morosely carries wine.

His road is rough with bog and bowlder,
And in the sky no planets shine.
Into the dark with stabbing glances
He peers, his careful steps are slow,
Lest on his breast as he advances
The staining wine should overflow.
I bear my amphora of sorrow,
Long brimming with the wine it hides;
There poison for each waiting morrow
Ferments within the painted sides.
I follow secret ways and hidden
To guard the evil vessel, lest
A careless touch should pour unbidden
Its bitterness upon my breast.

(*Babette Deutsch and Avraham Yarmolinsky*)

Vyacheslav Ivanov

1866–

THE HOLY ROSE

The holy Rose her leaves will soon unfold.
The tender bud of dawn already lies
Reddening on the wide, transparent skies.
Love's star is a white sail the still seas hold.
Here in the light-soaked space above the wold,
Through the descending dew the arches rise
Of the unseen cathedral, filled with cries
From the winged weavers threading it with gold.

Here on the hill, the cypress, in accord
With me, stands praying: a cowled eremite.
And on the rose's cheeks the tears fall light.
Upon my cell the patterned rays are poured.
And in the East, the purple vines bleed bright,
And seething overflow. . . . Hosanna, Lord!

(*Babette Deutsch and Avraham Yarmolinsky*)

Ivan Bunin

1870–

FLAX

SHE sits on tumulus Savoor, and stares,
Old woman Death, upon the crowded road.
Like a blue flame the small flax-flower flares
Thick through the meadows sowed.

And says old woman Death: "Hey, traveler!
Does any one want linen, linen fit
For funeral wear? A shroud, madam or sir,
I'll take cheap coin for it!"

And says serene Savoor: "Don't crow so loud!
Even the winding-sheet is dust, and cracks
And crumbles into earth, that from the shroud
May spring the sky-blue flax."

(Babette Deutsch and Avraham Yarmolinsky)

Valery Bryusov

1873–1924

RADIANT RANKS OF SERAPHIM

RADIANT ranks of seraphim
Stir the air about our bed.
With their windy wings and dim
Our hot cheeks are comforted.

Low the circling seraphs bend,
And we tremble and rejoice
At hosannas that ascend,
Winged with their unearthly voice.

Cloudy luminous faces hover,
And the wing-swept candles wane.
And our fiery breasts they cover
As with hidden holy rain.

(Babette Deutsch and Avraham Yarmolinsky)

Alexander Blok

1880–1921

RUSSIA

To sin, unshamed, to lose, unthinking,
The count of careless nights and days,
And then, while the head aches with drinking,
Steal to God's house, with eyes that glaze;

Thrice to bow down to earth, and seven
Times cross oneself beside the door,
With the hot brow, in hope of heaven,
Touching the spittle-covered floor;

With a brass farthing's gift dismissing
The offering, the holy Name
To mutter with loose lips, in kissing
The ancient, kiss-worn icon-frame;

And coming home, then, to be tricking
Some wretch out of the same small coin,
And with an angry hiccup, kicking
A lean cur in his trembling groin;

And where the icon's flame is quaking
Drink tea, and reckon loss and gain,
From the fat chest of drawers taking
The coupons wet with spittle-stain;

And sunk in feather-beds to smother
In slumber, such as bears may know,—
Dearer to me than every other
Are you, my Russia, even so.

(Babette Deutsch and Avraham Yarmolinsky)

ENGLISH

Anonymous

c. 1250

SUMER IS ICUMEN IN

Sumer is icumen in,
 Lhude sing cuccu;
Groweth sed and bloweth med
 And springth the wude nu.
  Sing cuccu!

Awe bleteth after lomb,
 Lhouth after calve cu;
Bulluc sterteth, bucke verteth,
 Murie sing cuccu.

Cuccu, cuccu, wel
 Singes thu, cuccu:
 Na swike thu naver nu;
Sing cuccu, nu,
 Sing cuccu,
 Sing cuccu, sing cuccu, nu.

Geoffrey Chaucer

1340?–1400

BALADE

From The Prologue to the Legend of Good Women

Hyd, Absolon, they gilte tresses clere;
Ester, ley thou thy meknesse al a-doun;
Hyd, Jonathas, al thy frendly manere;
Penalopee, and Marcia Catoun,
Mak of your wyfhod no comparisoun;
Hyde ye your beautes, Isoude and Eleyne,
Alceste is here, that al that may desteyne.

Thy faire bodye, lat hit nat appere,
Lavyne; and thou, Lucresse of Rome toun,
And Polixene, that boghte love so dere,
Eek Cleopatre, with al thy passioun,
Hyde ye your trouthe in love and your renoun;
And thou, Tisbe, that haſt for love swich peyne:
Alceſte is here, that al that may deſteyne.

Herro, Dido, Laudomia, alle in-fere,
Eek Phyllis, hanging for thy Demophoun,
And Canace, espyed by thy chere,
Ysiphile, betrayed with Jasoun,
Mak of your trouthe in love no boſt ne soun;
Nor Ypermiſtre or Adriane, ne pleyne;
Alceſte is here, that al that may deſteyne.

Anonymous

16th–17th centuries

BALLADS

Sir Patrick Spens

The king sits in Dumferling toune,
    Drinking the blude-reid wine:
"O whar will I get guid sailor,
    To sail this schip of mine?"

Up and spak an eldern knicht,
    Sat at the kings richt kne:
"Sir Patrick Spence is the beſt sailor,
    That sails upon the se."

The king has written a braid letter,
    And signd it wi his hand,
And sent it to Sir Patrick Spence,
    Was walking on the sand.

The firſt line that Sir Patrick red,
    A loud lauch lauched he;
The next line that Sir Patrick red,
    The teir blinded his ee.

"O what is this has don this deid,
  This ill deid don to me,
To send me out this time o' the yeir,
  To sail upon the se!

"Mak haſt, mak haſte, my mirry men all,
  Our guid schip sails the morne:"
"O say na sae, my maſter deir,
  For I feir a deadlie ſtorme.

"Late late yeſtreen I saw the new moone,
  Wi the auld moone in hir arme,
And I feir, I feir, my deir maſter,
  That we will cum to harme."

O our Scots nobles wer richt laith
  To weet their cork-heild schoone;
Bot lang owre a' the play wer playd,
  Thair hats they swam aboone.

O lang, lang may their ladies sit,
  Wi thair fans into their hand,
Or eir they se Sir Patrick Spence
  Cum sailing to the land.

O lang, lang may the ladies ſtand,
  Wi thair gold kems in their hairs,
Waiting for thair ain deir lords,
  For they'll se thame na mair.

Haf owre, haf owre to Aberdour,
  It's fiftie fadom deip,
And thair lies guid Sir Patrick Spence,
  Wi the Scots lords at his feit.

THE WIFE OF USHER'S WELL

1. THERE lived a wife at Usher's Well,
    And a wealthy wife was she;
  She had three ſtout and ſtalwart sons,
    And sent them oer the sea.

2. They hadna been a week from her,
   A week but barely ane,
Whan word came to the carline wife
   That her three sons were gane.

3. They hadna been a week from her,
   A week but barely three,
Whan word came to the carlin wife
   That her sons she'd never see.

4. "I wish the wind may never cease,
   Nor fashes in the flood,
Till my three sons come hame to me,
   In earthly flesh and blood."

5. It fell about the Martinmass,
   When nights are lang and mirk,
The carlin wife's three sons came hame,
   And their hats were o the birk.

6. It neither grew in syke nor ditch,
   Nor yet in ony sheugh;
But at the gates o Paradise,
   That birk grew fair eneugh.

   *   *   *   *   *

7. "Blow up the fire, my maidens,
   Bring water from the well;
For a' my house shall feast this night,
   Since my three sons are well."

8. And she has made to them a bed,
   She's made it large and wide,
And she's taen her mantle her about,
   Sat down at the bed-side.

   *   *   *   *   *

9. Up then crew the red, red cock,
   And up and crew the gray;
The eldest to the youngest said,
   " 'Tis time we were away."

10. The cock he hadna crawd but once,
   And clappd his wings at a',
When the youngest to the eldest said,
   "Brother, we must awa.

11. "The cock doth craw, the day doth daw,
   The channerin worm doth chide;
Gin we be mist out o our place,
   A sair pain we maun bide.

12. "Fare ye weel, my mother dear!
   Fareweel to barn and byre!
And fare ye weel, the bonny lass
   That kindles my mother's fire!"

Bonny Barbara Allan

1. It was in and about the Martinmas time,
   When the green leaves were a falling,
That Sir John Græme, in the West Country,
   Fell in love with Barbara Allan.

2. He sent his man down through the town,
   To the place where she was dwelling:
"O haste and come to my master dear,
   Gin ye be Barbara Allan."

3. O hooly, hooly rose she up,
   To the place where he was lying,
And when she drew the curtain by,
   "Young man, I think you're dying."

4. "O it's I'm sick, and very, very sick,
   And 'tis a' for Barbara Allan:"
"O the better for me ye's never be,
   Tho your heart's blood were a spilling.

5. "O dinna ye mind, young man," said she,
   "When ye was in the tavern a drinking,
That ye made the healths gae round and round,
   And slighted Barbara Allan?"

6. He turnd his face unto the wall,
   And death was with him dealing:
   "Adieu, adieu, my dear friends all,
   And be kind to Barbara Allan."

7. And slowly, slowly raise she up,
   And slowly, slowly left him,
   And sighing said, she could not stay,
   Since death of life had reft him.

8. She had not gane a mile but twa,
   When she heard the dead-bell ringing,
   And every jow that the dead-bell geid,
   It cry'd, Woe to Barbara Allan!

9. "O mother, mother, make my bed!
   O make it saft and narrow!
   Since my love died for me to-day,
   I'll die for him to-morrow."

LORD RANDAL

1. "O WHERE hae ye been, Lord Randal, my son?
   O where hae ye been, my handsome young man?"
   "I hae been to the wild wood; mother, make my bed
      soon,
   For I'm weary wi hunting, and fain wald lie down."

2. "Where gat ye your dinner, Lord Randal, my son?
   Where gat ye your dinner, my handsome, young
      man?"
   "I din'd wi my true-love; mother, make my bed
      soon,
   For I'm weary wi hunting, and fain wald lie down."

3. "What gat ye to your dinner, Lord Randal, my son?
   What gat ye to your dinner, my handsome young
      man?"
   "I gat eels boiled in broo; mother, make my bed
      soon,
   For I'm weary wi hunting, and fain wald lie down."

4. "What became of your bloodhounds, Lord Randal,
   my son?
   What became of your bloodhounds, my handsome
   young man?"
   "O they swelld and they died; mother, make my bed
   soon,
   For I'm weary wi hunting, and fain wald lie down."

5. "O I fear ye are poison'd, Lord Randal, my son!
   O I fear ye are poisond, my handsome young man!"
   "O yes! I am poisond; mother, make my bed soon,
   For I'm sick at the heart, and I fain wald lie down."

Edmund Spenser

1552–1599

AMORETTI

LXX

FRESH Spring, the herald of loves mighty king,
In whose cote-armor richly are displayd
All sorts of flowers the which on earth do spring,
In goodly colors gloriously arrayd,
Goe to my love, where she is carelesse layd,
Yet in her winters bowre, not well awake;
Tell her the joyous time wil not be ſtaid,
Unlesse she doe him by the forelock take:
Bid her therefore her selfe soone ready make,
To wayt on Love amongſt his lovely crew,
Where every one that misseth then her make
Shall be by him amearſt with penance dew.
Make haſt therefore, sweet love, whileſt it is prime;
For none can call againe the passèd time.

LXXV

One day I wrote her name upon the ſtrand,
But came the waves and washed it away:
Agayne I wrote it with a second hand,
But came the tyde, and made my paynes his pray.

Vayne man, sayd she, that doeſt in vaine assay,
A mortall thing so to immortalize,
For I my selve shall lyke to this decay,
And eek my name bee wyped out lykewize.
Not so, (quod I) let baser things devize
To dy in duſt, but you shall live by fame:
My verse your vertues rare shall eternize,
And in the hevens wryte your glorious name.
Where whenas death shall al the world subdew,
Our love shall live, and later life renew.

LXXIX

Men call you fayre, and you doe credit it,
For that your selfe ye dayly such doe see:
But the trew fayre, that is the gentle wit,
And vertuous mind, is much more praysd of me.
For all the reſt, how ever fayre it be,
Shall turne to nought and loose that glorious hew:
But onely that is permanent and free
From frayle corruption, that doth flesh ensew.
That is true beautie: that doth argue you
To be divine and borne of heavenly seed:
Deriv'd from that fayre Spirit, from whom al true
And perfeĉt beauty did at firſt proceed.
He onely fayre, and what he fayre hath made,
All other fayre lyke flowres untymely fade.

Sir Philip Sidney

1554–1586

A DITTY

My true-love hath my heart, and I have his,
By juſt exchange one for another given:
I hold his dear, and mine he cannot miss,
There never was a better bargain driven:
    My true-love hath my heart, and I have his.

His heart in me keeps him and me in one,
My heart in him his thoughts and senses guides:
He loves my heart, for once it was his own,
I cherish his because in me it bides:
    My true love hath my heart and I have his.

ASTROPHEL AND STELLA

I

Loving in truth, and fain in verse my love to show,
That she, dear she, might take some pleasure of my
    pain,—
Pleasure might cause her read, reading might make her
    know,
Knowledge might pity win, and pity grace obtain,—
I sought fit words to paint the blackest face of woe,
Studying inventions fine, her wits to entertain,
Oft turning others' leaves, to see if thence would flow
Some fresh and fruitful showers upon my sunburnt
    brain.
But words came halting forth, wanting Invention's stay;
Invention, nature's child, fled step-dame Study's blows;
And others' feet still seemed but strangers' in my way.
Thus, great with child to speak, and helpless in my
    throes,
Biting my truant pen, beating myself for spite;
"Fool," said my Muse to me, "look in thy heart, and
    write."

XXXI

With how sad steps, O Moon, thou climb'st the skies!
How silently, and with how wan a face!
What, may it be that even in heavenly place
That busy archer his sharp arrows tries?
Sure, if that long-with-love-acquainted eyes
Can judge of love, thou feel'st a lover's case,
I read it in thy looks; thy languished grace,
To me, that feel the like, thy state descries.
Then, even of fellowship, O Moon, tell me,
Is constant love deemed there but want of wit?

Are beauties there as proud as here they be?
Do they above love to be loved, and yet
Those lovers scorn whom that love doth possess?
Do they call virtue there ungratefulness?

Michael Drayton

1563–1631

From IDEA

SINCE there's no help, come, let us kiss and part!
Nay, I have done, you get no more of me;
And I am glad, yea, glad with all my heart,
That thus so cleanly I myself can free.
Shake hands for ever, cancel all our vows;
And when we meet at any time again,
Be it not seen in either of our brows,
That we one jot of former love retain.
Now at the last gasp of Love's latest breath,
When, his pulse failing, Passion speechless lie,
When Faith is kneeling by his bed of death,
And Innocence is closing up his eyes,—
Now, if thou wouldst, when all have given him over,
From death to life thou might'st him yet recover.

Christopher Marlowe

1564–1593

THE PASSIONATE SHEPHERD TO HIS LOVE

COME live with me and be my love,
And we will all the pleasures prove,
That valleys, groves, hills and fields,
Woods or steepy mountains yields.

And we will sit upon the rocks,
Seeing the shepherds feed their flocks
By shallow rivers, to whose falls
Melodious birds sing madrigals.

And I will make thee beds of roses,
And a thousand fragrant posies,
A cap of flowers and a kirtle
Embroidered all with leaves of myrtle;

A gown made of the finest wool,
Which from our pretty lambs we pull;
Fair-linéd slippers for the cold,
With buckles of the purest gold;

A belt of straw and ivy buds,
With coral clasps and amber studs;
And if these pleasures may thee move,
Come live with me and be my love.

The shepherd swains shall dance and sing
For thy delight each May morning;
If these delights thy mind may move,
Then live with me and be my love.

William Shakespeare

1564–1616

SONNETS

XII

WHEN I do count the clock that tells the time,
And see the brave day sunk in hideous night;
When I behold the violet past prime,
And sable curls all silvered o'er with white;
When lofty trees I see barren of leaves,
Which erst from heat did canopy the herd,
And summer's green all girded up in sheaves
Borne on the bier with the white and bristly beard,
Then of thy beauty do I question make,
That thou among the wastes of time must go,
Since sweets and beauties do themselves forsake
And die as fast as they see others grow;
And nothing 'gainst Time's scythe can make defense
Save breed, to brave him when he takes thee hence.

✗ XXIX

When, in disgrace with fortune and men's eyes,
I all alone beweep my outcast state
And trouble deaf heaven with my bootless cries
And look upon myself and curse my fate,
Wishing me like to one more rich in hope,
Featured like him, like him with friends possessed,
Desiring this man's art and that man's scope,
With what I most enjoy contented least;
Yet in these thoughts myself almost despising,
Haply I think on thee, and then my state,
Like to the lark at break of day arising
From sullen earth, sings hymns at heaven's gate;
For thy sweet love remembered such wealth brings
That then I scorn to change my state with kings.

XXX

When to the sessions of sweet silent thought
I summon up remembrance of things past,
I sigh the lack of many a thing I sought,
And with old woes new wail my dear time's waste:
Then can I drown an eye, unused to flow,
For precious friends hid in death's dateless night,
And weep afresh love's long since canceled woe,
And moan the expense of many a vanished sight:
Then can I grieve at grievances foregone,
And heavily from woe to woe tell o'er
The sad account of fore-bemoanèd moan,
Which I new pay as if not paid before.
But if the while I think on thee, dear friend,
All losses are restored and sorrows end.

XXXIII

Full many a glorious morning have I seen
Flatter the mountain-tops with sovereign eye,
Kissing with golden face the meadows green,
Gilding pale streams with heavenly alchemy;

Anon permit the basest clouds to ride
With ugly rack on his celestial face,
And from the forlorn world his visage hide,
Stealing unseen to west with this disgrace:
Even so my sun one early morn did shine
With all-triumphant splendor on my brow;
But out, alack! he was but one hour mine;
The region cloud hath masked him from me now.
Yet him for this my love no wit disdaineth;
Suns of the world may stain when heaven's sun staineth.

LIV

O, how much more doth beauty beauteous seem
By that sweet ornament which truth doth give!
The rose looks fair, but fairer we it deem
For that sweet odor which doth in it live.
The canker-blooms have full as deep a dye
As the perfuméd tincture of the roses,
Hang on such thorns, and play as wantonly
When summer's breath their maskéd buds discloses:
But, for their virtue only is their show,
They live unwooed and unrespected fade,
Die to themselves. Sweet roses do not so;
Of their sweet deaths are sweetest odors made:
And so of you, beauteous and lovely youth,
When that shall fade, my verse distills your truth.

LV

Not marble, nor the gilded monuments
Of princes, shall outlive this powerful rhyme;
But you shall shine more bright in these contents
Than unswept stone besmeared with sluttish time.
When wasteful war shall statues overturn,
And broils root out the work of masonry,
Nor Mars his sword nor war's quick fire shall burn
The living record of your memory.
'Gainst death and all-oblivious enmity
Shall you pace forth; your praise shall still find room

Even in the eyes of all posterity
That wear this world out to the ending doom.
So, till the judgment that yourself arise,
You live in this, and dwell in lovers' eyes.

LXIV

When I have seen by Time's fell hand defaced
The rich proud cost of outworn buried age;
When sometime lofty towers I see down-razed
And brass eternal slave to mortal rage;
When I have seen the hungry ocean gain
Advantage on the kingdom of the shore,
And the firm soil win of the watery main,
Increasing store with loss and loss with store;
When I have seen such interchange of state,
Or state itself confounded to decay;
Ruin hath taught me thus to ruminate,
That Time will come and take my love away.
This thought is as a death, which cannot choose
But weep to have that which it fears to lose.

LXV

Since brass, nor stone, nor earth, nor boundless sea,
But sad mortality o'er-sways their power,
How with this rage shall beauty hold a plea,
Whose action is no stronger than a flower?
O, how shall summer's honey breath hold out
Against the wreckful siege of battering days,
When rocks impregnable are not so stout,
Nor gates of steel so strong, but Time decays?
O fearful meditation; where, alack,
Shall Time's best jewel from Time's chest lie hid?
Or what strong hand can hold his swift foot back?
Or who his spoil of beauty can forbid?
O, none, unless this miracle have might,
That in black ink my love may still shine bright.

LXVI

Tired with all these, for restful death I cry,
As, to behold desert a beggar born,
And needy nothing trimmed in jollity,
And purest faith unhappily forsworn,
And gilded honor shamefully misplaced,
And maiden virtue rudely strumpeted,
And right perfection wrongfully disgraced,
And strength by limping sway disabléd,
And art made tongue-tied by authority,
And folly doctor-like controlling skill,
And simple truth miscalled simplicity,
And captive good attending captain ill:
Tired with all these, from these would I be gone,
Save that, to die, I leave my love alone.

LXXI

No longer mourn for me when I am dead
Than you shall hear the surly sullen bell
Give warning to the world that I am fled
From this vile world, with vilest worms to dwell:
Nay, if you read this line, remember not
The hand that writ it; for I love you so
That I in your sweet thoughts would be forgot
If thinking on me then should make you woe.
O, if, I say, you look upon this verse
When I perhaps compounded am with clay,
Do not so much as my poor name rehearse,
But let your love even with my life decay,
Lest the wise world should look into your moan
And mock you with me after I am gone.

LXXIII

That time of year thou mayst in me behold
When yellow leaves, or none, or few, do hang
Upon those boughs which shake against the cold,
Bare ruined choirs, where late the sweet birds sang.

In me thou see'st the twilight of such day
As after sunset fadeth in the west,
Which by and by black night doth take away,
Death's second self, that seals up all in rest.
In me thou see'st the glowing of such fire
That on the ashes of his youth doth lie,
As the death-bed whereon it must expire
Consumed with that which it was nourished by.
This thou perceivest, which makes thy love more strong,
To love that well which thou must leave ere long.

XC

Then hate me when thou wilt; if ever, now;
Now, while the world is bent my deeds to cross,
Join with the spite of fortune, make me bow,
And do not drop in for an after-loss:
Ah, do not, when my heart hath 'scaped this sorrow,
Come in the rearward of a conquered woe;
Give not a windy night a rainy morrow,
To linger out a purposed overthrow.
If thou wilt leave me, do not leave me last,
When other petty griefs have done their spite,
But in the onset come: so shall I taste
At first the very worst of fortune's might,
And other strains of woe, which now seem woe,
Compared with loss of thee will not seem so.

XCVII

How like a winter hath my absense been
From thee, the pleasure of the fleeting year!
What freezings have I felt, what dark days seen!
What old December's bareness everywhere!
And yet this time removed was summer's time,
The teeming autumn, big with rich increase,
Bearing the wanton burden of the prime,
Like widowed wombs after their lords' decease:
Yet this abundant issue seem to me

But hope of orphans and unfathered fruit;
For summer and his pleasures wait on thee,
And, thou away, the very birds are mute;
Or, if they sing, 'tis with so dull a cheer
That leaves look pale, dreading the winter's near.

XCVIII

From you have I been absent in the spring,
When proud-pied April dressed in all his trim
Hath put a spirit of youth in every thing,
That heavy Saturn laughed and leaped with him.
Yet nor the lays of birds nor the sweet smell
Of different flowers in odor and in hue
Could make me any summer's story tell,
Or from their proud lap pluck them where they grew;
Nor did I wonder at the lily's white,
Nor praise the deep vermilion in the rose;
They were but sweet, but figures of delight,
Drawn after you, you pattern of all those.
Yet seemed it winter still, and, you away,
As with your shadow I with these did play.

CVI

When in the chronicle of wasted time
I see descriptions of the fairest wights,
And beauty making beautiful old rhyme
In praise of ladies dead and lovely knights,
Then, in the blazon of sweet beauty's best,
Of hand, of foot, of lip, of eye, of brow,
I see their antique pen would have expressed
Even such a beauty as you master now
So all their praises are but prophecies
Of this our time, all you prefiguring;
And, for they looked but with divining eyes,
They had not skill enough your worth to sing:
For we, which now behold these present days,
Have eyes to wonder, but lack tongues to praise.

CVII

Not mine own fears, nor the prophetic soul
Of the wide world dreaming on things to come,
Can yet the lease of my true love control,
Supposed as forfeit to a confined doom.
The mortal moon hath her eclipse endured
And the sad augurs mock their own presage;
Incertainties now crown themselves assured
And peace proclaims olives of endless age.
Now with the drops of this most balmy time
My love looks fresh, and Death to me subscribes,
Since, spite of him, I'll live in this poor rhyme,
While he insults o'er dull and speechless tribes:
And thou in this shalt find thy monument,
When tyrants' crests and tombs of brass are spent.

CXVI

Let me not to the marriage of true minds
Admit impediments. Love is not love
Which alters when it alteration finds,
Or bends with the remover to remove:
O, no! it is an ever-fixèd mark
That looks on tempests and is never shaken;
It is the star to every wandering bark,
Whose worth's unknown, although his height be taken.
Love's not Time's fool, though rosy lips and cheeks
Within his bending sickle's compass come;
Love alters not with his brief hours and weeks,
But bears it out even to the edge of doom.
If this be error and upon me proved,
I never writ, nor no man ever loved.

CXXIX

The expense of spirit in a waste of shame
Is lust in action; and till action, lust
Is perjured, murderous, bloody, full of blame,
Savage, extreme, rude, cruel, not to trust,
Enjoyed no sooner but despisèd straight:

Past reason hunted, and no sooner had
Past reason hated, as a swallowed bait
On purpose laid to make the taker mad;
Mad in pursuit and in possession so;
Had, having, and in quest to have, extreme;
A bliss in proof, and proved, a very woe;
Before, a joy proposed; behind, a dream
All this the world well knows; yet none knows well
To shun the heaven that leads men to this hell.

CXXX

My mistress' eyes are nothing like the sun;
Coral is far more red than her lips' red:
If snow be white, why they her breasts are dun;
If hairs be wires, black wires grow on her head.
I have seen roses damasked, red and white,
But no such roses see I in her cheeks;
And in some perfumes is there more delight
Than in the breath that from my mistress reeks.
I love to hear her speak, yet well I know
That music hath a far more pleasing sound;
I grant I never saw a goddess go;
My mistress, when she walks, treads on the ground:
And yet, by heaven, I think my love as rare
As any she belied with false compare.

CXLVI

Poor soul, the center of my sinful earth,
Thrall to these rebel powers that thee array,
Why dost thou pine within and suffer death,
Painting thy outward walls so costly gay?
Why so large cost, having so short a lease,
Dost thou upon thy fading mansion spend?
Shall worms, inheritors of this excess,
Eat up thy charge? Is this thy body's end?
Then, soul, live thou upon thy servant's loss,
And let that pine to aggravate thy store;
Buy terms divine in selling hours of dross;

Within be fed, without be rich no more:
So shalt thou feed on Death, that feeds on men,
And Death once dead, there's no more dying then.

SONGS FROM THE PLAYS

From LOVE'S LABOR'S LOST

WHEN icicles hang by the wall,
 And Dick the shepherd blows his nail,
And Tom bears logs into the hall,
 And milk comes frozen home in pail,
When blood is nipped and ways be foul,
Then nightly sings the staring owl,
"Tu-whit, tu-who!" a merry note,
While greasy Joan doth keel the pot.

When all aloud the wind doth blow,
 And coughing drowns the parson's saw,
And birds sit brooding in the snow,
 And Marian's nose looks red and raw,
When roasted crabs hiss in the bowl,
Then nightly sings the staring owl,
"Tu-whit, tu-who!" a merry note,
While greasy Joan doth keel the pot.

From MUCH ADO ABOUT NOTHING

SIGH no more, ladies, sigh no more,
 Men were deceivers ever,
One foot in sea and one on shore,
 To one thing constant never:
Then sigh not so, but let them go,
 And be you blithe and bonny,
Converting all your sounds of woe
 Into Hey nonny, nonny.

Sing no more ditties, sing no moe,
 Of dumps so dull and heavy!
The fraud of men was ever so,
 Since summer first was leavy:

Then sigh not so, but let them go,
And be you blithe and bonny,
Converting all your sounds of woe
Into Hey nonny, nonny.

From As You Like It

UNDER the greenwood tree
Who loves to lie with me,
And turn his merry note
Unto the sweet birds' throat,
Come hither, come hither, come hither:
Here shall he see
No enemy
But winter and rough weather.

Who doth ambition shun
And loves to live i' the sun,
Seeking the food he eats
And pleased with what he gets,
Come hither, come hither, come hither:
Here shall he see
No enemy
But winter and rough weather.

———————

Blow, blow, thou winter wind,
Thou art not so unkind
As man's ingratitude;
Thy tooth is not so keen,
Because thou art not seen,
Although thy breath be rude.
Heigh ho! sing, heigh ho! unto the green holly:
Most friendship is feigning, most loving mere folly:
Then, heigh ho, the holly!
This life is most jolly.

Freeze, freeze, thou bitter sky
That dost not bite so nigh
As benefits forgot:

Though thou the waters warp,
Thy sting is not so sharp
    As friend remembered not.
Heigh ho! sing, heigh ho! etc.

———————

It was a lover and his lass,
  With a hey, and a ho, and a hey nonino,
That oe'r the green corn-field did pass
  In the spring time, the only pretty ring time,
When birds do sing, hey ding a ding, ding;
Sweet lovers love the spring.

Between the acres of the rye,
  With a hey, and a ho, and a hey nonino,
These pretty country folks would lie,
  In spring time, etc.

This carol they began that hour,
  With a hey, and a ho, and a hey nonino,
How that a life was but a flower
  In spring time, etc.

And therefore take the present time,
  With a hey, and a ho, and a hey nonino,
For love is crownèd with the prime
  In spring time, etc.

From TWELFTH NIGHT

O MISTRESS mine, where are you roaming?
O, stay and hear, your true love's coming,
  That can sing both high and low:
Trip no further, pretty sweeting,
Journeys end in lovers meeting,
  Every wise man's son doth know.

What is love? 'Tis not hereafter;
Present mirth hath present laughter;
  What's to come is still unsure:

In delay there lies no plenty;
Then come kiss me, sweet and twenty,
  Youth's a stuff will not endure.

From MEASURE FOR MEASURE

TAKE, O, take those lips away,
  That so sweetly were forsworn;
And those eyes, the break of day,
  Lights that do mislead the morn:
But my kisses bring again,
                    Bring again;
Seals of love, but sealed in vain,
                    Sealed in vain.

From CYMBELINE

HARK, hark! the lark at heaven's gate sings,
  And Phœbus 'gins arise,
His steeds to water at those springs
  On chaliced flowers that lies;
And winking Mary-buds begin
  To ope their golden eyes:
With every thing that pretty is,
  My lady sweet, arise;
    Arise, arise.

FEAR no more the heat o' the sun,
  Nor the furious winter's rages;
Thou thy worldly task hast done,
  Home art gone, and ta'en thy wages:
Golden lads and girls all must,
As chimney-sweepers, come to dust.

Fear no more the frowns o' the great;
  Thou art past the tyrant's stroke;
Care no more to clothe and eat;
  To thee the reed is as the oak:
The scepter, learning, psychic, must
All follow this, and come to dust.

Fear no more the lightning-flash,
   Nor the all-dreaded thunder-stone;
Fear not slander, censure rash;
   Thou hast finished joy and moan:
All lovers young, all lovers must
Consign to thee, and come to dust.

No exorciser harm thee!
   Nor no witchcraft charm thee!
Ghost unlaid forbear thee!
   Nothing ill come near thee!
Quiet consummation have;
And renownèd be thy grave!

From THE TEMPEST

FULL fathom five thy father lies;
   Of his bones are coral made;
Those are pearls that were his eyes;
   Nothing of him that doth fade
But doth suffer a sea-change
Into something rich and strange.
Sea-nymphs hourly ring his knell:

               Ding-dong.
Hark! now I hear them,—ding-dong, bell.

Where the bee sucks, there suck I;
In a cowslip's bell I lie;
There I couch when owls do cry.
On the bat's back I do fly
After summer merrily.
Merrily, merrily shall I live now
Under the blossom that hangs on the bough.

Ben Jonson

1573–1637

HYMN TO DIANA

From CYNTHIA'S REVELS

QUEEN and huntress, chaste and fair,
  Now the sun is laid to sleep,
Seated in thy silver chair,
  State in wonted manner keep:
    Hesperus entreats thy light,
    Goddess excellently bright.

Earth, let not thy envious shade
  Dare itself to interpose;
Cynthia's shining orb was made
  Heaven to clear when day did close:
    Bless us then with wished sight,
    Goddess excellently bright.

Lay thy bow of pearl apart
  And thy crystal-shining quiver;
Give unto the flying hart
  Space to breathe, how short soever:
    Thou that mak'st a day of night—
    Goddess excellently bright!

SONG TO CELIA

DRINK to me only with thine eyes,
  And I will pledge with mine;
Or leave a kiss but in the cup,
  And I'll not look for wine.
The thirst that from the soul doth rise
  Doth ask a drink divine;
But might I of Jove's nectar sup,
  I would not change for thine.

I sent thee late a rosy wreath,
   Not so much honoring thee
As giving it a hope that there
   It could not withered be.
But thou thereon didst only breathe,
   And sent'st it back to me;
Since when it grows, and smells, I swear,
   Not of itself but thee.

SIMPLEX MUNDITIIS

From EPICŒNE; OR, THE SILENT WOMAN

STILL to be neat, still to be dressed,
As you were going to a feast;
Still to be powdered, still perfumed:
Lady, it is to be presumed,
Though art's hid causes are not found,
All is not sweet, all is not sound.

Give me a look, give me a face
That makes simplicity a grace;
Robes loosely flowing, hair as free:
Such sweet neglect more taketh me
Than all the adulteries of art;
They strike mine eyes, but not my heart.

John Donne

1573–1631

SONG

Go and catch a falling star,
   Get with child a mandrake root,
Tell me where all past years are,
   Or who cleft the devil's foot,
Teach me to hear a mermaid's singing,
   Or to keep off envy's stinging,
      And find
      What wind
Serves to advance an honest mind.

If thou be'st born to strange sights,
   Things invisible go see,
Ride ten thousand days and nights,
   Till Age snow white hairs on thee;
Thou, when thou return'st, wilt tell me
All strange wonders that befell thee,
     And swear
     No where
Lives a woman true and fair.

If thou find'st one, let me know;
   Such a pilgrimage were sweet.
Yet do not; I would not go,
   Though at next door we might meet.
Though she were true when you met her,
And last till you write your letter,
     Yet she
     Will be
False, ere I come, to two or three.

LOVE'S DEITY

I LONG to talk with some old lover's ghost
   Who died before the god of love was born.
I cannot think that he who then loved most,
   Sunk so low as to love one which did scorn.
But since this god produced a destiny
And that vice-nature, custom, lets it be,
   I must love her that loves not me.

Sure, they which made him god, meant not so much,
   Nor he in his young godhead practiced it.
But when an even flame two hearts did touch,
   His office was indulgently to fit
Actives to passives. Correspondency
Only his subject was; it cannot be
   Love, till I love her who loves me.

But every modern god will not extend
  His vaſt prerogative as far as Jove.
To rage, to luſt, to write to, to commend,
  All is the purlieu of the god of love.
O! were we wakened by this tyranny
To ungod this child again, it could not be
  I should love her who loves not me.

Rebel and atheiſt too, why murmur I,
  As though I felt the worſt that love could do?
Love may make me leave loving, or might try
  A deeper plague, to make her love me too;
Which, since she loves before, I'm loth to see.
Falsehood is worse than hate; and that muſt be,
  If she whom I love, should love me.

THE FUNERAL

WHOEVER comes to shroud me, do not harm
    Nor queſtion much
That subtle wreath of hair about mine arm;
The myſtery, the sign you muſt not touch,
    For 'tis my outward soul,
Viceroy to that which, unto heav'n being gone,
    Will leave this to control
And keep these limbs, her provinces, from dissolution.

For if the sinewy thread my brain lets fall
    Through every part
Can tie those parts, and make me one of all;
Those hairs, which upward grew, and ſtrength and art
    Have from a better brain,
Can better do 't: except she meant that I
    By this should know my pain,
As prisoners then are manacled, when they're con-
    demned to die.

Whate'er she meant by 't, bury it with me,
    For since I am

Love's martyr, it might breed idolatry
If into other hands these reliques came
    As 't was humility
To afford to it all that a soul can do,
    So 't is some bravery
That, since you would have none of me, I bury some
      of you.

A HYMN TO GOD THE FATHER

Wilt thou forgive that sin where I begun,
    Which was my sin, though it were done before?
Wilt thou forgive that sin through which I run,
    And do run still, though still I do deplore?
When thou hast done, thou hast not done;
    For I have more.

Wilt thou forgive that sin which I have won
    Others to sin, and made my sins their door?
Wilt thou forgive that sin which I did shun
    A year or two, but wallowed in a score?
When thou hast done, thou hast not done;
    For I have more.

I have a sin of fear, that when I've spun
    My last thread, I shall perish on the shore;
But swear by thyself that at my death thy Son
    Shall shine as he shines now and heretofore;
And having done that, thou hast done;
    I fear no more.

Richard Barnefield

1574–1627

THE NIGHTINGALE

As it fell upon a day
In the merry month of May,
Sitting in a pleasant shade
Which a grove of myrtles made.

Beasts did leap and birds did sing,
Trees did grow and plants did spring;
Every thing did banish moan
Save the Nighingale alone:
She, poor bird, as all forlorn,
Leaned her breast up-till a thorn,
And there sung the dolefull'st ditty
That to hear it was great pity.
Fie, fie, fie, now would she cry;
Teru, teru, by and by;
That to hear her so complain
Scarce I could from tears refrain;
For her griefs so lively shown
Made me think upon mine own.
Ah! thought I, thou mourn'st in vain,
None takes pity on thy pain:
Senseless trees they cannot hear thee,
Ruthless beasts they will not cheer thee:
King Pandion he is dead,
All thy friends are lapped in lead;
All thy fellow birds do sing
Careless of thy sorrowing:
Even so, poor bird, like thee
None alive will pity me.

John Fletcher

1579–1625

ASPATIA'S SONG

From THE MAID'S TRAGEDY

LAY a garland on my hearse
    Of the dismal yew;
Maidens, willow branches bear;
    Say I diéd true.

My love was false, but I was firm
    From my hour of birth;
Upon my buried body lie
    Lightly, gently earth!

George Wither

1588–1667

THE LOVER'S RESOLUTION

SHALL I, wasting in despair,
Die, because a woman's fair?
Or make pale my cheeks with care
'Cause another's rosy are?
Be she fairer than the day,
Or the flowery meads in May,
    If she think not well of me,
    What care I how fair she be?

Shall my silly heart be pined,
'Cause I see a woman kind?
Or a well disposèd nature
Joinèd with a lovely feature?
Be she meeker, kinder, than
Turtle-dove or pelican,
    If she be not so to me,
    What care I how kind she be?

Shall a woman's virtues move
Me to perish for her love?
Or her well deserving known
Make me quite forget my own?
Be she with that goodness blest
Which may merit name of Best
    If she be not such to me,
    What care I how good she be?

'Cause her fortune seems too high,
Shall I play the fool and die?
She that bears a noble mind,
If not outward helps she find,
Thinks what with them he would do
That without them dares her woo;
    And unless that mind I see,
    What care I how great she be?

Great, or good, or kind, or fair,
I will ne'er the more despair;
If she loves me, this believe,
I will die ere she shall grieve;
If she slight me when I woo,
I can scorn, and let her go;
   For if she be not for me,
   What care I for whom she be?

William Browne

1590?–1645?

ON THE COUNTESS OF PEMBROKE

Underneath this sable hearse
Lies the subject of all verse:
Sidney's sister, Pembroke's mother:
Death, ere thou hast slain another
Fair, and learned, and good as she,
Time shall throw a dart at thee.

Marble piles let no man raise
To her name: in after days,
Some kind woman, born as she,
Reading this, like Niobe
Shall turn marble, and become
Both her mourner and her tomb.

Robert Herrick

1591–1674

AN ODE FOR BEN JONSON

Ah, Ben!
Say how, or when
Shall we, thy guests,
Meet at those lyric feasts
Made at the Sun,
The Dog, the Triple Tun?

Where we such clusters had,
As made us nobly wild, not mad;
And yet each verse of thine
Out-did the meat, out-did the frolic wine.

My Ben!
Or come again,
Or send to us
Thy wit's great overplus;
But teach us yet
Wisely to husband it,
Lest we that talent spend;
And having once brought to an end
That precious stock, the store
Of such a wit the world should have no more.

TO DAFFODILS

Fair daffodils, we weep to see
    You haste away so soon;
As yet the early rising sun
    Has not attained his noon.
        Stay, stay,
        Until the hasting day
            Has run
        But to the even-song;
And, having prayed together, we
    Will go with you along.

We have short time to stay as you,
    We have as short a spring;
As quick a growth to meet decay,
    As you, or anything.
        We die,
        As your hours do, and dry
            Away,
        Like to the summer's rain,
Or as the pearls of morning's dew,
    Ne'er to be found again.

UPON JULIA'S CLOTHES

Whenas in silks my Julia goes,
Then, then, methinks, how sweetly flows
That liquefaction of her clothes.

Next, when I cast mine eyes, and see
That brave vibration, each way free,
O, how that glittering taketh me!

SWEET DISORDER

A sweet disorder in the dress
Kindles in clothes a wantonness:
A lawn about the shoulders thrown
Into a fine distraction—
An erring lace, which here and there
Enthrals the crimson stomacher—
A cuff neglectful, and thereby
Ribbands to flow confusedly—
A winning wave, deserving note,
In the tempestuous petticoat—
A careless shoe-string, in whose tie
I see a wild civility—
Do more bewitch me than when art
Is too precise in every part.

✗ GRACE FOR A CHILD

Here a little child I stand,
Heaving up my either hand;
Cold as paddocks though they be,
Here I lift them up to Thee,
For a benison to fall
On our meat and on us all. Amen.

✗ TO THE VIRGINS TO MAKE MUCH OF TIME

Gather ye rosebuds while ye may,
    Old Time's still a-flying;
And this same flower that smiles to-day,
    To-morrow will be dying.

The glorious lamp of heaven, the sun,
　　The higher he's a-getting,
The sooner will his race be run,
　　And nearer he's to setting.

That age is blest which is the first,
　　When youth and blood are warmer;
But being spent, the worse and worst
　　Times still succeed the former.

Then be not coy, but use your time,
　　And while ye may, go marry;
For, having lost but once your prime,
　　You may forever tarry.

George Herbert

1593–1633

VIRTUE

Sweet day, so cool, so calm, so bright,
　　The bridal of the earth and sky;
The dew shall weep thy fall to-night,
　　For thou must die.

Sweet rose, whose hue, angry and brave,
　　Bids the rash gazer wipe his eye,
Thy root is ever in its grave,
　　And thou must die.

Sweet spring, full of sweet days and roses,
　　A box where sweets compacted lie,
My music shows ye have your closes,
　　And all must die.

Only a sweet and virtuous soul,
　　Like seasoned timber, never gives,
But though the whole world turn to coal,
　　Then chiefly lives.

PEACE

Sweet Peace, where dost thou dwell? I humbly crave,
    Let me once know.
  I sought thee in a secret cave,
    And ask'd, if Peace were there,
A hollow wind did seem to answer, No:
    Go seek elsewhere.

I did; and going did a rainbow note:
    Surely, thought I,
  This is the lace of Peace's coat:
    I will search out the matter.
But while I lookt the clouds immediately
    Did break and scatter.

Then went I to a garden and did spy
    A gallant flower,
  The crown Imperiall: Sure, said I,
    Peace at the root must dwell.
But when I digg'd, I saw a worm devoure
    What show'd so well.

At length I met a rev'rend good old man;
    Whom when for Peace
  I did demand, he thus began:
    There was a Prince of old
At Salem dwelt, who liv'd with good increase
    Of flock and fold.

He sweetly liv'd; yet sweetnesse did not save
    His life from foes.
  But after death out of his grave
    There sprang twelve stalks of wheat;
Which many wondring at, got some of those
    To plant and set.

It prosper'd strangely, and did soon disperse
    Through all the earth:

For they that taſte it do rehearse,
 That vertue lies therein;
A secret vertue, bringing peace and mirth
  By flight of sinne.

Take of this grain, which in my garden grows,
  And grows for you;
 Make bread of it: and that repose
 And peace, which ev'ry where
With so much earneſtness you do pursue
  Is onely there.

THE COLLAR

I STRUCK the board, and cried, "No more;
 I will abroad!
What, shall I ever sigh and pine?
My lines and life are free; free as the road,
 Loose as the wind, as large as ſtore.
  Shall I be ſtill in suit?
 Have I no harveſt but a thorn
 To let me blood, and not reſtore
What I have loſt with cordial fruit?
  Sure there was wine
 Before my sighs did dry it; there was corn
  Before my tears did drown it;
 Is the year only loſt to me?
  Have I no bays to crown it,
No flowers, no garlands gay; all blaſted,
  All waſted?
 Not so, my heart; but there is fruit,
  And thou haſt hands.
 Recover all thy sigh-blown age
On double pleasures; leave thy cold dispute
Of what is fit and not; forsake thy cage,
  Thy rope of sands
Which petty thoughts have made; and made to thee
 Good cable, to enforce and draw,
  And be thy law,

While thou didst wink and wouldst not see.
    Away! take heed;
    I will abroad.
Call in thy death's head there, tie up thy fears:
    He that forbears
    To suit and serve his need
    Deserves his load."
But as I raved, and grew more fierce and wild
    At every word,
   Methought I heard one calling, "Child";
   And I replied, "My Lord."

Thomas Carew

1594?–1639

DISDAIN RETURNED

He that loves a rosy cheek,
   Or a coral lip admires,
Or from star-like eyes doth seek
   Fuel to maintain his fires;
As old Time makes these decay,
So his flames must waste away.

But a smooth and steadfast mind,
   Gentle thoughts, and calm desires,
Hearts with equal love combined,
   Kindle never-dying fires.
Where these are not, I despise
Lovely cheeks or lips or eyes.

No tears, Celia, now shall win
   My resolved heart to return;
I have searched that soul within,
   And find nought but pride and scorn:
I have learned thy arts, and now
Can disdain as much as thou.
   Some power in my revenge convey
   That love to her I cast away.

ASK ME NO MORE

Ask me no more where Jove bestows,
When June is past, the fading rose;
For in your beauty's orient deep
These flowers, as in their causes, sleep.

Ask me no more whither do stray
The golden atoms of the day,
For, in pure love, heaven did prepare
Those powders to enrich your hair.

Ask me no more whither doth haste
The nightingale when May is past;
For in your sweet dividing throat
She winters, and keeps warm her note.

Ask me no more where those stars light
That downwards fall in dead of night,
For in your eyes they sit, and there
Fixèd become as in their sphere.

Ask me no more if east or west
The phœnix builds her spicy nest;
For unto you at last she flies,
And in your fragrant bosom dies.

James Shirley

1596–1666

A DIRGE

From The Contention of Ajax and Ulysses

The glories of our blood and state
  Are shadows, not substantial things;
There is no armor against fate;
Death lays his icy hand on kings:
    Scepter and crown
    Must tumble down,
And in the dust be equal made
With the poor crooked scythe and spade.

Some men with swords may reap the field,
   And plant fresh laurels where they kill;
But their strong nerves at last must yield;
   They tame but one another still:
      Early or late
      They stoop to fate,
And must give up their murmuring breath
When they, pale captives, creep to death.

The garlands wither on your brow;
   Then boast no more your mighty deeds;
Upon Death's purple altar now
   See where the victor-victim bleeds:
      Your heads must come
      To the cold tomb;
Only the actions of the just
Smell sweet, and blossom in their dust.

William Davenant

1606–1668

SONG

THE lark now leaves his watery nest,
   And climbing shakes his dewy wings.
He takes this window for the East,
   And to implore your light he sings—
Awake, awake; the morn will never rise
Till she can dress her beauty at your eyes.

The merchant bows unto the seaman's star,
   The plowman from the sun his season takes;
But still the lover wonders what they are
   Who look for day before his mistress wakes.
Awake, awake! break through your veils of lawn!
Then draw your curtains, and begin the dawn!

Edmund Waller

1606–1687

GO LOVELY ROSE!

Go, lovely Rose!
Tell her that wastes her time and me
That now she knows,
When I resemble her to thee,
How sweet and fair she seems to be.

Tell her that's young,
And shuns to have her graces spied,
That hadst thou sprung
In deserts, where no men abide,
Thou must have uncommended died.

Small is the worth
Of beauty from the light retired;
Bid her come forth,
Suffer herself to be desired,
And not blush so to be admired.

Then die; that she
The common fate of all things rare
May read in thee;
How small a part of time they share
That are so wondrous sweet and fair!

ON A GIRDLE

That which her slender waist confined,
Shall now my joyful temples bind;
No monarch but would give his crown,
His arms might do what this has done.

It was my heaven's extremest sphere,
The pale which held that lovely deer,
My joy, my grief, my hope, my love,
Did all within this circle move!

A narrow compass! and yet there
Dwelt all that's good, and all that's fair!
Give me but what this ribband bound,
Take all the rest the sun goes round!

John Milton

1608–1674

LYCIDAS

In this Monody the Author bewails a learned Friend, unfortu-
nately drowned in his passage from Chester on the Irish Seas,
1637; and, by occasion, foretells the ruin of our corrupted Clergy,
then in their height.

YET once more, O ye laurels, and once more,
Ye myrtles brown, with ivy never sere,
I come to pluck your berries harsh and crude,
And with forced fingers rude
Shatter your leaves before the mellowing year.
Bitter constraint and sad occasion dear
Compels me to disturb your season due;
For Lycidas is dead, dead ere his prime,
Young Lycidas, and hath not left his peer.
Who would not sing for Lycidas? he knew
Himself to sing, and build the lofty rhyme.
He must not float upon his watery bier
Unwept, and welter to the parching wind,
Without the meed of some melodious tear.
    Begin, then, Sisters of the sacred well
That from beneath the seat of Jove doth spring;
Begin, and somewhat loudly sweep the string.
Hence with denial vain and coy excuse:
So may some gentle Muse
With lucky words favor *my* destined urn,
And as he passes turn,
And bid fair peace be to my sable shroud!
    For we were nursed upon the self-same hill,
Fed the same flock, by fountain, shade, and rill;
Together both, ere the high lawns appeared
Under the opening eyelids of the Morn,

We drove a-field, and both together heard
What time the gray-fly winds her sultry horn,
Battening our flocks with the fresh dews of night,
Oft till the star that rose at evening bright
Toward heaven's descent had sloped his westering wheel.
Meanwhile the rural ditties were not mute;
Tempered to the oaten flute
Rough Satyrs danced, and Fauns with cloven heel
From the glad sound that would not be absent long;
And old Damœtas loved to hear our song.

But, oh; the heavy change, now thou art gone,
Now thou art gone and never must return!
Thee, Shepherd, the woods and desert caves,
With wild thyme and the gadding vine o'ergrown,
And all their echoes, mourn.
The willows, and the hazel copses green,
Shall now no more be seen
Fanning their joyous leaves to thy soft lays.
As killing as the canker to the rose,
Or taint-worm to the weanling herds that graze,
Or frost to flowers that their gay wardrobe wear,
When first the white-thorn blows;
Such, Lycidas, thy loss to shepherd's ear.

Where were ye, Nymphs, when the remorseless deep
Closed oe'r the head of your loved Lycidas?
For neither were ye playing on the steep
Where your old bards, the famous Druids, lie,
Nor on the shaggy top of Mona high,
Nor yet where Deva spreads her wizard stream.
Ay me! I fondly dream,
"Had ye been there," . . . for what could that have
    done?
What could the Muse herself that Orpheus bore,
The Muse herself, for her enchanting son,
Whom universal nature did lament,
When, by the rout that made the hideous roar,
His gory visage down the stream was sent,
Down the swift Hebrus to the Lesbian shore?

Alas! what boots it with uncessant care

To tend the homely, slighted, shepherd's trade,
And strictly mediate the thankless Muse?
Were it not better done, as others use,
To sport with Amaryllis in the shade,
Or with the tangles of Neæra's hair?
Fame is the spur that the clear spirit doth raise
(That last infirmity of noble mind)
To scorn delights and live laborious days;
But the fair guerdon when we hope to find,
And think to burst out into sudden blaze,
Comes the blind Fury with the abhorrèd shears
And slits the thin-spun life. "But not the praise,"
Phœbus replied, and touched my trembling ears:
"Fame is no plant that grows on mortal soil,
Nor in the glistering foil
Set off to the world, nor in broad rumor lies,
But lives and spreads aloft by those pure eyes
And perfect witness of all-judging Jove;
As he pronounces lastly on each deed,
Of so much fame in heaven expect thy meed."

O fountain Arethuse, and thou honored flood,
Smooth-sliding Mincius, crowned with vocal reeds,
That strain I heard was of a higher mood.
But now my oat proceeds,
And listens to the Herald of the Sea
That came in Neptune's plea.
He asked the waves, and asked the felon winds,
What hard mishap hath doomed this gentle swain?
And questioned every gust of rugged wings,
That blows from off each beakèd promontory.
They knew not of his story;
And sage Hippotades their answer brings,
That not a blast was from his dungeon strayed;
The air was calm, and on the level brine
Sleek Panopé with all her sisters played.
It was that fatal and perfidious bark,
Built in the eclipse, and rigged with curses dark,
That sunk so low that sacred head of thine.

Next, Camus, reverend sire, went footing slow,

His mantle hairy, and his bonnet sedge,
Inwrought with figures dim, and on the edge
Like to that sanguine flower inscribed with woe.
"Ah! what hath reft," quoth he, "my dearest pledge?"
Last came, and last did go,
The Pilot of the Galilean Lake;
Two massy keys he bore of metals twain
(The golden opes, the iron shuts amain).
He shook his mitred locks, and stern bespake:—
"How well could I have spared for thee, young swain,
Enow of such as, for their bellies' sake,
Creep, and intrude, and climb into the fold!
Of other care they little reckoning make
Than how to scramble at the shearers' feast
And shove away the worthy bidden guest.
Blind mouths! that scarce themselves know how to hold
A sheep-hook, or have learned ought else the least
That to the faithful herdman's art belongs!
What recks it them? What need they? They are sped;
And, when they list, their lean and flashy songs
Grate on their scrannel pipes of wretched straw;
The hungry sheep look up, and are not fed,
But, swoln with wind and the rank mist they draw,
Rot inwardly, and foul contagion spread;
Besides what the grim wolf with privy paw
Daily devours apace, and nothing said.
But that two-handed engine at the door
Stands ready to smite once, and smite no more."
    Return, Alphëus; the dread voice is past
That shrunk thy streams; return, Sicilian Muse,
And call the vales, and bid them hither cast
Their bells and flowerets of a thousand hues.
Ye valleys low, where the mild whispers use
Of shades, and wanton winds, and gushing brooks,
On whose fresh lap the swart star sparely looks,
Throw hither all your quaint enameled eyes
That on the green turf suck the honeyed showers,
And purple all the ground with vernal flowers.
Bring the rathe primrose that forsaken dies,

The tufted crow-toe, and pale jessamine,
The white pink, and the pansy freaked with jet,
The glowing violet,
The musk-rose, and the well-attired woodbine,
With cowslips wan that hang the pensive head,
And every flower that sad embroidery wears;
Bid amaranthus all his beauty shed,
And daffadillies fill their cups with tears,
To ſtrew the laureate hearse where Lycid lies.
For so, to interpose a little ease,
Let our frail thoughts dally with false surmise.
Ay me! whilſt thee the shores and sounding seas
Wash far away, where'er thy bones are hurled;
Whether beyond the ſtormy Hebrides,
Where thou perhaps under the whelming tide,
Visit'ſt the bottom of the monſtrous world;
Or whether thou, to our moiſt vows denied,
Sleep'ſt by the fable of Bellerus old,
Where the great Vision of the guarded mount
Looks toward Namancos and Bayona's hold.
Look homeward, Angel, now, and melt with ruth:
And, O ye dolphins, waft the hapless youth.

   Weep no more, woeful shepherds, weep no more,
For Lycidas, your sorrow, is not dead,
Sunk though he be beneath the watery floor.
So sinks the day-ſtar in the ocean bed,
And yet anon repairs his drooping head,
And tricks his beams, and with new-spangled ore
Flames in the forehead of the morning sky:
So Lycidas sunk low, but mounted high,
Through the dear might of Him that walked the waves,
Where, other groves and other ſtreams along,
With nectar pure his oozy locks he laves,
And hears the unexpressive nuptial song,
In the bleſt kingdoms meek of joy and love.
There entertain him all the Saints above,
In solemn troops, and sweet societies,
That sing, and singing in their glory move,
And wipe the tears for ever from his eyes.

Now, Lycidas, the shepherds weep no more;
Henceforth thou art the Genius of the shore,
In thy large recompense, and shalt be good
To all that wander in that perilous flood.

Thus sang the uncouth swain to the oaks and rills,
While the still morn went out with sandals gray;
He touched the tender stops of various quills,
With eager thought warbling his Doric lay:
And now the sun had stretched out all the hills,
And now was dropped into the western bay.
At last he rose, and twitched his mantle blue:
To-morrow to fresh woods, and pastures new.

ON HIS HAVING ARRIVED AT THE AGE OF TWENTY-THREE

How soon hath Time, the subtle thief of youth,
Stolen on his wing my three-and-twentieth year!
My hasting days fly on with full career,
But my late spring no bud or blossow shew'th.
Perhaps my semblance might deceive the truth
That I to manhood am arrived so near;
And inward ripeness doth much less appear,
That some more timely-happy spirits endu'th.
Yet, be it less or more, or soon or slow,
It shall be still in strictest measure even
To that same lot, however mean or high,
Toward which Time leads me, and the will of Heaven.
All is, if I have grace to use it so,
As ever in my great Task-Master's eye.

TO MR. H. LAWES ON HIS AIRS

Harry, whose tuneful and well-measured song
  First taught our English music how to span
  Words with just note and accent, not to scan
With Midas' ears, committing short and long,

Thy word and skill exempts thee from the throng,
  With praise enough for Envy to look wan;
  To after age thou shalt be writ the man
  That with smooth air couldst humor best our tongue.
Thou honor'st Verse, and Verse must lend her wing
  To honor thee, the priest of Phœbus' quire,
  That tunest their happiest lines in hymn or story.
Dante shall give Fame leave to set thee higher
  Than his Casella, whom he wooed to sing,
  Met in the milder shades of Purgatory.

TO MR. LAWRENCE

Lawrence, of virtuous father virtuous son,
  Now that the fields are dank, and ways are mire,
  Where shall we sometimes meet, and by the fire
  Help waste a sullen day, what may be won
From the hard season gaining? Time will run
  On smoother, till Favonius reinspire
  The frozen earth, and clothe in fresh attire
  The lily and rose, that neither sowed nor spun.
What neat repast shall feast us, light and choice,
  Of Attic taste, with wine, whence we may rise
  To hear the lute well touched or artful voice
Warble immortal notes and Tuscan air?
  He who of those delights can judge, and spare
  To interpose them oft, is not unwise.

✗ ON HIS BLINDNESS

When I consider how my light is spent
Ere half my days in this dark world and wide,
And that one talent which is death to hide
Lodged with me useless, though my soul more bent
To serve therewith my Maker, and present
My true account, lest He returning chide,
"Doth God exact day-labor, light denied?"
I fondly ask. But Patience, to prevent
That murmur, soon replies, "God doth not need

Either man's work or his own gifts. Who best
Bear his mild yoke, they serve him best. His state
Is kingly: thousands at his bidding speed,
And post o'er land and ocean without rest;
They also serve who only stand and wait."

ON THE LATE MASSACRE IN PIEDMONT

Avenge, O Lord, thy slaughtered saints, whose bones
Lie scattered on the Alpine mountains cold;
Even them who kept thy truth so pure of old,
When all our fathers worshiped stocks and stones,
Forget not: in thy book record their groans
Who were thy sheep, and in their ancient fold
Slain by the bloody Piedmontese, that rolled
Mother with infant down the rocks. Their moans
The vales redoubled to the hills, and they
To heaven. Their martyred blood and ashes sow
O'er all the Italian fields, where still doth sway
The triple Tyrant; that from these may grow
A hundredfold, who, having learnt thy way,
Early may fly the Babylonian woe.

Sir John Suckling

1609–1642

WHY SO PALE AND WAN?

From Aglaura

Why so pale and wan, fond lover?
   Prithee, why so pale?
Will, when looking well can't move her,
   Looking ill prevail?
   Prithee, why so pale?

Why so dull and mute, young sinner?
   Prithee, why so mute?
Will, when speaking well can't win her,
   Saying nothing do 't?
   Prithee, why so mute?

. Quit, quit for shame! This will not move;
　　This cannot take her.
If of herself she will not love,
　　Nothing can make her:
　　The devil take her!

✕ THE CONSTANT LOVER

OUT upon it, I have loved
　　Three whole days together!
And am like to love three more,
　　If it prove fair weather.

Time shall moult away his wings,
　　Ere he shall discover
In the whole wide world again
　　Such a constant lover.

But the spite on 't is, no praise
　　Is due at all to me:
Love with me had made no stays,
　　Had it any been but she.

Had it any been but she,
　　And that very face,
There had been at least ere this
　　A dozen dozen in her place.

Richard Lovelace

1618–1658

TO LUCASTA, ON GOING TO THE WARS

TELL me not, sweet, I am unkind,
　　That from the nunnery
Of thy chaste breast and quiet mind
　　To war and arms I fly.

True, a new mistress now I chase,
　　The first foe in the field;
And with a stronger faith embrace
　　A sword, a horse, a shield.

Yet this inconstancy is such
  As thou too shalt adore;
I could not love thee, dear, so much,
  Loved I not honor more.

TO ALTHEA, FROM PRISON

WHEN Love with unconfinèd wings
  Hovers within my gates,
And my divine Althea brings
  To whisper at the grates;
When I lie tangled in her hair
  And fettered to her eye,
The birds that wanton in the air
  Know no such liberty.

When flowing cups run swiftly round
  With no allaying Thames,
Our careless heads with roses bound,
  Our hearts with loyal flames;
When thirsty grief in wine we steep,
  When healths and draughts go free,
Fishes that tipple in the deep
  Know no such liberty.

When, like committed linnets, I
  With shriller throat shall sing
The sweetness, mercy, majesty,
  And glories of my king;
When I shall voice aloud how good
  He is, how great should be,
Enlarged winds, that curl the flood,
  Know no such liberty.

Stone walls do not a prison make,
  Nor iron bars a cage;
Minds innocent and quiet take
  That for an hermitage;

If I have freedom in my love,
    And in my soul am free,
Angels alone, that soar above,
    Enjoy such liberty.

Andrew Marvell

1621–1678

THE GARDEN

How vainly men themselves amaze,
To win the palm, the oak, or bays,
And their incessant labors see
Crowned from some single herb or tree
Whose short and narrow-vergèd shade
Does prudently their toils upbraid,
While all the flowers and trees do close
To weave the garlands of repose!

Fair quiet, have I found thee here,
And Innocence, thy sister dear?
Mistaken long, I sought you then
In busy companies of men.
Your sacred plants, if here below,
Only among the plants will grow;
Society is all but rude
To this delicious solitude.

No white nor red was ever seen
So amorous as this lovely green.
Fond lovers, cruel as their flame,
Cut in these trees their mistress' name.
Little, alas! they know or heed,
How far these beauties hers exceed!
Fair trees! wheres'e'er your bark I wound,
No name shall but your own be found.

When we have run our passion's heat,
Love hither makes his best retreat.
The gods, that mortal beauty chase,
Still in a tree did end their race;

Apollo hunted Daphne so,
Only that she might laurel grow;
And Pan did after Syrinx speed,
Not as a nymph, but for a reed.

What wondrous life is this I lead!
Ripe apples drop about my head;
The luscious clusters of the vine
Upon my mouth do crush their wine;
The nectarine, and curious peach,
Into my hands themselves do reach;
Stumbling on melons, as I pass,
Insnared with flowers, I fall on grass.

Meanwhile the mind, from pleasure less,
Withdraws into its happiness;—
The mind, that ocean where each kind
Does straight its own resemblance find;
Yet it creates, transcending these,
Far other worlds, and other seas,
Annihilating all that's made
To a green thought in a green shade.

Here at the fountain's sliding foot,
Or at some fruit-tree's mossy root,
Casting the body's vest aside,
My soul into the boughs does glide:
There, like a bird, it sits and sings,
Then whets and combs its silver wings,
And, till prepared for longer flight,
Waves in its plumes the various light.

Such was that happy garden-state,
While man there walked without a mate:
After a place so pure and sweet,
What other help could yet be meet!
But 'twas beyond a mortal's share
To wander solitary there:
Two paradises 'twere in one,
To live in paradise alone.

How well the skillful gardener drew
Of flowers, and herbs, this dial new;
Where, from above, the milder sun
Does through a fragrant zodiac run,
And, as it works, the industrious bee
Computes its time as well as we!
How could such sweet and wholesome hours
Be reckoned but with herbs and flowers?

TO HIS COY MISTRESS

Had we but world enough, and time,
This coyness, lady, were no crime.
We would sit down, and think which way
To walk, and pass our long love's day.
Thou by the Indian Ganges' side
Shouldst rubies find: I by the tide
Of Humber would complain. I would
Love you ten years before the flood,
And you should, if you please, refuse
Till the conversion of the Jews;
My vegetable love should grow
Vaster than empires and more slow;
An hundred years should go to praise
Thine eyes, and on thy forehead gaze;
Two hundred to adore each breast,
But thirty thousand to the rest;
An age at least to every part,
And the last age should show your heart.
For, lady, you deserve this state,
Nor would I love at lower rate.
   But at my back I always hear
Time's wingèd chariot hurrying near,
And yonder all before us lie
Deserts of vast eternity.
Thy beauty shall no more be found,
Nor, in thy marble vault, shall sound
My echoing song; then worms shall try
That long-preserved virginity,

And your quaint honor turn to dust,
And into ashes all my lust:
The grave's a fine and private place,
But none, I think, do there embrace.
  Now, therefore, while the youthful hue
Sits on thy skin like morning dew,
And while thy willing soul transpires
At every pore with instant fires,
Now let us sport us while we may,
And now, like amorous birds of prey,
Rather at once our time devour,
Than languish in his slow-chapped power.
Let us roll all our strength and all
Our sweetness up into one ball,
And tear our pleasures with rough strife
Through the iron gates of life;
Thus, though we cannot make our sun
Stand still, yet we will make him run.

Henry Vaughan

1622–1695

THE RETREAT

Happy those early days, when I
Shined in my angel-infancy!
Before I understood this place
Appointed for my second race,
Or taught my soul to fancy aught
But a white, celestial thought;
When yet I had not walked above
A mile or two from my first love,
And looking back—at that short space—
Could see a glimpse of his bright face;
When on some gilded cloud or flower
My gazing soul would dwell an hour,
And in those weaker glories spy
Some shadows of eternity;
Before I taught my tongue to wound
My conscience with a sinful sound.

Or had the black art to dispense
A several sin to every sense,
But felt through all this fleshly dress
Bright shoots of everlastingness.

  O, how I long to travel back,
And tread again that ancient track!
That I might once more reach that plain,
Where first I left my glorious train;
From whence the enlightened spirit sees
That shady city of palm trees.
But ah! my soul with too much stay
Is drunk, and staggers in the way!
Some men a forward motion love,
But I by backward steps would move;
And when this dust falls to the urn,
In that state I came, return.

John Dryden

1631–1700

TO THE MEMORY OF MR. OLDHAM

Farewell, too little, and too lately known,
Whom I began to think and call my own:
For sure our souls were near allied, and thine
Cast in the same poetic mold with mine.
One common note on either lyre did strike,
And knaves and fools we both abhorr'd alike.
To the same goal did both our studies drive;
The last set out the soonest did arrive.
Thus Nisus fell upon the slippery place,
While his young friend perform'd and won the race.
O early ripe! to thy abundant store
What could advancing age have added more?
It might (what nature never gives the young)
Have taught the numbers of thy native tongue.
But satire needs not those, and wit will shine
Thro' the harsh cadence of a rugged line:
A noble error, and but seldom made,
When poets are by too much force betray'd.

Thy generous fruits, tho' gather'd ere their prime,
Still shew'd a quickness; and maturing time
But mellows what we write to the dull sweets of
    rhyme.
Once more, hail and farewell; farewell, thou young,
But ah too short, Marcellus of our tongue;
Thy brows with ivy, and with laurels bound;
But fate and gloomy night encompass thee around.

SONG

From AMPHITRYON

FAIR Iris I love, and hourly I die,
But not for a lip, nor a languishing eye:
She's fickle and false, and there we agree,
For I am as false and as fickle as she.
We neither believe what either can say;
And, neither believing, we neither betray.
'Tis civil to swear, and say things of course;
We mean not the taking for better or worse.
When present, we love; when absent, agree:
I think not of Iris, nor Iris of me.
The legend of love no couple can find,
So easy to part, or so equally join'd.

SONG

From SECRET LOVE

I FEED a flame within, which so torments me,
That it both pains my heart, and yet contents me:
'Tis such a pleasing smart, and I so love it,
That I had rather die than once remove it.

Yet he for whom I grieve shall never know it;
My tongue does not betray, nor my eyes show it:
Not a sigh, not a tear, my pain discloses,
But they fall silently, like dew on roses.

Thus to prevent my love from being cruel,
My heart's the sacrifice, as 't is the fuel:

And while I suffer this, to give him quiet,
My faith rewards my love, tho' he deny it.

On his eyes will I gaze, and there delight me;
Where I conceal my love, no frown can fright me:
To be more happy, I dare not aspire;
Nor can I fall more low, mounting no higher.

A SONG FOR ST. CECILIA'S DAY

1687

FROM harmony, from heavenly harmony
    This universal frame began:
  When Nature underneath a heap
    Of jarring atoms lay
  And could not heave her head,
The tuneful voice was heard from high,
    "Arise, ye more than dead!"
Then cold and hot and moist and dry
In order to their stations leap,
    And Music's power obey.
From harmony, from heavenly harmony
    This universal frame began:
    From harmony to harmony
Through all the compass of the notes it ran,
The diapason closing full in man.

What passion cannot Music raise and quell?
    When Jubal struck the chorded shell,
  His listening brethren stood around,
  And, wondering, on their faces fell
  To worship that celestial sound:
Less than a god they thought there could not dwell
    Within the hollow of that shell
    That spoke so sweetly and so well.
What passion cannot Music raise and quell?

  The trumpet's loud clangor
    Excites us to arms,

With shrill notes of anger
   And mortal alarms.
The double double double beat
   Of the thundering drum
   Cries "Hark! the foes come;
Charge, charge! 'tis too late to retreat!"

The soft complaining flute
   In dying notes discovers
   The woes of hopeless lovers,
Whose dirge is whispered by the warbling lute.

   Sharp violins proclaim
Their jealous pangs and desperation,
Fury, frantic indignation,
Depth of pain, and height of passion
   For the fair disdainful dame.

But oh! what art can teach,
What human voice can reach
   The sacred organ's praise?
Notes inspiring holy love,
Notes that wing their heavenly ways
   To mend the choirs above.

Orpheus could lead the savage race,
And trees unrooted left their place,
   Sequacious of the lyre:
But bright Cecilia raised the wonder higher:
When to her organ vocal breath was given,
An angel heard, and straight appeared—
   Mistaking earth for heaven.

Grand Chorus

As from the power of sacred lays
   The spheres began to move,
And sung the great Creator's praise
   To all the blest above;
So when the last and dreadful hour
This crumbling pageant shall devour,

The trumpet shall be heard on high,
The dead shall live, the living die,
And Music shall untune the sky.

CHARACTERS FROM THE SATIRES

ACHITOPHEL

OF these the false Achitophel was first,
A name to all succeeding ages curst;
For close designs and crooked counsels fit,
Sagacious, bold, and turbulent of wit,
Restless, unfixed in principles and place,
In power unpleased, impatient of disgrace;
A fiery soul, which working out its way,
Fretted the pigmy body to decay
And o'er-informed the tenement of clay.
A daring pilot in extremity,
Pleased with the danger, when the waves went high,
He sought the storms; but, for a calm unfit,
Would steer too nigh the sands to boast his wit.
Great wits are sure to madness near allied
And thin partitions do their bounds divide;
Else, why should he, with wealth and honor blest,
Refuse his age the needful hours of rest?
Punish a body which he could not please,
Bankrupt of life, yet prodigal of ease?
And all to leave what with his toil he won
To that unfeathered two-legged thing, a son,
Got, while his soul did huddled notions try,
And born a shapeless lump, like anarchy.
In friendship false, implacable in hate,
Resolved to ruin or to rule the state;
To compass this the triple bond he broke,
The pillars of the public safety shook,
And fitted Israel for a foreign yoke;
Then, seized with fear, yet still affecting fame,
Usurped a patriot's all-atoning name.
So easy still it proves in factious times
With public zeal to cancel private crimes.

Zimri

Some of their chiefs were princes of the land;
In the first rank of these did Zimri stand,
A man so various that he seemed to be
Not one, but all mankind's epitome;
Stiff in opinions, always in the wrong,
Was everything by starts and nothing long;
But in the course of one revolving moon
Was chymist, fiddler, statesman, and buffoon;
Then all for women, painting, rhyming, drinking,
Besides ten thousand freaks that died in thinking.
Blest madman, who could every hour employ
With something new to wish or to enjoy!
Railing and praising were his usual themes,
And both, to show his judgment, in extremes:
So over violent or over civil
That every man with him was God or Devil.
In squandering wealth was his peculiar art;
Nothing went unrewarded but desert.
Beggared by fools whom still he found too late,
He had his jest, and they had his estate.
He laughed himself from Court; then sought relief
By forming parties, but could ne'er be chief:
For spite of him, the weight of business fell
On Absalom and wise Achitophel;
Thus wicked but in will, of means bereft,
He left not faction, but of that was left.

Og and Doeg

And hasten Og and Doeg to rehearse,
Two fools that crutch their feeble sense on verse,
Who by my Muse to all succeeding times
Shall live in spite of their own dogrel rhymes.
Doeg, though without knowing how or why,
Made still a blundering kind of melody;
Spurred boldly on, and dashed through thick and thin.
Through sense and nonsense, never out nor in;

Free from all meaning, whether good or bad,
And, in one word, heroically mad,
He was too warm on picking-work to dwell,
But faggoted his notions as they fell,
And, if they rhymed and rattled, all was well.
Spiteful he is not, though he wrote a satire,
For still there goes some thinking to ill-nature;
He needs no more than birds and beasts to think,
All his occasions are to eat and drink.
If he call rogue and rascal from a garret,
He means you no more mischief than a parrot;
The words for friend and foe alike were made,
To fetter them in verse is all his trade. . . .
Railing in other men may be a crime,
But ought to pass for mere instinct in him;
Instinct he follows and no farther knows,
For to write verse with him is to *transprose;*

'Twere pity treason at his door to lay
Who makes heaven's gate a lock to its own key;
Let him rail on, let his invective Muse
Have four and twenty letters to abuse,
Which if he jumbles to one line of sense,
Indict him of a capital offence.
In fire-works give him leave to vent his spite,
Those are the only serpents he can write;
The height of his ambition is, we know,
But to be master of a puppet-show;
On that one stage his works may yet appear,
And a month's harvest keeps him all the year.

    Now stop your noses, readers, all and some,
For here's a tun of midnight work to come,
Og from a treason-tavern rolling home.
Round as a globe, and liquored every chink,
Goodly and great he sails behind his link.
With all this bulk there's nothing lost in Og,
For every inch that is not fool is rogue: . . .
When wine has given him courage to blaspheme,
He curses God, but God before cursed him;

And if man could have reason, none has more,
That made his paunch so rich and him so poor.
With wealth he was not trusted, for Heaven knew
What 'twas of old to pamper up a Jew;
To what would he on quail and pheasant swell
That even on tripe and carrion could rebel?
But though Heaven made him poor, with reverence
    speaking,
He never was a poet of God's making;
The midwife laid her hand on his thick skull,
With this prophetic blessing—*Be thou dull;*
Drink, swear, and roar, forbear no lewd delight
Fit for thy bulk, do anything but write.
Thou art of lasting make, like thoughtless men,
A strong nativity—but for the pen;
Eat opium, mingle arsenic in thy drink,
Still thou mayest live, avoiding pen and ink.
I see, I see, 'tis counsel given in vain,
For treason, botched in rhyme, will be thy bane;
Rhyme is the rock on which thou art to wreck,
'Tis fatal to thy fame and to thy neck.
Why should thy meter good king David blast?
A psalm of his will surely be thy last.
Darest thou presume in verse to meet thy foes,
Thou whom the penny pamphlet foiled in prose?
Doeg, whom God for mankind's mirth has made,
O'ertops thy talent in thy very trade;
Doeg to thee, thy paintings are so coarse,
A poet is, though he's the poet's horse.
A double noose thou on thy neck dost pull
For writing treason and for writing dull;
To die for faction is a common evil,
But to be hanged for nonsense is the devil.
Hadst thou the glories of thy King exprest,
Thy praises had been satires at the best;
But thou in clumsy verse, unlicked, unpointed,
Hast shamefully defied the Lord's anointed:
I will not rake the dunghill of thy crimes,
For who would read thy life that reads thy rhymes?

But of king David's foes be this the doom,
May all be like the young man Absalom;
And for my foes may this their blessing be,
To talk like Doeg and to write like thee.

Sir Charles Sedley

1639?–1701

TO CELIA

Not, Celia, that I juster am,
　　Or better than the rest!
For I would change each hour like them,
　　Were not my heart at rest.

But I am tied to very thee
　　By every thought I have;
Thy face I only care to see,
　　Thy heart I only crave.

All that in woman is adored
　　In thy dear self I find;
For the whole sex can but afford
　　The handsome and the kind.

Why then should I seek further store
　　And still make love anew?
When change itself can give no more,
　　'Tis easy to be true.

Matthew Prior

1664–1721

A BETTER ANSWER

Dear Chloe, how blubbered is that pretty face!
　　Thy cheek all on fire, and thy hair all uncurled!
Prithee quit this caprice, and (as old Falstaff says)
　　Let us e'en talk a little like folks of this world.

How canst thou presume thou hast leave to destroy
   The beauties which Venus but lent to thy keeping?
Those looks were designed to inspire love and joy;
   More ordinary eyes may serve people for weeping.

To be vexed at a trifle or two that I writ,
   Your judgment at once and my passion you wrong;
You take that for fact which will scarce be found wit:
   Od's life! must one swear to the truth of a song?

What I speak, my fair Chloe, and what I write, shows
   The difference there is betwixt nature and art:
I court others in verse, but I love thee in prose;
   And they have my whimsies, but thou hast my heart.

The god of us verse-men (you know, child), the sun,
   How after his journeys he sets up his rest;
If at morning o'er earth 'tis his fancy to run,
   At night he reclines on his Thetis's breast.

So when I am wearied with wandering all day,
   To thee, my delight, in the evening I come:
No matter what beauties I saw in my way;
   They were but my visits, but thou art my home.

Then finish, dear Chloe, this pastoral war,
   And let us like Horace and Lydia agree;
For thou art a girl as much brighter than her
   As he was a poet sublimer than me.

AN ODE

THE merchant, to secure his treasure,
   Conveys it in a borrowed name:
Euphelia serves to grace my measure,
   But Chloe is my real flame.

My softest verse, my darling lyre
   Upon Euphelia's toilet lay,
When Chloe noted her desire
   That I should sing, that I should play.

My lyre I tune, my voice I raise;
  But with my numbers mix my sighs;
And whilst I sing Euphelia's praise,
  I fix my soul on Chloe's eyes.

Fair Chloe blushed, Euphelia frowned,
  I sung and gazed, I played and trembled:
And Venus to the Loves around
  Remarked how ill we all dissembled.

Joseph Addison

1672–1719

HYMN

The spacious firmament on high,
With all the blue ethereal sky,
And spangled heavens, a shining frame,
Their great Original proclaim.
The unwearied Sun from day to day
Does his Creator's power display;
And publishes to every land
The work of an Almighty hand.

Soon as the evening shades prevail,
The Moon takes up the wondrous tale;
And nightly to the listening Earth
Repeats the story of her birth:
Whilst all the stars that round her burn,
And all the planets in their turn,
Confirm the tidings as they roll,
And spread the truth from pole to pole.

What though in solemn silence all
Move round the dark terrestrial ball;
What though nor real voice nor sound
Amidst their radiant orbs be found?
In Reason's ear they all rejoice,
And utter forth a glorious voice;
Forever singing as they shine,
"The Hand that made us is divine."

Alexander Pope

1688–1744

ODE ON SOLITUDE

HAPPY the man whose wish and care
  A few paternal acres bound,
Content to breathe his native air
    In his own ground.

Whose herds with milk, whose fields with bread,
  Whose flocks supply him with attire,
Whose trees in summer yield him shade,
    In winter fire.

Bless'd who can unconcern'dly find
  Hours, days, and years slide soft away,
In health of body, peace of mind,
    Quiet by day;

Sound sleep by night: study and ease
  Together mix'd; sweet recreation;
And innocence, which most does please,
    With Meditation.

Thus let me live, unseen, unknown,
  Thus unlamented let me die;
Steal from the world, and not a stone
    Tell where I lie.

CHARACTERS FROM THE SATIRES

ATTICUS

PEACE to all such! but were there one whose fires
True genius kindles, and fair fame inspires;
Blest with each talent, and each art to please,
And born to write, converse, and live with ease,
Should such a man, too fond to rule alone,
Bear, like the Turk, no brother near the throne,

View him with scornful, yet with jealous eyes,
And hate for arts that caused himself to rise;
Damn with faint praise, assent with civil leer,
And, without sneering, teach the rest to sneer;
Willing to wound, and yet afraid to strike,
Just hint a fault, and hesitate dislike;
Alike reserved to blame, or to commend,
A timorous foe, and a suspicious friend;
Dreading e'en fools, by flatterers besieged,
And so obliging, that he ne'er obliged;
Like Cato, give his little senate laws,
And sit attentive to his own applause:
While wits and Templars every sentence raise.
And wonder with a foolish face of praise—
Who but must laugh, if such a man there be?
Who would not weep, if Atticus were he?

SPORUS

Let Sporus tremble—— What? that thing of silk,
Sporus, that mere white curd of ass's milk?
Satire or sense, alas! can Sporus feel,
Who breaks a butterfly upon a wheel?
Yet let me flap this bug with gilded wings,
This painted child of dirt, that stinks and stings;
Whose buzz the witty and the fair annoys,
Yet wit ne'er tastes, and beauty ne'er enjoys:
So well-bred spaniels civilly delight
In mumbling of the game they dare not bite.
Eternal smiles his emptiness betray,
As shallow streams run dimpling all the way.
Whether in florid impotence he speaks,
And, as the prompter breathes, the puppet squeaks;
Or at the ear of Eve, familiar toad!
Half froth, half venom, spits himself abroad,
In puns, or politics, or tales, or lies,
Or spite, or smut, or rhymes, or blasphemies.
His wit all see-saw, between that and this,
Now high, now low, now master up, now miss,

And he himself one vile antithesis.
Amphibious thing! that acting either part,
The trifling head, or the corrupted heart;
Fop at the toilet, flatterer at the board,
Now trips a lady, and now struts a lord.
Eve's temper thus the Rabbins have express'd,
A cherub's face, a reptile all the rest.
Beauty that shocks you, parts that none will trust,
Wit that can creep, and pride that licks the dust.

WHARTON

WHARTON! the scorn and wonder of our days,
Whose ruling passion was the lust of praise:
Born with whate'er could win it from the wise,
Women and fools must like him, or he dies:
Though wondering senates hung on all he spoke,
The club must hail him master of the joke.
Shall parts so various aim at nothing new?
He'll shine a Tully and a Wilmot too.
Then turns repentant, and his God adores
With the same spirit that he drinks and whores;
Enough if all around him but admire,
And now the punk applaud, and now the friar.
Thus with each gift of Nature and of art,
And wanting nothing but an honest heart;
Grown all to all, from no one vice exempt,
And most contemptible, to shun contempt;
His passion still, to covet general praise,
His life, to forfeit it a thousand ways;
A constant bounty which no friend has made;
An angel tongue, which no man can persuade;
A fool, with more of wit than half mankind,
Too rash for thought, for action too refined;
A tyrant to the wife his heart approves;
A rebel to the very king he loves;
He dies, sad outcast of each Church and State,
And, harder still! flagitious, yet not great.
Ask you why WHARTON broke through every rule?
'Twas all for fear the knaves should call him fool.

CHLOE

"Yet Chloe sure was form'd without a spot."—
Nature in her then err'd not, but forgot.
"With every pleasing, every prudent part,
Say, what can Chloe want?"—She wants a heart.
She speaks, behaves, and acts, just as she ought,
But never, never reached one generous thought.
Virtue she finds too painful an endeavor,
Content to dwell in decencies for ever.
So very reasonable, so unmoved,
As never yet to love, or to be loved.
She, while her lover pants upon her breast,
Can mark the figures on an Indian chest;
And when she sees her friend in deep despair,
Observes how much a chintz exceeds mohair!
Forbid it, Heaven, a favor or a debt
She e'er should cancel—but she may forget.
Safe is your secret still in Chloe's ear;
But none of Chloe's shall you ever hear.
Of all her dears she never slander'd one,
But cares not if a thousand are undone.
Would Chloe know if you're alive or dead?
She bids her footman put it in her head.
Chloe is prudent—would you too be wise?
Then never break your heart when Chloe dies.

Henry Carey

1693?–1743

SALLY IN OUR ALLEY

Of all the girls that are so smart
    There's none like pretty Sally;
She is the darling of my heart,
    And she lives in our alley.
There is no lady in the land
    Is half so sweet as Sally;
She is the darling of my heart,
    And she lives in our alley.

Her father he makes cabbage-nets
    And through the ſtreets does cry 'em;
Her mother she sells laces long
    To such as please to buy 'em:
But sure such folks could ne'er beget
    So sweet a girl as Sally!
She is the darling of my heart,
    And she lives in our alley.

When she is by, I leave my work,
    I love her so sincerely;
My maſter comes like any Turk,
    And bangs me moſt severely:
But let him bang his bellyful,
    I'll bear it all for Sally;
She is the darling of my heart,
    And she lives in our alley.

Of all the days that's in the week
    I dearly love but one day—
And that's the day that comes betwixt
    A Saturday and Monday;
For then I'm dreſt all in my beſt
    To walk abroad with Sally;
She is the darling of my heart,
    And she lives in our alley.

My maſter carries me to church,
    And often am I blamèd
Because I leave him in the lurch
    As soon as text is namèd;
I leave the church in sermon-time
    And slink away to Sally;
She is the darling of my heart,
    And she lives in our alley.

When Chriſtmas comes about again,
    O then I shall have money;
I'll board it up, and, box and all,
    I'll give it to my honey:

I would it were ten thousand pound,
   I'd give it all to Sally;
She is the darling of my heart,
   And she lives in our alley.

My master and the neighbors all
   Make game of me and Sally,
And, but for her, I'd better be
   A slave and row a galley;
But when my seven long years are out
   O then I'll marry Sally,—
O then we'll wed, and then we'll bed,
   But not in our alley!

William Shenstone

1714–1763

WRITTEN AT AN INN AT HENLEY

To thee, fair freedom! I retire
   From flattery, cards, and dice, and din;
Nor art thou found in mansions higher
   Than the low cot or humble inn.

'Tis here with boundless power I reign;
   And every health which I begin
Converts dull port to bright champagne;
   Such freedom crowns it, at an inn.

I fly from pomp, I fly from plate!
   I fly from falsehood's specious grin!
Freedom I love, and form I hate,
   And choose my lodgings at an inn.

Here, waiter! take my sordid ore,
   Which lacqueys else might hope to win;
It buys, what courts have not in store,
   It buys me freedom at an inn.

Whoe'er has traveled life's dull round,
   Where'er his stages may have been,
May sigh to think he still has found
   The warmest welcome at an inn.

Thomas Gray

1716–1771

x ELEGY

WRITTEN IN A COUNTRY CHURCH-YARD

THE Curfew tolls the knell of parting day,
  The lowing herd winds slowly o'er the lea,
The plowman homeward plods his weary way,
  And leaves the world to darkness and to me.

Now fades the glimmering landscape on the sight,
  And all the air a solemn ſtillness holds,
Save where the beetle wheels his droning flight,
  And drowsy tinklings lull the diſtant folds;

Save that from yonder ivy-mantled tower
  The moping owl does to the moon complain
Of such as, wandering near her secret bower,
  Moleſt her ancient solitary reign.

Beneath those rugged elms, that yew-tree's shade,
  Where heaves the turf in many a moldering heap,
Each in his narrow cell for ever laid,
  The rude Forefathers of the hamlet sleep.

The breezy call of incense-breathing Morn,
  The swallow twittering from the ſtraw-built shed,
The cock's shrill clarion, or the echoing horn,
  No more shall rouse them from their lowly bed.

For them no more the blazing hearth shall burn,
  Or busy housewife ply her evening care:
No children run to lisp their sire's return,
  Or climb his knees the envied kiss to share.

Oft did the harveſt to their sickle yield,
  Their furrow oft the ſtubborn glebe has broke;
How jocund did they drive their team afield!
  How bowed the woods beneath their ſturdy ſtroke.

Let not Ambition mock their useful toil,
  Their homely joys, and destiny obscure;
Nor Grandeur hear with a disdainful smile
  The short and simple annals of the poor.

The boast of heraldry, the pomp of power,
  And all that beauty, all that wealth e'er gave,
Await alike the inevitable hour.
  The paths of glory lead but to the grave.

Nor you, ye Proud, impute to These the fault,
  If Memory o'er their Tomb no Trophies raise,
Where through the long-drawn isle and fretted vault
  The pealing anthem swells the note of praise.

Can storied urn or animated bust
  Back to its mansion call the fleeting breath?
Can Honor's voice provoke the silent dust,
  Or Flattery soothe the dull cold ear of Death?

Perhaps in this neglected spot is laid
  Some heart once pregnant with celestial fire;
Hands, that the rod of empire might have swayed,
  Or waked to ecstasy the living lyre.

But Knowledge to their eyes her ample page
  Rich with the spoils of time did ne'er unroll;
Chill Penury repressed their noble rage,
  And froze the genial current of the soul.

Full many a gem of purest ray serene,
  The dark unfathomed caves of ocean bear:
Full many a flower is born to blush unseen,
  And waste its sweetness on the desert air.

Some village Hampden, that with dauntless breast
  The little tyrant of his fields withstood,
Some mute inglorious Milton here may rest,
  Some Cromwell guiltless of his country's blood.

The applause of listening senates to command,
  The threats of pain and ruin to despise,
To scatter plenty o'er a smiling land,
  And read their history in a nation's eyes,

Their lot forbade: nor circumscribed alone
  Their growing virtues, but their crimes confined;
Forbade to wade through slaughter to a throne,
  And shut the gates of mercy on mankind,

The struggling pangs of conscious truth to hide,
  To quench the blushes of ingenuous shame,
Or heap the shrine of Luxury and Pride
  With incense kindled at the Muse's flame.

Far from the madding crowd's ignoble strife,
  Their sober wishes never learned to stray;
Along the cool sequestered vale of life
  They kept the noiseless tenor of their way.

Yet even these bones from insult to protect,
  Some frail memorial still erected nigh,
With uncouth rhymes and shapeless sculpture decked,
  Implores the passing tribute of a sigh.

Their name, their years, spelt by the unlettered muse,
  The place of fame and elegy supply;
And many a holy text around she strews,
  That teach the rustic moralist to die.

For who, to dumb Forgetfulness a prey,
  This pleasing anxious being e'er resigned,
Left the warm precincts of the cheerful day,
  Nor cast one longing lingering look behind?

On some fond breast the parting soul relies,
  Some pious drops the closing eye requires;
Even from the tomb the voice of Nature cries,
  Even in our ashes live their wonted fires.

For thee, who mindful of the unhonored dead
  Dost in these lines their artless tale relate;
If chance, by lonely contemplation led,
  Some kindred spirit shall inquire thy fate,—

Haply some hoary-headed swain may say,
  "Oft have we seen him at the peep of dawn
Brushing with hasty steps the dews away
  To meet the sun upon the upland lawn.

"There at the foot of yonder nodding beech
  That wreathes its old fantastic roots so high,
His listless length at noontide would he stretch,
  And pore upon the brook that babbles by.

"Hard by yon wood, now smiling as in scorn,
  Muttering his wayward fancies he would rove,
Now drooping, woeful-wan, like one forlorn,
  Or crazed with care, or crossed in hopeless love.

"One morn I missed him on the customed hill,
  Along the heath, and near his favorite tree;
Another came; nor yet beside the rill,
  Nor up the lawn, nor at the wood was he;

"The next, with dirges due in sad array
  Slow through the church-way path we saw him
    borne.—
Approach and read (for thou canst read) the lay,
  Graved on the stone beneath yon aged thorn."

(THE EPITAPH)

Here rests his head upon the lap of Earth
  A Youth to Fortune and to Fame unknown.
Fair Science frowned not on his humble birth,
  And Melancholy marked him for her own.

Large was his bounty, and his soul sincere,
  Heaven did a recompense as largely send:
He gave to Misery all he had, a tear,
  He gained from Heaven ('twas all he wished) a
    friend.

No farther seek his merits to disclose,
  Or draw his frailties from their dread abode
(There they alike in trembling hope repose),
  The bosom of his Father and his God.

William Collins

1721-1759

ODE TO EVENING

If aught of oaten stop, or pastoral song,
May hope, chaste Eve, to soothe thy modest ear,
  Like thy own solemn springs,
  Thy springs and dying gales,

O nymph reserved, while now the bright-haired sun
Sits in yon western tent, whose cloudy skirts,
  With brede ethereal wove,
  O'erhang his wavy bed:

Now air is hushed, save where the weak-eyed bat,
With short shrill shriek, flits by on leathern wing,
  Or where the beetle winds
  His small but sullen horn,

As oft he rises 'midst the twilight path,
Against the pilgrim borne in heedless hum:
  Now teach me, maid composed,
  To breathe some softened strain,

Whose numbers, stealing through thy darkening vale
May not unseemly with its stillness suit,
  As, musing slow, I hail
  Thy genial loved return!

For when thy folding-star arising shows
His paly circlet, at his warning lamp
  The fragrant Hours, the elves
  Who slept in buds the day,

And many a nymph who wreathes her brows with
    sedge,
And sheds the freshening dew, and, lovelier still
  The pensive Pleasures sweet,
  Prepare thy shadowy ear:

Then lead, calm votaress, where some sheety lake
Cheers the lone heath, or some time-hallowed pile
  Or upland fallows gray
  Reflect its last cool gleam.

Of if chill blustering winds, or driving rain,
Forbid my willing feet, be mine the hut
  That from the mountain's side
  Views wilds, and swelling floods,

And hamlets brown, and dim-discovered spires,
And hears their simple bell, and marks o'er all
  Thy dewy fingers draw
  The gradual dusky veil.

While Spring shall pour his showers, as oft he wont,
And bathe thy breathing tresses, meekest Eve!
  While summer loves to sport
  Beneath thy lingering light;

While sallow Autumn fills thy lap with leaves;
Or Winter, yelling through the troublous air,
  Affrights thy shrinking train,
  And rudely rends thy robes;

So long, regardful of thy quiet rule,
Shall Fancy, Friendship, Science, rose-lipped Health,
  Thy gentlest influence own,
  And hymn thy favorite name!

ODE

WRITTEN IN THE BEGINNING OF THE YEAR 1746

How sleep the brave, who sink to rest
By all their country's wishes blest!

When Spring, with dewy fingers cold,
Returns to deck their hallowed mold,
She there shall dress a sweeter sod
Than Fancy's feet have ever trod.

By fairy hands their knell is rung;
By forms unseen their dirge is sung;
There Honor comes, a pilgrim gray,
To bless the turf that wraps their clay;
And Freedom shall awhile repair,
To dwell, a weeping hermit, there!

Oliver Goldsmith

1728–1774

SONG

From THE VICAR OF WAKEFIELD

WHEN lovely woman stoops to folly,
    And finds too late that men betray,
What charm can soothe her melancholy?
    What art can wash her guilt away?

The only art her guilt to cover,
    To hide her shame from every eye,
To give repentance to her lover,
    And wring his bosom, is— to die.

William Blake

1757–1827

THE PIPER

PIPING down the valleys wild,
    Piping songs of pleasant glee,
On a cloud I saw a child,
    And he laughing said to me:

"Pipe a song about a Lamb!"
    So I piped with merry cheer.
"Piper, pipe that song again;"
    So I piped: he wept to hear.

"Drop thy pipe, thy happy pipe;
　　Sing thy songs of happy cheer:"
So I sang the same again,
　　While he wept with joy to hear.

"Piper, sit thee down and write
　　In a book, that all may read."
So he vanished from my sight,
　　And I plucked a hollow reed,

And I made a rural pen,
　　And I stained the water clear,
And I wrote my happy songs
　　Every child may joy to hear.

THE CLOD AND THE PEBBLE

"Love seeketh not itself to please,
　　Nor for itself hath any care,
But for another gives its ease,
　　And builds a Heaven in Hell's despair."

So sung a little Clod of Clay,
　　Trodden with the cattle's feet,
But a Pebble of the brook
　　Warbled out these meters meet:

"Love seeketh only Self to please,
　　To bind another to Its delight,
Joys in another's loss of ease,
　　And builds a Hell in Heaven's despite."

THE SICK ROSE

O Rose, thou art sick!
　　The invisible worm,
That flies in the night,
　　In the howling storm,

Has found out thy bed
　　Of crimson joy;
And his dark secret love
　　Does thy life destroy.

THE TIGER

Tyger, tyger: burning bright
In the forests of the night,
What immortal hand or eye
Could frame thy fearful symmetry?

In what distant deeps or skies
Burnt the fire of thine eyes?
On what wings dare he aspire?
What the hand dare seize the fire?

And what shoulder, and what art,
Could twist the sinews of thy heart?
And, when thy heart began to beat,
What dread hand, and what dread feet?

What the hammer? what the chain?
In what furnace was thy brain?
What the anvil? what dread grasp
Dare its deadly terrors clasp?

When the stars threw down their spears,
And watered heaven with their tears,
Did he smile his work to see?
Did he who made the Lamb make thee?

Tyger, tyger: burning bright
In the forests of the night,
What immortal hand or eye,
Dare frame thy fearful symmetry?

AH, SUNFLOWER

Ah, Sunflower! weary of time,
Who countest the steps of the Sun;
Seeking after that sweet golden clime,
Where the traveler's journey is done;
Where the Youth pined away with desire,
And the pale Virgin shrouded in snow,
Arise from their graves, and aspire
Where my Sun-flower wishes to go!

THE GARDEN OF LOVE

I WENT to the Garden of Love,
And saw what I never had seen:
A Chapel was built in the midst,
Where I used to play on the green.

And the gates of this chapel were shut,
And "Thou shalt not" writ over the door;
So I turned to the Garden of Love,
That so many sweet flowers bore;

And I saw it was fillèd with graves,
And tombstones where flowers should be;
And priests in black gowns were walking their rounds,
And binding with briars my joys and desires.

A POISON TREE

I WAS angry with my friend:
I told my wrath, my wrath did end.
I was angry with my foe:
I told it not, my wrath did grow.

And I watered it in fears,
Night and morning with my tears;
And I sunnèd it with smiles,
And with soft deceitful wiles.

And it grew both day and night,
Till it bore an apple bright;
And my foe beheld it shine,
And he knew that it was mine,

And into my garden stole,
When the night had veiled the pole:
In the morning glad I see
My foe outstretched beneath the tree.

From MILTON

AND did those feet in ancient time
　　Walk upon England's mountains green?
And was the holy Lamb of God
　　On England's pleasant pastures seen?

And did the Countenance Divine
　　Shine forth upon our clouded hills?
And was Jerusalem builded here
　　Among these dark Satanic Mills?

Bring me my Bow of burning gold!
　　Bring me my Arrows of desire!
Bring me my Spear! O clouds, unfold!
　　Bring me my Chariot of fire!

I will not cease from Mental Fight,
　　Nor shall my Sword sleep in my hand,
Till we have built Jerusalem
　　In England's green and pleasant Land.

Robert Burns

1759–1796

HIGHLAND MARY

YE banks and braes, and streams around
　　The castle o' Montgomery,
Green be your woods and fair your flowers,
　　Your waters never drumlie!
There Summer first unfald her robes,
　　And there the langest tarry;
For there I took the last fareweel,
　　O' my sweet Highland Mary.

How sweetly bloomed the gay, green birk,
　　How rich the hawthorn's blossom,
As underneath their fragrant shade
　　I clasped her to my bosom!

The golden hours on angel wings
    Flew o'er me and my dearie;
For dear to me as light and life
    Was my sweet Highland Mary.

Wi' monie a vow and locked embrace
    Our parting was fu' tender;
And, pledging aft to meet again,
    We tore oursels asunder.
But O, fell Death's untimely frost,
    That nipt my flower sae early!
Now green's the sod, and cauld's the clay,
    That wraps my Highland Mary!

O pale, pale now, those rosy lips,
    I aft hae kissed sae fondly;
And closed for ay, the sparkling glance
    That dwalt on me sae kindly;
And moldering now in silent dust
    That heart that lo'ed me dearly!
But still within my bosom's core
    Shall live my Highland Mary.

SONG: MARY MORISON

O MARY, at thy window be!
    It is the wished, the trysted hour.
Those smiles and glances let me see,
    That makes the miser's treasure poor.
How blythely wad I bide the stoure,
    A weary slave frae sun to sun,
Could I the rich reward secure—
    The lovely Mary Morison!

Yestreen, when to the trembling string
    The dance gaed through the lighted ha',
To thee my fancy took its wing,
    I sat, but neither heard nor saw:

Though this was fair, and that was braw,
  And yon the toaſt of a' the town,
I sighed, and said amang them a':
  "Ye are na Mary Morison!"

O Mary, canſt thou wreck his peace
  Who for thy sake wad gladly die?
Or canſt thou break that heart of his
  Whase only faut is loving thee?
If love for love thou wilt na gie,
  At leaſt be pity to me shown:
A thought ungentle canna be
  The thought o' Mary Morison.

YE FLOWERY BANKS

YE flowery banks o' bonie Doon,
  How can ye blume sae fair?
How can ye chant, ye little birds,
  And I sae fu' o' care?

Thou'll break my heart, thou bonie bird,
  That sings upon the bough:
Thou minds me o' the happy days
  When my fause luve was true!

Thou'll break my heart, thou bonie bird,
  That sings beside thy mate:
For sae I sat, and sae I sang,
  And wiſt na o' my fate!

Aft hae I rov'd by bonie Doon
  To see the woodbine twine,
And ilka bird sang o' its luve,
  And sae did I o' mine.

Wi' lightsome heart I pu'd a rose
  Frae aff its thorny tree,
And my fause luver staw my rose,
  But left the thorn wi' me.

OF A' THE AIRTS

Of a' the airts the wind can blaw
  I dearly like the west,
For there the bonie lassie lives,
  The lassie I lo'e best.
There wild woods grow, and rivers row,
  And monie a hill between,
But day and night, my fancy's flight
  Is ever wi' my Jean.

I see her in the dewy flowers—
  I see her sweet an' fair.
I hear her in the tunefu' birds—
  I hear her charm the air.
There's not a bonie flower that springs
  By fountain, shaw, or green;
There's not a bonie bird that sings,
  But minds me o' my Jean.

A RED, RED ROSE

O, my luve is like a red, red rose,
  That's newly sprung in June.
O my luve is like the melodie,
  That's sweetly played in tune.

As fair art thou, my bonie lass,
  So deep in luve am I,
And I will luve thee still, my dear,
  Till a' the seas gang dry.

Till a' the seas gang dry, my dear,
  And the rocks melt wi' the sun!
And I will luve thee still, my dear,
  While the sands o' life shall run.

And fare thee weel, my only luve,
  And fare thee weel awhile!
And I will come again, my luve,
  Though it were ten thousand mile!

FLOW GENTLY, SWEET AFTON

Flow gently, sweet Afton, among thy green braes!
Flow gently, I'll sing thee a song in thy praise!
My Mary's asleep by thy murmuring stream—
Flow gently, sweet Afton, disturb not her dream!

Thou stock dove whose echo resounds through the glen,
Ye wild whistling blackbirds in yon thorny den,
Thou green-crested lapwing, thy screaming forbear—
I charge you, disturb not my slumbering fair!

How lofty, sweet Afton, thy neighboring hills,
Far marked with the courses of clear winding rills!
There daily I wander, as noon rises high,
My flocks and my Mary's sweet cot in my eye.

How pleasant thy banks and green valleys below,
Where wild in the woodlands the primroses blow;
There oft, as mild Evening weeps over the lea,
The sweet-scented birk shades my Mary and me.

Thy crystal stream, Afton, how lovely it glides,
And winds by the cot where my Mary resides!
How wanton thy waters her snowy feet lave,
As, gathering sweet flowerets, she stems thy clear wave!

Flow gently, sweet Afton, among thy green braes!
Flow gently, sweet river, the theme of my lays!
My Mary's asleep by thy murmuring stream—
Flow gently, sweet Afton, disturb not her dream!

MY HEART'S IN THE HIGHLANDS

Farewell to the Highlands, farewell to the North,
The birth-place of valor, the country of worth!
Wherever I wander, wherever I rove,
The hills of the Highlands for ever I love.

My heart's in the Highlands, my heart is not here,
My heart's in the Highlands, a-chasing the deer,
A-chasing the wild deer and following the roe—
My heart's in the Highlands, wherever I go!

Farewell to the mountains high-covered with snow,
Farewell to the straths and green valleys below,
Farewell to the forests and wild-hanging woods,
Farewell to the torrents and loud-pouring floods!

My heart's in the Highlands, my heart is not here,
My heart's in the Highlands, a-chasing the deer,
A-chasing the wild deer and following the roe—
My heart's in the Highlands, wherever I go!

JOHN ANDERSON MY JO

John Anderson my jo, John,
  When we were first acquent,
Your locks were like the raven,
  Your bonie brow was brent;
But now your brow is beld, John,
  Your locks are like the snaw,
But blessings on your frosty pow,
  John Anderson my jo!

John Anderson my jo, John,
  We clamb the hill thegither,
And monie a cantie day, John,
  We've had wi' ane anither;
Now we maun totter down, John,
  And hand in hand we'll go,
And sleep thegither at the foot,
  John Anderson my jo!

SONG: GREEN GROW THE RASHES

Green grow the rashes, O;
Green grow the rashes, O;
The sweetest hours that e'er I spend,
  Are spent amang the lasses, O.

There's nought but care on every han',
    In every hour that passes, O:
What signifies the life o' man,
    An 'twere na for the lasses, O.

The war'ly race may riches chase,
    An' riches still may fly them, O;
An' though at last they catch them fast,
    Their hearts can ne'er enjoy them, O.

But gie me a cannie hour at e'en,
    My arms about my dearie, O,
An' war'ly cares, an' war'ly men
    May a' gae tapsalteerie, O!

For you sae douce, ye sneer at this;
    Ye're nought but senseless asses, O;
The wisest man the warl' e'er saw,
    He dearly loved the lasses, O.

Auld Nature swears, the lovely dears
    Her noblest work she classes, O:
Her prentice han' she tried on man,
    An' then she made the lasses, O.

TAM GLEN

My heart is a-breaking, dear tittie,
    Some counsel unto me come len'.
To anger them a' is a pity,
    But what will I do wi' Tam Glen?

I'm thinking, wi' sic a braw fellow
    In poortith I might wak a fen'.
What care I in riches to wallow,
    If I mauna marry Tam Glen?

There's Lowrie, the laird o' Dumeller:
    "Guid-day to you," brute! he comes ben.
He brags and he blaws o' his siller,
    But when will he dance like Tam Glen?

My minnie does conſtantly deave me,
  And bids me beware o' young men.
They flatter, she says, to deceive me—
  But wha can think sae o' Tam Glen?

My daddie says, gin I'll forsake him,
  He'll gie me guid hunder marks ten.
But if it's ordained I maun tak him,
  O, wha will I get but Tam Glen?

Yeſtreen at the valentines' dealing,
  My heart to my mou gied a ſten,
For thrice I drew ane without failing,
  And thrice it was written, "Tam Glen"!

The laſt Halloween I was waukin
  My droukit sark-sleeve, as ye ken—
His likeness came up the house ſtaukin,
  And the very gray breeks o' Tam Glen!

Come, counsel, dear tittie, don't tarry!
  I'll gie ye my bonie black hen,
Gif ye will advise me to marry
  The lad I lo'e dearly, Tam Glen.

AULD LANG SYNE

SHOULD auld acquaintance be forgot,
  And never brought to mind?
Should auld acquaintance be forgot,
  And auld lang syne?

Cho.—For auld lang syne, my dear,
  For auld lang syne,
We'll tak a cup o' kindness yet
  For auld lang syne!

And surely ye'll be your pint-ſtowp,
  And surely I'll be mine,
And we'll tak a cup o' kindness yet
  For auld lang syne!

We twa hae run about the braes,
  And pou'd the gowans fine,
But we've wandered monie a weary fit
  Sin' auld lang syne.

We two hae paidl'd in the burn
  Frae morning sun till dine,
But seas between us braid hae roared
  Sin' auld lang syne.

And there's a hand, my trusty fiere,
  And gie's a hand o' thine,
And we'll tak a right guid-willie waught
  For auld lang syne!

WILLIE BREWED A PECK O' MAUT

O, WILLIE brew'd a peck o' maut,
An' Rob an' Allan cam to see.
Three blyther hearts that lee-lang night
Ye wad na found in Christendie.

Cho.—We are na fou, we're nae that fou,
But just a drappie in our e'e!
The cock may craw, the day may daw,
And ay we'll taste the barley bree!

Here are we met, three merry boys,
Three merry boys, I trow, are we;
An' mony a night we've merry been,
And mony mae we hope to be!

It is the moon, I ken her horn,
That's blinkin' in the lift sae hie:
She shines sae bright to wyle us hame,
But, by my sooth, she'll wait a wee!

Wha first shall rise to gang awa,
A cuckold, coward loun is he!
What first beside his chair shall fa'
He is the King amang us three!

William Wordsworth

1770–1850

INFLUENCE OF NATURAL OBJECTS

Wisdom and Spirit of the universe!
Thou Soul, that art the Eternity of thought!
And giv'ſt to forms and images a breath
And everlaſting motion! not in vain,
By day or ſtar-light, thus from my firſt dawn
Of childhood didſt thou intertwine for me
The passions that build up our human soul;
Not with the mean and vulgar works of Man;
But with high objeᴄts, with enduring things,
With life and nature; purifying thus
The elements of feeling and of thought,
And sanᴄtifying by such discipline
Both pain and fear,—until we recognize
A grandeur in the beatings of the heart.

Nor was this fellowship vouchsafed to me
With ſtinted kindness. In November days,
When vapors rolling down the valleys made
A lonely scene more lonesome; among woods
At noon; and 'mid the calm of summer nights,
When, by the margin of the trembling lake,
Beneath the gloomy hills, homeward I went
In solitude, such intercourse was mine:
Mine was it in the fields both day and night,
And by the water, all the summer long.
And in the froſty season, when the sun
Was set, and, visible for many a mile,
The cottage-windows through the twilight blazed,
I heeded not the summons: happy time
It was indeed for all of us; for me
It was a time of rapture! Clear and loud
The village-clock tolled six—I wheeled about,
Proud and exulting like an untired horse
That cares not for his home.—All shod with ſteel
We hissed along the polished ice, in games

Confederate, imitative of the chase
And woodland pleasures,—the resounding horn,
The pack loud-chiming, and the hunted hare.
So through the darkness and the cold we flew,
And not a voice was idle: with the din
Smitten, the precipices rang aloud;
The leafless trees and every icy crag
Tinkled like iron; while far-distant hills
Into the tumult sent an alien sound
Of melancholy, not unnoticed while the stars,
Eastward, were sparkling clear, and in the west
The orange sky of evening died away.

   Not seldom from the uproar I retired
Into a silent bay, or sportively
Glanced sideway, leaving the tumultuous throng,
To cut across the reflex of a star;
Image, that flying still before me, gleamed
Upon the glassy plain: and oftentimes,
When we had given our bodies to the wind,
And all the shadowy banks on either side
Came sweeping through the darkness, spinning still
The rapid line of motion, then at once
Have I, reclining back upon my heels,
Stopped short; yet still the solitary cliffs
Wheeled by me—even as if the earth had rolled
With visible motion her diurnal round!
Behind me did they stretch in solemn train,
Feebler and feebler, and I stood and watched
Till all was tranquil as a summer sea.

SHE DWELT AMONG THE UNTRODDEN WAYS

    SHE dwelt among the untrodden ways
      Beside the springs of Dove,
  A Maid whom there were none to praise
      And very few to love:

  A violet by a mossy stone
      Half hidden from the eye!

—Fair as a star, when only one
    Is shining in the sky.

She lived unknown, and few could know
    When Lucy ceased to be;
But she is in her grave, and, oh,
    The difference to me!

I TRAVELED AMONG UNKNOWN MEN

I TRAVELED among unknown men,
    In lands beyond the sea;
Nor, England! did I know till then
    What love I bore to thee.

'Tis past, that melancholy dream!
    Nor will I quit thy shore
A second time; for still I seem
    To love thee more and more.

Among thy mountains did I feel
    The joy of my desire;
And she I cherished turned her wheel
    Beside an English fire.

Thy mornings showed, thy nights concealed
    The bowers where Lucy played;
And thine too is the last green field
    That Lucy's eyes surveyed.

A SLUMBER DID MY SPIRIT SEAL

A SLUMBER did my spirit seal;
    I had no human fears;
She seemed a thing that could not feel
    The touch of earthly years.

No motion has she now, no force;
    She neither hears nor sees;
Rolled round in earth's diurnal course,
    With rocks, and stones, and trees.

THE SOLITARY REAPER

Behold her, single in the field,
Yon solitary Highland Lass!
Reaping and singing by herself;
Stop here, or gently pass!
Alone she cuts and binds the grain,
And sings a melancholy strain;
O listen! for the Vale profound
Is overflowing with the sound.

No Nightingale did ever chaunt
More welcome notes to weary bands
Of travelers in some shady haunt,
Among Arabian sands:
A voice so thrilling ne'er was heard
In spring-time from the Cuckoo-bird,
Breaking the silence of the seas
Among the farthest Hebrides.

Will no one tell me what she sings?—
Perhaps the plaintive numbers flow
For old, unhappy, far-off things,
And battles long ago:
Or is it some more humble lay,
Familiar matter of to-day?
Some natural sorrow, loss, or pain,
That has been, and may be again?

Whate'er the theme, the Maiden sang
As if her song could have no ending;
I saw her singing at her work,
And o'er the sickle bending;—
I listened, motionless and still;
And, as I mounted up the hill,
The music in my heart I bore,
Long after it was heard no more.

LONDON 1802

Milton! thou shouldst be living at this hour:
England hath need of thee: she is a fen
Of stagnant waters: altar, sword, and pen,
Fireside, the heroic wealth of hall and bower,
Have forfeited their ancient English dower
Of inward happiness. We are selfish men;
Oh! raise us up, return to us again;
And give us manners, virtue, freedom, power.
Thy soul was like a Star, and dwelt apart;
Thou hadst a voice whose sound was like the sea:
Pure as the naked heavens, majestic, free,
So didst thou travel on life's common way,
In cheerful godliness; and yet thy heart
The lowliest duties on herself did lay.

COMPOSED UPON WESTMINSTER BRIDGE
SEPT. 3, 1802

Earth has not anything to show more fair:
Dull would he be of soul who could pass by
A sight so touching in its majesty:
This city now doth like a garment wear
The beauty of the morning; silent, bare,
Ships, towers, domes, theaters, and temples lie
Open unto the fields, and to the sky;
All bright and glittering in the smokeless air.
Never did sun more beautifully steep
In his first splendor, valley, rock, or hill;
Ne'er saw I, never felt, a calm so deep!
The river glideth at his own sweet will:
Dear God! the very houses seem asleep;
And all that mighty heart is lying still!

IT IS A BEAUTEOUS EVENING, CALM AND FREE

It is a beauteous evening, calm and free,
The holy time is quiet as a Nun

Breathless with adoration: the broad sun
Is sinking down in its tranquillity;
The gentleness of heaven broods o'er the Sea:
Listen! the mighty Being is awake,
And doth with his eternal motion make
A sound like thunder—everlastingly.
Dear Child! dear Girl! that walkest with me here,
If thou appear untouched by solemn thought,
Thy nature is not therefore less divine:
Thou liest in Abraham's bosom all the year,
And worship'st at the Temple's inner shrine,
God being with thee when we know it not.

✗ THE WORLD IS TOO MUCH WITH US

The world is too much with us: late and soon,
Getting and spending, we lay waste our powers:
Little we see in Nature that is ours;
We have given our hearts away, a sordid boon!
This Sea that bares her bosom to the moon;
The winds that will be howling at all hours,
And are up-gathered now like sleeping flowers;
For this, for everything, we are out of tune;
It moves us not.—Great God! I'd rather be
A Pagan suckled in a creed outworn;
So might I, standing on this pleasant lea,
Have glimpses that would make me less forlorn;
Have sight of Proteus rising from the sea;
Or hear old Triton blow his wreathèd horn.

ODE TO DUTY

Stern Daughter of the Voice of God!
O Duty! if that name thou love,
Who art a light to guide, a rod
To check the erring, and reprove;
Thou, who art victory and law
When empty terrors overawe;
From vain temptations dost set free;
And calm'st the weary strife of frail humanity!

There are who ask not if thine eye
Be on them; who, in love and truth,
Where no misgiving is, rely
Upon the genial sense of youth:
Glad Hearts! without reproach or blot;
Who do thy work, and know it not:
O if through confidence misplaced
They fail, thy saving arms, dread Power, around them
    cast.

Serene will be our days and bright,
And happy will our nature be,
When love is an unerring light,
And joy its own security.
And they a blissful course may hold
Even now, who, not unwisely bold,
Live in the spirit of this creed;
Yet seek thy firm support, according to their need.

I, loving freedom, and untried;
No sport of every random gust,
Yet being to myself a guide,
Too blindly have reposed my trust:
And oft, when in my heart was heard
Thy timely mandate, I deferred
The task, in smoother walks to stray;
But thee I now would serve more strictly, if I may.

Through no disturbance of my soul,
Or strong compunction in me wrought,
I supplicate for thy control;
But in the quietness of thought:
Me this unchartered freedom tires;
I feel the weight of chance-desires:
My hopes no more must change their name,
I long for a repose that ever is the same.

Stern Lawgiver! yet thou dost wear
The Godhead's most benignant grace;

Nor know we anything so fair
As is the smile upon thy face:
Flowers laugh before thee on their beds
And fragrance in thy footing treads;
Thou dost preserve the stars from wrong;
And the most ancient heavens, through Thee, are fresh
    and strong.

To humbler functions, awful Power!
I call thee: I myself commend
Unto thy guidance from this hour;
Oh, let my weakness have an end!
Give unto me, made lowly wise,
The spirit of self-sacrifice;
The confidence of reason give;
And in the light of truth thy Bondman let me live!

ODE

Intimations of Immortality from Recollections of Early Childhood

I

There was a time when meadow, grove and stream,
The earth, and every common sight,
    To me did seem
    Appareled in celestial light,
The glory and the freshness of a dream.
It is not now as it hath been of yore;—
    Turn wheresoe'er I may,
    By night or day,
The things which I have seen I now can see no more.

II

    The Rainbow comes and goes,
    And lovely is the Rose;
    The Moon doth with delight

Look round her when the heavens are bare;
 Waters on a starry night
 Are beautiful and fair;
 The sunshine is a glorious birth;
 But yet I know, where'er I go,
That there hath passed away a glory from the earth.

III

Now, while the birds thus sing a joyous song,
 And while the young lambs bound
 As to the tabor's sound,
To me alone there came a thought of grief:
A timely utterance gave that thought relief,
 And I again am strong.
The cataracts blow their trumpets from the steep;
No more shall grief of mine the season wrong;
I hear the Echoes through the mountains throng,
The Winds come to me from the fields of sleep,
 And all the earth is gay;
 Land and sea
 Give themselves up to jollity,
 And with the heart of May
 Doth every Beast keep holiday;—
 Thou Child of Joy,
Shout round me, let me hear thy shouts, thou happy
 Shepherd-boy!

IV

Ye blessèd Creatures, I have heard the call
 Ye to each other make; I see
The heavens laugh with you in your jubilee;
 My heart is at your festival,
 My head hath its coronal,
The fullness of your bliss, I feel—I feel it all.
 Oh evil day! if I were sullen
 While Earth herself is adorning
 This sweet May-morning,
 And the Children are culling
 On every side,

In a thousand valleys far and wide,
　　Fresh flowers; while the sun shines warm,
And the Babe leaps up on his Mother's arm:—
　　I hear, I hear, with joy I hear!
　　—But there's a Tree, of many, one,
A single Field which I have looked upon,
Both of them speak of something that is gone:
　　The Pansy at my feet
　　Doth the same tale repeat:
Whither is fled the visionary gleam?
Where is it now, the glory and the dream?

v

Our birth is but a sleep and a forgetting:
The Soul that rises with us, our life's Star,
　　Hath had elsewhere its setting,
　　　And cometh from afar:
　　Not in entire forgetfulness,
　　And not in utter nakedness,
But trailing clouds of glory do we come
　　From God, who is our home:
Heaven lies about us in our infancy!
Shades of the prison-house begin to close
　　Upon the growing Boy,
But he beholds the light, and whence it flows,
　　He sees it in his joy;
The Youth, who daily farther from the east
　　Muſt travel, ſtill is Nature's Prieſt,
　　And by the vision splendid
　　Is on his way attended;
At length the Man perceives it die away,
And fade into the light of common day.

VI

Earth fills her lap with pleasures of her own;
Yearnings she hath in her own natural kind.
And, even with something of a Mother's mind,
　　And no unworthy aim,
　　The homely Nurse doth all she can

To make her Foster-child, her Inmate Man,
    Forget the glories he hath known,
And that imperial palace whence he came.

VII

Behold the Child among his new-born blisses,
A six years' Darling of a pigmy size!
See, where 'mid work of his own hand he lies,
Fretted by sallies of his mother's kisses,
With light upon him from his father's eyes!
See, at his feet, some little plan or chart,
Some fragment from his dream of human life,
Shaped by himself with newly-learnèd art;
      A wedding or a festival,
      A mourning or a funeral;
      And this hath now his heart,
     And unto this he frames his song:
      Then will he fit his tongue
To dialogues of business, love, or strife;
      But it will not be long
      Ere this be thrown aside,
      And with new joy and pride
The little Actor cons another part;
Filling from time to time his "humorous stage"
With all the Persons, down to palsied Age,
That Life brings with her in her equipage;
      As if his whole vocation
      Were endless imitation.

VIII

Thou, whose exterior semblance doth belie
      Thy Soul's immensity;
Thou best Philosopher, who yet dost keep
Thy heritage, thou Eye among the blind,
That, deaf and silent, read'st the eternal deep,
Haunted for ever by the eternal mind,—
      Mighty Prophet! Seer blest!
      On whom those truths do rest,

Which we are toiling all our lives to find,
In darkness lost, the darkness of the grave;
Thou, over whom thy Immortality
Broods like the Day, a Master o'er a Slave,
A Presence which is not to be put by;
Thou little Child, yet glorious in the might
Of heaven-born freedom on thy being's height,
Why with such earnest pains dost thou provoke
The years to bring the inevitable yoke,
Thus blindly with thy blessedness at strife?
Full soon thy Soul shall have her earthly freight,
And custom lie upon thee with a weight,
Heavy as frost, and deep almost as life!

IX

O joy! that in our embers
Is something that doth live,
That nature yet remembers
What was so fugitive!
The thought of our past years in me doth breed
Perpetual benediction: not indeed
For that which is most worthy to be blest—
Delight and liberty, the simple creed
Of Childhood, whether busy or at rest,
With new-fledged hope still fluttering in his breast:—
Not for these I raise
The song of thanks and praise;
But for those obstinate questionings
Of sense and outward things,
Fallings from us, vanishings;
Blank misgivings of a Creature
Moving about in worlds not realized,
High instincts before which our mortal nature
Did tremble like a guilty Thing surprised:
But for those first affections,
Those shadowy recollections,
Which, be they what they may,
Are yet the fountain-light of all our day,

Are yet a master-light of all our seeing;
   Uphold us, cherish, and have power to make
Our noisy years seem moments in the being
Of the eternal Silence: truths that wake,
      To perish never:
Which neither listlessness, nor mad endeavor,
      Nor Man nor Boy,
Nor all that is at enmity with joy,
Can utterly abolish or destroy!
      Hence in a season of calm weather
      Though inland far we be,
Our Souls have sight of that immortal sea
      Which brought us hither,
      Can in a moment travel thither,
And see the Children sport upon the shore,
And hear the mighty waters rolling evermore.

                    x

Then sing, ye Birds, sing, sing a joyous song!
      And let the young Lambs bound
      As to the tabor's sound!
We in thought will join your throng,
      Ye that pipe and ye that play,
      Ye that through your hearts to-day
      Feel the gladness of the May!
What though the radiance which was once so bright
Be now for ever taken from my sight,
   Though nothing can bring back the hour
Of splendor in the grass, of glory in the flower;
      We will grieve not, rather find
      Strength in what remains behind;
      In the primal sympathy
      Which having been must ever be;
      In the soothing thoughts that spring
      Out of human suffering;
      In the faith that looks through death,
In years that bring the philosophic mind.

XI

And O, ye Fountains, Meadows, Hills, and Groves,
Forebode not any severing of our loves!
Yet in my heart of hearts I feel your might;
I only have relinquished one delight
To live beneath your more habitual sway.
I love the Brooks which down their channels fret,
Even more than when I tripped lightly as they;
The innocent brightness of a new-born Day
      Is lovely yet;
The Clouds that gather round the setting sun
Do take a sober coloring from an eye
That hath kept watch o'er man's mortality;
Another race hath been, and other palms are won.
Thanks to the human heart by which we live,
Thanks to its tenderness, its joys, and fears,
To me the meanest flower that blows can give
Thoughts that do often lie too deep for tears.

Sir Walter Scott

1771–1832

SOLDIER, REST! THY WARFARE O'ER

From THE LADY OF THE LAKE

SOLDIER, rest! thy warfare o'er,
   Sleep the sleep that knows not breaking;
Dream of battled fields no more,
   Days of danger, nights of waking.
In our isle's enchanted hall,
   Hands unseen thy couch are strewing,
Fairy strains of music fall,
   Every sense in slumber dewing.
Soldier, rest! thy warfare o'er,
Dream of fighting fields no more:
Sleep the sleep that knows not breaking,
Morn of toil, nor night of waking.

No rude sound shall reach thine ear,
  Armor's clang, or war-steed champing,
Trump nor pibroch summon here
  Mustering clan, or squadron tramping.
Yet the lark's shrill fife may come
  At the daybreak from the fallow,
And the bittern sound his drum,
  Booming from the sedgy shallow.
Ruder sounds shall none be near,
Guards nor warders challenge here,
Here's no war-steed's neigh and champing,
Shouting clans or squadrons stamping.

Huntsman, rest! thy chase is done;
  While our slumbrous spells assail ye,
Dream not, with the rising sun,
  Bugles here shall sound reveillé.
Sleep! the deer is in his den;
  Sleep! thy hounds are by thee lying;
Sleep! nor dream in yonder glen
How thy gallant steed lay dying.
Huntsman, rest! thy chase is done;
Think not of the rising sun,
For at dawning to assail ye,
Here no bugles sound reveillé.

Samuel Taylor Coleridge
1772–1834

KUBLA KHAN

In Xanadu did Kubla Khan
A stately pleasure-dome decree:
Where Alph, the sacred river, ran
Through caverns measureless to man
  Down to a sunless sea.
So twice five miles of fertile ground
With walls and towers were girdled round:
And here were gardens bright with sinuous rills

Where blossomed many an incense-bearing tree;
And here were forests ancient as the hills,
Enfolding sunny spots of greenery.

But oh! that deep romantic chasm which slanted
Down the green hill athwart a cedarn cover!
A savage place! as holy and enchanted
As e'er beneath a waning moon was haunted
By woman wailing for her demon-lover!
And from this chasm, with ceaseless turmoil seething,
As if this earth in fast thick pants were breathing,
A mighty fountain momently was forced;
Amid whose swift half-intermitted burst
Huge fragments vaulted like rebounding hail,
Or chaffy grain beneath the thresher's flail:
And 'mid these dancing rocks at once and ever
It flung up momently the sacred river.
Five miles meandering with a mazy motion
Through wood and dale the sacred river ran,
Then reached the caverns measureless to man,
And sank in tumult to a lifeless ocean:
And 'mid this tumult Kubla heard from far
Ancestral voices prophesying war!
  The shadow of the dome of pleasure
   Floated midway on the waves;
  Where was heard the mingled measure
   From the fountain and the caves.
 It was a miracle of rare device,
 A sunny pleasure-dome with caves of ice!

  A damsel with a dulcimer
  In a vision once I saw:
  It was an Abyssinian maid,
  And on her dulcimer she played,
  Singing of Mount Abora.
  Could I revive within me
  Her symphony and song,
  To such a deep delight 't would win me,
That with music loud and long,

I would build that dome in air,
That sunny dome! those caves of ice!
And all who heard should see them there,
And all should cry, Beware! Beware!
His flashing eyes, his floating hair!
Weave a circle round him thrice,
And close your eyes with holy dread,
For he on honey-dew hath fed,
And drunk the milk of Paradise.

Charles Lamb

1775–1834

THE OLD FAMILIAR FACES

I HAVE had playmates, I have had companions,
In my days of childhood, in my joyful school-days;
All, all are gone, the old familiar faces.

I have been laughing, I have been carousing,
Drinking late, sitting late, with my bosom cronies;
All, all are gone, the old familiar faces.

I loved a love once, fairest among women;
Closed are her doors on me, I must not see her—
All, all are gone, the old familiar faces.

I have a friend, a kinder friend has no man;
Like an ingrate, I left my friend abruptly;
Left him, to muse on the old familiar faces.

Ghost-like I paced round the haunts of my childhood.
Earth seemed a desert I was bound to traverse,
Seeking to find the old familiar faces.

Friend of my bosom, thou more than a brother,
Why were not thou born in my father's dwelling?
So might we talk of the old familiar faces—

How some they have died, and some they have left me,
And some are taken from me; all are departed;
All, all are gone, the old familiar faces.

Walter Savage Landor

1775–1864

ROSE AYLMER

Ah what avails the sceptered race,
  Ah what the form divine!
What every virtue, every grace!
  Rose Aylmer, all were thine.
Rose Aylmer, whom these wakeful eyes
  May weep, but never see,
A night of memories and of sighs
  I consecrate to thee.

PAST RUINED ILION

Past ruined Ilion Helen lives,
  Alcestis rises from the shades;
Verse calls them forth; 'tis verse that gives
  Immortal youth to mortal maids.

Soon shall Oblivion's deepening veil
  Hide all the peopled hills you see,
The gay, the proud, while lovers hail
  These many summers you and me.

ON HIS SEVENTY-FIFTH BIRTHDAY

I strove with none; for none was worth my strife,
  Nature I loved, and next to Nature, Art;
I warmed both hands before the fire of life,
  It sinks, and I am ready to depart.

DIRCE

From Pericles and Aspasia

Stand close around, ye Stygian set,
  With Dirce in one boat conveyed,
Or Charon, seeing, may forget
  That he is old, and she a shade.

Thomas Love Peacock

1785–1866

THE WAR-SONG OF DINAS VAWR

From THE MISFORTUNES OF ELPHIN

THE mountain sheep are sweeter,
But the valley sheep are fatter;
We therefore deemed it meeter
To carry off the latter.
We made an expedition;
We met a host, and quelled it;
We forced a strong position,
And killed the men who held it.

On Dyfed's richest valley,
Where herds of kine were brousing,
We made a nightly sally,
To furnish our carousing.
Fierce warriors rushed to meet us;
We met them, and o'erthrew them:
They struggled hard to beat us;
But we conquered them, and slew them.

As we drove our prize at leisure,
The king marched forth to catch us:
His rage surpassed all measure,
But his people could not match us.
He fled to his hall-pillars;
And, ere our force we led off,
Some sacked his house and cellars,
While others cut his head off.

We there, in strife bewild'ring,
Spilt blood enough to swim in:
We orphaned many children,
And widowed many women.

The eagles and the ravens
We glutted with our foemen;
The heroes and the cravens,
The spearmen and the bowmen.

We brought away from battle,
And much their land bemoaned them,
Two thousand head of cattle,
And the head of him who owned them:
Ednyfed, King of Dyfed,
His head was borne before us;
His wine and beasts supplied our feasts,
And his overthrow, our chorus.

George Gordon, Lord Byron

1788-1824

SHE WALKS IN BEAUTY

She walks in beauty, like the night
  Of cloudless climes and starry skies;
And all that's best of dark and bright
  Meet in her aspect and her eyes:
Thus mellowed to that tender light
  Which heaven to gaudy day denies.

One shade the more, one ray the less,
  Had half impaired the nameless grace
Which waves in every raven tress,
  Or softly lightens o'er her face;
Where thoughts serenely sweet express
  How pure, how dear their dwelling-place.

And on that cheek, and o'er that brow,
  So soft, so calm, yet eloquent,
The smiles that win, the tints that glow,
  But tell of days in goodness spent,
A mind at peace with all below,
  A heart whose love is innocent!

SO, WE'LL GO NO MORE A-ROVING

So, we'll go no more a-roving
　　So late into the night,
Though the heart be still as loving,
　　And the moon be still as bright.

For the sword outwears its sheath,
　　And the soul wears out the breast,
And the heart must pause to breathe,
　　And Love itself have rest.

Though the night was made for loving,
　　And the day returns too soon,
Yet we'll go no more a-roving
　　By the light of the moon.

Percy Bysshe Shelley

1792–1822

TO ——

Music, when soft voices die,
Vibrates in the memory—
Odors, when sweet violets sicken,
Live within the sense they quicken.

Rose leaves, when the rose is dead,
Are heaped for the belovèd's bed;
And so thy thoughts, when thou art gone,
Love itself shall slumber on.

THE INDIAN SERENADE

I arise from dreams of thee
In the first sweet sleep of night,
When the winds are breathing low,
And the stars are shining bright:
I arise from dreams of thee,
And a spirit in my feet
Hath led me—who knows how?
To thy chamber window, Sweet!

The wandering airs they faint
On the dark, the silent ſtream—
The Champak odors fail
Like sweet thoughts in a dream;
The nightingale's complaint,
It dies upon her heart;—
As I muſt on thine,
Oh, belovèd as thou art!

Oh lift me from the grass!
I die! I faint! I fail!
Let thy love in kisses rain
On my lips and eyelids pale.
My cheek is cold and white, alas!
My heart beats loud and faſt;—
Oh! press it to thine own again,
Where it will break at laſt.

TO NIGHT

SWIFTLY walk over the weſtern wave,
    Spirit of Night
  Out of the miſty eaſtern cave,
Where, all the long and lone daylight,
Thou woveſt dreams of joy and fear,
Which make thee terrible and dear,—
    Swift be thy flight!

Wrap thy form in a mantle gray,
    Star-inwrought!
Blind with thine hair the eyes of Day;
Kiss her until she be wearied out;
Then wander o'er city, and sea, and land,
Touching all with thine opiate wand—
    Come, long-sought!

When I arose and saw the dawn,
    I sighed for thee;
When light rode high, and the dew was gone,

And noon lay heavy on flower and tree,
And the weary Day turned to his rest,
Lingering like an unloved guest,
    I sighed for thee.

Thy brother Death came, and cried,
    Wouldst thou me?
Thy sweet child Sleep, the filmy-eyed,
Murmured like a noon-tide bee,
Shall I nestle near thy side?
Wouldst thou me?—And I replied,
    No, not thee!

Death will come when thou art dead,
    Soon, too soon—
Sleep will come when thou art fled;
Of neither would I ask the boon
I ask of thee, belovèd Night—
Swift be thine approaching flight,
    Come soon, soon!

CHORUS FROM HELLAS

The world's great age begins anew,
    The golden years return,
The earth doth like a snake renew
    Her winter weeds outworn:
Heaven smiles, and faiths and empires gleam,
Like wrecks of a dissolving dream.

A brighter Hellas rears its mountains
    From waves serener far;
A new Peneus rolls his fountains
    Against the morning star.
Where fairer Tempes bloom, there sleep
Young Cyclads on a sunnier deep.

A loftier Argo cleaves the main,
    Fraught with a later prize;

Another Orpheus sings again,
   And loves, and weeps, and dies.
A new Ulysses leaves once more
Calypso for his native shore.

Oh, write no more the tale of Troy,
   If earth Death's scroll muſt be!
Nor mix with Laian rage the joy
   Which dawns upon the free:
Although a subtler Sphinx renew
Riddles of death Thebes never knew.

Another Athens shall arise,
   And to remoter time
Bequeath, like sunset to the skies,
   The splendor of its prime;
And leave, if naught so bright may live,
All earth can take or Heaven can give.

Saturn and Love their long repose
   Shall burſt, more bright and good
Than all who fell, than One who rose,
   Than many unsubdued:
Not gold, not blood, their altar dowers,
But votive tears and symbol flowers.

Oh, cease! muſt hate and death return?
   Cease! muſt men kill and die?
Cease! drain not to its dregs the urn
   Of bitter prophecy.
The world is weary of the paſt,
Oh, might it die or reſt at laſt!

OZYMANDIAS

I MET a traveler from an antique land
Who said: Two vaſt and trunkless legs of ſtone
Stand in the desert. Near them, on the sand,
Half sunk, a shattered visage lies, whose frown,

And wrinkled lip, and sneer of cold command,
Tell that its sculptor well those passions read
Which yet survive, stamped on these lifeless things,
The hand that mocked them and the heart that fed;
And on the pedestal these words appear:
"My name is Ozymandias, king of kings:
Look on my works, ye Mighty, and despair!"
Nothing beside remains. Round the decay
Of that colossal wreck, boundless and bare
The lone and level sands stretch far away.

· ODE TO THE WEST WIND

I

O WILD West Wind, thou breath of Autumn's being,
Thou, from whose unseen presence the leaves dead
Are driven, like ghosts from an enchanter fleeing.

Yellow, and black, and pale, and hectic red,
Pestilence-stricken multitudes: O thou,
Who chariotest to their dark wintry bed

The wingèd seeds, where they lie cold and low,
Each like a corpse within its grave, until
Thine azure sister of the Spring shall blow

Her clarion o'er the dreaming earth, and fill
(Driving sweet buds like flocks to feed in air)
With living hues and odors plain and hill:

Wild Spirit, which art moving everywhere;
Destroyer and preserver; hear, oh, hear!

II

Thou on whose stream, 'mid the steep sky's commotion,
Loose clouds like earth's decaying leaves are shed,
Shook from the tangled boughs of Heaven and Ocean

Angels of rain and lightning: there are spread
On the blue surface of thine airy surge,
Like the bright hair uplifted from the head

Of some fierce Mænad, even from the dim verge
Of the horizon to the zenith's height,
The locks of the approaching storm. Thou dirge

Of the dying year, to which this closing night
Will be the dome of a vast sepulcher,
Vaulted with all thy congregated might

Of vapors, from whose solid atmosphere
Black rain, and fire, and hail will burst: oh, hear!

III

Thou who didst waken from his summer dreams
The blue Mediterranean, where he lay
Lulled by the coil of his crystàlline streams,

Beside a pumice isle in Baiæ's bay,
And saw in sleep old palaces and towers
Quivering within the wave's intenser day.

All overgrown with azure moss and flowers
So sweet, the sense faints picturing them! Thou
For whose path the Atlantic's level powers

Cleave themselves into chasms, while far below
The sea-blooms and the oozy woods which wear
The sapless foliage of the ocean, know

Thy voice, and suddenly grow gray with fear,
And tremble and despoil themselves: oh, hear!

IV

If I were a dead leaf thou mightest bear;
If I were a swift cloud to fly with thee;
A wave to pant beneath thy power, and share

The impulse of thy strength, only less free
Than thou, O uncontrollable! If even
I were as in my boyhood, and could be

The comrade of thy wanderings over Heaven,
As then, when to outstrip thy skiey speed
Scarce seemed a vision; I would ne'er have striven

As thus with thee in prayer in my sore need.
Oh, lift me as a wave, a leaf, a cloud!
I fall upon the thorns of life! I bleed!

A heavy weight of hours has chained and bowed
One too like thee: tameless, and swift, and proud.

v

Make me thy lyre, even as the forest is:
What if my leaves are falling like its own!
The tumult of thy mighty harmonies

Will take from both a deep, autumnal tone,
Sweet though in sadness. Be thou, Spirit fierce,
My spirit! Be thou me, impetuous one!

Drive my dead thoughts over the universe
Like withered leaves to quicken a new birth!
And, by the incantation of this verse,

Scatter, as from an unextinguished hearth
Ashes and sparks, my words among mankind!
Be through my lips to unawakened earth

The trumpet of a prophecy! O wind,
If Winter comes, can Spring be far behind?

John Keats

1795–1821

ODE TO A NIGHTINGALE

MY heart aches, and a drowsy numbness pains
    My sense, as though of hemlock I had drunk,

Or emptied some dull opiate to the drains
  One minute past, and Lethe-wards had sunk:
'Tis not through envy of thy happy lot,
  But being too happy in thine happiness,—
    That thou, light-wingèd Dryad of the trees,
      In some melodious plot
    Of beechen green, and shadows numberless,
      Singest of summer in full-throated ease.

O for a draught of vintage! that hath been
  Cooled a long age in the deep-delvèd earth,
Tasting of Flora and the country green,
  Dance, and Provençal song, and sunburnt mirth!
O for a beaker full of the warm South,
  Full of the true, the blushful Hippocrene,
    With beaded bubbles winking at the brim,
      And purple-stainèd mouth;
    That I might drink, and leave the world unseen,
      And with thee fade away into the forest dim:

Fade far away, dissolve, and quite forget
  What thou among the leaves hast never known,
The weariness, the fever, and the fret
  Here, where men sit and hear each other groan;
Where palsy shakes a few, sad, last gray hairs,
  Where youth grows pale, and specter-thin, and dies;
    Where but to think is to be full of sorrow
      And leaden-eyed despairs,
    Where Beauty cannot keep her lustrous eyes,
      Or new Love pine at them beyond to-morrow.

Away! away! for I will fly to thee,
  Not charioted by Bacchus and his pards,
But on the viewless wings of Poesy,
  Though the dull brain perplexes and retards:
Already with thee! tender is the night,
  And haply the Queen-Moon is on her throne,
    Clustered around by all her starry Fays;
      But here there is no light,

Save what from heaven is with the breezes blown
   Through verdurous glooms and winding mossy
     ways.

I cannot see what flowers are at my feet,
   Nor what soft incense hangs upon the boughs,
But, in embalmèd darkness, guess each sweet
   Wherewith the seasonable month endows
The grass, the thicket, and the fruit-tree wild;
   White hawthorn, and the pastoral eglantine;
     Fast-fading violets covered up in leaves;
      And mid-May's eldest child,
   The coming musk-rose, full of dewy wine,
     The murmurous haunt of flies on summer eves.

Darkling I listen; and for many a time
   I have been half in love with easeful Death,
Called him soft names in many a musèd rhyme,
   To take into the air my quiet breath;
Now more than ever seems it rich to die,
   To cease upon the midnight with no pain,
     While thou art pouring forth thy soul abroad
      In such an ecstasy!
   Still wouldst thou sing, and I have ears in vain—
     To thy high requiem become a sod.

Thou wast not born for death, immortal Bird!
   No hungry generations tread thee down;
The voice I hear this passing night was heard
   In ancient days by emperor and clown:
Perhaps the self-same song that found a path
   Through the sad heart of Ruth, when, sick for home,
     She stood in tears amid the alien corn;
      The same that oft-times hath
   Charmed magic casements, opening on the foam
     Of perilous seas, in faery lands forlorn.

Forlorn! the very word is like a bell
   To toll me back from thee to my sole self!

Adieu! the fancy cannot cheat so well
  As she is famed to do, deceiving elf.
Adieu! adieu! thy plaintive anthem fades
  Past the near meadows, over the still stream,
    Up the hill-side; and now 'tis buried deep
      In the next valley-glades:
  Was it a vision, or a waking dream?
    Fled is that music:—Do I wake or sleep?

ODE ON A GRECIAN URN

Thou still unravished bride of quietness,
  Thou foster-child of silence and slow time,
Sylvan historian, who canst thus express
  A flowery tale more sweetly than our rhyme:
What leaf-fringed legend haunts about thy shape
  Of deities or mortals, or of both,
    In Tempe or the dales of Arcady?
What men or gods are these? What maidens loth?
What mad pursuit? What struggle to escape?
    What pipes and timbrels? What wild ecstasy?

Heard melodies are sweet, but those unheard
  Are sweeter; therefore, ye soft pipes, play on;
Not to the sensual ear, but, more endeared,
  Pipe to the spirit ditties of no tone:
Fair youth, beneath the trees, thou canst not leave
  Thy song, nor ever can those trees be bare;
    Bold Lover, never, never canst thou kiss,
Though winning near the goal—yet, do not grieve;
  She cannot fade, though thou hast not thy bliss,
    For ever wilt thou love, and she be fair!

Ah, happy, happy boughs! that cannot shed
  Your leaves, nor ever bid the Spring adieu;
And, happy melodist, unwearièd,
  For ever piping songs for ever new;
More happy love! more happy, happy love!
  For ever warm and still to be enjoyed,
    For ever panting, and for ever young;

All breathing human passion far above,
    That leaves a heart high-sorrowful and cloyed,
        A burning forehead, and a parching tongue.

Who are these coming to the sacrifice?
    To what green altar, O mysterious priest,
Lead'st thou that heifer lowing at the skies,
    And all her silken flanks with garlands dressed?
What little town by river or sea shore,
    Or mountain-built with peaceful citadel,
        Is emptied of its folk, this pious morn?
And, little town, thy streets for evermore
    Will silent be; and not a soul to tell
        Why thou art desolate, can e'er return.

O Attic shape! Fair attitude! with brede
    Of marble men and maidens overwrought,
With forest branches and the trodden weed;
    Thou, silent form, dost tease us out of thought
As doth eternity: Cold Pastoral!
    When old age shall this generation waste,
        Thou shalt remain, in midst of other woe
Than ours, a friend to man, to whom thou say'st,
    "Beauty is truth, truth beauty,"—that is all
        Ye know on earth, and all ye need to know.

TO AUTUMN

Season of mists and mellow fruitfulness,
    Close bosom-friend of the maturing sun:
Conspiring with him how to load and bless
    With fruit the vines that round the thatch-eves run;
To bend with apples the mossed cottage-trees,
    And fill all fruit with ripeness to the core;
        To swell the gourd, and plump the hazel shells
With a sweet kernel; to set budding more,
    And still more, later flowers for the bees,
    Until they think warm days will never cease,
        For Summer has o'er-brimmed their clammy cells.

Who hath not seen thee oft amid thy store?
    Sometimes whoever seeks abroad may find

Thee sitting careless on a granary floor,
  Thy hair soft-lifted by the winnowing wind;
Or on a half-reaped furrow sound asleep,
  Drowsed with the fume of poppies, while thy hook
    Spares the next swath and all its twinèd flowers:
And sometimes like a gleaner thou dost keep
  Steady thy laden head across a brook;
  Or by a cider-press, with patient look,
    Thou watchest the last oozings hours by hours.

Where are the songs of Spring? Ay, where are they?
  Think not of them, thou hast thy music too,—
While barrèd clouds bloom the soft-dying day,
  And touch the stubble-plains with rosy hue;
Then in a wailful choir the small gnats mourn
  Among the river sallows, borne aloft
    Or sinking as the light wind lives or dies;
And full-grown lambs loud bleat from hilly bourn;
  Hedge-crickets sing; and now with treble soft
  The red-breast whistles from a garden-croft;
    And gathering swallows twitter in the skies.

WHEN I HAVE FEARS THAT I MAY
CEASE TO BE

WHEN I have fears that I may cease to be
Before my pen has gleaned my teeming brain,
Before high-pilèd books, in charact'ry,
Hold like rich garners the full-ripened grain;
When I behold, upon the night's starred face,
Huge cloudy symbols of a high romance,
And think that I may never live to trace,
Their shadows, with the magic hand of chance;
And when I feel, fair creature of an hour
That I shall never look upon thee more,
Never have relish in the faery power
Of unreflecting love;—then on the shore
Of the wide world I stand alone, and think,
Till Love and Fame to nothingness do sink.

LA BELLE DAME SANS MERCI

O WHAT can ail thee, knight-at-arms,
   Alone and palely loitering?
The sedge has withered from the lake,
   And no birds sing.

O what can ail thee, knight-at-arms,
   So haggard and so woe-begone?
The squirrel's granary is full,
   And the harvest's done.

I see a lily on thy brow
   With anguish moist and fever dew,
And on thy cheek a fading rose
   Fast withereth too.

I met a lady in the meads,
   Full beautiful—a faery's child;
Her hair was long, her foot was light,
   And her eyes were wild.

I made a garland for her head,
   And bracelets too, and fragrant zone;
She looked at me as she did love,
   And made sweet moan.

I set her on my pacing steed,
   And nothing else saw all day long,
For sidelong would she bend, and sing
   A faery's song.

She found me roots of relish sweet,
   And honey wild, and manna dew,
And sure in language strange she said—
   "I love thee true!"

She took me to her elfin grot,
   And there she wept and sighed full sore,
And there I shut her wild wild eyes
   With kisses four.

And there she lullèd me asleep,
  And there I dreamed—ah! woe betide!
The latest dream I ever dreamed
  On the cold hill's side.

I saw pale kings and princes too,
  Pale warriors, death-pale were they all;
They cried—"La Belle Dame sans Merci
  Thee hath in thrall!"

I saw their starved lips in the gloam,
  With horrid warning gapèd wide,
And I awoke and found me here,
  On the cold hill's side.

And this is why I sojourn here,
  Alone and palely loitering,
Though the sedge is withered from the lake
  And no birds sing.

John Henry, Cardinal Newman

1801–1890

THE PILLAR OF THE CLOUD

Lead, Kindly Light, amid the encircling gloom,
        Lead Thou me on!
The night is dark, and I am far from home!
        Lead Thou me on.
Keep Thou my feet; I do not ask to see
The distant scene—one step enough for me.

I was not ever thus, nor prayed that Thou
        Shouldst lead me on.
I loved to choose and see my path, but now
        Lead Thou me on!
I loved the garish day, and, spite of fears,
Pride ruled my will: remember not past years.

So long Thy power hath blest me, sure it still
    Will lead me on,
O'er moor and fen, o'er crag and torrent till
    The night is gone,
And with the morn those angel faces smile
Which I have loved long since, and lost awhile.

Alfred, Lord Tennyson

1809–1892

MARIANA

WITH blackest moss the flower-pots
    Were thickly crusted, one and all:
The rusted nails fell from the knots
    That held the pear to the gable-wall.
The broken sheds looked sad and strange:
    Unlifted was the clinking latch;
    Weeded and worn the ancient thatch
Upon the lonely moated grange.
    She only said, "My life is dreary,
        He cometh not," she said;
    She said, "I am aweary, aweary,
        I would that I were dead!"

Her tears fell with the dews at even;
    Her tears fell ere the dews were dried;
She could not look on the sweet heaven,
    Either at morn or eventide.
After the flitting of the bats,
    When thickest dark did trance the sky,
    She drew her casement-curtain by,
And glanced athwart the glooming flats.
    She only said, "The night is dreary,
        He cometh not," she said;
    She said, "I am aweary, aweary,
        I would that I were dead!"

Upon the middle of the night,
    Waking she heard the night-fowl crow:

The cock sung out an hour ere light;
From the dark fen the oxen's low
Came to her: without hope of change,
In sleep she seemed to walk forlorn,
Till cold winds woke the gray-eyed morn
About the lonely moated grange.
She only said, "My life is dreary,
He cometh not," she said;
She said, "I am aweary, aweary,
I would that I were dead!"

About a stone-cast from the wall
A sluice with blackened waters slept,
And o'er it many, round and small,
The clustered marish-mosses crept.
Hard by a poplar shook alway,
All silver-green with gnarlèd bark:
For leagues no other tree did mark
The level waste, the rounding gray.
She only said, "The night is dreary,
He cometh not," she said;
She said, "I am aweary, aweary,
I would that I were dead!"

And ever when the moon was low,
And the shrill winds were up and away,
In the white curtain, to and fro,
She saw the gusty shadow sway.
But when the moon was very low,
And wild winds bound within their cell,
The shadow of the poplar fell
Upon her bed, across her brow.
She only said, "My life is dreary,
He cometh not," she said;
She said, "I am aweary, aweary,
I would that I were dead!"

All day within the dreamy house,
The doors upon their hinges creaked;

The blue fly sung in the pane; the mouse
  Behind the moldering wainscot shrieked,
Or from the crevice peered about.
  Old faces glimmered through the doors,
  Old foosteps trod the upper floors,
Old voices called her from without.
    She only said, "My life is dreary,
      He cometh not," she said;
    She said, "I am aweary, aweary,
      I would that I were dead!"

The sparrow's chirrup on the roof,
  The slow clock ticking, and the sound
Which to the wooing wind aloof
  The poplar made, did all confound
Her sense; but most she loathed the hour
  When the thick-moted sunbeam lay
  Athwart the chambers, and the day
Was sloping toward his western bower.
    Then said she, "I am very dreary,
      He will not come," she said;
    She wept, "I am aweary, aweary,
      O God, that I were dead!"

SONG FROM MAUD

COME into the garden, Maud,
  For the black bat, night, has flown,
Come into the garden, Maud,
  I am here at the gate alone;
And the woodbine spices are wafted abroad,
  And the musk of the rose is blown.

For a breeze of morning moves,
  And the planet of love is on high,
Beginning to faint in the light that she loves
  On a bed of daffodil sky,
To faint in the light of the sun she loves,
  To faint in his light, and to die.

All night have the roses heard
   The flute, violin, bassoon;
All night has the casement jessamine stirred
   To the dancers dancing in tune;
Till a silence fell with the waking bird,
   And a hush with the setting moon.

I said to the lily, "There is but one,
   With whom she has heart to be gay.
When will the dancers leave her alone?
   She is weary of dance and play."
Now half to the setting moon are gone,
   And half to the rising day;
Low on the sand and loud on the stone
   The last wheel echoes away.

I said to the rose, "The brief night goes
   In babble and revel and wine.
O young lord-lover, what sighs are those,
   For one that will never be thine
But mine, but mine," so I sware to the rose,
   "Forever and ever, mine."

And the soul of the rose went into my blood,
   As the music clashed in the Hall;
And long by the garden lake I stood,
   For I heard your rivulet fall
From the lake to the meadow and on to the wood,
   Our wood, that is dearer than all;

From the meadow your walks have left so sweet
   That whenever a March-wind sighs
He sets the jewel-print of your feet
   In violets blue as your eyes,
To the woody hollows in which we meet
   And the valleys of Paradise.

The slender acacia would not shake
   One long milk-bloom on the tree;

The white lake-blossom fell into the lake
   As the pimpernel dozed on the lea;
But the rose was awake all night for your sake,
   Knowing your promise to me;
The lilies and roses were all awake,
   They sighed for the dawn and thee.

Queen rose of the rosebud garden of girls,
   Come hither, the dances are done,
In gloss of satin and glimmer of pearls,
   Queen lily and rose in one;
Shine out, little head, sunning over with curls,
   To the flowers, and be their sun.

There has fallen a splendid tear
   From the passion-flower at the gate.
She is coming, my dove, my dear;
   She is coming, my life, my fate.
The red rose cries, "She is near, she is near;"
   And the white rose weeps, "She is late;"
The larkspur listens, "I hear, I hear;"
   And the lily whispers, "I wait."

She is coming, my own, my sweet;
   Were it ever so airy a tread,
My heart would hear her and beat,
   Were it earth in an earthy bed;
My dust would hear her and beat,
   Had I lain for a century dead,
Would start and tremble under her feet,
   And blossom in purple and red.

BREAK, BREAK, BREAK

Break, break, break,
   On thy cold gray stones, O Sea!
And I would that my tongue could utter
   The thoughts that arise in me.

O well for the fisherman's boy,
　That he shouts with his sister at play!
O well for the sailor lad,
　That he sings in his boat on the bay!

And the stately ships go on
　To their haven under the hill;
But O for the touch of a vanished hand,
　And the sound of a voice that is still!

Break, break, break,
　At the foot of thy crags, O Sea!
But the tender grace of a day that is dead
　Will never come back to me.

SONGS FROM THE PRINCESS

I

Tears, idle tears, I know not what they mean,
Tears from the depth of some divine despair
Rise in the heart, and gather to the eyes,
In looking on the happy autumn-fields,
And thinking of the days that are no more.

Fresh as the first beam glittering on a sail,
That brings our friends up from the underworld,
Sad as the last which reddens over one
That sinks with all we love below the verge;
So sad, so fresh, the days that are no more.

Ah, sad and strange as in dark summer dawns
The earliest pipe of half-awakened birds
To dying ears, when unto dying eyes
The casement slowly grows a glimmering square;
So sad, so strange, the days that are no more.

Dear as remembered kisses after death,
And sweet as those by hopeless fancy feigned
On lips that are for others; deep as love,
Deep as first love, and wild with all regret;
O Death in Life, the days that are no more!

2

The splendor falls on castle walls
   And snowy summits old in story;
The long light shakes across the lakes,
   And the wild cataract leaps in glory.
Blow, bugle, blow, set the wild echoes flying,
Blow, bugle; answer, echoes, dying, dying, dying.

O, hark, O, hear! how thin and clear,
   And thinner, clearer, farther going!
O, sweet and far from cliff and scar
   The horns of elfland faintly blowing!
Blow, let us hear the purple glens replying,
Blow, bugle; answer, echoes, dying, dying, dying.

O love, they die in yon rich sky,
   They faint on hill or field or river;
Our echoes roll from soul to soul,
   And grow for ever and for ever.
Blow, bugle, blow, set the wild echoes flying,
And answer, echoes, answer, dying, dying, dying.

Robert Browning

1812–1889

PORPHYRIA'S LOVER

The rain set early in to-night,
   The sullen wind was soon awake,
It tore the elm-tops down for spite,
   And did its worst to vex the lake:
I listened with heart fit to break.
When glided in Porphyria; straight
   She shut the cold out and the storm,
And kneeled and made the cheerless grate
   Blaze up, and all the cottage warm;
Which done, she rose, and from her form
Withdrew the dripping cloak and shawl,

And laid her soiled gloves by, untied
Her hat and let the damp hair fall,
 And, laſt, she sat down by my side
And called me. When no voice replied,
She put my arm about her waiſt,
 And made her smooth white shoulder bare
And all her yellow hair displaced,
 And, ſtooping, made my cheek lie there,
And spread, o'er all, her yellow hair,
Murmuring how she loved me—she
 Too weak, for all her heart's endeavor,
To set its ſtruggling passion free
 From pride, and vainer ties dissever,
And give herself to me forever.
But passion sometimes would prevail,
 Nor could to-night's gay feaſt reſtrain
A sudden thought of one so pale
 For love of her, and all in vain:
So, she was come through wind and rain.
Be sure I looked up at her eyes
 Happy and proud; at laſt I knew
Porphyria worshiped me; surprise
 Made my heart swell, and ſtill it grew
While I debated what to do.
That moment she was mine, mine, fair,
 Perfeƈtly pure and good: I found
A thing to do, and all her hair
 In one long yellow ſtring I wound
Three times her little throat around,
And ſtrangled her. No pain felt she;
 I am quite sure she felt no pain.
As a shut bud that holds a bee,
 I warily oped her lids: again
Laughed the blue eyes without a ſtain.
And I untightened next the tress
 About her neck; her cheek once more
Blushed bright beneath my burning kiss:
 I propped her head up as before,
Only, this time my shoulder bore

Her head, which droops upon it still:
   The smiling rosy little head,
So glad it has its utmost will,
   That all it scorned at once is fled,
And I, its love, am gained instead!
Porphyria's love: she guessed not how
   Her darling one wish would be heard.
And thus we sit together now,
   And all night long we have not stirred,
And yet God has not said a word!

MY LAST DUCHESS

FERRARA

That's my last Duchess painted on the wall,
Looking as if she were alive. I call
That piece a wonder, now: Frà Pandolf's hands
Worked busily a day, and there she stands.
Will 't please you sit and look at her? I said
"Frà Pandolf" by design, for never read
Strangers like you that pictured countenance,
The depth and passion of its earnest glance,
But to myself they turned (since none puts by
The curtain I have drawn for you, but I)
And seemed as they would ask me, if they durst,
How such a glance came there; so, not the first
Are you to turn and ask thus. Sir, 't was not
Her husband's presence only, called that spot
Of joy into the Duchess' cheek: perhaps
Frà Pandolf chanced to say, "Her mantle laps
Over my lady's wrist too much," or "Paint
Must never hope to reproduce the faint
Half-flush that dies along her throat:" such stuff
Was courtesy, she thought, and cause enough
For calling up that spot of joy. She had
A heart—how shall I say?—too soon made glad,
Too easily impressed; she liked whate'er
She looked on, and her looks went everywhere.
Sir, 't was all one! My favor at her breast,

The dropping of the daylight in the West,
The bough of cherries some officious fool
Broke in the orchard for her, the white mule
She rode with round the terrace—all and each
Would draw from her alike the approving speech,
Or blush, at least. She thanked men,—good! but thanked
Somehow—I know not how—as if she ranked
My gift of a nine-hundred-years-old name
With anybody's gift. Who'd stooped to blame
This sort of trifling? Even had you skill
In speech—(which I have not)—to make your will
Quite clear to such an one, and say, "Just this
Or that in you disgusts me; here you miss,
Or there exceed the mark"—and if she let
Herself be lessoned so, nor plainly set
Her wits to yours, forsooth, and made excuse,
—E'en then would be some stooping; and I choose
Never to stoop. Oh, sir, she smiled, no doubt,
Whene'er I passed her; but who passed without
Much the same smile? This grew; I gave commands;
Then all smiles stopped together. There she stands
As if alive. Will 't please you rise? We'll meet
The company below, then. I repeat
The Count your master's known munificence
Is ample warrant that no just pretense
Of mine for dowry will be disallowed;
Though his fair daughter's self, as I avowed
At starting, is my object. Nay, we'll go
Together down, sir. Notice Neptune, though,
Taming a sea-horse, thought a rarity,
Which Claus of Innsbruck cast in bronze for me!

HOME-THOUGHTS, FROM ABROAD

OH, to be in England
Now that April's there,
And whoever wakes in England
Sees, some morning, unaware,

That the lowest boughs and the brushwood sheaf
Round the elm-tree bole are in tiny leaf,
While the chaffinch sings on the orchard bough
In England—now!

And after April, when May follows,
And the whitethroat builds, and all the swallows?
Hark, where my blossomed pear-tree in the hedge
Leans to the field and scatters on the clover
Blossoms and dewdrops—at the bent spray's edge—
That's the wise thrush; he sings each song twice over,
Lest you should think he never could recapture
The first fine careless rapture!
And though the fields look rough with hoary dew,
All will be gay when noontide wakes anew
The buttercups, the little children's dower
—Far brighter than this gaudy melon-flower!

HOME-THOUGHTS, FROM THE SEA

Nobly, nobly Cape Saint Vincent to the Northwest died
    away;
Sunset ran, one glorious blood-red, reeking into Cadiz
    Bay;
Bluish 'mid the burning water, full in face Trafalgar
    lay;
In the dimmest Northeast distance dawned Gibraltar
    grand and gray;
"Here and here did England help me: how can I help
    England?"—say
Whoso turns as I, this evening, turn to God to praise
    and pray,
While Jove's planet rises yonder, silent over Africa.

MEETING AT NIGHT

The gray sea and the long black land;
And the yellow half-moon large and low;
And the startled little waves that leap
In fiery ringlets from their sleep,

As I gain the cove with pushing prow,
And quench its speed i' the slushy sand.
Then a mile of warm sea-scented beach;
Three fields to cross till a farm appears;
A tap at the pane, the quick sharp scratch
And blue spurt of a lighted match,
And a voice less loud, through its joys and fears,
Than the two hearts beating each to each!

PARTING AT MORNING

Round the cape of a sudden came the sea,
And the sun looked over the mountain's rim;
And straight was a path of gold for him,
And the need of a world of men for me.

Arthur Hugh Clough

1819–1861

WHERE LIES THE LAND?

Where lies the land to which the ship would go?
Far, far ahead, is all her seamen know.
And where the land she travels from? Away,
Far, far behind, is all that they can say.

On sunny noons upon the deck's smooth face,
Linked arm in arm, how pleasant here to pace;
Or, o'er the stern reclining, watch below
The foaming wake far widening as we go.

On stormy nights when wild northwesters rave,
How proud a thing to fight with wind and wave!
The dripping sailor on the reeling mast
Exults to bear, and scorns to wish it past.

Where lies the land to which the ship would go?
Far, far ahead, is all her seamen know.
And where the land she travels from? Away,
Far, far behind, is all that they can say.

SAY NOT THE STRUGGLE NOUGHT AVAILETH

Say not the struggle nought availeth,
    The labor and the wounds are vain,
The enemy faints not, nor faileth,
    And as things have been they remain.

If hopes were dupes, fears may be liars;
    It may be, in yon smoke concealed,
Your comrades chase e'en now the fliers,
    And, but for you, possess the field.

For while the tired waves, vainly breaking,
    Seem here no painful inch to gain,
Far back, through creeks and inlets making,
    Comes silent, flooding in, the main.

And not by eastern windows only,
    When daylight comes, comes in the light,
In front, the sun climbs slow, how slowly,
    But westward, look, the land is bright.

Matthew Arnold
1822–1888

REQUIESCAT

Strew on her roses, roses,
    And never a spray of yew!
In quiet she reposes;
    Ah, would that I did too!

Her mirth the world required;
    She bathed it in smiles of glee.
But her heart was tired, tired,
    And now they let her be.

Her life was turning, turning,
    In mazes of heat and sound.
But for peace her soul was yearning,
    And now peace laps her round.

Her cabined, ample spirit,
It fluttered and failed for breath.
To-night it doth inherit
The vasty hall of death.

DOVER BEACH

THE sea is calm to-night,
The tide is full, the moon lies fair
Upon the straits;—on the French coast the light
Gleams and is gone; the cliffs of England stand,
Glimmering and vast, out in the tranquil bay,
Come to the window, sweet is the night-air!
Only, from the long line of spray
Where the sea meets the moon-blanched land,
Listen! you hear the grating roar
Of pebbles which the waves draw back, and fling,
At their return, up the high strand,
Begin, and cease, and then again begin,
With tremulous cadence slow, and bring
The eternal note of sadness in.

Sophocles long ago
Heard it on the Ægean, and it brought
Into his mind the turbid ebb and flow
Of human misery; we
Find also in the sound a thought,
Hearing it by this distant northern sea.

The sea of faith
Was once, too, at the full, and round earth's shore
Lay like the folds of a bright girdle furled.
But now I only hear
Its melancholy, long, withdrawing roar,
Retreating, to the breath
Of the night-wind, down the vast edges drear
And naked shingles of the world.

Ah, love, let us be true
To one another! for the world, which seems

To lie before us like a land of dreams,
So various, so beautiful, so new,
Hath really neither joy, nor love, nor light,
Nor certitude, nor peace, nor help for pain;
And we are here as on a darkling plain
Swept with confused alarms of struggle and flight,
Where ignorant armies clash by night.

Christina Rossetti

1830–1894

SONG

When I am dead, my dearest,
    Sing no sad songs for me;
Plant thou no roses at my head,
    Nor shady cypress tree:
Be the green grass above me
    With showers and dewdrops wet;
And if thou wilt, remember,
    And if thou wilt, forget.

I shall not see the shadows,
    I shall not feel the rain;
I shall not hear the nightingale
    Sing on, as if in pain;
And dreaming through the twilight
    That doth not rise nor set,
Haply I may remember,
    And haply may forget.

A BIRTHDAY

My heart is like a singing bird
    Whose nest is in a watered shoot;
My heart is like an apple-tree
    Whose boughs are bent with thick-set fruit;
My heart is like a rainbow shell
    That paddles in a halcyon sea;
My heart is gladder than all these,
    Because my love is come to me.

Raise me a dais of silk and down;
  Hang it with vair and purple dyes;
Carve it in doves and pomegranates,
  And peacocks with a hundred eyes;
Work it in gold and silver grapes,
  In leaves and silver fleur-de-lys;
Because the birthday of my life
  Is come, my love is come to me.

REMEMBER

REMEMBER me when I am gone away,
Gone far away into the silent land;
When you can no more hold me by the hand,
Nor I half turn to go, yet turning stay.
Remember me when no more, day by day,
You tell me of our future that you planned:
Only remember me; you understand
It will be late to counsel then or pray.
Yet if you should forget me for a while
And afterwards remember, do not grieve:
For if the darkness and corruption leave
A vestige of the thoughts that once I had,
Better by far you should forget and smile
Than that you should remember and be sad.

Algernon Charles Swinburne

1837–1909

THE GARDEN OF PROSERPINE

HERE, where the world is quiet,
  Here, where all trouble seems
Dead winds' and spent waves' riot
  In doubtful dreams of dreams;
I watch the green field growing
For reaping folk and sowing,
For harvest-time and mowing,
  A sleepy world of streams.

I am tired of tears and laughter,
    And men that laugh and weep;
Of what may come hereafter
    For men that sow to reap:
I am weary of days and hours,
Blown buds of barren flowers,
Desires and dreams and powers,
    And everything but sleep.

Here life has death for neighbor,
    And far from eye or ear
Wan waves and wet winds labor,
    Weak ships and spirits steer;
They drive adrift, and whither
They wot not who make thither;
But no such winds blow hither,
    And no such things grow here.

No growth of moor or coppice,
    No heather-flower or vine
But bloomless buds of poppies,
    Green grapes of Proserpine,
Pale beds of blowing rushes,
Where no leaf blooms or blushes
Save this whereout she crushes
    For dead men deadly wine.

Pale, without name or number,
    In fruitless fields of corn,
They bow themselves and slumber
    All night till light is born;
And like a soul belated,
In hell and heaven unmated,
By cloud and mist abated
    Comes out of darkness morn.

Though one were strong as seven,
    He too with death shall dwell,
Nor wake with wings in heaven,
    Nor weep for pains in hell;

Though one were fair as roses,
His beauty clouds and closes,
And well though love reposes,
    In the end it is not well.

Pale, beyond porch and portal,
    Crowned with calm leaves, she stands
Who gathers all things mortal
    With cold immortal hands;
Her languid lips are sweeter
Than love's who fears to greet her
To men that mix and meet her
    From many times and lands.

She waits for each and other,
    She waits for all men born;
Forgets the earth her mother,
    The life of fruits and corn;
And spring and seed and swallow
Take wing for her and follow
Where summer song rings hollow
    And flowers are put to scorn.

There go the loves that wither,
    The old loves with wearier wings;
And all dead years draw thither,
    And all disastrous things;
Dead dreams of days forsaken,
Blind buds that snows have shaken,
Wild leaves that winds have taken,
    Red strays of ruined springs.

We are not sure of sorrow,
    And joy was never sure;
To-day will die to-morrow;
    Time stoops to no man's lure;
And love, grown faint and fretful,
With lips but half regretful
Sighs, and with eyes forgetful
    Weeps that no loves endure.

From too much love of living,
   From hope and fear set free,
We thank with brief thanksgiving
   Whatever gods may be
That no life lives for ever;
That dead men rise up never;
That even the weariest river
   Winds somewhere safe to sea.

Then star nor sun shall waken,
   Nor any change of light:
Nor sound of waters shaken,
   Nor any sound or sight:
Nor wintry leaves nor vernal,
Nor days nor things diurnal:
Only the sleep eternal
   In an eternal night.

CHORUS

From ATALANTA IN CALYDON

WHEN the hounds of spring are on winter's traces,
   The mother of months in meadow or plain
Fills the shadows and windy places
   With lisp of leaves and ripple of rain;
And the brown bright nightingale amorous
Is half assuaged for Itylus,
For the Thracian ships and the foreign faces,
   The tongueless vigil, and all the pain.

Come with bows bent and with emptying of quivers,
   Maiden most perfect, lady of light,
With a noise of winds and many rivers,
   With a clamor of waters, and with might;
Bind on thy sandals, O thou most fleet,
Over the splendor and speed of thy feet;
For the faint east quickens, the wan west shivers,
   Round the feet of the day and the feet of the night.

Where shall we find her, how shall we sing to her,
  Fold our hands round her knees, and cling?
O that man's heart were as fire and could spring to her,
  Fire, or the strength of the streams that spring!
For the stars and the winds are unto her
As raiment, as songs of the harp-player;
For the risen stars and the fallen cling to her,
  And the southwest-wind, and the west-wind sing.

For winter's rains and ruins are over,
  And all the season of snows and sins;
The days dividing lover and lover,
  The light that loses, the night that wins;
And time remembered is grief forgotten,
And frosts are slain and flowers begotten,
And in green underwood and cover
  Blossom by blossom the spring begins.

The full streams feed on flower of rushes,
  Ripe grasses trammel a traveling foot,
The faint fresh flame of the young year flushes
  From leaf to flower and flower to fruit;
And fruit and leaf are as gold and fire,
And the oat is heard above the lyre,
And the hoofèd heel of a satyr crushes
  The chestnut-husk at the chestnut-root.

And Pan by noon and Bacchus by night,
  Fleeter of foot than the fleet-foot kid,
Follows with dancing and fills with delight
  The Mænad and the Bassarid;
And soft as lips that laugh and hide
The laughing leaves of the trees divide,
And screen from seeing and leave in sight
  The god pursuing, the maiden hid.

The ivy falls with the Bacchanal's hair
  Over her eyebrows hiding her eyes;
The wild vine slipping down leaves bare
  Her bright breast shortening into sighs;

The wild vine slips with the weight of its leaves,
But the berried ivy catches and cleaves
To the limbs that glitter, the feet that scare
  The wolf that follows, the fawn that flies.

Thomas Hardy

1840–1928

DRUMMER HODGE

They throw in Drummer Hodge, to rest
  Uncoffined—just as found:
His landmark is a kopje-crest
  That breaks the veldt around;
And foreign constellations west
  Each night above his mound.

Young Hodge the Drummer never knew—
  Fresh from his Wessex home—
The meaning of the broad Karoo,
  The Bush, the dusty loam,
And why uprose to nightly view
  Strange stars amid the gloam.

Yet portion of the unknown plain
  Will Hodge for ever be;
His homely Northern breast and brain
  Grow to some Southern tree,
And strange-eyed constellations reign
  His stars eternally.

HAP

If but some vengeful god would call to me
From up the sky, and laugh: "Thou suffering thing,
Know that thy sorrow is my ecstasy,
That thy love's loss is my hate's profiting!"

Then would I bear it, clench myself, and die,
Steeled by the sense of ire unmerited;
Half-eased in that a Powerfuller than I
Had willed and meted me the tears I shed.

But not so. How arrives it joy lies slain,
And why unblooms the best hope ever sown?
—Crass Casualty obstructs the sun and rain,
And dicing Time for gladness casts a moan. . . .
These purblind Doomsters had as readily strown
Blisses about my pilgrimage as pain.

LET ME ENJOY

(Minor Key)

LET me enjoy the earth no less
Because the all-enacting Might
That fashioned forth its loveliness
Had other aims than my delight.

About my path there flits a Fair,
Who throws me not a word or sign;
I'll charm me with her ignoring air,
And laud the lips not meant for mine.

From manuscripts of moving song
Inspired by scenes and dreams unknown,
I'll pour out raptures that belong
To other, as they were my own.

And some day hence, towards Paradise
And all its blest—if such should be—
I will lift glad, afar-off eyes,
Though it contain no place for me.

ON AN INVITATION TO THE UNITED STATES

MY ardors for emprize nigh lost
Since Life has bared its bones to me,
I shrink to seek a modern coast
Whose riper times have yet to be;
Where the new regions claim them free
From that long drip of human tears
Which peoples old in tragedy
Have left upon the centuried years.

For, wonning in these ancient lands,
  Enchased and lettered as a tomb,
And scored with prints of perished hands,
  And chronicled with dates of doom,
Though my own Being bear no bloom
I trace the lives such scenes enshrine,
  Give past exemplars present room,
And their experience count as mine.

Alice Meynell

1850–1923

THE SHEPHERDESS

She walks—the lady of my delight—
  A shepherdess of sheep.
Her flocks are thoughts. She keeps them white;
  She guards them from the steep;
She feeds them on the fragrant height,
  And folds them in for sleep.

She roams maternal hills and bright,
  Dark valleys safe and deep.
Into that tender breast at night
  The chastest stars may peep.
She walks—the lady of my delight—
  A shepherdess of sheep.

She holds her little thoughts in sight,
  Though gay they run and leap.
She is so circumspect and right;
  She has her soul to keep.
She walks—the lady of my delight—
  A shepherdess of sheep.

Alfred Edward Housman

1859–

WITH RUE MY HEART IS LADEN

With rue my heart is laden
  For golden friends I had.

For many a rose-lipt maiden
  And many a lightfoot lad.

By brooks too broad for leaping
  The lightfoot boys are laid;
The rose-lipt girls are sleeping
  In fields where roses fade.

WHITE IN THE MOON

White in the moon the long road lies,
  The moon stands blank above;
White in the moon the long road lies
  That leads me from my love.

Still hangs the hedge without a gust,
  Still, still the shadows stay:
My feet upon the moonlit dust
  Pursue the ceaseless way.

The world is round, so travelers tell,
  And straight though reach the track,
Trudge on, trudge on, 'twill all be well,
  The way will guide one back.

But ere the circle homeward hies
  Far, far it must remove:
White in the moon the long road lies
  That leads me from my love.

LOVELIEST OF TREES

Loveliest of trees, the cherry now
Is hung with bloom along the bough,
And stands about the woodland ride
Wearing white for Eastertide.

Now, of my threescore years and ten,
Twenty will not come again,
And take from seventy springs a score,
It only leaves me fifty more.

And since to look at things in bloom
Fifty springs are little room,
About the woodlands I will go
To see the cherry hung with snow.

FAR IN A WESTERN BROOKLAND

Far in a western brookland
    That bred me long ago
The poplars stand and tremble
    By pools I used to know.

There, in the windless night-time,
    The wanderer, marveling why,
Halts on the bridge to hearken
    How soft the poplars sigh.

He hears: long since forgotten
    In fields where I was known,
Here I lie down in London
    And turn to rest alone.

There, by the starlit fences,
    The wanderer halts and hears
My soul that lingers sighing
    About the glimmering weirs.

Rudyard Kipling

1865–

RECESSIONAL

God of our fathers, known of old,
    Lord of our far-flung battle-line,
Beneath whose awful Hand we hold
    Dominion over palm and pine—
Lord God of Hosts, be with us yet,
Lest we forget—lest we forget!

The tumult and the shouting dies;
  The captains and the kings depart:
Still stands Thine ancient sacrifice,
  An humble and a contrite heart.
Lord God of Hosts, be with us yet,
Lest we forget—lest we forget!

Far-called, our navies melt away;
  On dune and headland sinks the fire:
Lo, all our pomp of yesterday
  Is one with Nineveh and Tyre!
Judge of the Nations, spare us yet,
Lest we forget—lest we forget!

If, drunk with sight of power, we loose
  Wild tongues that have not Thee in awe,
Such boastings as the Gentiles use,
  Or lesser breeds without the Law—
Lord God of Hosts, be with us yet,
Lest we forget—lest we forget!

For heathen heart that puts her trust
  In reeking tube and iron shard,
All valiant dust that builds on dust,
  And guarding, calls not Thee to guard,
For frantic boast and foolish word—
Thy Mercy on Thy People, Lord!

                              Amen.

Ernest Dowson ·

1867–1900

VITAE SUMMA BREVIS SPEM NOS VETAT
INCOHARE LONGAM

They are not long, the weeping and the laughter,
  Love and desire and hate:
I think they have no portion in us after
  We pass the gate.

They are not long, the days of wine and roses:
    Out of a misty dream
Our path emerges for a while, then closes
    Within a dream.

William Henry Davies

1870–

LEISURE

WHAT is this life, if full of care,
We have no time to stand and stare.

No time to stand beneath the boughs
And stare as long as sheep or cows.

No time to see, when woods we pass,
Where squirrels hide their nuts in grass.

No time to see, in broad daylight,
Streams full of stars, like stars at night.

No time to turn at Beauty's glance,
And watch her feet, how they can dance.

No time to wait till her mouth can
Enrich that smile her eyes began.

A poor life this if, full of care,
We have no time to stand and stare.

Walter de la Mare

1873–

THE LISTENERS

"Is there anybody there?" said the Traveler,
    Knocking on the moonlit door;
And his horse in the silence champed the grasses
    Of the forest's ferny floor;
And a bird flew up out of the turret,
    Above the Traveler's head:
And he smote upon the door again a second time;
    "Is there anybody here?" he said.

But no one descended to the Traveler;
   No head from the leaf-fringed sill
Leaned over and looked into his gray eyes,
   Where he stood perplexed and still.
But only a host of phantom listeners
   That dwelt in the lone house then
Stood listening in the quiet of the moonlight
   To that voice from the world of men:
Stood thronging the faint moonbeams on the dark stair,
   That goes down to the empty hall,
Hearkening in the air stirred and shaken
   By the lonely Traveler's call.
And he felt in his heart their strangeness,
   Their stillness answering his cry,
While his horse moved, cropping the dark turf,
   Neath the starred and leafy sky;
For he suddenly smote on the door, even
   Louder, and lifted his head:—
"Tell them I came, and no one answered,
   That I kept my word," he said.
Never the least stir made the listeners,
   Though every word he spake
Fell echoing through the shadowiness of the still house
   From the one man left awake:
Ay, they heard his foot upon the stirrup,
   And the sound of iron on stone,
And how the silence surged softly backward,
   When the plunging hoofs were gone.

John Masefield

1878–

SONNET

From LOLLINGDON DOWNS

HERE in the self is all that man can know
Of Beauty, all the wonder, all the power,
All the unearthly color, all the glow,
Here in the self which withers like a flower;

Here in the self which fades as hours pass,
And droops and dies and rots and is forgotten
Sooner, by ages, than the mirroring glass
In which it sees its glory still unrotten.
Here in the flesh, within the flesh, behind,
Swift in the blood and throbbing on the bone,
Beauty herself, the universal mind,
Eternal April wandering alone;
The God, the holy Ghost, the atoning Lord,
Here in the flesh, the never yet explored.

Aldous Huxley

1894–

FIRST PHILOSOPHER'S SONG

A POOR degenerate from the ape
Whose hands are four, whose tail's a limb,
I contemplate my flaccid shape
And know I may not rival him,

Save with my mind—a nimbler beast
Possessing a thousand sinewy tails,
A thousand hands, with which it scales,
Greedy of luscious truth, the greased

Poles and the coco palms of thought,
Thrids easily through the mangrove maze
Of metaphysics, walks the taut
Frail dangerous liana ways

That link across wide gulfs remote
Analogies between tree and tree;
Outruns the hare, outhops the goat;
Mind fabulous, mind sublime and free!

But oh, the sound of simian mirth!
Mind, issued from the monkey's womb,
Is still umbilical to earth,
Earth its home and earth its tomb.

Robert Graves

1895–

LOST LOVE

His eyes are quickened so with grief,
He can watch a grass or leaf
Every instant grow; he can
Clearly through a flint wall see,
Or watch the startled spirit flee
From the throat of a dead man.
Across two counties he can hear,
And catch your words before you speak.
The woodlouse or the maggot's weak
Clamor rings in his sad ear;
And noise so slight it would surpass
Credence:—drinking sound of grass,
Worm talk, clashing jaws of moth
Chumbling holes in cloth:
The groan of ants who undertake
Gigantic loads for honor's sake,
Their sinews creak, their breath comes thin:
Whir of spiders when they spin.
And minute whispering, mumbling, sighs
Of idle grubs and flies.
This man is quickened so with grief,
He wanders god-like or like thief
Inside and out, below, above,
Without relief seeking lost love.

IRISH

From the Gaelic
Colum-Cille

6th century

(Attributed)

FAREWELL TO IRELAND

Alas for the voyage, O High King of Heaven,
    Enjoined upon me,
For that I was on the red plain of bloody Cooldrevin
    Was present to see.

How happy the son is of Dima; no sorrow
    For him is designed,
He is having, this hour, round his own hill in Durrow,
    The wish of his mind.

The sound of the winds in the elms, like strings of
    A harp being played,
The note of a blackbird that claps with the wings of
    Delight in the shade.

With him in Ros-Grencha the cattle are lowing
    At earliest dawn,
On the brink of the summer the pigeons are cooing
    And doves in the lawn.

Three things am I leaving behind me, the very
    Most dear that I know,
Tir-Leedach I'm leaving, and Durrow and Derry;
    Alas, I must go!

Yet my visit and feasting with Comgall have eased me
    At Cainneach's right hand,
And all but thy government, Eiré, have pleased me,
    Thou waterful land.

(Douglas Hyde)

Hugh O'Donnell

16th century

(Attributed)

DARK ROSALEEN

O MY dark Rosaleen,
 Do not sigh, do not weep!
The priests are on the ocean green,
 They march along the deep.
There's wine from the royal Pope,
 Upon the ocean green;
And Spanish ale shall give you hope,
 My dark Rosaleen!
 My own Rosaleen!
Shall glad your heart, shall give you hope,
Shall give you health and help, and hope,
 My Dark Rosaleen.

O hills, and through dales,
 Have I roamed for your sake;
All yesterday I sailed with sails
 On river and on lake.
The Erne, at its highest flood,
 I dashed across unseen,
For there was lightning in my blood,
 My dark Rosaleen!
 My own Rosaleen!
Oh! there was lightning in my blood,
Red lightning lightened through my blood,
 My Dark Rosaleen!

All day long in unrest,
 To and fro do I move,
The very soul within my breast
 Is wasted for you, love!
The heart in my bosom faints
 To think of you, my Queen,

My life of life, my saint of saints,
  My dark Rosaleen!
  My own Rosaleen!
To hear your sweet and sad complaints,
My life, my love, my saint of saints,
  My Dark Rosaleen!

Woe and pain, pain and woe,
  Are my lot, night and noon,
To see your bright face clouded so,
  Like to the mournful moon.
But yet will I rear your throne
  Again in golden sheen;
'Tis you shall reign, shall reign alone,
  My dark Rosaleen!
  My own Rosaleen!
'Tis you shall have the golden throne,
'Tis you shall reign, shall reign alone,
  My Dark Rosaleen!

Over dews, over sands
  Will I fly for your weal
Your holy, delicate white hands
  Shall girdle me with steel.
At home in your emerald bowers,
  From morning's dawn till e'en,
You'll pray for me, my flower of flowers,
  My dark Rosaleen!
  My fond Rosaleen!
You'll think of me through daylight's hours,
My virgin flower, my flower of flowers,
  My Dark Rosaleen!

I could scale the blue air,
  I could plow the high hills,
Oh, I could kneel all night in prayer,
  To heal your many ills!
And one beamy smile from you
  Would float like light between

My toils and me, my own, my true,
　My dark Rosaleen!
　My fond Rosaleen!
Would give me life and soul anew,
A second life, a soul anew,
　My Dark Rosaleen!

O! the Erne shall run red
　With redundance of blood,
The earth shall rock beneath our tread,
　And flames wrap hill and wood,
And gun-peal, and slogan cry
　Wake many a glen serene,
Ere you shall fade, ere you shall die,
　My dark Rosaleen!
　My own Rosaleen!
The Judgment Hour muſt firſt be nigh
Ere you can fade, ere you can die,
　My Dark Rosaleen!

(James Clarence Mangan)

O'Gnive

16th century

THE DOWNFALL OF THE GAEL

My heart is in woe,
And my soul deep in trouble,—
For the mighty are. low,
And abased are the noble:

The Sons of the Gael
Are in exile and mourning,
Worn, weary, and pale
As spent pilgrims returning;

Or men who, in flight
From the field of disaſter,
Beseech the black night
On their flight to fall faſter;

Or seamen aghast
When their planks gape asunder
And the waves fierce and fast
Tumble through in hoarse thunder;

Or men whom we see
That have got their death-omen,—
Such wretches are we
In the chains of our foemen!

Our courage is fear,
Our nobility vileness,
Our hope is despair,
And our comeliness foulness.

There is mist on our heads,
And a cloud chill and hoary
Of black sorrow, sheds
An eclipse on our glory.

From Boyne to the Linn
Has the mandate been given,
That the children of Finn
From their country be driven.

That the sons of the king—
Oh, the treason and malice!—
Shall no more ride the ring
In their own native valleys;

No more shall repair
Where the hill foxes tarry,
Nor forth to the air
Fling the hawk at her quarry:

For the plain shall be broke
By the share of the stranger,
And the stone-mason's stroke
Tell the woods of their danger;

The green hills and shore
Be with white keeps disfigured,
And the Mote of Rathmore
Be the Saxon churl's haggard!

The land of the lakes
Shall no more know the prospect
Of valleys and brakes—
So transformed is her aspect!

The Gael cannot tell,
In the uprooted wildwood
And the red ridgy dell,
The old nurse of his childhood:

The nurse of his youth
Is in doubt as she views him,
If the wan wretch, in truth,
Be the child of her bosom.

We starve by the board,
And we thirst amid wassail—
For the guest is the lord,
And the host is the vassal.

Through the woods let us roam,
Through the wastes wild and barren;
We are strangers at home!
We are exiles in Erin!

And Erin's a bark
O'er the wide waters driven!
And the tempest howls dark,
And her side planks are riven!

And in billows of might
Swell the Saxon before her,—
Unite, oh, unite!
Or the billows burst o'er her!

(*Sir Samuel Ferguson*)

Egan O'Rahilly

18th century

LAMENT FOR BANBA

O my land! O my love!
    What a woe, and how deep,
Is thy death to my long mourning soul!
    God alone, God above,
    Can awake thee from sleep,
Can release thee from bondage and dole!
    Alas, alas, and alas!
        For the once proud people of Banba!

As a tree in its prime,
    Which the ax layeth low,
Didst thou fall, O unfortunate land!
    Not by time, nor thy crime,
    Came the shock and the blow.
They were given by a false felon hand!
    Alas, alas, and alas!
        For the once proud people of Banba!

O, my grief of all griefs
    Is to see how thy throne
Is usurped, whilst thyself art in thrall!
    Other lands have their chiefs,
    Have their kings, thou alone
Art a wife, yet a widow withal!
    Alas, alas, and alas!
        For the once proud people of Banba!

The high house of O'Neill
    Is gone down to the dust,
The O'Brien is clanless and banned;
    And the steel, the red steel
    May no more be the trust
Of the Faithful and Brave in the land!
    Alas, alas, and alas!
        For the once proud people of Banba!

True, alas! Wrong and Wrath
    Were of old all too rife.
Deeds were done which no good man admires
    And perchance Heaven hath
    Chastened us for the strife
And the blood-shedding ways of our sires!
    Alas, alas, and alas!
        For the once proud people of Banba!

But, no more! This our doom,
    While our hearts yet are warm,
Let us not over weakly deplore!
    For the hour soon may loom
    When the Lord's mighty hand
Shall be raised for our rescue once more!
    And all our grief shall be turned into joy
      For the still proud people of Banba!

          (James Clarence Mangan)

Raferty

d. 1835

I AM RAFERTY

I AM Raferty the Poet
    Full of hope and love,
With eyes that have no light,
    With gentleness that has no misery.

Going west upon my pilgrimage
    By the light of my heart,
Feeble and tired
    To the end of my road.

Behold me now,
    And my face to the wall,
A-playing music
    Unto empty pockets.

          (Douglas Hyde)

Anonymous

A POEM TO BE SAID ON HEARING THE BIRDS SING

A FRAGRANT prayer upon the air
My child taught me,
Awaken there, the morn is fair,
The birds sing free;
Now dawns the day, awake and pray,
And bend the knee;
The Lamb who lay beneath the clay
Was slain for thee.

(Douglas Hyde)

Thomas Moore

1779–1852

HOW OFT HAS THE BANSHEE CRIED

How oft has the Banshee cried!
How oft has death untied
Bright links that Glory wove,
Sweet bonds entwined by Love!
Peace to each manly soul that sleepeth;
Rest to each faithful eye that weepeth;
Long may the fair and brave
Sigh o'er the hero's grave!

We're fallen on evil days!
Star after star decays,
Every bright name that shed
Light o'er the land is fled.
Dark falls the tear of him that mourneth
Lost joy, or hope that ne'er returneth:
But brightly flows the tear
Wept o'er a hero's bier.

Quenched are our beacon lights—
Thou, of the Hundred Fights!

Thou, on whose burning tongue
Truth, peace and freedom hung!
Both mute—but long as valor shineth,
Or mercy's soul at war repineth,
So long shall Erin's pride
Tell how they lived and died.

Anonymous

THE WEARIN' O' THE GREEN

Oh, Paddy dear! and did ye hear the news that's goin'
round?
The shamrock is forbid by law to grow on Irish ground!
No more St. Patrick's day we'll keep; his color can't be
seen,
For there's a cruel law ag'in' the Wearin' o' the Green!

I met with Napper Tandy, and he took me by the hand,
And he said, "How's poor ould Ireland, and how does
she stand?"
"She's the most distressful country that ever yet was seen,
For they're hanging men and women there for the
Wearin' o' the Green."

An' if the color we must wear is England's cruel red,
Let it remind us of the blood that Ireland has shed;
Then pull the shamrock from your hat, and throw it on
the sod,
An' never fear, 'twill take root there, though under foot
'tis trod.

When law can stop the blades of grass from growin' as
they grow,
An' when the leaves in summer time their color dare not
show,
Then I will change the color, too, I wear in my caubeen;
But till that day, plaise God, I'll stick to the Wearin' o'
the Green.

Katherine Tynan

1861–

THE DOVES

THE house where I was born,
Where I was young and gay,
Grows old amid its corn,
Amid its scented hay.

Moan of the cushat dove,
In silence rich and deep;
The old head I love
Nods to its quiet sleep.

Where once were nine and ten
Now two keep house together;
The doves moan and complain
All day in the still weather.

What wind, bitter and great,
Has swept the country's face,
Altered, made desolate
The heart-remembered place?

What wind, bitter and wild,
Has swept the towering trees
Beneath whose shade a child
Long since gathered heartease?

Under the golden eaves
The house is still and sad,
As though it grieves and grieves
For many a lass and lad.

The cushat doves complain
All day in the still weather;
Where once were nine or ten
But two keep house together.

William Butler Yeats

1865–

TO AN ISLE IN THE WATER

Shy one, shy one,
Shy one of my heart,
She moves in the firelight
Pensively apart.

She carries in the dishes,
And lays them in a row.
To an isle in the water
With her would I go.

She carries in the candles,
And lights the curtained room,
Shy in the doorway
And shy in the gloom;

And shy as a rabbit,
Helpful and shy.
To an isle in the water
With her would I fly.

WHEN YOU ARE OLD

When you are old and gray and full of sleep,
And nodding by the fire, take down this book,
And slowly read, and dream of the soft look
Your eyes had once, and of their shadows deep;

How many loved your moments of glad grace,
And loved your beauty with love false or true;
But one man loved the pilgrim soul in you,
And loved the sorrows of your changing face.

And bending down beside the glowing bars
Murmur, a little sadly, how love fled
And paced upon the mountains overhead
And hid his face amid a crowd of stars.

THE EVERLASTING VOICES

O sweet everlasting Voices be still;
Go to the guards of the heavenly fold
And bid them wander obeying your will
Flame under flame, till Time be no more;
Have you not heard that our hearts are old,
That you call in birds, in wind on the hill,
In shaken boughs, in tide on the shore?
O sweet everlasting Voices be still.

THE COLD HEAVEN

Suddenly I saw the cold and rook-delighting Heaven
That seemed as though ice burned and was but the more
    ice,
And thereupon imagination and heart were driven
So wild that every casual thought of that and this
Vanished, and left but memories, that should be out of
    season
With the hot blood of youth, of love crossed long ago;
And I took all the blame out of all sense and reason,
Until I cried and trembled and rocked to and fro,
Riddled with light. Ah! when the ghost begins to
    quicken,
Confusion of the death-bed over, is it sent
Out naked on the roads, as the books say, and stricken
By the injustice of the skies for punishment?

TO A FRIEND WHOSE WORK HAS COME TO NOTHING

Now all the truth is out,
Be secret and take defeat
From any brazen throat,
For how can you compete,
Being honor bred, with one
Who, were it proved he lies
Were neither shamed in his own
Nor in his neighbors' eyes?

Bred to a harder thing
Than Triumph, turn away
And like a laughing string
Whereon mad fingers play
Amid a place of stone,
Be secret and exult,
Because of all things known
That is most difficult.

George William Russell ("A. E.")
1867–

A MOUNTAIN WIND

THE cold limbs of the air
Brush by me on the hill,
Climb to the utmost crag,
Leap out, then all is still.

Ah, but what high intent
In the cold will of wind;
What scepter would it grasp
To leave these dreams behind!

Trail of celestial things:
White centaurs, winged in flight,
Through the fired heart sweep on,
A hurricane of light.

I have no plumes for air:
Earth hugs to it my bones.
Leave me, O sky-born powers,
Brother to grass and stones.

A HOLY HILL

BE still: be still: nor dare
    Unpack what you have brought,
Nor loosen on this air
    Red gnomes of your thought.

Uncover: bend the head
   And let the feet be bare:
This air that thou breathest
   Is holy air.

Sin not against the Breath,
   Using ethereal fire
To make seem as faery
   A wanton desire.

Know that this granite height
   May be a judgment throne,
Dread thou the unmovable will,
   The wrath of stone.

THE LONELY

Lone and forgotten
Through a long sleeping,
In the heart of age
A child woke weeping.

No invisible mother
Was nigh him there
Laughing and nodding
From earth and air.

No elfin comrades
Came at his call,
And the earth and the air
Were blank as a wall.

The darkness thickened
Upon him creeping,
In the heart of age
A child lay weeping.

IMMORTALITY

We must pass like smoke or live within the spirit's fire;
For we can no more than smoke unto the flame return

If our thought has changed to dream, our will unto
    desire,
  As smoke we vanish though the fire may burn.

Lights of infinite pity star the gray dusk of our days:
Surely here is soul: with it we have eternal breath:
In the fire of love we live, or pass by many ways,
  By unnumbered ways of dream to death.

John Millington Synge

1871–1909

PRELUDE

STILL south I went and west and south again,
  Through Wicklow from the morning till the night,
And far from cities, and the sights of men,
  Lived with the sunshine and the moon's delight.

I knew the stars, the flowers, and the birds,
  The gray and wintry sides of many glens,
And did but half remember human words,
  In converse with the mountains, moors, and fens.

IN KERRY

WE heard the thrushes by the shore and sea,
And saw the golden star's nativity,
Then round we went the lane by Thomas Flynn,
Across the church where bones lie out and in;
And there I asked beneath a lonely cloud
Of strange delight, with one bird singing loud,
What change you'd wrought in graveyard, rock and sea,
This new wild paradise to wake for me. . . .
Yet knew no more than knew those merry sins
Had built this stack of thigh-bones, jaws and shins.

Moira O'Neill

CORRYMEELA

OVER here in England I'm helpin' wi' the hay,
And I wisht I was in Ireland the livelong day;
Weary on the English hay, an' sorra take the wheat!
Och! Corrymeela, an' the blue sky over it.

There's a deep dumb river flowin' by beyont the heavy
trees,
This livin' air is moithered wi' the hummin' o' the bees;
I wisht I'd hear the Claddagh burn go runnin' through
the heat,
Past Corrymeela, wi' the blue sky over it.

The people that's in England is richer nor the Jews,
There's not the smallest young gossoon but thravels in
his shoes!
I'd give the pipe between me teeth to see a barefut child,
Och! Corrymeela, an' the low south wind.

Here's hands so full o' money an' hearts so full o' care,
By the luck o' love! I'd still go light for all I did go bare.
"God save ye, colleen dhas," I said; the girl she thought
me wild!
Fair Corrymeela, an' the low south wind.

D'ye mind me now, the song at night is mortal hard to
raise,
The girls are heavy goin' here, the boys are ill to plase;
When ones't I'm out this workin' hive, 'tis I'll be back
again—
Aye, Corrymeela, in the same soft rain.

The puff o' smoke from one ould roof before an English
town!
For a *shaugh* wid Andy Feelan here I'd give a silver
crown,
For a curl o' hair like Mollie's ye'll ask the like in vain,
Sweet Corrymeela, an' the same soft rain.

Thomas MacDonagh

1878–1916

JOHN-JOHN

I DREAMT laſt night of you, John-John,
And thought you called to me;
And when I woke this morning, John,
Yourself I hoped to see;
But I was all alone, John-John,
Though ſtill I heard your call;
I put my boots and bonnet on,
And took my Sunday shawl,
And went full sure to find you, John,
    At Nenagh fair.

The fair was just the same as then,
Five years ago to-day,
Wen firſt you left the thimble-men
And came with me away;
For there again were thimble-men
And shooting galleries,
And card-trick men and maggie-men,
Of all sorts and degrees;
But not a sight of you, John-John,
    Was anywhere.

I turned my face to home again,
And called myself a fool
To think you'd leave the thimble-men
And live again by rule,
To go to mass and keep the faſt
And till the little patch;
My wish to have you home was paſt
Before I raised the latch
And pushed the door and saw you, John,
    Sitting down there.

How cool you came in here, begad,
As if you owned the place!

But rest yourself there now, my lad,
'Tis good to see your face;
My dream is out, and now by it
I think I know my mind:
At six o'clock this house you'll quit,
And leave no grief behind;—
But until six o'clock, John-John,
        My bit you'll share.

The neighbors' shame of me began
When first I brought you in;
To wed and keep a tinker man
They thought a kind of sin;
But now this three years since you ve gone
'Tis pity me they do,
And that I'd rather have, John-John,
Than that they'd pity you,
Pity for me and you, John-John,
        I could not bear.

Oh, you're my husband right enough,
But what's the good of that?
You know you never were the stuff
To be the cottage cat,
To watch the fire and hear me lock
The door and put out Shep—
But there, now, it is six o'clock
And time for you to step.
God bless and keep you far, John-John!
        And that's my prayer.

Seumas O'Sullivan

1878–

THE STARLING LAKE

My sorrow that I am not by the little dún
By the lake of the starlings at Rosses under the hill,
And the larks there, singing over the fields of dew,
Or evening there and the sedges still.

For plain I see now the length of the yellow sand,
And Lissadell far off and its leafy ways,
And the holy mountain whose mighty heart
Gathers into it all the colored days.
My sorrow that I am not by the little dún
By the lake of the starlings at evening when all is still,
And still in whispering sedges the herons stand,
'Tis there I would nestle at rest till the quivering moon
Uprose in the golden quiet over the hill.

Padraic Pearse

1880–1916

IDEAL

NAKED I saw thee,
O beauty of beauty!
And I blinded my eyes
For fear I should flinch.

I heard thy music,
O sweetness of sweetness!
And I shut my ears
For fear I should fail.

I kissed thy lips
O sweetness of sweetness!
And I hardened my heart
For fear of my ruin.

I blinded my eyes
And my ears I shut,
I hardened my heart
And my love I quenched.

I turned my back
On the dream I had shaped,
And to this road before me
My face I turned.

I set my face
To the road here before me,
To the work that I see,
To the death that I shall meet.

(Translated from the Gaelic by Thomas MacDonagh)

Padraic Colum

1881–

RIVER-MATES

I'LL be an otter, and I'll let you swim
A mate beside me; we will venture down
A deep, dark river, when the sky above
Is shut of the sun; spoilers are we,
Thick-coated; no dog's tooth can bite at our veins,
With eyes and ears of poachers; deep-earthed ones
Turned hunters; let him slip past
The little vole; my teeth are on an edge
For the King-fish of the River!

    I hold him up
The glittering salmon that smells of the sea;
I hold him high and whistle!
    Now we go
Back to our earths; we will tear and eat
Sea-smelling salmon; you will tell the cubs
I am the Booty-bringer, I am the Lord
Of the River; the deep, dark, full and flowing River!

A DROVER

To Meath of the pastures,
From wet hills by the sea,
Through Leitrim and Longford
Go my cattle and me.

I hear in the darkness
Their slipping and breathing.
I name them the bye-ways
They're to pass without heeding.

Then the wet, winding roads,
Brown bogs with black water;
And my thoughts on white ships
And the King o' Spain's daughter.

O! farmer, strong farmer!
You can spend at the fair
But your face you must turn
To your crops and your care.

And soldiers—red soldiers!
You've seen many lands;
But you walk two by two,
And by captain's commands.

O! the smell of the beasts,
The wet wind in the morn;
And the proud and hard earth
Never broken for corn;

And the crowds at the fair,
The herds loosened and blind,
Loud words and dark faces
And the wild blood behind.

(O! strong men with your best
I would strive breast to breast
I could quiet your herds
With my words, with my words.)

I will bring you, my kine,
Where there's grass to the knee;
But you'll think of scant croppings
Harsh with salt of the sea.

Joseph Campbell

1881–

THE BLIND MAN AT THE FAIR

O to be blind!
To know the darkness that I know.
The stir I hear is empty wind,
The people idly come and go.

The sun is black, tho' warm and kind,
The horsemen ride, the ſtreamers blow
Vainly in the fluky wind,
For all is darkness where I go.

The cattle bellow to their kind,
The mummers dance, the jugglers throw,
The thimble-rigger speaks his mind—
But all is darkness where I go.

I feel the touch of womankind,
Their dresses flow as white as snow;
But beauty is a withered rind
For all is darkness where I go.

Laſt night the moon of Lammas shined,
Rising high and setting low;
But light is nothing to the blind—
All, all is darkness where they go.

White roads I walk with vacant mind,
White cloud-shapes round me drifting slow,
White lilies waving in the wind—
And darkness everywhere I go.

THE OLD WOMAN

As a white candle
    In a holy place,
So is the beauty
    Of an aged face.

As the spent radiance
    Of the winter sun,
So is a woman
    With her travail done.

Her brood gone from her,
    And her thoughts as ſtill
As the waters
    Under a ruined mill.

James Stephens

1882–

DEIRDRE

Do not let any woman read this verse;
It is for men, and after them their sons
And their sons' sons.

The time comes when our hearts sink utterly;
When we remember Deirdre and her tale,
And that her lips are dust.

Once she did tread the earth; men took her hand;
They looked into her eyes and said their say,
And she replied to them.

More than a thousand years it is since she
Was beautiful: she trod the living grass;
She saw the clouds.

A thousand years! The grass is still the same,
The clouds as lovely as they were that time
When Deirdre was alive.

But there has never been a woman born
Who was so beautiful, not one so beautiful
Of all the women born.

Let all men go apart and mourn together;
No man can ever love her; not a man
Can ever be her lover.

No man can bend before her; no man say—
What could one say to her? There are no words
That one could say to her!

Now she is but a story that is told
Beside the fire! No man can ever be
The friend of that poor queen.

THE DAISIES

In the scented bud of the morning—O,
    When the windy grass went rippling far,
I saw my dear one walking slow,
    In the field where the daisies are.

We did not laugh and we did not speak
    As we wandered happily to and fro;
I kissed my dear on either cheek,
    In the bud of the morning—O.

A lark sang up from the breezy land,
    A lark sang down from a cloud afar,
And she and I went hand in hand
    In the field where the daisies are.

THE GOAT PATHS

The crooked paths go every way
Upon the hill—they wind about
Through the heather in and out
Of the quiet sunniness.
And there the goats, day after day,
Stray in sunny quietness,
Cropping here and cropping there,
As they pause and turn and pass,
Now a bit of heather spray,
Now a mouthful of the grass.

In the deeper sunniness,
In the place where nothing stirs,
Quietly in quietness,
In the quiet of the furze,
For a time they come and lie
Staring on the roving sky.

If you approach they run away,
They leap and stare, away they bound,
With a sudden angry sound,
To the sunny quietude;

Crouching down where nothing stirs
In the silence of the furze,
Crouching down again to brood
In the sunny solitude.

If I were as wise as they,
I would stray apart and brood,
I would beat a hidden way
Through the quiet heather spray
To a sunny solitude;

And should you come I'd run away,
I would make an angry sound,
I would start and turn and bound
To the deeper quietude,
To the place where nothing stirs
In the silence of the furze.

In that airy quietness
I would think as long as they;
Through the quiet sunniness
I would stray away to brood
By a hidden, beaten way
In the sunny solitude,

I would think until I found
Something I can never find,
Something lying on the ground,
In the bottom of my mind.

James Joyce

1882–

I HEAR AN ARMY

I HEAR an army charging upon the land,
And the thunder of horses plunging, foam about their
knees:
Arrogant, in black armor, behind them stand,
Disdaining the reins, with fluttering whips, the
charioteers.

They cry unto the night their battle-name:
I moan in sleep when I hear afar their whirling laughter.
They cleave the gloom of dreams, a blinding flame,
Clanging, clanging upon my heart as upon an anvil.

They come shaking in triumph their long, green hair:
They come out of the sea and run shouting by the
    shore.
My heart, have you no wisdom thus to despair?
My love, my love, my love, why have you left me alone?

Joseph Plunkett

1887–1916

THE SPARK

BECAUSE I used to shun
Death and the mouth of hell
And count my battles won
If I should see the sun
The blood and smoke dispel,

Because I used to pray
That living I might see
The dawning light of day
Set me upon my way
And from my fetters free,
Because I used to seek
Your answer to my prayer
And that your soul should speak
For strengthening of the weak
To struggle with despair,

Now I have seen my shame
That I should thus deny
My soul's divinest flame,
Now shall I shout your name,
Now shall I seek to die.

By any hands but these
In battle or in flood,
On any lands or seas,
No more shall I spare ease,
No more shall I spare blood

When I have need to fight
For heaven or for your heart,
Against the powers of light
Or darkness I shall smite
Until their might depart,

Because I know the spark
Of God has no eclipse,
Now Death and I embark
And sail into the dark
With laughter on our lips.

Francis Ledwidge

1891–1917

LAMENT FOR THE POETS: 1916

I HEARD the Poor Old Woman say:
"At break of day the fowler came,
And took my blackbirds from their songs
Who loved me well thro' shame and blame.

No more from lovely distances
Their songs shall bless me mile by mile,
Nor to white Ashbourne call me down
To wear my crown another while.

With bended flowers the angels mark
For the skylark the place they lie,
From there its little family
Shall dip their wings first in the sky.

And when the first surprise of flight
Sweet songs excite, from the far dawn
Shall there come blackbirds loud with love,
Sweet echoes of the singers gone.

But in the lonely hush of eve
Weeping I grieve the silent bills."
I heard the Poor Old Woman say
In Derry of the little hills.

ARDAN MÓR

As I was climbing Ardan Mór
From the shore of Sheelin lake,
I met the herons coming down
Before the water's wake.

And they were talking in their flight
Of dreamy ways the herons go
When all the hills are withered up
Nor any waters flow.

AMERICAN

From the American Indian

LOVE SONG (Papago)

EARLY I rose
In the blue morning;
My love was up before me,
It came running up to me from the doorways of the
    Dawn.

On Papago Mountain
The dying quarry
Looked at me with my love's eyes.

(Mary Austin)

NEITHER SPIRIT NOR BIRD (Shoshone)

NEITHER spirit nor bird;
That was my flute you heard
Laſt night by the river.
When you came with your wicker jar
Where the river drags the willows,
That was my flute you heard,
Wacoba, Wacoba,
Calling, Come to the willows!

Neither the wind nor a bird
Ruſtled the lupine blooms.
That was my blood you heard
Answer your garment's hem
Whispering through the grasses;
That was my blood you heard
By the wild rose under the willows.

That was no beast that stirred,
That was my heart you heard,
Pacing to and fro
In the ambush of my desire,
To the music my flute let fall.
Wacoba, Wacoba,
That was my heart you heard
Leaping under the willows.

(Mary Austin)

COME NOT NEAR MY SONGS (Shoshone)

Come not near my songs,
You who are not my lover,
Lest from out that ambush
Leaps my heart upon you!

When my songs are glowing
As an almond thicket
With the bloom upon it,
Lies my heart in ambush
All amid my singing;
Come not near my songs,
You who are not my lover!

Do not hear my songs,
You who are not my lover!
Over-sweet the heart is,
Where my love has bruised it,
Breathe you not that fragrance,
You who are not my lover.
Do not stoop above my song,
With its languor on you,
Lest from out my singing,
Leaps my heart upon you!

(Mary Austin)

LAMENT OF A MAN FOR HIS SON (Paiute)

Son, my son!
I will go up to the mountain
And there I will light a fire

To the feet of my son's spirit,
And there will I lament him;
Saying,
O my son,
What is my life to me, now you are departed?

Son, my son,
In the deep earth
We softly laid thee
In a chief's robe,
In a warrior's gear.
Surely there,
In the spirit land
Thy deeds attend thee!
Surely,
The corn comes to the ear again!
But I, here,
I am the stalk that the seed-gatherers
Descrying empty, afar, left standing.
Son, my son!
What is my life to me, now you are departed?

(Mary Austin)

THE GRASS ON THE MOUNTAIN (Paiute)

Oh, long long
The snow has possessed the mountains.

The deer have come down and the big-horn,
They have followed the Sun to the south
To feed on the mesquite pods and the bunch grass.
Loud are the thunder drums
In the tents of the mountains.
Oh, long, long
Have we eaten chia seeds
And dried deer's flesh of the summer killing.
We are wearied of our huts
And the smoky smell of our garments.

We are sick with desire of the sun
And the grass on the mountain.

(Mary Austin)

HUNTING-SONG (Navaho)

Comes the deer to my singing,
Comes the deer to my song,
Comes the deer to my singing.

He, the blackbird, he am I,
Bird beloved of the wild deer,
Comes the deer to my singing.

From the Mountain Black,
From the summit,
Down the trail, coming, coming now,
Comes the deer to my singing.

Through the blossoms,
Through the flowers, coming, coming now,
Comes the deer to my singing.

Through the flower dew-drops,
Coming, coming now,
Comes the deer to my singing.

Through the pollen, flower pollen,
Coming, coming now,
Comes the deer to my singing.

Starting with his left fore-foot,
Stamping, turns the frightened deer.
Comes the deer to my singing.

Quarry mine, blessed am I
In the luck of the chase.
Comes the deer to my singing.

Comes the deer to my singing,
Comes the deer to my song,
Comes the deer to my singing.

(*Natalie Curtis*)

SONG OF THE HORSE (Navaho)

How joyous his neigh!
Lo, the Turquoise Horse of Johano-ai,
How joyous his neigh!
There on precious hides outspread standeth he;
How joyous his neigh!
There on tips of fair fresh flowers feedeth he;
How joyous his neigh!
There of mingled waters holy drinketh he;
How joyous his neigh!
There he spurneth dust of glittering grains;
How joyous his neigh!
There in mist of sacred pollen hidden, all hidden he;
How joyous his neigh!
There his offspring may grow and thrive for evermore;
How joyous his neigh!

(Natalie Curtis)

SONG OF THE RAIN CHANT (Navaho)

Far as man can see,
    Comes the rain,
    Comes the rain with me.

From the Rain-Mount,
Rain-Mount far away,
    Comes the rain,
    Comes the rain with me.

'Mid the lightnings,
'Mid the lightning zigzag,
'Mid the lightning flashing,
    Comes the rain,
    Comes the rain with me.

'Mid the swallows,
'Mid the swallows blue,
Chirping glad together,
    Comes the rain,
    Comes the rain with me.

Through the pollen,
Through the pollen blest.
All in pollen hidden
Comes the rain,
Comes the rain with me.

Far as man can see,
Comes the rain,
Comes the rain with me.

(*Natalie Curtis*)

KOROSTA KATZINA SONG (Hopi)

1

YELLOW butterflies
Over the blossoming virgin corn,
With pollen-painted faces
Chase one another in brilliant throng.

2

Blue butterflies
Over the blossoming virgin beans,
With pollen-painted faces
Chase one another in brilliant streams.

3

Over the blossoming corn,
Over the virgin corn
Wild bees hum;
Over the blossoming corn,
Over the virgin beans
Wild bees hum.

4

Over your field of growing corn
All day shall hang the thunder-cloud;
Over your field of growing corn
All day shall come the rushing rain.

(*Natalie Curtis*)

CORN-GRINDING SONG (Laguna)

Butterflies, butterflies,
Now fly away to the blossoms,
Fly, blue-wing,
Fly, yellow-wing,
Now fly away to the blossoms,
Fly, red-wing,
Fly, white-wing,
Now fly away to the blossoms,
Butterflies, away!
Butterflies, butterflies,
Now fly away to the blossoms.
Butterflies, away!

(Natalie Curtis)

THE VOICE THAT BEAUTIFIES THE LAND
(Navaho)

1

The voice that beautifies the land!
The voice above,
The voice of the thunder,
Among the dark clouds
Again and again it sounds,
The voice that beautifies the land.

2

The voice that beautifies the land!
The voice below,
The voice of the grasshopper,
Among the flowers and grasses
Again and again it sounds,
The voice that beautifies the land.

(Washington Matthews)

SONG TO THE MOUNTAINS (Pawnee)

1

MOUNTAINS loom upon the path we take;
Yonder peak now rises sharp and clear;
Behold! It ſtands with its head uplifted,
Thither we go, since our way lies there.

2

Mountains loom upon the path we take;
Yonder peak now rises sharp and clear;
Behold! We climb, drawing near its summit;
Steeper grows the way and slow our ſteps.

3

Mountains loom upon the path we take;
Yonder peak that rises sharp and clear,
Behold us now on its head uplifted;
Planting there our feet, we ſtand secure.

4

Mountains loom upon the path we take;
Yonder peak that rose so sharp and clear,
Behold us now on its head uplifted;
Reſting there at laſt we sing our song.

(Alice C. Fletcher)

A LOVER'S LAMENT (Tewa)

MY little breath, under the willows by the water-side we
used to sit,
And there the yellow cottonwood bird came and sang.
That I remember and therefore I weep.
Under the growing corn we used to sit,
And there the little leaf bird came and sang.
That I remember and therefore I weep.
There on the meadow of yellow flowers we used to walk.
Alas! how long ago that we two walked in that pleasant
way.

Then everything was happy, but alas! how long ago.
There on the meadow of crimson flowers we used to
  walk.
Oh, my little breath, now I go there alone in sorrow.

(H. J. Spinden)

THE COYOTE AND THE LOCUST (Zuñi)

Locust, locust, playing a flute,
  Locust, locust, playing a flute!
Away up on the pine-tree bough,
  Closely clinging,
  Playing a flute,
  Playing a flute!

(Frank Cushing)

OJIBWA WAR SONGS

1

Hear my voice, Birds of War!
I prepare a feast for you to feed on;
I see you cross the enemy's lines;
Like you I shall go.
I wish the swiftness of your wings;
I wish the vengeance of your claws;
I muster my friends;
I follow your flight.
Ho, you young men warriors,
Bear your angers to the place of fighting!

2

From the south they came, Birds of War—
Hark! to their passing scream.
I wish the body of the fiercest,
As swift, as cruel, as strong.
I cast my body to the chance of fighting.
Happy I shall be to lie in that place,
In that place where the fight was,
Beyond the enemy's line.

3

Here on my breast have I bled!
See—see! these are fighting-scars!
Mountains tremble at my yell!
I strike for life.

(*H. H. Schoolcraft*)

THREE SONGS FROM THE HAIDA

(Queen Charlotte's Island, British Columbia)

LOVE SONG

BEAUTIFUL is she, this woman,
As the mountain flower;
But cold, cold, is she,
Like the snowbank
Behind which it blooms.

THE BEAR'S SONG

(*Whoever can sing this one is admitted forever to the
friendship of the bears*)

I HAVE taken the woman of beauty
For my wife;
I have taken her from her friends.
I hope her kinsmen will not come
And take her away from me.
I will be kind to her.
Berries, berries I will give her from the hill
And roots from the ground.
I will do everything to please her.
For her I made this song and for her I sing it.

SONG FOR FINE WEATHER

O GOOD Sun,
Look thou down upon us:
Shine, shine on us, O Sun,
Gather up the clouds, wet, black, under thy arms,—

That the rains may cease to fall.
Because thy friends are all here on the beach
Ready to go fishing—
Ready for the hunt.
Therefore look kindly on us, O Good Sun!
Give us peace within our tribe
And with all our enemies.
Again, again we call—
Hear us, hear us, O Good Sun!

(Constance Lindsay Skinner)

Ralph Waldo Emerson

1803–1882

THE RHODORA

ON BEING ASKED, WHENCE IS THE FLOWER?

In May, when sea-winds pierced our solitudes,
I found the fresh Rhodora in the woods,
Spreading its leafless blooms in a damp nook,
To please the desert and the sluggish brook.
The purple petals, fallen in the pool,
Made the black water with their beauty gay;
Here might the red-bird come his plume to cool,
And court the flower that cheapens his array.
Rhodora! if the sages ask thee why
This charm is wasted on the earth and sky,
Tell them, dear, that if eyes were made for seeing,
Then Beauty is its own excuse for being:
Why thou wert there, O rival of the rose!
I never thought to ask, I never knew:
But, in my simple ignorance, suppose
The self-same Power that brought me there brought you.

BRAHMA

If the red slayer think he slays,
    Or if the slain think he is slain,
They know not well the subtle ways
    I keep, and pass, and turn again.

Far or forgot to me is near;
    Shadow and sunlight are the same;
The vanished gods to me appear;
    And one to me are shame and fame.

They reckon ill who leave me out;
    When me they fly, I am the wings;
I am the doubter and the doubt,
    And I the hymn the Brahmin sings.

The strong gods pine for my abode,
    And pine in vain the sacred Seven;
But thou, meek lover of the good!
    Find me, and turn thy back on heaven.

CONCORD HYMN

SUNG AT THE COMPLETION OF THE BATTLE MONUMENT,
JULY 4, 1837

By the rude bridge that arched the flood,
    Their flag to April's breeze unfurled,
Here once the embattled farmers stood,
    And fired the shot heard round the world.

The foe long since in silence slept;
    Alike the conqueror silent sleeps;
And Time the ruined bridge has swept
    Down the dark stream which seaward creeps.

On this green bank, by this soft stream,
    We set to-day a votive stone;
That memory may their dead redeem,
    When, like our sires, our sons are gone.

Spirit, that made those heroes dare
    To die, and leave their children free,
Bid Time and Nature gently spare
    The shaft we raise to them and thee.

THE PROBLEM

I LIKE a church; I like a cowl;
I love a prophet of the soul;
And on my heart monastic aisles
Fall like sweet strains, or pensive smiles:
Yet not for all his faith can see
Would I that cowlèd churchman be.

Why should the vest on him allure,
Which I could not on me endure?

Not from a vain or shallow thought
His awful Jove young Phidias brought,
Never from lips of cunning fell
The thrilling Delphic oracle;
Out from the heart of nature rolled
The burdens of the Bible old;
The litanies of nations came,
Like the volcano's tongue of flame,
Up from the burning core below,—
The canticles of love and woe:
The hand that rounded Peter's dome
And groined the aisles of Christian Rome
Wrought in a sad sincerity;
Himself from God he could not free;
He builded better than he knew;—
The conscious stone to beauty grew.

Know'st thou what wove yon woodbird's nest
Of leaves, and feathers from her breast?
Or how the fish outbuilt her shell,
Painting with morn each annual cell?
Or how the sacred pine-tree adds
To her old leaves new myriads?
Such and so grew these holy piles,
Whilst love and terror laid the tiles.
Earth proudly wears the Parthenon,
As the best gem upon her zone,

And Morning opes with haste her lids
To gaze upon the Pyramids;
O'er England's abbeys bends the sky,
As on its friends, with kindred eye;
For out of Thought's interior sphere
These wonders rose to upper air;
And Nature gladly gave them place,
Adopted them into her race,
And granted them an equal date
With Andes and with Ararat.

These temples grew as grows the grass;
Art might obey, but not surpass.
The passive Master lent his hand
To the vast soul that o'er him planned;
And the same power that reared the shrine
Bestrode the tribes that knelt within.
Ever the fiery Pentecost
Girds with one flame the countless host,
Trances the heart through chanting choirs,
And through the priest the mind inspires.
The word unto the prophet spoken
Was writ on tables yet unbroken;
The word by seers or sibyls told,
In groves of oak, or fanes of gold,
Still floats upon the morning wind,
Still whispers to the willing mind.
One accent of the Holy Ghost
The heedless world hath never lost.
I know what say the fathers wise,—
The Book itself before me lies,
Old *Chrysostom,* best Augustine,
And he who blent both in his line,
The younger *Golden Lips* or mines,
Taylor, the Shakespeare of divines.
His words are music in my ear,
I see his cowlèd portrait dear;
And yet, for all his faith could see,
I would not the good bishop be.

GIVE ALL TO LOVE

Give all to love;
Obey thy heart;
Friends, kindred, days,
Estate, good-fame,
Plans, credit and the Muse,—
Nothing refuse.

'Tis a brave master;
Let it have scope:
Follow it utterly,
Hope beyond hope:
High and more high
It dives into noon,
With wing unspent,
Untold intent;
But it is a god,
Knows its own path
And the outlets of the sky.

It was never for the mean;
It requireth courage stout.
Souls above doubt,
Valor unbending,
It will reward,—
They shall return
More than they were,
And ever ascending.

Leave all for love;
Yet, hear me, yet,
One word more thy heart behoved,
One pulse more of firm endeavor,—
Keep thee to-day,
To-morrow, forever,
Free as an Arab
Of thy beloved.

Cling with life to the maid;
But when the surprise,
First vague shadow of surmise
Flits across her bosom young,
Of a joy apart from thee,
Free be she, fancy-free;
Nor thou detain her vesture's hem,
Nor the palest rose she flung
From her summer diadem.

Though thou loved her as thyself,
As a self of purer clay,
Though her parting dims the day,
Stealing grace from all alive;
Heartily know,
When half-gods go,
The gods arrive.

Henry Wadsworth Longfellow

1807–1882

MY LOST YOUTH

OFTEN I think of the beautiful town
   That is seated by the sea;
Often in thought go up and down
The pleasant streets of that dear old town,
   And my youth comes back to me.
      And a verse of a Lapland song
      Is haunting my memory still:
      "A boy's will is the wind's will,
And the thoughts of youth are long, long thoughts."

I can see the shadowy lines of its trees,
   And catch, in sudden gleams,
The sheen of the far-surrounding seas,
And islands that were the Hesperides
   Of all my boyish dreams.
      And the burden of that old song,
      It murmurs and whispers still:
      "A boy's will is the wind's will,
And the thoughts of youth are long, long thoughts."

I remember the black wharves and the slips,
   And the sea-tides tossing free;
And Spanish sailors with bearded lips,
And the beauty and mystery of the ships,
   And the magic of the sea.
     And the voice of that wayward song
     Is singing and saying still:
     "A boy's will is the wind's will,
And the thoughts of youth are long, long thoughts."

I remember the bulwarks by the shore,
   And the fort upon the hill;
The sunrise gun, with its hollow roar,
The drum-beat repeated o'er and o'er,
   And the bugle wild and shrill.
     And the music of that old song
     Throbs in my memory still:
     "A boy's will is the wind's will,
And the thoughts of youth are long, long thoughts."

I remember the sea-fight far away,
   How it thundered o'er the tide!
And the dead captains, as they lay
In their graves, o'erlooking the tranquil bay
   Where they in battle died.
     And the sound of that mournful song
     Goes through me with a thrill:
     "A boy's will is the wind's will,
And the thoughts of youth are long, long thoughts."

I can see the breezy dome of groves,
   The shadows of Deering's Woods;
And the friendships old and the early loves
Come back with a Sabbath sound, as of doves
   In quiet neighborhoods.
     And the verse of that sweet old song,
     It flutters and murmurs still:
     "A boy's will is the wind's will,
And the thoughts of youth are long, long thoughts."

I remember the gleams and glooms that dart
　Across the school-boy's brain;
The song and the silence in the heart,
That in part are prophecies, and in part
　Are longings wild and vain.
　　And the voice of that fitful song
　　Sings on, and is never still:
　　"A boy's will is the wind's will,
And the thoughts of youth are long, long thoughts."

There are things of which I may not speak;
　There are dreams that cannot die;
There are thoughts that make the strong heart weak,
And bring a pallor into the cheek,
　And a mist before the eye.
　　And the words of that fatal song
　　Come over me like a chill:
　　"A boy's will is the wind's will,
And the thoughts of youth are long, long thoughts."

Strange to me now are the forms I meet
　When I visit the dear old town;
But the native air is pure and sweet,
And the trees that o'ershadow each well-known street,
　As they balance up and down,
　　Are singing the beautiful song,
　　Are sighing and whispering still:
　　"A boy's will is the wind's will,
And the thoughts of youth are long, long thoughts."

And Deering's Woods are fresh and fair,
　And with joy that is almost pain
My heart goes back to wander there,
And among the dreams of the days that were,
　I find my lost youth again.
　　And the strange and beautiful song,
　　The groves are repeating it still:
　　"A boy's will is the wind's will,
And the thoughts of youth are long, long thoughts."

CHAUCER

An old man in a lodge within a park;
The chamber walls depicted all around
With portraitures of huntsman, hawk, and hound,
And the hurt deer. He listeneth to the lark,
Whose song comes with the sunshine through the dark
Of painted glass in leaden lattice bound;
He listeneth and he laugheth at the sound,
Then writeth in a book like any clerk.
He is the poet of the dawn, who wrote
The Canterbury Tales, and his old age
Made beautiful with song; and as I read
I hear the crowing cock, I hear the note
Of lark and linnet, and from every page
Rise odors of plowed field or flowery mead.

Edgar Allan Poe

1809–1849

TO HELEN

Helen, thy beauty is to me
    Like those Nicæan barks of yore,
That gently, o'er a perfumed sea,
    The weary, wayworn wanderer bore
    To his own native shore.

On desperate seas long wont to roam,
    Thy hyacinth hair, thy classic face,
Thy Naiad airs have brought me home
    To the glory that was Greece
    And the grandeur that was Rome.

Lo! in yon brilliant window-niche
    How statue-like I see thee stand,
The agate lamp within thy hand!
    Ah, Psyche, from the regions which
    Are Holy Land!

ULALUME

THE skies they were ashen and sober;
　　The leaves they were crispèd and sere—
　　The leaves they were withering and sere:
It was night, in the lonesome October
　　Of my most immemorial year;
It was hard by the dim lake of Auber,
　　In the misty mid region of Weir—
It was down by the dank tarn of Auber,
　　In the ghoul-haunted woodland of Weir.

Here once, through an alley Titanic,
　　Of cypress, I roamed with my Soul—
　　Of cypress, with Psyche, my Soul.
These were days when my heart was volcanic
　　As the scoriac rivers that roll—
　　As the lavas that restlessly roll
Their sulphurous currents down Yaanek
　　In the ultimate climes of the Pole—
That groan as they roll down Mount Yaanek
　　In the realms of the Boreal Pole.

Our talk had been serious and sober,
　　But our thoughts they were palsied and sere—
　　Our memories were treacherous and sere—
For we knew not the month was October,
　　And we marked not the night of the year—
　　(Ah, night of all nights in the year!)
We noted not the dim lake of Auber,
　　(Though once we had journeyed down here)
Remembered not the dank tarn of Auber,
　　Nor the ghoul-haunted woodland of Weir.

And now, as the night was senescent
　　And star-dials pointed to morn—
　　As the star-dials hinted of morn—
At the end of our path a liquescent
　　And nebulous luster was born.

Out of which a miraculous crescent
   Arose with a duplicate horn—
Astarte's bediamonded crescent
   Distinct with its duplicate horn.

And I said—"She is warmer than Dian;
   She rolls through an ether of sighs—
   She revels in a region of sighs:
She has seen that the tears are not dry on
   These cheeks, where the worm never dies,
And has come past the stars of the Lion
   To point us the path to the skies—
   To the Lethean peace of the skies—
Come up, in despite of the Lion,
   To shine on us with her bright eyes—
Come up through the lair of the Lion,
   With love in her luminous eyes."

But Psyche, uplifting her finger,
   Said—"Sadly this star I mistrust—
   Her pallor I strangely mistrust—
Oh, hasten!—oh, let us not linger!
   Oh, fly!—let us fly!—for we must."
In terror she spoke, letting sink her
   Wings till they trailed in the dust—
In agony sobbed, letting sink her
   Plumes till they trailed in the dust—
   Till they sorrowfully trailed in the dust.

I replied—"This is nothing but dreaming:
   Let us on by this tremulous light!
   Let us bathe in this crystalline light!
Its sybillic splendor is beaming
   With Hope and in Beauty to-night:—
   See! it flickers up the sky through the night!
Ah, we safely may trust to its gleaming,
   And be sure it will lead us aright:
We safely may trust to a gleaming
   That cannot but guide us aright,
   Since it flickers up to Heaven through the night."

Thus I pacified Psyche and kissed her,
    And tempted her out of her gloom—
    And conquered her scruples and gloom;
And we passed to the end of a vista,
    But were stopped by the door of a tomb—
    By the door of a legended tomb;
And I said—"What is written, sweet sister,
    On the door of this legended tomb?"
    She replied—"Ulalume—Ulalume!—
    'Tis the vault of thy lost Ulalume!"

Then my heart it grew ashen and sober
    As the leaves that were crispèd and sere—
    As the leaves that were withering and sere;
And I cried—"It was surely October
    On *this* very night of last year
    That I journeyed—I journeyed down here—
    That I brought a dread burden down here!
    On this night of all nights in the year,
    Ah, what demon has tempted me here?
Well I know, now, this dim lake of Auber—
    This misty mid region of Weir—
Well I know, now, this dank tarn of Auber—
    This ghoul-haunted woodland of Weir."

ANNABEL LEE

It was many and many a year ago,
    In a kingdom by the sea
That a maiden there lived whom you may know
    By the name of Annabel Lee;—
And this maiden she lived with no other thought
    Than to love and be loved by me.

I was a child and *she* was a child,
    In this kingdom by the sea,
But we loved with a love that was more than love—
    I and my Annabel Lee—
With a love that the wingèd seraphs in Heaven
    Coveted her and me.

And this was the reason that, long ago,
In this kingdom by the sea,
A wind blew out of a cloud, chilling
My beautiful Annabel Lee;
So that her high-born kinsmen came
And bore her away from me,
To shut her up in a sepulcher
In this kingdom by the sea.

The angels, not half so happy in Heaven,
Went envying her and me:—
Yes!—that was the reason (as all men know,
In this kingdom by the sea)
That the wind came out of the cloud, by night,
Chilling and killing my Annabel Lee.

But our love it was stronger by far than the love
Of those who were older than we—
Of many far wiser than we—
And neither the angels in Heaven above,
Nor the demons down under the sea,
Can ever dissever my soul from the soul
Of the beautiful Annabel Lee:—

For the moon never beams without bringing me dreams
Of the beautiful Annabel Lee;
And the stars never rise but I feel the bright eyes
Of the beautiful Annabel Lee;
And so, all the night-tide, I lie down by the side
Of my darling,—my darling,—my life and my bride,
In the sepulcher there by the sea—
In her tomb by the sounding sea.

Henry David Thoreau

1817–1862

SMOKE

Light-winged Smoke, Icarian bird,
Melting thy pinions in thy upward flight;
Lark without song, and messenger of dawn,

Circling above the hamlets as thy nest;
Or else, departing dream, and shadowy form
Of midnight vision, gathering up thy skirts;
By night star-veiling, and by day
Darkening the light and blotting out the sun;
Go thou, my incense, upward from this hearth,
And ask the gods to pardon this clear flame.

MIST

Low-anchored cloud,
Newfoundland air,
Fountain-head and source of rivers,
Dew-cloth, dream-drapery,
And napkin spread by fays;
Drifting meadow of the air,
Where bloom the daisied banks and violets,
And in whose fenny labyrinth
The bittern booms and heron wades;
Spirit of lakes and seas and rivers,
Bear only perfumes and the scent
Of healing herbs to just men's fields.

Walt Whitman

1819–1892

I SAW IN LOUISIANA A LIVE-OAK GROWING

I saw in Louisiana a live-oak growing,
All alone stood it, and the moss hung down from the
    branches;
Without any companion it grew there, uttering joyous
    leaves of dark green,
And its look, rude, unbending, lusty, made me think of
    myself;
But I wonder'd how it could utter joyous leaves, stand-
    ing alone there, without its friend, its lover near—
    for I knew I could not;
And I broke off a twig with a certain number of leaves
    upon it, and twined around it a little moss,

And brought it away—and I have placed it in sight
  in my room;
It is not needed to remind me as of my own dear
  friends,
(For I believe lately I think of little else than of them:)
Yet it remains to me a curious token—it makes me
  think of manly love;
For all that, and though the live-oak glistens there in
  Louisiana, solitary, in a wide flat space,
Uttering joyous leaves all its life, without a friend, a
  lover, near,
I know very well I could not.

A NOISELESS, PATIENT SPIDER

A NOISELESS, patient spider,
I mark'd, where, on a little promontory, it stood, iso-
  lated;
Mark'd how, to explore the vacant, vast surrounding,
It launch'd forth filament, filament, filament, out of
  itself;
Ever unreeling them—ever tirelessly speeding them.

And you, O my Soul, where you stand,
Surrounded, surrounded, in measureless oceans of space,
Ceaselessly musing, venturing, throwing,—seeking the
  spheres, to connect them;
Till the bridge you will need, be form'd—till the ductile
  anchor hold;
Till the gossamer thread you fling, catch somewhere, O
  my Soul.

OUT OF THE CRADLE ENDLESSLY ROCKING

OUT of the cradle endlessly rocking,
Out of the mocking-bird's throat, the musical shuttle,
Out of the Ninth-month midnight,
Over the sterile sands and the fields beyond, where the
  child leaving his bed wandered alone, bareheaded,
  barefoot,

Down from the showered halo,
Up from the mystic play of shadows twining and twist-
    ing as if they were alive,
Out from the patches of briers and blackberries,
From the memories of the bird that chanted to me,
From your memories, sad brother, form the fitful risings
    and fallings I heard,
From under that yellow half-moon late-risen and swollen
    as if with tears,
From those beginning notes of yearning and love there
    in the mist,
From the thousand responses of my heart never to cease,
From the myriad thence-aroused words,
From the word stronger and more delicious than any,
From such as now they start the scene revisiting,
As a flock, twittering, rising, or overhead passing,
Borne hither, ere all eludes me, hurriedly,
A man, yet by these tears a little boy again,
Throwing myself on the sand, confronting the waves,
I, chanter of pains and joys, uniter of here and hereafter,
Taking all hints to use them, but swiftly leaping beyond
    them,
A reminiscence sing.

Once Paumanok,
When the lilac-scent was in the air and Fifth-month
    grass was growing,
Up this seashore in some briers,
Two feathered guests from Alabama, two together,
And their nest, and four light-green eggs spotted with
    brown,
And every day the he-bird to and fro near at hand,
And every day the she-bird crouched on her nest, silent,
    with bright eyes,
And every day I, a curious boy, never too close, never
    disturbing them,
Cautiously peering, absorbing, translating.

Shine! shine! shine!
Pour down your warmth, great sun!
While we bask, we two together.

Two together!
Winds blow south, or winds blow north,
Day come white, or night come black,
Home, or rivers and mountains from home,
Singing all time, minding no time,
While we two keep together.

Till of a sudden,
Maybe killed, unknown to her mate,
One forenoon the she-bird crouched not on the nest,
Nor returned that afternoon, nor the next,
Nor ever appeared again.

And thenceforward all summer in the sound of the sea,
And at night under the full of the moon in calmer
weather,
Over the hoarse surging of the sea,
Or flitting from brier to brier by day,
I saw, I heard at intervals the remaining one, the he-
bird,
The solitary guest from Alabama.

Blow! blow! blow!
Blow up sea-winds along Paumanok's shore;
I wait and I wait till you blow my mate to me.

Yes, when the stars glistened,
All night long on the prong of a moss-scalloped stake,
Down almost amid the slapping waves,
Sat the lone singer wonderful causing tears.

He called on his mate,
He poured forth the meanings which I of all men know.

Yes, my brother, I know,—
The rest might not, but I have treasured every note,
For more than once dimly down to the beach gliding,
Silent, avoiding the moonbeams, blending myself with
    the shadows,
Recalling now the obscure shapes, the echoes, the sounds
    and sights after their sorts,
The white arms out in the breakers tirelessly tossing,
I, with bare feet, a child, the wind wafting my hair,
Listened long and long.
Listened to keep, to sing, now translating the notes,
Following you, my brother.

Soothe! soothe! soothe!
Close on its wave soothes the wave behind,
And again another behind embracing and lapping, every
    one close,
But my love soothes not me, not me.

Low hangs the moon, it rose late,
It is lagging—O I think it is heavy with love, with love.

O madly the sea pushes upon the land,
With love, with love.

O night! do I not see my love fluttering out among the
    breakers?
What is that little black thing I see there in the white?

Loud! loud! loud!
Loud I call to you, my love!

High and clear I shoot my voice over the waves,
Surely you must know who is here, is here,
You must know who I am, my love.

Low-hanging moon!
What is that dusky spot in your brown yellow?
O it is the shape, the shape of my mate!
O moon, do not keep her from me any longer,

Land! land! O land!
Whichever way I turn, O I think you could give me my
*   mate back again if you only would,*
For I am almost sure I see her dimly whichever way I
*   look.*

O rising stars!
Perhaps the one I want so much will rise, will rise with
*   some of you.*

O throat! O trembling throat!
Sound clearer through the atmosphere!
Pierce the woods, the earth,
Somewhere listening to catch you must be the one I
*   want.*

Shake out carols!
Solitary here, the night's carols!
Carols of lonesome love! death's carols!
Carols under that lagging, yellow, waning moon!
O under that moon where she droops almost down into
*   the sea!*
O reckless despairing carols!

But soft! sink low!
Soft! let me just murmur,
And do you wait a moment, you husky-noised sea,
For somewhere I believe I heard my mate responding
*   to me,*
So faint, I must be still, be still to listen,
But not altogether still, for then she might not come
*   immediately to me.*

Hither, my love!
Here I am! here!
With this just-sustained note I announce myself to you,
This gentle call is for you my love, for you.

Do not be decoyed elsewhere:
That is the whistle of the wind, it is not my voice,
That is the fluttering, the fluttering of the spray,
Those are the shadows of leaves.

O darkness! O in vain!
O I am very sick and sorrowful.

O brown halo in the sky near the moon, drooping upon
    the sea!
O troubled reflection in the sea!
O throat! O throbbing heart!
And I singing uselessly, uselessly all the night.

O past! O happy life! O songs of joy!
In the air, in the woods, over fields,
Loved! loved! loved! loved! loved!
But my mate no more, no more with me!
We two together no more.

The aria is sinking.
All else continuing, the stars shining,
The winds blowing, the notes of the bird continuous
    echoing,
With angry moans the fierce old mother incessantly
    moaning,
On the sands of Paumanok's shore gray and rustling,
The yellow half-moon enlarged, sagging down, droop-
    ing, the face of the sea almost touching,
The boy ecstatic, with his bare feet the waves, with his
    hair the atmosphere dallying,
The love in the heart long pent, now loose, now at last
    tumultuously bursting,
The aria's meaning, the ears, the soul, swiftly depositing,
The strange tears down the cheeks coursing,
The colloquy there, the trio, each uttering,
The undertone, the savage old mother incessantly crying,
To the boy's soul's questions sullenly timing, some
    drowned secret hissing,
To the outsetting bard.

Demon or bird (said the boy's soul)

Is it indeed toward your mate you sing? or is it really
    to me?

For I, that was a child, my tongue's use sleeping, now
    I have heard you,

Now in a moment I know what I am for, I awake,

And already a thousand singers, a thousand songs,
    clearer, louder and more sorrowful than yours,

A thousand warbling echoes have started to life within
    me, never to die.

O you singer solitary, singing by yourself, projecting me,

O solitary me listening, never more shall I cease per-
    petuating you,

Never more shall I escape, never more the reverberations,

Never more the cries of unsatisfied love be absent from
    me,

Never again leave me to be the peaceful child I was
    before what there in the night,

By the sea under the yellow and sagging moon,

The messenger there aroused, the fire, the sweet hell
    within,

The unknown want, the destiny of me.

O give me the clew! (it lurks in the night here some-
    where)

O if I am to have so much, let me have more!

A word then, (for I will conquer it)

The word final, superior to all,

Subtle, sent up—what is it?—I listen;

Are you whispering it, and have been all the time, you
    sea-waves?

Is that it from your liquid rims and wet sands?

Whereto answering, the sea,

Delaying not, hurrying not,

Whispered me through the night, and very plainly be-
    fore daybreak,

Lisped to me the low and delicious word death,
And again death, death, death, death,
Hissing melodious, neither like the bird nor like my
    aroused child's heart,
But edging near as privately for me, rustling at my feet,
Creeping thence steadily up to my ears and laving me
    softly all over,
Death, death, death, death, death.

Which I do not forget,
But fuse the song of my dusky demon and brother,
That he sang to me in the moonlight on Paumanok's
    gray beach,
With the thousand responsive songs at random,
My own songs awaked from that hour,
And with them the key, the word up from the waves,
The word of the sweetest song and all songs,
That strong and delicious word which, creeping to my
    feet,
(Or like some old crone rocking the cradle, swathed in
    sweet garments, bending aside)
The sea whispered me.

WHEN LILACS LAST IN THE DOORYARD BLOOMED

I

WHEN lilacs last in the dooryard bloomed,
And the great star early drooped in the western sky at
    night,
I mourned, and yet shall mourn with ever-returning
    spring.

Ever-returning spring, trinity sure to me you bring,
Lilac blooming perennial and drooping star in the west,
And thought of him I love.

II

O powerful western fallen star!
O shades of night—O moody, tearful night!

O great star disappeared—O the black murk that hides
    the star!
O cruel hands that hold me powerless—O helpless soul
    of me!
O harsh surrounding cloud that will not free my soul.

III

In the dooryard fronting an old farmhouse near the
    white-washed palings,
Stands the lilac-bush tall-growing with heart-shaped
    leaves of rich green,
With many a pointed blossom rising delicate, with the
    perfume strong I love,
With every leaf a miracle—and from this bush in the
    dooryard,
With delicate-colored blossoms and heart-shaped leaves
    of rich green,
A sprig with its flower I break.

IV

In the swamp in secluded recesses,
A shy and hidden bird is warbling a song.
Solitary the thrush,
The hermit withdrawn to himself, avoiding the settle-
    ments,
Sings by himself a song.

Song of the bleeding throat,
Death's outlet song of life (for well dear brother I know,
If thou wast not granted to sing thou wouldst surely
    die.)

V

Over the breast of the spring, the land, amid cities,
Amid lanes and through old woods, where lately the
    violets peeped from the ground, spotting the gray
    débris,

Amid the grass in the fields each side of the lanes, pass-
    ing the endless grass,
Passing the yellow-speared wheat, every grain from its
    shroud in the dark-brown fields uprisen,
Passing the apple-tree blows of white and pink in the
    orchards,
Carrying a corpse to where it shall rest in the grave,
Night and day journeys a coffin.

VI

Coffin that passes through lanes and streets,
Through day and night with the great cloud darkening
    the land,
With the pomp of the inlooped flags with the cities
    draped in black,
With the show of the States themselves as of crape-
    veiled women standing,
With processions long and winding and the flambeaus
    of the night,
With the countless torches lit, with the silent sea of
    faces and the unbared heads,
With the waiting depot, the arriving coffin, and the
    somber faces,
With dirges through the night, with the thousand voices
    rising strong and solemn,
With all the mournful voices of the dirges poured
    around the coffin,
The dim-lit churches and the shuddering organs—where
    amid these you journey,
With the tolling tolling bells' perpetual clang,
Here, coffin that slowly passes,
I give you my sprig of lilac.

VII

(Nor for you, for one alone,
Blossoms and branches green to coffins all I bring,
For fresh as the morning, thus would I chant a song
    for you, O sane and sacred death.

All over bouquets of roses,
O death, I cover you over with roses and early lilies,
But mostly and now the lilac that blooms the first,
Copious I break, I break the sprigs from the bushes,
With loaded arms I come, pouring for you,
For you, and the coffins all of you, O death.)

VIII

O western orb sailing the heaven,
Now I know what you must have meant as a month
    since I walked,
As I walked in silence the transparent shadowy night,
As I saw you had something to tell as you bent to me
    night after night,
As you drooped from the sky low down as if to my
    side (while the other stars all looked on),
As we wandered together the solemn night (for some-
    thing, I know not what, kept me from sleep),
As the night advanced, and I saw on the rim of the west
    how full you were of woe,
As I stood on the rising ground in the breeze in the cool
    transparent night,
As I watched where you passed and was lost in the
    netherward black of the night,
As my soul in its trouble dissatisfied sank, as where you,
    sad orb,
Concluded, dropped in the night, and was gone.

IX

Sing on, there in the swamp,
O singer bashful and tender! I hear your notes, I hear
    your call,
I hear, I come presently, I understand you;
But a moment I linger, for the lustrous star has detained
    me,
The star, my departing comrade, holds and detains me.

X

O how shall I warble myself for the dead one there I
loved?
And how shall I deck my song for the large sweet soul
that has gone?
And what shall my perfume be for the grave of him I
love?

Sea-winds blown from east and west,
Blown from the Eastern sea and blown from the Western
sea, till there on the prairies meeting,
These, and with these, and the breath of my chant,
I'll perfume the grave of him I love.

XI

O what shall I hang on the chamber walls?
And what shall the pictures be that I hang on the walls,
To adorn the burial-house of him I love?

Pictures of growing spring and farms and homes,
With the Fourth-month eve at sundown, and the gray
smoke lucid and bright,
With floods of the yellow gold of the gorgeous, indolent,
sinking sun, burning, expanding the air,
With the fresh sweet herbage under foot, and the pale
green leaves of the trees prolific,
In the distance the flowing gaze, the breast of the river,
with a wind-dapple here and there,
With ranging hills on the banks, with many a line
against the sky, and shadows,
And the city at hand with dwellings so dense, and
stacks of chimneys,
And all the scenes of life and the workshops, and the
workmen homeward returning.

XII

Lo, body and soul—this land,
My own Manhattan with spires, and the sparkling and
hurrying tides, and the ships,

The varied and ample land, the South and the North in
    the light, Ohio's shores and the flashing Missouri,
And ever the far-spreading prairies covered with grass
    and corn.

Lo, the most excellent sun so calm and haughty,
The violet and purple morn with just-felt breezes,
The gentle soft-born measureless light,
The miracle spreading, bathing all, the fulfilled noon,
The coming eve delicious, the welcome night and the
    stars,
Over my cities shining all, enveloping man and land.

XIII

Sing on, sing on you gray-brown bird,
Sing from the swamps, the recesses, pour your chant
    from the bushes,
Limitless out of the dusk, out of the cedars and pines.
Sing on dearest brother, warble your reedy song,
Loud human song, with voice of uttermost woe.

O liquid and free and tender!
O wild and loose to my soul—O wondrous singer!
You only I hear—yet the star holds me (but will soon
    depart),
Yet the lilac with mastering odor holds me.

XIV

Now while I sat in the day and looked forth,
In the close of the day with its light and the fields
    of spring, and the farmers preparing their crops,
In the large unconscious scenery of my land with its
    lakes and forests,
In the heavenly aerial beauty (after the perturbed winds
    and the storms),
Under the arching heavens of the afternoon swift pass-
    ing, and the voices of children and women,
The many-moving sea-tides, and I saw the ships how
    they sailed,

And the summer approaching with richness, and the
    fields all busy with labor,
And the infinite separate houses, how they all went on,
    each with its meals and minutia of daily usages,
And the streets how their throbbings throbbed, and the
    cities pent—lo, then and there,
Falling upon them all and among them all, enveloping
    me with the rest,
Appeared the cloud, appeared the long black trail,
And I knew death, its thought, and the sacred knowl-
    edge of death.

Then with the knowledge of death as walking one side
    of me,
And the thought of death close-walking the other side
    of me,
And I in the middle as with companions, and as holding
    the hands of companions,
I fled forth to the hiding, receiving night that talks not,
Down to the shores of the water, the path by the swamp
    in the dimness.
To the solemn shadowy cedars and ghostly pines so still.
And the singer so shy to the rest received me,
The gray-brown bird I know received us comrades three,
And he sang the carol of death, and a verse for him
    I love.

From deep secluded recesses,
From the fragrant cedars and the ghostly pines so still,
Came the carol of the bird.

And the charm of the carol rapt me,
As I held as if by their hands my comrades in the night,
And the voice of my spirit tallied the song of the bird.

Come lovely and soothing death,
Undulate round the world, serenely arriving, arriving,
In the day, in the night, to all, to each,
Soon or later delicate death.

Praised be the fathomless universe,
For life and joy, and for objects and knowledge curious,
And for love, sweet love—but praise! praise! praise!
For the sure-enwinding arms of cool-enfolding death.

Dark mother always gliding near with soft feet,
Have none chanted for thee a chant of fullest welcome?
Then I chant it for thee, I glorify thee above all,
I bring thee a song that when thou must indeed come,
    come unfalteringly.

Approach, strong deliveress!
When it is so, when thou hast taken them, I joyously
    sing the dead,
Lost in the loving floating ocean of thee,
Laved in the flood of thy bliss, O death.

From me to thee glad serenades,
Dances for thee I propose, saluting thee, adornments and
    feastings for thee,
And the sights of the open landscapes and the high-
    spread sky are fitting,
And life and the fields, and the huge and thoughtful
    night.
The night in silence under many a star,
The ocean shore and the husky whispering wave whose
    voice I know,
And the soul turning to thee, O vast and well-veiled
    death,
And the body gratefully nestling close to thee.

Over the tree-tops I float thee a song,
Over the rising and sinking waves, over the myriad
    fields and the prairies wide,
Over the dense-packed cities all the teeming wharves
    and ways,
I float this carol with joy, with joy to thee O death.

XV

To the tally of my soul,
Loud and strong kept up the gray-brown bird,
With pure deliberate notes, spreading, filling the night.

Loud in the pines and cedars dim,
Clear in the freshness moist and the swamp-perfume,
And I with my comrades there in the night.

While my sight that was bound in my eyes unclosed,
As to long panoramas of visions.

And I saw askant the armies,
I saw as in noiseless dreams hundreds of battle-flags,
Borne through the smoke of the battles and pierced with
    missiles I saw them,
And carried hither and yon through the smoke, and torn
    and bloody,
And at last but a few shreds left on the staffs (and all in
    silence),
And the staffs all splintered and broken.

I saw battle-corpses, myriads of them,
And the white skeletons of young men, I saw them,
I saw the débris and débris of all the slain soldiers of
    the war,
But I saw they were not as was thought,
They themselves were fully at rest, they suffered not,
The living remained and suffered, the mother suffered,
And the wife and the child and the musing comrade
    suffered,
And the armies that remained suffered.

XVI

Passing the visions, passing the night,
Passing, unloosing the hold of my comrades' hands,
Passing the song of the hermit bird and the tallying song
    of my soul,

Victorious song, death's outlet song, yet varying, ever-
altering song,

As low and wailing, yet clear the notes, rising and falling, flooding the night,

Sadly sinking and fainting, as warning and warning,
and yet again bursting with joy,

Covering the earth and filling the spread of the heaven,

As that powerful psalm in the night I heard from
recesses,

Passing, I leave thee lilac with heart-shaped leaves,

I leave thee there in the door-yard, blooming, returning
with spring.

I cease from my song for thee,

From my gaze on thee in the west, fronting the west,
communing with thee,

O comrade lustrous with silver face in the night.

Yet each to keep and all, retrievements out of the night,

The song, the wondrous chant of the gray-brown bird,

And the tallying chant, the echo aroused in my soul,

With the lustrous and drooping star with the countenance full of woe,

With the holders holding my hand nearing the call of
the bird,

Comrades mine, and I in the midst, and their memory
ever to keep, for the dead I loved so well,

For the sweetest, wisest soul of all my days and lands—
and this for his dear sake,

Lilac and star and bird twined with the chant of my
soul,

There in the fragrant pines and the cedars dusk and
dim.

Emily Dickinson

1830–1886

SUCCESS

Success is counted sweetest
By those who ne'er succeed.
To comprehend a nectar
Requires sorest need.

Not one of all the purple host
Who took the flag to-day
Can tell the definition,
So clear, of victory,

As he, defeated, dying,
On whose forbidden ear
The distant strains of triumph
Break, agonized and clear.

A WOUNDED DEER LEAPS HIGHEST

A WOUNDED deer leaps highest,
I've heard the hunter tell;
'Tis but the ecstasy of death,
And then the brake is still.

The smitten rock that gushes,
The trampled steel that springs:
A cheek is always redder
Just where the hectic stings!

Mirth is the mail of anguish,
In which it cautious arm,
Let anybody spy the blood
And "You're hurt" exclaim!

EXCLUSION

THE soul selects her own society,
Then shuts the door;
On her divine majority
Obtrude no more.

Unmoved, she notes the chariot's pausing
At her low gate;
Unmoved, an emperor is kneeling
Upon her mat.

I've known her from an ample nation
Choose one;
Then close the valves of her attention
Like stone.

SUSPENSE

ELYSIUM is as far as to
The very nearest room,
If in that room a friend await
Felicity or doom.

What fortitude the soul contains,
That is can so endure
The accent of a coming foot,
The opening of a door!

George Santayana

1863–

I WOULD I MIGHT FORGET THAT I AM I

I WOULD I might forget that I am I,
And break the heavy chain that binds me fast,
Whose links about myself my deeds have cast.
What in the body's tomb doth buried lie
Is boundless; 'tis the spirit of the sky,
Lord of the future, guardian of the past,
And soon must forth, to know his own at last.
In his large life to live, I fain would die.
Happy the dumb beast, hungering for food,
But calling not his suffering his own;
Blessèd the angel, gazing on all good,
But knowing not he sits upon a throne;
Wretched the mortal, pondering his mood,
And doomed to know his aching heart alone.

AS IN THE MIDST OF BATTLE THERE IS ROOM

As in the midst of battle there is room
For thoughts of love, and in foul sin for mirth;
As gossips whisper of a trinket's worth
Spied by the death-bed's flickering candle-gloom;
As in the crevices of Cæsar's tomb

The sweet herbs flourish on a little earth:
So in this great disaster of our birth
We can be happy, and forget our doom.
For morning, with a ray of tenderest joy
Gilding the iron heaven, hides the truth,
And evening gently woos us to employ
Our grief in idle catches. Such is youth;
Till from that summer's trance we wake, to find
Despair before us, vanity behind.

Edwin Arlington Robinson

1869–

LUKE HAVERGAL

Go to the western gate, Luke Havergal,
There where the vines cling crimson on the wall,
And in the twilight wait for what will come.
The leaves will whisper there of her, and some,
Like flying words, will strike you as they fall;
But go, and if you listen she will call.
Go to the western gate, Luke Havergal—
Luke Havergal.

No, there is not a dawn in eastern skies
To rift the fiery night that's in your eyes;
But there, where western glooms are gathering,
The dark will end the dark, if anything:
God slays Himself with every leaf that flies,
And hell is more than half of paradise.
No, there is not a dawn in eastern skies—
In eastern skies.

Out of a grave I come to tell you this,
Out of a grave I come to quench the kiss
That flames upon your forehead with a glow
That blinds you to the way that you must go.
Yes, there is yet one way to where she is,
Bitter, but one that faith may never miss.
Out of a grave I come to tell you this—
To tell you this.

There is the western gate, Luke Havergal,
There are the crimson leaves upon the wall.
Go, for the winds are tearing them away,—
Nor think to riddle the dead words they say,
Nor any more to feel them as they fall;
But go, and if you trust her she will call.
There is the western gate, Luke Havergal—
Luke Havergal.

MINIVER CHEEVY

MINIVER CHEEVY, child of scorn,
  Grew lean while he assailed the seasons;
He wept that he was ever born,
  And he had reasons.

Miniver loved the days of old
  When swords were bright and steeds were prancing;
The vision of a warrior bold
  Would set him dancing.

Miniver sighed for what was not,
  And dreamed, and rested from his labors;
He dreamed of Thebes and Camelot,
  And Priam's neighbors.

Miniver mourned the ripe renown
  That made so many a name so fragrant;
He mourned Romance, now on the town,
  And Art, a vagrant.

Miniver loved the Medici,
  Albeit he had never seen one;
He would have sinned incessantly
  Could he have been one.

Miniver cursed the commonplace
  And eyed a khaki suit with loathing;
He missed the mediæval grace
  Of iron clothing.

Miniver scorned the gold he sought,
  But sore annoyed was he without it;
Miniver thought, and thought, and thought,
  And thought about it.

Miniver Cheevy, born too late,
  Scratched his head and kept on thinking;
Miniver coughed, and called it fate,
  And kept on drinking.

MR. FLOOD'S PARTY

OLD Eben Flood, climbing alone one night
Over the hill between the town below
And the forsaken upland hermitage
That held as much as he should ever know
On earth again of home, paused warily.
The road was his with not a native near;
And Eben, having leisure, said aloud,
For no man else in Tilbury Town to hear:

"Well, Mr. Flood, we have the harvest moon
Again, and we may not have many more;
The bird is on the wing, the poet says,
And you and I have said it here before.
Drink to the bird." He raised up to the light
The jug that he had gone so far to fill,
And answered huskily: "Well, Mr. Flood,
Since you propose it, I believe I will."

Alone, as if enduring to the end
A valiant armor of scarred hopes outworn,
He stood there in the middle of the road
Like Roland's ghost winding a silent horn.
Below him, in the town among the trees,
Where friends of other days had honored him,
A phantom salutation of the dead
Rang thinly till old Eben's eyes were dim.

Then, as a mother lays her sleeping child
Down tenderly, fearing it may awake,
He set the jug down slowly at his feet
With trembling care, knowing that most things break;
And only when assured that on firm earth
It stood, as the uncertain lives of men
Assuredly did not, he paced away,
And with his hand extended paused again:

"Well, Mr. Flood, we have not met like this
In a long time; and many a change has come
To both of us, I fear, since last it was
We had a drop together. Welcome home!"
Convivially returning with himself,
Again he raised the jug up to the light;
And with an acquiescent quaver said:
"Well, Mr. Flood, if you insist, I might.

"Only a very little, Mr. Flood—
For auld lang syne. No more, sir; that will do."
So, for the time, apparently it did,
And Eben evidently thought so too;
For soon amid the silver loneliness
Of night he lifted up his voice and sang,
Secure, with only two moons listening,
Until the whole harmonious landscape rang—

"For auld lang syne." The weary throat gave out,
The last word wavered; and the song being done,
He raised again the jug regretfully
And shook his head, and was again alone.
There was not much that was ahead of him,
And there was nothing in the town below—
Where strangers would have shut the many doors
That many friends had opened long ago.

THE SHEAVES

WHERE long the shadows of the wind had rolled,
Green wheat was yielding to the change assigned;

And as by some vast magic undivined
The world was turning slowly into gold.
Like nothing that was ever bought or sold
It waited there, the body and the mind;
And with a mighty meaning of a kind
That tells the more the more it is not told.
So in a land where all days are not fair,
Fair days went on till on another day
A thousand golden sheaves were lying there,
Shining and still, but not for long to stay—
As if a thousand girls with golden hair
Might rise from where they slept and go away.

Amy Lowell

1874–1925

PATTERNS

I WALK down the garden paths,
And all the daffodils
Are blowing, and the bright blue squills.

I walk down the patterned garden paths
In my stiff, brocaded gown.
With my powdered hair and jeweled fan,
I too am a rare
Pattern. As I wander down
The garden paths.

My dress is richly figured,
And the train
Make a pink and silver stain
On the gravel, and the thrift
Of the borders.
Just a plate of current fashion,
Tripping by in high-heeled, ribboned shoes.
Not a softness anywhere about me,
Only whale-bone and brocade.
And I sink on a seat in the shade
Of a lime tree. For my passion

Wars against the stiff brocade.
The daffodils and squills
Flutter in the breeze
As they please.
And I weep;
For the lime tree is in blossom
And one small flower has dropped upon my bosom.

And the plashing of waterdrops
In the marble fountain
Comes down the garden paths.
The dripping never stops.
Underneath my stiffened gown
Is the softness of a woman bathing in a marble basin,
A basin in the midst of hedges grown
So thick, she cannot see her lover hiding,
But she guesses he is near,
And the sliding of the water
Seems the stroking of a dear
Hand upon her.
What is Summer in a fine brocaded gown!
I should like to see it lying in a heap upon the ground,
All the pink and silver crumpled up on the ground.

I would be the pink and silver as I ran along the paths,
And he would stumble after,
Bewildered by my laughter.
I should see the sun flashing from his sword hilt and
    the buckles on his shoes.
I would choose
To lead him in a maze along the patterned paths,
A bright and laughing maze for my heavy-booted lover,
Till he caught me in the shade,
And the buttons of his waistcoat bruised my body as he
    clasped me,
Aching, melting, unafraid.
With the shadows of the leaves and the sundrops,
And the plopping of the waterdrops,
All about us in the open afternoon—

I am very like to swoon
With the weight of this brocade,
For the sun sifts through the shade.

Underneath the fallen blossom
In my bosom,
Is a letter I have hid.
It was brought to me this morning by a rider from the
　　Duke.
"Madam, we regret to inform you that Lord Hartwell
Died in action Thursday se'n night."
As I read it in the white, morning sunlight,
The letters squirmed like snakes.
"Any answer, Madam," said my footman.
"No," I told him.
"See that the messenger takes some refreshment.
No, no answer."
And I walked into the garden,
Up and down the patterned paths,
In my stiff, correct brocade.
The blue and yellow flowers stood up proudly in the sun,
Each one.
I stood upright too,
Held rigid to the pattern
By the stiffness of my gown.
Up and down I walked,
Up and down.

In a month he would have been my husband.
In a month, here, underneath this lime,
He would have broken the pattern;
He for me, and I for him,
He as Colonel, I as Lady,
On this shady seat.
He had a whim
That sunlight carried blessing.
And I answered, "It shall be as you have said."
Now he is dead.

In Summer and in Winter I shall walk
Up and down
The patterned garden paths
In my stiff, brocaded gown.
The squills and daffodils
Will give place to pillared roses, and to asters, and to
    snow.
I shall go
Up and down,
In my gown.
Gorgeously arrayed,
Boned and stayed.
And the softness of my body will be guarded from
    embrace
By each button, hook and lace.
For the man who should loose me is dead,
Fighting with the Duke in Flanders,
In a pattern called a war.
Christ! What are patterns for?

Robert Frost

1875–

THE RUNAWAY

ONCE when the snow of the year was beginning to fall,
We stopped by a mountain pasture to say "Whose colt?"
A little Morgan had one forefoot on the wall,
The other curled at his breast. He dipped his head
And snorted at us. And then he had to bolt.
We heard the miniature thunder where he fled,
And we saw him, or thought we saw him, dim and gray,
Like a shadow against the curtain of falling flakes.
"I think the little fellow's afraid of the snow.
He isn't winter-broken. It isn't play
With the little fellow at all. He's running away.
I doubt if even his mother could tell him, 'Sakes,
It's only weather.' He'd think she didn't know!
Where is his mother? He can't be out alone."

And now he comes again with a clatter of stone
And mounts the wall again with whited eyes
And all his tail that isn't hair up straight.
He shudders his coat as if to throw off flies.
"Whoever it is that leaves him out so late,
When other creatures have gone to stall and bin,
Ought to be told to come and take him in."

AN OLD MAN'S WINTER NIGHT

ALL out of doors looked darkly in at him
Through the thin frost, almost in separate stars,
That gathers on the pane in empty rooms.
What kept his eyes from giving back the gaze
Was the lamp tilted near them in his hand.
What kept him from remembering what it was
That brought him to that creaking room was age.
He stood with barrels round him—at a loss.
And having scared the cellar under him
In clomping there, he scared it once again
In clomping off;—and scared the outer night,
Which has its sounds, familiar, like the roar
Of trees and crack of branches, common things,
But nothing so like beating on a box.
A light he was to no one but himself
Where now he sat, concerned with he knew what,
A quiet light, and then not even that.
He consigned to the moon, such as she was,
So late-arising, to the broken moon
As better than the sun in any case
For such a charge, his snow upon the roof,
His icicles along the wall to keep;
And slept. The log that shifted with a jolt
Once in the stove, disturbed him and he shifted,
And eased his heavy breathing, but still slept.
One aged man—one man—can't keep a house,
A farm, a countryside, or if he can,
It's thus he does it of a winter night.

THE OVEN BIRD

There is a singer everyone has heard,
Loud, a mid-summer and a mid-wood bird,
Who makes the solid tree trunks sound again.
He says that leaves are old and that for flowers
Mid-summer is to spring as one to ten.
He says the early petal-fall is past
When pear and cherry bloom went down in showers
On sunny days a moment overcast;
And comes that other fall we name the fall.
He says the highway dust is over all.
The bird would cease and be as other birds
But that he knows in singing not to sing.
The question that he frames in all but words
Is what to make of a diminished thing.

THE TUFT OF FLOWERS

I went to turn the grass once after one
Who mowed it in the dew before the sun.

The dew was gone that made his blade so keen
Before I came to view the leveled scene.

I looked for him behind an isle of trees;
I listened for his whetstone on the breeze.

But he had gone his way, the grass all mown,
And I must be, as he had been—alone,

"As all must be," I said within my heart,
"Whether they work together or apart."

But as I said it, swift there passed me by
On noiseless wing a bewildered butterfly.

Seeking with memories grown dim o'er night
Some resting flower of yesterday's delight.

And once I marked his flight go round and round,
As where some flower lay withering on the ground.

And then he flew as far as eye could see,
And then on tremulous wing came back to me.

I thought of questions that have no reply,
And would have turned to toss the grass to dry;

But he turned first, and led my eye to look
At a tall tuft of flowers beside a brook,

A leaping tongue of bloom the scythe had spared
Beside a reedy brook the scythe had bared.

I left my place to know them by their name,
Finding them butterfly weed when I came.

The mower in the dew had loved them thus,
By leaving them to flourish, not for us,

Nor yet to draw one thought of ours to him.
But from sheer morning gladness at the brim.

The butterfly and I had lit upon,
Nevertheless, a message from the dawn,

That made me hear the wakening birds around,
And hear his long scythe whispering to the ground,

And feel a spirit kindred to my own;
So that henceforth I worked no more alone;

But glad with him, I worked as with his aid,
And weary, sought at noon with him the shade;

And dreaming, as it were, held brotherly speech
With one whose thought I had not hoped to reach.

"Men work together," I told him from the heart,
"Whether they work together or apart."

Carl Sandburg

1878–

GRASS

PILE the bodies high at Austerlitz and Waterloo.
Shovel them under and let me work—
      I am the grass; I cover all.

And pile them high at Gettysburg
And pile them high at Ypres and Verdun.
Shovel them under and let me work.
Two years, ten years, and passengers ask the conductor:
      What place is this?
      Where are we now?

      I am the grass.
      Let me work.

THREE SPRING NOTATIONS ON BIPEDS

I

THE down drop of the blackbird,
The wing catch of arrested flight,
The stop midway and then off:
   off for triangles, circles, loops
   of new hieroglyphs—
This is April's way: a woman:
"O yes, I'm here again and your **heart**
   knows I was coming."

2

White pigeons rush at the sun,
A marathon of wing feats is on:
"Who most loves danger? Who most loves
   wings? Who somersaults for God's sake
   in the name of wing power
   in the sun and blue
   on an April Thursday."

So ten winged heads, ten winged feet,
   race their white forms over Elmhurst.
They go fast: once the ten together were
   a feather of foam bubble, a chrysanthemum
   whirl speaking to silver and azure.

3

The child is on my shoulders.
In the prairie moonlight the child's legs
   hang over my shoulders.
She sits on my neck and I hear her calling
   me a good horse.
She slides down—and into the moon silver of
   a prairie stream
She throws a stone and laughs at the clug-clug.

Nicholas Vachel Lindsay

1879–

THE EAGLE THAT IS FORGOTTEN

(JOHN P. ALTGELD)

SLEEP softly . . . eagle forgotten . . . under the stone.
Time has its way with you there, and the clay has its
   own.

"We have buried him now," thought your foes, and in
   secret rejoiced.
They made a brave show of their mourning, their hatred
   unvoiced.
They had snarled at you, barked at you, foamed at you,
   day after day.
Now you were ended. They praised you . . . and laid
   you away.

The others, that mourned you in silence and terror and
   truth,
The widow bereft of her crust, and the boy without
   youth,

The mocked and the scorned and the wounded, the lame
and the poor,
That should have remembered forever, . . . Remember
no more.

Where are those lovers of yours, on what name do they
call,
The lost, that in armies wept over your funeral pall?
They call on the names of a hundred high-valiant ones,
A hundred white eagles have risen, the sons of your
sons.
The zeal in their wings is a zeal that your dreaming
began.
The valor that wore out your soul in the service of man.

Sleep softly . . . eagle forgotten . . . under the stone.
Time has its way with you there, and the clay has its
own.
Sleep on, O brave-hearted, O wise man that kindled the
flame—
To live in mankind is far more than to live in a name,
To live in mankind, far, far more than . . . to live in
a name.

Ezra Pound

THE GARDEN

1885–

En robe de parade.
Samain

LIKE a skein of loose silk blown against a wall
She walks by the railing of a path in Kensington
Gardens,
And she is dying piece-meal of a sort of emotional
anæmia.

And round about there is a rabble
Of the filthy, sturdy, unkillable infants of the very poor.
They shall inherit the earth.

In her is the end of breeding.
Her boredom is exquisite and excessive.
She would like some one to speak to her,
And is almost afraid that I will commit that indiscretion.

"H. D."

1886–

ADONIS

I

EACH of us like you
has died once,
each of us like you
has passed through drift of wood-leaves
cracked and bent
and tortured and unbent
in the winter frost—
then burnt into gold points,
lighted afresh,
crisp amber, scales of gold-leaf,
gold turned and re-welded
in the sun-heat.

Each of us like you
has died once,
each of us has crossed an old wood-path
and found the winter leaves
so golden in the sun-fire
that even the live wood-flowers
were dark.

II

Not the gold on the temple-front
where you stand
is as gold as this,
not the gold that fastens your sandal,
nor the gold reft

through your chiseled locks
is as gold as this laſt year's leaf,
not all the gold hammered and wrought
and beaten
on your lover's face,
brow and bare breaſt
is as golden as this.

Each of us like you
has died once,
each of us like you
ſtands apart, likc you
fit to be worshiped.

OREAD

Whirl up, sea—
Whirl your pointed pines,
Splash your great pines
On our rocks,
Hurl your green over us,
Cover us with your pools of fir.

Robinson Jeffers

1887–

NIGHT

The ebb slips from the rock, the sunken
Tide-rocks lift ſtreaming shoulders
Out of the slack, the slow weſt
Sombering its torch; a ship's light
Shows faintly, far out,
Over the weight of the prone ocean
On the low cloud.

Over the dark mountain, over the dark pinewood,
Down the long dark valley along the shrunken river,
Returns the splendor without rays, the shining of
    shadow,

Peace-bringer, the matrix of all shining and quieter of
　　shining.

Where the shore widens on the bay she opens dark wings

And the ocean accepts her glory. O soul worshipful of
　　her

You like the ocean have grave depths where she dwells
　　always,

And the film of waves above that takes the sun takes also

Her, with more love. The sun-lovers have a blond
　　favorite,

A father of lights and noises, wars, weeping and
　　laughter,

Hot labor, luſt and delight and the other blemishes.
　　Quietness

Flows from her deeper fountain; and he will die; and
　　she is immortal.

Far off from here the slender

Flocks of the mountain foreſt

Move among ſtems like towers

Of the old redwoods to the ſtream,

No twig crackling; dip shy

Wild muzzles into the mountain water

Among the dark ferns.

O passionately at peace you being secure will pardon

The blasphemies of glowworms, the lamp in my tower,
　　the fretfulness

Of cities, the crescents of the planets, the pride of the
　　ſtars.

This Auguſt night in a rift of cloud Antares reddens,

The great one, the ancient torch, a lord among loſt
　　children,

The earth's orbit doubled would not girdle his greatness,
　　one fire

Globed, out of grasp the mind enormous; but to you
　　O Night

What? Not a spark? What flicker of a spark in the faint
　　far glimmer

Of a lost fire dying in the desert, dim coals of a sand-
pit the Bedouins
Wandered from at dawn. . . . Ah singing prayer to
what gulfs tempted
Suddenly are you more lost? To us the near-hand
mountain
Be a measure of height, the tide-worn cliff at the sea-
gate a measure of continuance.

The tide, moving the night's
Vastness with lonely voices,
Turns, the deep dark-shining
Pacific leans on the land,
Feeling his cold strength
To the outmost margins: you Night will resume
The stars in your time.

O passionately at peace when will that tide draw shore-
ward?
Truly the spouting fountains of light, Antares, Arcturus,
Tire of their flow, they sing one song but they think
silence.
The striding winter giant Orion shines, and dreams
darkness.
And life, the flicker of men and moths and wolf on the
hill,
Though furious for continuance, passionately feeding,
passionately
Remaking itself upon its mates, remembers deep inward
The calm mother, the quietness of the womb and the
egg,
The primal and the latter silences: dear Night it is
memory
Prophesies, prophecy that remembers, the charm of the
dark.
And I and my people, we are willing to love the fourscore years
Heartily; but as a sailor loves the sea, when the helm
is for harbor.

Have men's minds changed,
Or the rock hidden in the deep of the waters of the soul
Broken the surface? A few centuries
Gone by, was none dared not to people
The darkness beyond the stars with harps and habita-
        tions.
But now, dear is the truth. Life is grown sweeter and
        lonelier,
And death is no evil.

CONTINENT'S END

At the equinox when the earth was veiled in a late rain,
        wreathed with wet poppies, waiting spring,
The ocean swelled for a far storm and beat its boundary,
        the ground-swell shook the beds of granite.

I gazing at the boundaries of granite and spray, the
        established sea-marks, felt behind me
Mountain and plain, the immense breadth of the conti-
        nent, before me the mass and doubled stretch of
        water.

I said: You yoke the Aleutian seal-rocks with the lava
        and coral sowings that flower the south,
Over your flood the life that sought the sunrise faces
        ours that has followed the evening star.

The long migrations meet across you and it is nothing
        to you, you have forgotten us, mother.
You were much younger when we crawled out of the
        womb and lay in the sun's eye on the tideline.

It was long and long ago; we have grown proud since
        then and you have grown bitter; life retains
Your mobile soft unquiet strength; and envies hardness,
        the insolent quietness of stone.

The tides are in our veins, we still mirror the stars, life
        is your child, but there is in me
Older and harder than life and more impartial, the eye
        that watched before there was an ocean.

That watched you fill your beds out of the condensation
of thin vapor and watched you change them,
That saw you soft and violent wear your boundaries
down, eat rock, shift places with the continents.

Mother, though my son's measure is like your surf-
beat's ancient rhythm I never learned it of you.
Before there was any water there were tides of fire, both
our tones flow from the older fountain.

Thomas Stearns Eliot

1888–

MORNING AT THE WINDOW

They are rattling breakfast plates in basement kitchens,
And along the trampled edges of the street
I am aware of the damp souls of housemaids
Sprouting despondently at area gates.

The brown waves of fog toss up to me
Twisted faces from the bottom of the street,
And tear from a passer-by with muddy skirts
An aimless smile that hovers in the air
And vanishes along the level of the roofs.

Edna St. Vincent Millay

1892–

✗ SONNET

Euclid alone has looked on Beauty bare.
Let all who prate of Beauty hold their peace,
And lay them prone upon the earth and cease
To ponder on themselves, the while they stare
At nothing, intricately drawn nowhere
In shapes of shifting lineage; let geese
Gabble and hiss, but heroes seek release

From dusty bondage into luminous air.
O blinding hour, O holy, terrible day,
When first the shaft into his vision shone
Of light anatomized! Euclid alone
Has looked on Beauty bare. Fortunate they
Who, though once only and then but far away,
Have heard her massive sandal set on stone.

FACULTAD DE FILOSOFÍA Y LETRAS
INSTITUTO DE FILOLOGÍA HISPÁNICA
"DOCTOR AMADO ALONSO"

PEDRO HENRÍQUEZ UREÑA
ESTUDIOS DE VERSIFICACIÓN ESPAÑOLA

PUBLICACIONES DEL INSTITUTO DE FILOLOGÍA
HISPÁNICA
"DOCTOR AMADO ALONSO"
DIRECTOR: MARCOS A. MORINIGO

PEDRO HENRÍQUEZ UREÑA

ESTUDIOS DE VERSIFICACIÓN ESPAÑOLA

UNIVERSIDAD DE BUENOS AIRES
DEPARTAMENTO EDITORIAL

El Instituto de Filología Hispánica publica este volumen como un homenaje y un testimonio de reconocimiento a la obra de maestro que Pedro Henríquez Ureña realizó en él durante muchos años, en estrecha colaboración con su director Amado Alonso.

Los estudios de Pedro Henríquez Ureña en materia de versificación tienen un valor capital, que no ha disminuído con los años. En algunos aspectos, como en el de la versificación irregular, puede decirse que su libro constituye la piedra angular; en otros, como en el del endecasílabo y el alejandrino, aunque retoma temas ya elaborados por investigadores anteriores, los enriquece y perfecciona en forma definitiva.

Aparecen reunidos aquí por primera vez todos sus trabajos dedicados a la versificación española, excepción hecha de alguna reseña o nota breve. Así se pone al alcance de los estudiosos artículos perdidos en revistas difíciles de hallar, y además se ofrece La versificación irregular en la poesía castellana *y* El endecasílabo castellano *con las adiciones y correcciones que su autor había dejado preparadas para una futura edición, dándole al primero el título de* La poesía castellana de versos fluctuantes *según sus deseos.*

El Instituto deja constancia de su especial gratitud a la esposa e hijas del autor, que facilitaron los materiales y permitieron la publicación de esta obra, y a las Profesoras Ana María Barrenechea y Emma Susana Speratti Piñero que participaron en la recolección y ordenamiento de esos materiales.

M. A. M.

LA POESÍA CASTELLANA
DE VERSOS FLUCTUANTES

PRÓLOGO

Cuando en 1917 di a conocer el fragmento épico de *Roncesvalles*, pensaba, al examinar su interesantísima versificación: «¡Adiós las ilusiones de los partidarios de la regularidad silábica del *Mio Cid*!» Creía poder dar ya como indisputable que los juglares de gesta y los juglares de metros más cortos, por ejemplo, los autores de *Santa María Egipcíaca* o de *Elena y María*, usaban habitualmente un metro de desigual número de sílabas, metro que deberá estudiarse en adelante sin los prejuicios propios de los que creen que en todo caso deben imperar los principios de la métrica isosilábica.

Pero aquel anisosilabismo, que bien puede señalarse como uno de los caracteres primordiales de la literatura española, necesitaba ser estudiado, no sólo en algunos textos antiguos, sino sistemáticamente en toda su extensión, a través de las más varias épocas de la poesía. Porque aunque la métrica llamada irregular, con el tiempo, cesa de ostentarse arrogante en grandes obras literarias y va relegándose poco a poco a manifestaciones fugaces, casi furtivas, éstas pululan en todo el campo literario como flora silvestre imposible de desarraigar. Y entonces, en vez de las viejas formas, se imponen otros tipos de versificación anisosílaba, tipos rítmicos, ligados al canto y al baile.

Al estudio de todas las épocas de esa versificación variamente irregular ha consagrado el Sr. Henríquez Ureña el presente libro, donde ha organizado por primera vez una vasta materia que comprende desde los orígenes medievales hasta la lírica de las zarzuelas y del género chico y hasta la revolución contemporánea iniciada por Rubén Darío.

Bajo el atractivo de una materia hasta hoy tan desatendida, el autor no siempre se limita a su propio campo; pero no tenemos sino que agradecerle cuando alguna vez se deja llevar irresistiblemente fuera de la versificación para agrupar algunos asuntos de la poesía lírica, de modo que, en ocasiones, deja de hacer un estudio de formas para esbozar el de algunos temas poéticos. Eso vamos ganando.

En este libro hallamos felizmente vencidas las principales di-

11

ficultades de la sistematización de una materia hasta hoy no tratada en su conjunto. Para descubrir las breves muestras de un verso relegado a condición inferior, Henríquez Ureña ha realizado una vasta exploración bibliográfica; para comprender e interpretar formas poéticas, hasta ahora descuidadas, ha llevado su atención en direcciones nuevas y originales, ilustrando con fortuna los contactos y mezclas de los varios principios de la versificación que luchan y conviven.

Desde su primera edición, este libro ha sido base indispensable para todos los trabajos de métrica referentes al sector especial por él tratado. Ahora, en segunda edición, sale enriquecido con perspectivas nuevas, afianzado en sus teorías, depurado en su nomenclatura y tan esmeradamente revisado en todo, que acrece su utilidad en gran manera. Y bien puede decirse que Henríquez Ureña, penetrando la esencia musical de esta métrica antes desconocida, abriendo el espíritu del lector a gustar bellezas que antes dejaban insensible a la crítica, ha conquistado una nueva provincia para la historia literaria.

R. Menéndez Pidal

ADVERTENCIA

Este libro se escribió de 1916 a 1920, parte en los Estados Unidos, parte en España. Se publicó en 1920. Las principales reseñas que sobre él se escribieron son las de *The Times Literary Supplement*, de Londres, 18 de agosto de 1921 —anónima, según la costumbre del diario—; William Paton Ker, en la *Modern Language Review*, de Cambridge, 1923, tomo XVIII, págs. 226-229; George Tyler Northup, en *Modern Philology*, de Chicago, 1922, tomo XIX, págs. 434-435; K. Sneyders de Vogel, en *Neophilologus*, de Amsterdam, 1922, tomo VII, págs. 299-300: Jules Ronjat, en la *Revue des Langues Romanes*, de Montpellier, 1923, tomo LXII, págs. 447-448; Gonzalo Zaldumbide, en *Hispania*, de París, 1920; Federico García Godoy, en *Letras*, de Santo Domingo, 1920; Armando Donoso, en *La Nación*, de Buenos Aires, 1921.

Como el libro, en razón de su asunto, recorre gran parte de la poesía española, se le ha consultado y citado con mucha frecuencia. Se han aceptado en general sus conclusiones, aunque con alguna que otra reserva, apuntada más que formulada. Única actitud negativa, la de Julio Cejador y Frauca, en su obra antológica *La verdadera poesía castellana*: como siempre, se contenta con negar la idea ajena, sin aportar demostraciones.

Agotada la primera edición desde 1928, tuve que esperar a 1931 para hallar tiempo que dedicar a la preparación de la segunda. He revisado cuidadosamente el texto, retocando la expresión siempre que lo creí necesario, rectificando los datos cuando lo exigían los resultados de nuevas investigaciones, ajenas o propias, agregando materiales nuevos (desde luego, todos los que aparecían en los apéndices de la primera edición quedan ahora incorporados en el texto), estableciendo mejor ordenación aquí y allí. Sólo tres modificaciones sustanciales he introducido: considerar que los poetas de la Edad Media trataban los grupos de vocales según el uso de la pronunciación normal de su tiempo, salvo Berceo, que empleó artificial y sistemáticamente el hiato, y en parte López de Ayala; designar con el nombre de *acentual*, en vez de *rítmica*, la versificación irregular de los cantares populares y sus deriva-

13

ciones a partir del siglo xv; atribuirle al verso acentual en español más raíz castellana que antes, restándole importancia al influjo galaico-portugués. Finalmente, he agregado al índice alfabético de nombres de personas un índice de temas.

PEDRO HENRÍQUEZ UREÑA

INTRODUCCIÓN

La versificación castellana se considera, generalmente, como versificación silábica, al igual que la italiana o la francesa. Su fundamento primario es la costumbre de tratar las sílabas como isócronas: no cabe diferenciarlas, para la métrica, en largas y breves, porque no lo son de modo permanente, según su estructura; la duración de cualquier sílaba varía según su posición en el grupo fónico y según el valor afectivo que se le atribuya [1]. De ahí se deriva el isosilabismo, es decir, el hecho, frecuente en todas las lenguas romances, de que cada tipo de verso tenga número fijo de sílabas. Y el principio del isosilabismo se combina con el de los acentos de intensidad (el *ictus*): uno, el final, como obligatorio; otros, los interiores, como necesarios o como voluntarios, según la longitud del renglón [2].

Pero sí puede decirse, en téíminos generales, que la versificación castellana es silábica cuando sólo se quiere contraponerla

---

[1] Véase Tomás Navarro Tomás, *La cantidad silábica en unos versos de Rubén Darío*, en la *Revista de Filología Española*, 1922, tomo IX, págs. 1-29, y la tercera edición de su *Manual de pronunciación española*, Madrid, 1926 (§ 180, *Cantidad silábica*). Mi trabajo *En busca del verso puro*, páginas 253 a 270 de este volumen, ensaya definir el fundamento de toda versificación: la simple serie de grupos fónicos semejantes; pero este principio se combina generalmente con apoyos rítmicos: igualdad en el número de sílabas, pies cuantitativos, juego de tonos o de acentos de intensidad, rima, aliteración.

[2] En el presente estudio, los versos se denominarán siempre a la manera usual en nuestro idioma, que es semejante a la italiana y contraria a la francesa e inglesa; a saber: contando una sílaba después de la última acentuada, aunque de hecho falte, según ocurre en los versos agudos. El verso tipo será, pues, el verso cuya terminación se llama en otras lenguas femenina y entre nosotros grave o llana; no el verso de terminación masculina, llamada entre nosotros aguda. Así, son igualmente octosilábicos estos dos del romance viejo de *Fontefrida*:

> Do todas las avecicas...
> Ni casar contigo, no...

Creyendo que el carácter del trabajo no lo requiere, no me he decidido a adoptar el sistema que investigadores como Hanssen aplican en análisis mé-

15

a la cuantitativa de los griegos y de los latinos clásicos, sólo parcialmente cabe afirmar que es isosilábica, como la francesa, la provenzal o la italiana. La mayor parte de los versos escritos en nuestro idioma están gobernados por la igualdad de medida silábica, y en mayor o menor escala por el ritmo de acentos; pero existen otras formas de versificación donde el isosilabismo no aparece o apenas se insinúa [1].

I. Una de estas formas es meramente artificial y pertenece a la poesía de gabinete: son aquellos versos en que, desde el siglo XVI hasta el XX, se ha ensayado resucitar en castellano la métrica *cuantitativa* de la antigüedad clásica, y en particular el hexámetro. No abundan estos ensayos, ni forman escuela, y, si se omiten unos pocos, como los de Esteban Manuel de Villegas en el siglo XVII o los de Rubén Darío y Guillermo Valencia en el nuestro, poca importancia artística cabe atribuirles.

II. Otra forma es la *amétrica;* versos cuya medida no es fija, sino que fluctúa entre determinados límites; entre once sílabas y diez y ocho, por ejemplo, o entre siete y diez.

III. Otra, en fin, es la versificación puramente *acentual*, donde el número de sílabas fluctúa también, pero la acentuación produce efectos bien definidos, relacionados con la música o al menos con el origen lírico de los versos [2].

La significación de la medida silábica es conocida teóricamente en castellano desde que el autor del *Libro de Alejandro*, en el siglo XIII, definió su versificación —con más orgullo que verdad— como de «sílabas contadas». Si durante más de cien años no hallamos ninguna nueva alusión al cuento de sílabas, después, en todo el siglo XV, los poetas cultos declaran su adhesión al principio silábico, y hasta expresan su desdén de quienes lo ignoran. El gran maestro del humanismo español, Nebrija, lo reconoce tam-

---

tricos minuciosos y que consiste en denominar cada verso según el número estricto, aritmético, de sus sílabas.

A veces emplearé términos de la métrica clásica, pero adaptados a la silábica y acentual; en vez de la sílaba larga, debe pensarse en la acentuada, y en vez de la breve en la inacentuada: troqueo *(caso)*, yambo *(casó)*, dáctilo *(célebre)*, anfíbraco *(celébre)*, anapesto *(celebré)*.

[1] En rigor, después del movimiento simbolista, no es posible atribuir carácter de isosilabismo invariable a la poesía de ninguna lengua romance. Pero, a lo menos, era lícito, treinta años atrás, atribuirlo a la francesa, a la provenzal y a la italiana; no así a ninguno de los tres idiomas románicos de España: entre éstos, el catalán es el que se ha mantenido más cerca del isosilabismo, pero la influencia española y portuguesa ha roto la uniformidad.

[2] A falta de otro término más específico, usaré el de *versificación acentual* para designar exclusivamente aquella que deriva su carácter peculiar de los acentos y no adopta el principio del número igual de sílabas; llamaré *silábicos* aun a los versos donde la acentuación tiene tanta importancia como el cuento de sílabas, según ocurre con nuestros endecasílabos yámbicos. Faltando la igualdad de medida silábica, los versos que llamo *acentuales* se distinguen por la acentuación, que establece, ya pies o golpes, como en el metro de gaita gallega, ya alternancia de renglones largos y cortos, como en la seguidilla antigua.

bién en la poesía de su tiempo, pero comienza a echarle sombra con su deseo de introducir el sistema cuantitativo en el verso español. Todavía en el siglo XVI saben ver claro preceptistas como el sagaz maestro Alonso López Pinciano; pero el *fantasma de la cantidad*, evocado por la aberración de Nebrija, continúa reapareciendo y acaba por dominar en el siglo de los académicos, el XVIII. Sólo durante el siglo XIX se logra desterrarlo, especialmente desde que el fundador de la moderna gramática española, Andrés Bello, publica sus breves *Principios de ortología y métrica* (1835). Bello todavía emplea términos de la poética clásica —el de pie, por ejemplo—, pero los moderniza y en general restablece sobre sus verdaderos principios el estudio del verso español [1].

La importancia del principio silábico y del acentual, demostrada con la práctica de los poetas cultos durante los siglos XVIII y XIX, no ocultó a los ojos de Bello la existencia de metros castellanos que no cabían dentro de sus fórmulas: así, la versificación del *Cantar de Mio Cid* o la de arte mayor. En su tratado, corto, didáctico, no juzgó conveniente introducir la discusión de tales versos (sólo da explicaciones sobre las peculiaridades del arte mayor), puesto que no estaban en uso entre los hombres de letras contemporáneos suyos. En trabajos especiales sí expresó sus ideas sobre el verso épico [2].

Los preceptistas posteriores a Bello cayeron en el hábito de reducir la poesía castellana a los metros silábicos, de acuerdo con la práctica de los versificadores cultos del siglo XIX: así, hay quienes hablan del verso de arte mayor como simple dodecasílabo; pero a fines de la centuria la simplificadora teoría se vió atacada por dos flancos. En primer lugar, los nuevos poetas de América, con Rubén Darío al frente, y luego los de España, se lanzaron a ensayar toda especie de formas métricas desusadas, hasta llegar al moderno *verso libre;* al mismo tiempo, las investigaciones eruditas ponían a discusión los problemas relativos a la versificación amétrica de los castellanos medievales [3] y a la acentual de los gallegos y portugueses.

Mucho queda por hacer. El estudio de la versificación caste-

---

[1] Véase TOMÁS NAVARRO TOMÁS, *Historia de algunas opiniones sobre la cantidad silábica española*, en la *Revista de Filología Española*, 1921, tomo VIII, págs. 30-57. Error frecuente, pero no general, ha sido confundir el acento español, que es de intensidad, con la cantidad o con el tono. En Juan del Encina (1496) comienza el error de atribuir a las sílabas acentuadas mayor duración que a las inacentuadas.

[2] *Obras completas* de Bello, 15 vols., Santiago de Chile, 1881-1893; véanse tomos II, VI y VIII. — Sobre el papel de Bello en el estudio de estas cuestiones, véase MARCELINO MENÉNDEZ Y PELAYO, *Historia de la poesía hispanoamericana*, Madrid, 2 vols., 1911-1913 (vol. I, págs. 367-371), y su prólogo a los *Diálogos literarios* de José Coll y Vehí.

[3] Observa con razón MENÉNDEZ PIDAL (*Poesía juglaresca y juglares*, pág. 342) que la ametría de los poemas medievales va de acuerdo con la frecuente indecisión de la rima entre consonante y asonante.

17

llana es mucho menos sencillo de lo que hasta hace poco parecía [1]. No sólo hay que tomar en cuenta la versificación irregular, amétrica, cuyo análisis apasiona en estos momentos a cuantos se interesan en los viejos cantares épicos: hay que tomar en cuenta también el vasto cuerpo de poesía meramente acentual, o a veces sólo irregular con tendencia al ritmo de acentos, que se descubre en España desde el siglo xv y perdura hasta nuestros días entre el pueblo. De estos metros, solamente dos se han estudiado: el decasílabo y endecasílabo anapésticos, muy brevemente pero con gran precisión, por Milá; la seguidilla, con extensión y minuciosidad, por Hanssen. Aquí aspiro a recoger, clasificándolas sumariamente, las manifestaciones de la poesía castellana fuera de los moldes del isosilabismo; sólo omitiré los ensayos de métrica cuantitativa a la manera latina.

Junto a la irregularidad del verso se presenta otra, menor en importancia: la irregularidad de las combinaciones estróficas, en virtud de la cual no sólo se mezclan versos de diferentes medidas, sino que las estrofas, en vez de repetirse con arreglo al principio de la isometría, se suceden en desorden. Nuestra poesía culta practica la heterometría: en las silvas, por ejemplo; la poesía popular también la conoce.

---

[1] Véase, por ejemplo, las cuestiones que toco en el trabajo *El endecasílabo castellano* (págs. 271-347).

CAPÍTULO I

LA VERSIFICACIÓN IRREGULAR EN LA POESÍA
DE LA EDAD MEDIA

(1100-1400)

§ 1. GENERALIDAD DE LA FLUCTUACIÓN EN LA MEDIDA DEL VERSO. — El isosilabismo no podía ser el punto de partida, sino la meta, para el verso español primitivo. Es de suponer que ninguna versificación alcanza, apenas nace, regularidad completa. De las formas imperfectas y vagas de su poesía primitiva, cada idioma escoge y define, de acuerdo con su propio genio, los tipos de su versificación [1].

[1] Los orígenes primeros de la versificación española, sus antecedentes latinos en la Edad Media, no los estudiaré; no son indispensables para determinar el carácter de ninguno de nuestros tipos métricos. Sólo me referiré, en ocasiones, a la influencia de la versificación de otras lenguas romances, especialmente la galaicoportuguesa,
La versificación de las lenguas romances se enlaza con los metros silábicos latinos, ya populares, ya eclesiásticos, y el verso español debe su origen unas veces al latino, otras veces al románico extranjero, otras, en fin —al menos en parte—, a tendencias autóctonas. Pero aun los orígenes latinos o románicos no encadenarían el verso español al isosilabismo: al pasar de una lengua a otra, el verso pudo fácilmente perder la regularidad silábica y apoyarse en la rima como elemento primordial, según ocurre con frecuencia en los refranes, en los juegos y en las adivinanzas infantiles. Cabe mencionar, a este propósito, el proceso de descomposición que ocurre en la poesía francesa de la Edad Media, esencialmente silábica, cuando los normandos la trasplantan a Inglaterra: según unos (Gaston Paris, Johan Vising, Paul Meyer), se trata sólo de irregularidades producidas por cambios de pronunciación y tal vez mala inteligencia de la métrica; según otros, la irregularidad va más hondo, y se debe a la influencia del verso acentual de los ingleses (Atkinson, Suchier, Förster). TOBLER resume así la cuestión: «Aun las obras más imperfectas dejan adivinar más o menos la especie de verso francés que les ha servido de modelo, pero hay que reconocer, asimismo, que aun las mejores no pudieron llegar a una imitación perfecta» (*Le vers français ancien et moderne*, traducción francesa de Breul y Sudre, París, 1895, pág. 11). La irregularidad se produce también en el tránsito de los poetas franceses a Italia: véase el artículo de ELLIJAH CLARENCE HILLS, *Irregular epic metres: a comparative study of the metre of the Poem of the Cid and of certain Anglo-Norman, Franco-Ita-*

19

Al leer la poesía española medieval, la escrita hasta fines del siglo xiv, desde luego advertimos que nunca ofrece absoluta regularidad silábica, absoluta precisión métrica, comparable a la de los poetas modernos, sino diversos grados de irregularidad, de fluctuación, que se escalonan desde la relativa anarquía del *Cantar de Mio Cid* hasta la uniformidad artificial de Berceo. Hay manuscritos que nos hacen atribuir a impericia de los copistas buena parte de las irregularidades métricas; pero es imposible atribuírselas todas: no es lógico creer que, en un medio literario donde todos los poetas supiesen medir los versos, todos los copistas fuesen incapaces de atenerse a medidas silábicas justas; los manuscritos medievales, en las demás lenguas romances, nos ofrecen testimonio abundante de lo contrario.

La irregularidad, generalmente, es mayor en la poesía más antigua que en la posterior; es mayor, asimismo, en la poesía juglaresca, escrita para todo el pueblo, que en las obras de los clérigos, escritas principalmente para lectores [1]. A veces los versos españoles medievales son tipos de transición que están pasando lentamente de la etapa amétrica a la etapa silábica: se ve que la versificación española primitiva, anterior a la que conocemos, era irregular. Más allá del tipo primitivo, amétrico, y sin ser silábico tampoco, ni transición entre esos dos, existe todavía el tipo acentual; en él, bajo la influencia de la música, el verso adquiere ritmo marcado, que se apoya en el acento. Comparados con el tipo silábico, los otros dos son fluctuantes; el número de sílabas nunca es fijo en ellos, sino que cambia con mayor o menor frecuencia,

lian and Venetian epic poems, en el tomo I del *Homenaje a Menéndez Pidal*, Madrid, 1925, reimpreso en su tomo de *Hispanic studies*, Palo Alto, 1929: sostiene que «los hombres que compusieron estos poemas parecen haberse satisfecho con un cuento aproximado de sílabas. Emplearon la asonancia —o en ocasiones la rima consonante— y dividieron los renglones en dos hemistiquios, pero no sintieron la necesidad del número fijo de sílabas». Véase, además, R. MENÉNDEZ PIDAL, *Posía juglaresca y juglares*, Madrid, 1926, págs. 348-349.

Debe recordarse que en el latín de la Edad Media se encuentran ejemplos de versificación llena de irregularidades, a veces como degeneración de los metros cuantitativos (especialmente en España: véanse los hexámetros que trae HÜBNER en las *Inscriptiones Hispanae Christianae*, núm. 123), y se encuentra prosa rimada, que hasta servía para el canto: su popularidad durante los siglos ix y xii explicaría su posible influencia sobre el verso español. Consúltese el trabajo de H. GAVEL, *De coro, decorar*, en el tomo I del *Homenaje a Menéndez Pidal*, especialmente la nota de la pág. 148: llega a suponer que el verso regular francés procediera de la prosa latina tomada a través de formas efímeras de versificación irregular.

[1] Aunque la distinción entre poesía culta y poesía popular, de todo el pueblo, en la Edad Media, no equivalga precisamente a la distinción moderna, recordemos que no es invención de nuestra época, sino que la hemos heredado de aquélla; para la versificación, y para todas las cuestiones de orden técnico, tiene importancia. Pero hay que poner en cuenta las revolucionarias ideas del gran libro de D. RAMÓN MENÉNDEZ PIDAL, *Poesía juglaresca y juglares*, Madrid, 1924: la diferencia entre el juglar y el clérigo se escalonaba en transiciones, y poetas como el Arcipreste de Hita usaban los metros de clerecía para fines juglarescos.

dentro de límites mayores o menores, según la longitud del paradigma silábico a que se aproximan [1].

§ 2. EL VERSO ÉPICO. — El verso de la epopeya nacional hubo de ser amétrico desde su origen. En su forma más antigua fluctúa entre once y diez y ocho sílabas; el documento más arcaico va más lejos aún: entre diez y veinte sílabas. Sobre la anarquía del verso ejercen acción moderadora la asonancia, al final del renglón, y la cesura, hacia la mitad o poco antes.

[1] Creo innecesario repetir la discusión de los diversos puntos que toco, puesto que es fácil encontrarla, de acuerdo con las indicaciones bibliográficas, en los autores a cuya opinión me adhiero. Indico, cuando las juzgo importantes, opiniones contrarias a las que acojo.

La cuestión fundamental sobre los orígenes del verso español, la teoría del verso amétrico, tiene su principal defensor en MENÉNDEZ PIDAL. Véase, especialmente, lo que dice en sus notas a *Elena y María* (en la *Revista de Filología Española*, Madrid, 1914, I, págs. 93-96), donde opone el verso irregular de España al isosilábico francés; en la reseña sobre el trabajo de H. R. Lang que se indicará más adelante *(Revista de Filología Española*, 1916, III, págs. 338-344); en el estudio sobre *Roncesvalles (Revista de Filología Española*, 1917, IV, especialmente página 123); en *Algunos caracteres primordiales de la literatura española*, en el *Bulletin Hispanique*, de Burdeos, 1918, donde hace (págs. 208-211) consideraciones generales sobre la versificación castellana medieval y en *Poesía juglaresca y juglares*, págs. 215, 266, 342-344, 348-350, 359-361, 407 y 462-467.

La opinión favorable a la tesis del verso amétrico puede encontrarse en España, no sólo sugerida por MANUEL MILÁ y FONTANALS *(De la poesía heroico-popular en España*, 1874; reimpreso como tomo VIII de sus *Obras completas*, ocho volúmenes, Barcelona, 1888-1896), sino en PEDRO JOSÉ PIDAL (introducción al *Cancionero de Juan Alfonso de Baena*, Madrid, 1851) y en ANTONIO GARCÍA GUTIÉRREZ (discurso de entrada en la Real Academia Española, 1862).

GOTTFRIED BAIST se acerca a esta opinión en su *Spanische Litteratur*, en el *Grundriss der romanischen Philologie*, de Gröber, segunda parte, vol. II, págs. 389-390. Véanse, además, las ideas posteriores que ha expresado en el *Kritischer Jahresbericht über die Fortschritte der romanischen Philologie*, de Erlangen (VI, 1, pág. 381), transcritas luego por Hanssen en su artículo sobre Juan de Mena (véase *infra*).

El catedrático de la Universidad de Chile, FRIEDRICH HANSSEN, que al principio oponía reparos a la idea de la versificación amétrica, acaba por aceptarla: véase, entre otros, su artículo sobre el *Cid*, publicado en la *Revue de Dialectologie Romane*, de Bruselas, 1909, y en los *Anales de la Universidad de Chile*, de Santiago, 1911, y su *Compte-rendu*, también sobre el *Cid*, en el *Bulletin de Dialectologie Romane*, de Bruselas, 1912. Los trabajos de Hanssen sobre métrica son tantos, y figuran en publicaciones tan diversas, que resulta difícil conocerlos todos. Indicaré los principales: *Sobre el hiato en la antigua versificación castellana*, Santiago de Chile (1896); *Miscelánea de versificación castellana* (en los *Anales de la Universidad de Chile*, 1897); *Un himno de Juan Ruiz (Anales*, 1899); *Sobre las coplas 1.656-1.661 del Arcipreste (Anales*, 1900); *Zur spanischen und portugiesischen Metrik* (publicaciones de la Deutsche Wissenschaftliche Verein, de Chile, Valparaíso, 1900); *Zur lateinischen und romanischen Metrik* (publicaciones de la Deutsche Verein, Valparaíso, 1901); *Los versos de las Cantigas de Santa María del Rey Alfonso X* y las *Notas a la versificación de D. Juan Manuel (Anales*, 1901); *Los metros de los cantares de Juan Ruiz (Anales*, 1902); *Metrische Studien zu Alfonso und Berceo* (Deutsche Verein, Valparaíso, 1903); *El metro del Poema de Fernán González (Anales*, 1904); *El arte mayor de Juan de Mena (Anales*, 1906); *Notas a la Vida de Santo Do-*

21

Nunca adquirió fijeza silábica. En el *Cantar de Mio Cid* (siglo XII) [1], y en el fragmento de *Roncesvalles* (siglo XIII) [2], la fluctuación obedece a curiosa fórmula descubierta por Menéndez Pidal en los versos de medida segura: abriendo la serie con la medida que abunda más (14 sílabas), las otras se seguirán, de acuerdo con el orden de frecuencia, alternándose con regularidad matemática: 14, [15], [13], [16], [12], [17], [11], [18].

mingo de Silos escrita por Berceo (Anales, 1907); *La seguidilla (Anales,* 1909); *Notas del Poema del Cid (Anales,* 1911; véase *supra); Compte-rendu* sobre el *Cid,* tomos II y III de la edición de Menéndez Pidal *(Bulletin de Dialectologie Romane,* 1912); *Los endecasílabos de Alfonso X (Bulletin Hispanique,* 1913); *Los alejandrinos de Alfonso X (Anales,* 1913); *Die jambischen Metra Alfons des X (Modern Language Notes,* Baltimore, 1914); *La elisión y la sinalefa en el Libro de Alejandro (Revista de Filología Española,* 1916).

EDMUND STENGEL, en su tratado sobre la versificación de las lenguas romances *(Romanische Verslehre,* en el *Grundriss der romanischen Philologie,* de Gröber, segunda parte, vol. I; véanse, particularmente, las págs. 5 a 10), mantiene, como principio fundamental de ella, el isosilabismo; no habla de tipos amétricos, y sólo acepta los rítmicos o acentuales encerrándolos dentro de la unidad silábica. En todo lo que atañe a Castilla y Portugal, el trabajo de Stengel está muy anticuado y pobre o inexacto en noticias.

El catedrático de la Universidad de Yale, HENRY ROSEMAN LANG, niega que el verso del *Cantar del Mio Cid* sea amétrico, y, en general, no se inclina a aceptar el principio amétrico en castellano; sí acepta, tanto para Castilla como para Portugal, el principio acentual, pero acaso lo haga encerrándolo dentro de moldes silábicos, con pocas licencias: no he encontrado ningún pasaje suyo explícito sobre la cuestión. Véanse sus diversos trabajos sobre la poesía galaicoportuguesa, que se indicarán en el capítulo siguiente, y las muy extensas *Notes on the metre of the Poem of the Cid* (en la *Romanic Review* de Nueva York, 1914, 1917, 1918): hay allí gran caudal de observaciones importantes, pero es lamentable que aparezcan desordenadas, por la forma polémica del trabajo.

CAROLINA MICHAËLIS DE VASCONCELLOS ha formulado opiniones muy interesantes sobre la versificación acentual: las comentaré al tratar de la poesía galaicoportuguesa.

[1] La teoría de Milá, que considera verso irregular el del *Cantar de Mio Cid,* acabará por imponerse, gracias a los análisis y razonamientos de MENÉNDEZ PIDAL, quien la ha hecho suya, renovándola en muchos sentidos: véase su edición crítica del poema *Cantar de Mio Cid: texto, gramática y vocabulario,* 3 vols. con paginación corrida, Madrid, 1908-1911 (consúltense, sobre todo, las págs. 76 a 103 y 1174). Lang se opone a esta teoría, para sostener, con Cornu, la del doble octosílabo, en sus ya mencionadas *Notes.* A la parte de esas *Notes* publicada en 1914 ha contestado, en parte, Menéndez Pidal en la *Revista de Filología Española,* 1916, págs. 241-244 y 338-344; las últimas se refieren a la métrica. Estimo que hay derecho a repetir las palabras de PIO RAJNA, *Osservazioni e dubbi concernenti la storia delle romanze spagnuole,* en la *Romanic Review,* 1915: «A parer mio, più non è da dubitare.»

En su edición crítica, Menéndez Pidal expone la historia de las opiniones sobre el metro del *Cid:* las más importantes son la de Diez, Wolf, Bello, Damas Hinard, Restori, Saroïhandy, Cornu, Milá, Baist y Lidforss.

[2] *Roncesvalles, un nuevo cantar de gesta español del siglo XIII,* texto, de sólo cien versos, con estudio de Menéndez Pidal en la *Revista de Filología Española,* 1917; para la métrica, págs. 123-138. Véanse, además, los comentarios de Aurelio M. Espinosa en la revista *Hispania,* de Palo Alto, California, 1917 (págs. 37-39), y de S. G. Morley, en la *Romanic Review,* 1918 (págs. 347-350): uno y otro apoyan decididamente la teoría del verso amétrico.

Dentro del desorden métrico del *Cantar*, luchan tres paradigmas aspirando a definirse y a dominar formando series: el alejandrino, que sirve de eje principal; el verso de diez y seis sílabas, que le sigue de cerca, y —caso curioso— el endecasílabo, semejante al de la epopeya francesa, con cesura después de la cuarta sílaba. *Roncesvalles* es todavía idéntico en tendencias.

Después el metro épico se aproxima al tipo de diez y seis sílabas, en los versos que se descubren a través de las prosificaciones de la *Crónica General* (fines del siglo XIII) y sus derivadas (siglos XIV y XV), en el *Cantar de los Infantes de Lara* (siglo XIV) y en el *Cantar de Rodrigo* (hacia 1400)[1].

§ 3. EL VERSO DE LOS ROMANCES. — El romance lo conocemos cuando se acerca al término de su evolución hacia el molde silábico, y la cesura se está convirtiendo en pausa, disolviéndose el verso largo en dos cortos, que tienden a regularizarse bajo la influencia del octosílabo lírico:

> ...Vido venir un navío — navegando por la mare;
> mariuero que dentro viene —diziendo viene este cantare...[2]

Aun los más viejos, entre los *romances viejos* conocidos, son cuando mucho de fines del siglo XIV. A pesar de su reciente

[1] Sobre las prosificaciones, véanse MENÉNDEZ PIDAL, *La leyenda de los Infantes de Lara* (Madrid, 1896) y su disertación sobre *La Crónica General de España* (recepción en la Academia de la Historia, Madrid, 1916; reimpresa en sus *Estudios literarios*, Madrid, s. a. [1920]). En el estudio sobre *Roncesvalles* modifica parcialmente, en cuanto a la métrica, los resultados de *Los Infantes de Lara*. En la gesta de los *Infantes* y en el *Cantar de Rodrigo* predomina ya el verso de diez y seis sílabas: «se desquicia el eje, pero no aumenta la regularidad». Véase también JULIO PUYOL Y ALONSO, *Cantar de gesta de D. Sancho II de Castilla* (Madrid, 1911): adopta la teoría de Milá sobre el verso irregular (pág. 14).
Es posible que en las *Crónicas* existiera —junto con la evidente costumbre de prosificar las narraciones épicas, advertida desde antes de Milá por eruditos como PEDRO JOSÉ PIDAL (introducción al *Cancionero de Baena*) y JOSÉ AMADOR DE LOS RÍOS *(Historia crítica de la literatura española*, 7 vols., Madrid, 1861-1865)—, la tendencia a poner en prosa rítmica, con versos intercalados, algunos pasajes que tuvieran calor poético, pero que originariamente estaban en prosa. Véase este fragmento de la *Primera Crónica General* (pág. 310 de la edición de Menéndez Pidal, Nueva Biblioteca de Autores Españoles, Madrid, 1906): «Maldita sea la sanna | del traydor Julián, ca mucho fue perseuerada; | maldita sea la su yra, ca mucho fue dura et mala, | ca sandio fue él con su rauia... | matador de su sennor, enemigo de su casa... | amargo es el su nombre en la boca de quil nombra; | duelo et pesar faze la su remembrança...» El original es la prosa latina de D. Rodrigo, el arzobispo toledano, en su *De rebus Hispaniae* (libro III, cap. XX): «Maledictus furor impius Iuliani quia pertinax, et indignatio quia dura, vesanus furia... homicida in dominum, hostis in domesticos... memoria eius in omni ore amarescet...»
[2] *Lieder des Juan Rodriguez del Padron*, publicados por Hugo Albert Rennert según el manuscrito del Museo Británico en la *Zeitschrift für romanische Philologie*, Halle, 1893. El romance citado, sin embargo, es probable que no sea original del poeta gallego, sino que haya sido copiado junto con poesías suyas.

fecha, en los romances viejos se hallan muchas irregularidades: hasta en los atribuídos a Carvajal, poeta de corte. Romances populares con todos los versos estrictamente silábicos no son fáciles de hallar hasta ya entrado el siglo XVI: la frecuente supresión o adición de una sílaba persistió, probablemente, porque así lo permitía la música con que se les cantaba [1].

§ 4. EL VERSO DEL MESTER DE CLERECÍA. — Cuando pasamos de la obra de los juglares a la de los clérigos, vemos que el alejandrino del mester de clerecía alcanzó, en manos de su principal cultivador, Gonzalo de Berceo (¿1180-1247?), artificiosa uniformidad silábica, a pesar de ser aún relativamente nuevo, «nueva maestría», como se le llama en el anónimo *Libro de Apolonio*:

> Quiero fer una prosa en román paladino
> en qual suele el pueblo fablar con su uezino,
> ca non so tan letrado por fer otro latino:
> bien ualdrá, como creo, un vaso de bon vino [2].

[1] Ejemplos de romances irregulares: los de *Infantes de Lara*, los de *Roncesvalles*, los de *Gaiferos*, el del *Conde Dirlos* (muchas fluctuaciones), los del *Conde Claros*, los de *Reinaldos de Montalván*, los de *Calaínos*, el del *Palmero*. La cuestión del origen de los romances —y, por lo tanto, de su versificación— ha suscitado discusiones recientes. LANG, en sus *Notes* sobre el *Cid*, niega el abolengo épico que se les atribuye desde Milá, y que había sido propuesto antes por Bello (1843) y Damas Hinard: para Lang, a quien apoya J. D. M. FORD *(Main currents of Spanish literature*, Nueva York, 1919), el romance es tan antiguo como el cantar de gesta. RAYMOND FOULCHÉ-DELBOSC, en *Essai sur les origines du romancero*, (París, 1912), duda también de que los romances procedan de las gestas, pero suponiéndolos muy modernos. La tesis de Milá y de Menéndez y Pelayo *(Antología de poetas líricos castellanos*: véanse, en particular, vol. XI, páginas 82 a 127) la sostiene hoy MENÉNDEZ PIDAL: además de las obras suyas arriba indicadas, consúltense *L'épopée castillane à travers la littérature espagnole* (traducción francesa de Henry Mérimée, París, 1910), *El romancero español* (Nueva York, publicaciones de la Hispanic Society,.1910), *Los orígenes del romancero*, en la *Revista de Libros*, de Madrid, 1914, págs. 3-14. y sus estudios *Poesía popular y romancero*, en la *Revista de Filología Española*, 1914, 1915, 1916, sobre todo los artículos del tercer año, págs. 239 y siguientes. Menéndez Pidal sostiene ahora, especialmente en el discurso sobre *La Crónica General* (págs. 42-45), la probabilidad de que existieran desde el principio narraciones poéticas breves parecidas a los romances —de unos cien versos de extensión— y todavía otras narraciones de longitud mediana —de quinientos a seiscientos versos—. Da nuevo desarrollo a estas ideas en *Poesía juglaresca y juglares*: véanse, especialmen'e, págs. 317-326, 371-374, y, sobre los romances, 413-422.

Véanse, por último, el artículo ya citado de PIO RAJNA, poco favorable a la tesis, y el interesantísimo de S. GRISWOLD MORLEY, *Are the spanish romances written in quatrains?* (en la *Romanic Review*, 1916), que apoya a Menéndez Pidal y prueba que los romances se escribieron en series indefinidas, como *laisses* o *tirades*, y no en cuartetas, hasta fines del siglo XVI. GEORGES CIROT, *Le mouvement quaternaire dans les romances* (en el *Bulletin Hispanique*, abril a junio de 1919), acepta los resultados de las investigaciones de Morley, y trata de completarlos con nuevos puntos de vista. Vuelve sobre el tema BERNARD FRANZEN SWEDELIUS, *Is the Spanish «romance» always quaternary?* (en *Modern Language Notes*, 1924).

[2] Cito la segunda estrofa de la *Vida de Santo Domingo de Silos* según la edición crítica de J. D. Fitz-Gerald (París, 1904; para las enmiendas y los ver-

Berceo obtiene la regularidad mediante el empleo artificial, forzado, del hiato; nunca emplea la sinalefa: sólo la elisión; paradójicamente, su regularidad resulta una manera de irregularidad, pues la pronunciación normal del español exige la sinalefa, y, leídos naturalmente, sin los hiatos anormales, los versos cojean [1].

El caso de Berceo es excepcional: es el único versificador que podemos declarar correcto, si bien anormalmente correcto, en todo el trecho que va desde el *Cantar de Mio Cid* y el *Misterio de los Reyes Magos* hasta D. Pero López de Ayala. Fuera de Berceo, los alejandrinos del mester de clerecía presentan irregularidades a menudo; puede decirse que las hay en uno de cada cuatro versos.

El alejandrino aparece en su época formativa en los más antiguos documentos, en donde se hallan el *Misterio de los Reyes Magos* y la *Disputa del alma y del cuerpo*, que pertenecen al siglo XII o a los comienzos del XIII [2].

Luego, en la época de Berceo, el poema que también se le ha querido adjudicar, el *Libro de Alejandro*, presenta un grado de irregularidad mucho mayor que la existente en las obras indiscutibles del Maestro. Y esto ocurre a pesar de que el autor proclama en conocidísimo verso, el principio silábico: «síllauas cuntadas». Sus hemistiquios octosilábicos (alrededor de una cuarta parte del total como ya se observa en la *Disputa*) podrían explicarse por influjo del octosilabismo, que quizá comenzaría entonces a

sos imperfectos, véanse las páginas XXXI a XXXIX). Después de Fitz-Gerald se ha avanzado en el estudio de los textos de Berceo con ayuda de nuevos manuscritos: ediciones de Antonio G. Solalinde *(El sacrificio de la misa*, Madrid, 1913; *Milagros de Nuestra Señora*, Madrid, 1922) y de Charles Carroll Marden *(Cuatro poemas de Berceo* —de los *Milagros*—, Madrid, 1928; *Veintitrés milagros*, Madrid, 1920, y *Martirio de San Lorenzo*, en las *Publications of the Modern Language Association*, 1930).

[1] Sobre la cuaderna vía en conjunto y para Berceo, existen los trabajos de carácter general ya mencionados de HANSSEN, sus *Metrische Studien zu Alfonso und Berceo* (1903) y sus *Notas a la Vida de Santo Domingo de Silos* (1907); el libro de FITZ-GERALD relativo al *Santo Domingo, Versification of the Cuaderna Via* (Nueva York, 1905); el de RUFINO LANCHETAS, *Gramática y vocabulario... de Berceo*, Madrid, 1900 (págs. 1.023-1.042: superficial); MENÉNDEZ Y PELAYO, *Antología de poetas líricos castellanos* (vol. II, págs. XXXI-XXXVIII, y vol. IV, págs. XXXVI-XXXVII); MENÉNDEZ PIDAL, *Poesía juglaresca y juglares*, págs. 350-354. Fitz-Gerald describe así la versificación de Berceo: «La cuaderna vía consiste en coplas de cuatro versos en monorrima; cada verso consta de dos hemistiquios, cada hemistiquio tiene seis sílabas si la terminación es aguda, siete si es grave y ocho si es esdrújula... Sólo hay un acento métrico en cada hemistiquio, y cae invariablemente en la sexta sílaba... El hiato entre palabras es absolutamente obligatorio y, en consecuencia, la sinalefa está prohibida con igual rigor. El poeta estaba en libertad para usar o no de la contracción, de la apócope y de la aféresis; en casos especiales, tal vez de la síncope... No tenía trabas [o pocas] en el uso de la diálisis y de la sinícesis [diéresis y sinéresis]...»

[2] Véase ESPINOSA, *Notes on the versification of El Misterio de los Reyes Magos*, en la *Romanic Review*, 1915. Al alejandrino del siglo XII, tanto en el *Misterio* y la *Disputa* como en el *Cid*, resulta aventurado suponerle influjo francés, pues no hay pruebas de que este verso exista en Francia antes que en España. El influjo francés probablemente comienza con la cuaderna vía.

adquirir importancia en la epopeya, o por similitud con la anacrusis de la lírica galaicoportuguesa, que ya se cultivaba en Castilla; aunque así fuera, otras desviaciones mayores indican impericia técnica [1].

La irregularidad es algo menor en el *Libro de Apolonio* — uno de cada cinco versos — (principios del siglo XIII) [2]. Es mayor en el *Poema de Fernán González* (escrito hacia 1255): la reconstrucción de Marden, demasiado rigurosa, reduce las desviaciones a poco menos de la vigésima parte del total; en ellas se cree descubrir la influencia del cantar de gesta en que pudo inspirarse el poeta de clerecía, porque abundan los hemistiquios octosilábicos que son fórmulas de epopeya; pero la irregularidad general de los cantares de gesta autoriza a suponer que la influencia se extiende a toda la irregularidad del *Fernán González* [3].

Todavía más rigurosa que la labor de Marden es la de Pietsch sobre la versión de los *Disticha Catonis* (siglo XIII) al reducirlos a alejandrinos perfectos, compuestos de dos hemistiquios heptasilábicos. De hecho, en las primitivas ediciones los hemistiquios fluctúan entre cinco y diez sílabas [4].

El *Poema de José* y la *Vida de San Ildefonso*, que se sitúan entre el siglo XIII y el XIV, no indican ningún avance en precisión métrica; tampoco los *Proverbios en rimo del sabio Salomón* ni el *Libro de la miseria del hombre*, donde el verso de diez y seis sílabas se sobrepone continuamente al alejandrino. Sí hay avance en la

---

[1] No hay estudio extenso sobre la métrica del *Alejandro*, pero pueden consultarse las valiosas indicaciones de ALFRED MOREL-FATIO en *Romania* (1875, págs. 53-57), las de LANG en sus *Notes* sobre el *Cid* (1914, págs. 24-25), y el trabajo de HANSSEN sobre *La elisión y la sinalefa en el «Libro de Alejandro»* (1916): abunda la elisión, pero no se excluye, como en Berceo, la sinalefa. Véase, además, MENÉNDEZ PIDAL, *Poesía juglaresca y juglares*, págs. 355-359; para él, el autor del *Alejandro* es Juan Lorenzo Segura, el clérigo de Astorga.

[2] Véase MARDEN, edición crítica del *Libro de Apolonio*, 2 vols., Baltimore, 1917-1922: trata de la versificación, sin afirmaciones definitivas, en las págs. 29-35 del tomo II.

[3] Véase la edición crítica del *Poema de Fernán González*, hecha por MARDEN (Baltimore, 1904; consúltense las págs. L-LIII) y el estudio de HANSSEN, *El metro del Poema de Fernán González* (1904). Además, MENÉNDEZ PIDAL, *Poesía juglaresca y juglares*, págs. 359-361.

[4] Véase *Preliminary notes on two old Spanish versions of the Disticha Catonis*, de KARL PIETSCH (Decennial Publications of the University of Chicago, 1902): además del texto regularizado de la versión en mester de clerecía, copia las citas que de ellas se hacen en el tratado del *Credo*, obra del maestro Alfonso de Valladolid (1270-1349), antes atribuída a San Pedro Pascual (véase la rectificación de MENÉNDEZ PIDAL en el artículo *Sobre la bibliografía de San Pedro Pascual*, en el *Bulletin Hispanique*, 1902, págs. 298-301). Como ejemplo de la versificación irregular conservada en las impresiones del siglo XVI, véanse las citas que hacen JOSÉ MARÍA SBARBI, *Monografía sobre los refranes, adagios y proverbios castellanos* (Madrid, 1891, pág. 172), MENÉNDEZ Y PELAYO, *Bibliografía hispanolatina clásica* (Madrid, 1902, págs. 302-304), y JAKOB ULRICH, *Eine spanische Bearbeitung des Pseudo-Cato*, en las *Romanische Forschungen*, de Erlangen, tomo XVI, 1906.

descripción de batalla que forma parte de la traducción, en prosa y verso, de la *Crónica Troyana* [1].

Podría esperarse medida exacta en poeta de tantos dones como fué el Arcipreste de Hita (¿1283-1350?); pero se ve que nunca le preocupó con relación a su verso narrativo: el octonario se mezcla con los alejandrinos constantemente, y la fluctuación es general: la versificación está «exenta de toda preocupación erudita de *sílabas cuntadas*», dice Menéndez Pidal, quien considera al Arcipreste poeta de espíritu y hábitos juglarescos más que clericales [2]. Sólo en la segunda mitad del siglo XVI volveremos a encontrar exactitud semejante a la de Berceo en la última obra del mester de clerecía, el *Rimado de Palacio*, de D. Pero López de Ayala (1332-1407): es probable que todo el poema se haya compuesto de versificación regular; comienza en alejandrinos correctos; pero, a contar desde la copla 296, los manuscritos sufren — aunque mucho menos que en el caso del Arcipreste — la invasión del verso de diez y seis sílabas. Ayala no proscribía la sinalefa, pero usaba el hiato hasta el abuso.

§ 5. EL VERSO DE ARTE MAYOR. — El arte mayor, que nace para Castilla en el siglo XIV y dura en auge hasta mediado el XVI, pertenece, en su pleno desarrollo, a la poesía posterior a 1400; pero todavía puede aducirse como ejemplo de la fluctuación medieval, que lo afecta en sus comienzos. Es un tipo de versificación, no amétrica, sino acentual; probablemente nace como evolución castellana de ritmos derivados de la poesía galaicoportuguesa, según la opinión de Santillana, o emparentados con ella estrechamente. Anunciado, de modo vago e imperfecto, en algunos de los dísticos *(ensiemplos)* que D. Juan Manuel (1282-1348) insertó en su *Conde Lucanor*, y en las coplas del arcipreste de Hita que principian: «Miércoles a tercia el cuerpo de Cristo...», aparece definido ya en un *dictado* de D. Pero López de Ayala, «La nao de Sant Pedro passa grant tormenta...», en la *Danza de la muerte* y en la *Revelación de un ermitaño*. Luego lo emplean, y lo perfeccionan,

[1] Véanse los pasajes en verso, extractados por ANTONIO PAZ Y MELIA, de la traducción mixta (en la *Revue Hispanique*, 1899), y el estudio de SOLALINDE, *Las versiones españolas del Roman de Troie* (en la *Revista de Filología Española*, 1916; consúltese la pág. 155).

El *Poema de José* (o *Alhadiz de Yúçuf*) no es el único producto de la literatura aljamiada escrito en mester de clerecía; se pueden citar, por lo menos, los versos iniciales de *La alabanza de Mahoma*, obra muy posterior. La literatura aljamiada reproduce, a veces tardíamente, formas de la española cristiana.

[2] Véase *Poesía juglaresca y juglares*, págs. 265-275. JULIO PUYOL Y ALONSO, *El Arcipreste de Hita* (Madrid, 1916), enumera y describe los metros del *Libro de buen amor* (véase caps. VIII y IX) sin hacer estudio de ellos. No hay estudio sobre el metro narrativo del poema, excepto el trabajo, que no he leído, de ERIK STAAFF, en *Nordisk Tidsskrift for Filologi*, Copenhague, 3.ª serie, vol. 15; según los comentarios de Hanssen *(Bulletin de Dialectologie Romane*, 1912, págs. 136-137), el hispanista escandinavo acepta la *fluctuación*.

muchos poetas del siglo xv; finalmente, muchos también, pero ya pocos de importancia, lo manejan entre 1500 y 1550. Desde entonces pasa a la categoría de metro arcaico [1].

En manos de versificadores inhábiles, el arte mayor se convierte más de una vez en madeja informe de sílabas [2]. En su pleno desarrollo, representado por Juan de Mena (1411-1456), consistía en dodecasílabos divididos en dos hemistiquios iguales, y combinados libremente con versos de una y aun dos sílabas menos — según el modo castellano de contarlas —, pero de ritmo semejante, con cuatro acentos que pocas veces faltan. Muy de tarde en tarde se introducen también versos con una sílaba más al principio, y así resulta que, en virtud de la acentuación, se equivalen rítmicamente estos cuatro hemistiquios: «Aristótiles cérca...»; «Con nuéstro Macías...»; «Piédras y dárdos...», e «Hízo perdér...»

En la mayoría de los casos, la libertad rítmica se reduce a combinar los dodecasílabos con endecasílabos de gaita gallega, anapésticos (Bello y Hanssen prefieren llamarlos dactílicos, por el ictus frecuente en la primera sílaba):

> Nin baten las alas ya los alciones,
> nin tientan jugando de se rociar,
> los quales amansan la furia del mar
> con sus cantares e lánguidos sones...
>
> Los míseros cuerpos ya non respirauan,
> mas so las aguas andauan ocultos... [3].

[1] Las licencias del arte mayor fueron sucintamente descritas por BELLO en su *Ortología y métrica*. MOREL-FATIO, en su estudio *L'arte mayor et l'hendécasyllabe* (en *Romania*, 1894), trata de explicar por qué alternaban versos enteros con versos procatalécticos; su teoría resultó inaceptable: exigía alterar el acento de las palabras, «Vayan de gentés...» en vez de «Vayan de géntes...» (ocurre en cantares españoles antiguos como «Pisaré yo el polvó...», y modernos como «Tres hojitas tiene, madre, el arbolé...», pero resultaría incomprensible en versos no destinados al canto ni a la burla), y no tomaba en cuenta los hemistiquios donde ni siquiera podía variarse la acentuación, puesto que ya eran agudos de por sí: «Es a saber...», «Hizo perder...». FOULCHÉ-DELBOSC, en su *Étude sur le Laberinto de Juan de Mena* (en la *Revue Hispanique*, 1902; hay traducción castellana de ADOLFO BONILLA Y SAN MARTÍN, *Juan de Mena y el arte mayor*, Madrid, 1903), estableció las verdaderas reglas del arte mayor resolviendo el problema definitivamente. Véase, además, M. MENÉNDEZ Y PELAYO, *Antología* (vol. IV, págs. xxxiv y xciv a xcvi; vol. V, págs. cxcv a cxcvii; vol. XIII págs. 199-211); todos los trabajos generales de HANSSEN, y los relativos a D. Juan Manuel (1901), a Juan de Mena (1906) y a las coplas 1.656-1.661 del Arcipreste (1900): adviértase que la numeración de las coplas «En ti es mi esperanza...», es allí la de Janer en la antigua Biblioteca de Autores Españoles, vol. LVII, y que en las ediciones de Ducamin, Cejador y Reyes les corresponden los números 1.684 a 1.689. Hanssen sugiere que las licencias pueden provenir del canto. El trabajo de JOHN SCHMITT, *Sul verso de arte mayor* (en los *Rendiconti della Reale Accademia dei Lincei*, Roma, 1905), propone hipótesis sobre cuestiones de origen; yerra a veces en el análisis de los hemistiquios acentuados en la cuarta sílaba.

[2] Ejemplo: los versos de Sánchez de Jahén en el *Cancionero de Baena* (núms. 123, 125 y 127).

[3] Coplas 171 y 185 del *Laberinto de Fortuna*, de Juan de Mena.

La excepción —relativa— es el Marqués de Santillana (1398-1458), quien conocía mejor que nadie en su tiempo los primores de la versificación silábica; su verso de arte mayor tiene casi siempre doce sílabas, como el de los poetas que lo emplearon cuando dejó de estar en boga:

> O lúcido Jove, la mi mano guía,
> despierta el engenio, aviva la mente,
> el rústico modo aparta e desvía
> e torna mi lengua, de ruda, eloquente... [1].

§ 6. La polimetría del «Misterio de los Reyes Magos».

— Hubo todavía otros metros, que los juglares o los clérigos usaron, sobre todo en la lírica; metros cortos que, antes del siglo XIV, extreman la fluctuación, a veces en igual grado que el *Cantar de Mio Cid*, y que, cuando sobreviven, se van haciendo más y más regulares.

El *Misterio de los Reyes Magos* (siglo XII), obra de clérigo, es caso especial. Junto con el alejandrino, presenta versos de nueve y de siete sílabas. Los escasos ejemplos de otras medidas (cuatro, cinco, seis, ocho) son mucho menos importantes: los tetrasílabos y pentasílabos son meros *quebrados* de los versos largos, y como tales se emplean, anunciando la futura copla de pie quebrado; los hexasílabos y octosílabos tal vez pudieran resolverse, mediante enmiendas, en versos de otras medidas, siete y nueve. En general, el autor del drama trata de medir sus versos, con escasa pericia, y conscientemente mezcla cuatro tipos de verso, cuando menos. Hasta donde lo permite el estado actual del texto, se discierne que el poeta buscó una variedad dentro de la cual había regularidad; cada una de las diversas combinaciones que introduce (excepto el pasaje extravagante de los versos 125 a 137) es aproximadamente regular en sí. El *Misterio* inicia, según Menéndez y Pelayo, «la tendencia polimétrica que siempre ha caracterizado al teatro español» [2], la tendencia procede, en realidad, del drama latino eclesiástico de la Edad Media.

§ 7. Los metros cortos fluctuantes.

— La combinación de temas o de poesías intitulada *Razón de amor* con los *Denuestos del agua y el vino* (siglo XIII) presenta el fenómeno de la fluc-

---

[1] Invocación en la *Comedieta de Ponza*. He llegado a suponer que Santillana escribía sólo dodecasílabos en su arte mayor y que los endecasílabos serían descuidos de copistas; pero sólo el estudio de los manuscritos más autorizados permitiría decidirlo.

[2] M. Menéndez y Pelayo, *Antología*, vol. II, pág. XXIX; hay una equivocación: el *Misterio* no contiene versos de diez y seis sílabas. Aurelio M. Espinosa, *Notes on the versification of El Misterio de los Reyes Magos*, muy útil, aunque una que otra vez su modo de medir se preste a discusión; véase, sin embargo, su artículo posterior, *Synalepha in Old Spanish Poetry*, en la *Romanic Review*, 1917.

tuación, no la mezcla consciente de versos distintos en busca de variedad. Los versos son principalmente eneasílabos y octosílabos. Rara vez los hay menores de ocho; pero no escasean los de once y doce [1].

Menéndez Pidal considera el poemita juglaresco de *Elena y María* (hacia 1280), la cántica de velador («Eya velar») inserta en el *Duelo de la Virgen*, de Berceo, y la larga *Vida de Santa María Egipcíaca* como ejemplos de verso francamente irregular. En el primero predomina el octosílabo; en las otras dos, el eneasílabo. La fluctuación tiene en estos poemas fórmulas curiosas, de alternancia y contraste, como en los poemas épicos [2]. El eneasílabo predomina también en otra obra juglaresca, de versificación muy ruda, el *Libro de los tres reyes de Oriente*.

> E quando conell estudieron
> e el estrella nunqua le vieron...

> Dixo que de que fuera nado
> nunqua oyera tan negro mandado...

(Reyes de Oriente)

> Mas el cuidado mayor
> que ha aquel tu señor,
> de su salteria rrezar,
> e sos molaziellos ensenar;
> la batalla faz con sus manos
> quando bautiza sus afijados...

(Elena y María)

Durante el siglo XIV, la fluctuación comienza a disminuir. Los *ensiemplos* de D. Juan Manuel, en *El Conde Lucanor*, presentan varios tipos métricos, que van de diez hasta diez y seis sílabas. Todos fluctúan de modo muy curioso en cuanto a la acentuación musical (excepto en los pocos ejemplos de arte mayor); pero el principio isosilábico se aplica con bastante exactitud: el autor debió de intentar aplicarlo conscientemente, puesto que el título de sus perdidas *Reglas de cómo se debe trovar* indica que conocía el arte trovadoresco [3].

No sucede igual cosa con los dísticos, generalmente amétricos, de Clemente Sánchez de Vercial, en su *Libro de los ejemplos*

---

[1] Véase MENÉNDEZ PIDAL, *Poesía juglaresca y juglares*, páginas 42 y 186.

[2] Véanse las notas de MENÉNDEZ PIDAL a *Elena y María* y a *Roncesvalles;* además, *Poesía juglaresca y juglares*, págs. 347-349 y 380-381. HANSSEN, en la *Miscelánea* y en el trabajo sobre Mena, trata de reconstruir, sobre moldes silábicos, la cántica de Berceo; pero, a mi juicio, son infructuosos sus esfuerzos: como Baist y Menéndez Pidal, creo irregular la versificación de la cántica.

[3] MILÁ, *Vida y escritos del Infante...* (*Obras*, vol. IV, págs. 149-150); MENÉNDEZ Y PELAYO, *Antología*, vol. III, págs. CXV-CXVII (incluye, por error, los tetrasílabos); HANSSEN, *Notas a la versificación de D. Juan Manuel*, 1901. — BAIST (*Spanische Litteratur*, pág. 390) se equivoca al declarar amétricos los versos del príncipe.

(entre 1400 y 1420), ni con los versos del Arcipreste de Hita, cuya medida fluctúa, tanto en su cuaderna vía y su incipiente arte mayor como en sus canciones, donde se hallan desde los tetrasílabos hasta los endecasílabos. En las canciones, la fluctuación proviene a menudo de la práctica de la catalexis, semejante a la de los poetas galaicoportugueses, y especialmente de la licencia de igualar los versos agudos con los llanos de igual longitud numérica, aritmética, pero no métrica (ley de Mussafia):

> Por que en grand gloria
> estás e con plazer,
> yo en tu memoria
> algo quiero fazer...

Su octosílabo lírico está bien definido, aunque a ratos le falte o le sobre [1].

Todavía cabe hallar ejemplos de fluctuación de la medida en otras composiciones influídas por la lírica galaicoportuguesa, como el *cossante* rítmico de D. Diego Hurtado de Mendoza el viejo, almirante de Castilla (muerto en 1404):

> A aquel árbol que mueve la foxa...

y la *pregunta* de Fray Lope del Monte *(Cancionero de Baena,* núm. 345), en que predomina el decasílabo bipartito:

> El sol eclipsi, la luna llena...

§ 8. EL OCTOSÍLABO EN LA POESÍA LÍRICA. — El octosílabo lírico se impone desde mediados del siglo XIV. El *Poema de Alfonso XI* (de fines del siglo), especie de gesta híbrida hispanogalaica, desarrolla su asunto épico en estrofas de tipo lírico, cuartetas octosilábicas, con irregularidades, en rimas alternas [2].

Precisamente Alfonso X el Sabio y su biznieto el rey a quien canta aquel poema aparecen como eslabones de la transición entre la poesía de Galicia y Portugal y la canción trovadoresca de Castilla. La composición atribuída a Alfonso el Sabio (¿1220?-1284) que comienza:

---

[1] Sobre la catalexis, y sobre la ley de Mussafia, se hablará en el capítulo siguiente. — Sobre los metros líricos del *Libro de buen amor,* véase MENÉNDEZ Y PELAYO, *Antología,* vol. IV, pág. c; PUYOL, *El arcipreste de Hita;* HANSSEN, trabajos de carácter general y los especiales, *Un himno de Juan Ruiz* («Ave María gloriosa...»), en 1899; *Sobre las coplas 1.656-1.661,* en 1900, y *Los metros de los cantares de Juan Ruiz,* en 1902. — En mi trabajo sobre *El endecasílabo castellano* he puesto en duda que el Arcipreste usara este tipo métrico, porque lleva rima interior; ahora creo, con Menéndez y Pelayo y Puyol, que sí lo empleó, con cesura después de la cuarta sílaba («Quiero seguir — a ti, flor de las flores...»).

[2] Véase MENÉNDEZ PIDAL, *Poesía juglaresca y juglares,* págs. 383-384.

Senhora, por amor de Dios,
aved algún duelo de mí...

y la de Alfonso XI (1311-1350):

En un tiempo cogí flores
del muy nobre paraíso...

escritas ambas en castellano contaminado de gallego, son las producciones más antiguas de carácter trovadoresco existentes en nuestro idioma. Sus octosílabos tienden a mantenerse dentro de la medida, gracias al influjo de la versificación silábica del Occidente hispánico [1].

De ellos, a través del Arcipreste, y de los trozos líricos intercalados en la versión mixta de la *Crónica Troyana*, se pasa a López de Ayala y a los poetas del *Cancionero de Baena*, que pertenecen a los últimos años del siglo XIV y primeros del XV. Hay pocas vacilaciones en los octosílabos de Ayala, que él emplea, ya solos, ya en combinación con versos de diez y seis sílabas. Poquísimas vacilaciones en el gran *Cancionero:* allí el octosílabo es ya la medida justa que recibió su perfección en manos del Marqués de Santillana e inundó el siglo XV [2].

Desde entonces, el octosílabo, ya sea en romances, ya sea en canciones líricas, es el metro popular por excelencia en el idioma castellano y no ha perdido prestigio entre los hombres de letras.

§ 9. EL HEPTASÍLABO. — El verso de siete sílabas, conocido ya por el autor del *Misterio*, reaparece, como vástago del alejandrino dividido por la rima; en los *Proverbios* del Rabí Santob (siglo XIV) y en la *Crónica Troyana* (primeros versos sobre Troilo y Briseida). Allí se desliza, a veces, hacia el octosílabo, como los hemistiquios del mester de clerecía:

---

[1] Véanse MENÉNDEZ Y PELAYO, *Antología*, vol. III, pág. XLIII; THEOPHILO BRAGA y CAROLINA MICHAËLIS DE VASCONCELLOS, *Geschichte der portugiesischen Litteratur*, en el *Grundriss*, de Gröber (§ 34); MENÉNDEZ PIDAL, *Poesía juglaresca y juglares*, págs. 255-256: recuerda también al trovador anónimo (hacia 1190) cuya canción cita el catalán Ramón Vidal de Besalú, «Tal dona no quiero servir...».

[2] Sobre Ayala, véase MENÉNDEZ Y PELAYO, *Antología*, vol. IV, págs. XXV y XXXIII-XXXIV (pero la descripción de la cántiga «Sennor, si tú has dado...» es inexacta: no está en heptasílabos y alejandrinos, sino en octosílabos y versos de diez y seis sílabas).

Sobre el Arcipreste, HANSSEN, *Los metros de los cantares de Juan Ruiz*, 1902. Hay unas cuantas irregularidades en los octosílabos del *Cancionero de Lope de Stúñiga* (edición de Madrid, 1872; véanse páginas 144-150, 180, 186, 190, 203). También las hay en el *Cancionero Herberay* (columnas 451-567 del tomo I del *Ensayo de una biblioteca española de libros raros y curiosos*, de BARTOLOMÉ JOSÉ GALLARDO, 4 vols., Madrid, 1863-1889); por ejemplo: la composición que comienza «Mi bien, si por agora...».

>Non me tengan por corto,
>que mucho judío largo
>non trahería lo que porto,
>nin leuaría tanto cargo... [1].

Apunta en D. Juan Manuel. En el Arcipreste aparece de cuando en cuando, mezclado con otros tipos para formar estrofas [2]. Falta en el *Cancionero de Baena* y demás colecciones del siglo xv y principios del xvi; sólo surge cuando viene de Italia en compañía del endecasílabo. Apenas si, entre tanto, sobrevive en la poesía acentual del pueblo; pero, dentro de ella, llega a hacerse importante en la seguidilla.

§ 10. EL HEXASÍLABO. — El verso de seis sílabas, si no muy abundante, persiste desde su aparición en la cántiga de serrana del Arcipreste

>Cerca la Tablada...

y en su cántiga de loores

>Ventura astrosa...

El Arcipreste lo maneja sin fluctuaciones apenas, mejor que ningún otro verso.

Formando contraste con los de Juan Ruiz, los hexasílabos de la *Serranilla de la Zarzuela* (popular, de principios del siglo xv) fluctúan, hasta el punto de hacer pensar en las futuras seguidillas:

>Yo me yva, mi madre,
>a Villa Reale;
>errara yo el camino
>en fuerte lugare...
>O será porquerizo
>de Villa Real... [3].

---

[1] Véase MENÉNDEZ Y PELAYO, *Antología*, vol. III, pág. cxxiv.

[2] HANSSEN, artículos indicados a propósito del Arcipreste. Consúltense también para los hexasílabos.

[3] R. MENÉNDEZ PIDAL, *Serranilla de la Zarzuela*, en los *Studi Medievali* de Turín (vol. II, 1906-1907, págs. 263-270). Reconstruye la Serranilla según las citas de Francisco Salinas, *De musica*, 1577, Juan López de Úbeda, *Cancionero y vergel de plantas divinas*, 1588, y Lope de Vega, auto de *La venta de la Zarzuela* y comedias *El sol parado* y *Las paces de los reyes*.

Es posible que ya se imitara la *Serranilla de la Zarzuela* en uno de los cantares (núm. 402) del *Cancionero musical de los siglos XV y XVI*, publicado por Francisco Asenjo Barbieri (Madrid, 1890):

>So ell encina encina,
>so ell encina.

>Yo me iba, mi madre,
>a la romería;
>para ir más devota
>fuí sin compañía:
>so ell encina...

Encontramos el hexasílabo en unas cuantas poesías del *Cancionero de Baena* [1]; de allí pasa al Marqués de Santillana, quien lo pule en sus Serranillas y lo trasmite a Alvarez Gato y a Juan del Encina. Paralelamente se desarrolla entre el pueblo, que lo usa en villancicos y endechas [2].

§ 11. EL PENTASÍLABO Y EL TETRASÍLABO. — Los versos de cinco y de cuatro sílabas se utilizan sólo como complementarios. Después del *Misterio*, el inevitable Arcipreste es el primero en usarlos:

> Santa María,
> luz del día,
> tú me guía
> todavía.

El verso de cuatro sílabas, fluctuante a menudo entre seis y dos, se unió al de ocho para formar la única combinación de dos clases distintas de verso que adquiere importancia o logra persistir en la poesía castellana medieval. Esta combinación, que en su forma típica recibe el nombre de copla de pie quebrado, se encuentra desde el siglo XIV en la *Doctrina cristiana*, de Pedro de Veragüe, en la versión mixta de la *Crónica Troyana* (profecía de Casandra) y en el Arcipreste [3]. En poetas posteriores llegó a ser uniforme y exacta respecto del verso más largo; pero hubo siempre más libertad — verdadero resto de la antigua fluctuación — respecto del más corto. Había, además, la sinalefa y la compensación entre

Y quizá también en otra canción del *Cancionero* (núm. 380), sobre Menga la del Bustar:

> Yo me iba, la mi madre,
> a Santa María del Pino...

Después la imita Fray José de Valdivielso, en el siglo XVII *(Romancero espiritual*, edición de Madrid, 1880, pág. 269).

[1] Juan Alfonso de Baena («Muy alto rey digno...» y «Muy alto benigno...»); Alfonso Álvarez de Villasandino («Vysso enamorado...» y «Señor Juan Ffurtado...»); Fray Diego de Valencia («Todos tus donseles...»); Garci Ferrandes de Jerena («Convenme vivir...» y «Virgen, flor d'espina...»); Juan de Mena («Desque vos miré...»); Álvar Ruiz de Toro («Señor, el estornino...»: poesía cuyo metro fluctúa).

[2] Véanse, por ejemplo, las composiciones del *Cancionero Herberay*, que llevan los motes «Soy garridilla e pierdo sazón...» y «Que non es valedero...» (y quizá sean también populares las que comienzan «Vos soys la morada...», «Pues mi pena veys...», «Quiçá si pensáys...», «La yra de Dios...», «Quien biue sufriendo...», «Quien gasta su vida...» y «Temiendo aquel día...»: en todas ellas el lenguaje es pobre y el metro fluctúa a veces); luego, las composiciones anónimas populares, que llevan los números 14, 92, 102, 127, 150, 188, 237, 245, 304, 394, 402, 420 y 423, en el *Cancionero musical de los siglos XV y XVI, transcrito y comentado por Francisco Asenjo Barbieri* (Madrid, 1890). Véase AMADOR DE LOS RÍOS, *Historia de la literatura española*, volumen II, págs. 501 y 502.

[3] MENÉNDEZ Y PELAYO, *Antología*, vol. III, pág. CXXXVII; HANSSEN, artículos en que se refiere al Arcipreste.

el largo y el corto, si aquél terminaba en vocal o en rima aguda:

> Cual nunca tuuo amador,
> ni menos la voluntad
> de tal manera...

> Si presupongo c'os veo,
> luego la tengo cobrada
> y socoɪrida [1].

Ejemplos de varios grados de libertad pueden hallarse en el gran *Cancionero*, en poesías del coleccionador Juan Alfonso de Baeɪa («De vyl gente sarracena...») y de Villasandino («Generoɕa, Muy fermosa...» y «Álvaro, sseñor, non vystes...»); luego, en el *Cancionero de Stúñiga* (coleccionado hacia la mitad del siglo xv): el *desir* de Moxica: «Soys vos, desid, amigo...».

La copla de pie quebrado, perfeccionada por Santillana y los Manrique, subsistió a través del siglo xvi, y Tirso la usó todavía en sus comedias. Desde luego, a partir de Santillana, los versos adquieren fijeza silábica, y no se permite otra licencia que la del *enjambement* entre largo y corto.

§ 12. RESUMEN. — Desde el siglo xii hasta fines del xiv, el fenómeno de la fluctuación existe, salvo excepciones bien contadas, en toda la versificación española, pero con caracteres diversos y en grados distintos. Es general, eso sí: la irregularidad métrica estaba en todas partes, *en el ambiente,* y no sólo en los asendereados copistas [2].

La tradición de las formas amétricas, que según todos los indicios es nacional, castellana, influye en los poemas heroicos y en obras breves de carácter juglaresco, aunque sean imitaciones de poesía culta extranjera: así en el caso de *Elena y María*. Hoy mismo perdura en refranes del pueblo:

> El que en gastos va muy lejos
> no hará casa con azulejos...

> Bocado de mal pan,
> no lo comas ni lo des a tu can... [3]

Las formas amétricas después de haber sido las dominantes —y en su origen probablemente las únicas— de la versifica-

---

[1] Jorge Manrique, coplas del *Castillo de amor*. Véase A. M. ESPINOSA, *La sinalefa entre versos en la versificación española*, en la *Romanic Review*, abril-junio, 1925, y *La compensación entre versos en la poesía española*, en la *Romanic Review*, octubre-diciembre, 1925.

[2] Como ejemplo del hábito de la versificación irregular entre los juglares véanse los *Fragmentos del programa de un juglar cazurro* que transcribe MENÉNDEZ PIDAL en *Poesía juglaresca y juglares*, págs. 462-467, y los comentarios, págs. 300-307.

[3] Hay ejemplos abundantes en J. MORAWSKI, *Les formules rimées dans la langue espagnole* (en la *Revista de Filología Española*, 1927).

ción castellana, luchan con la tendencia a las «sílabas contadas» de que daban ejemplo la poesía latina medieval, la provenzal, la francesa, la galaicoportuguesa: así lo vemos desde el siglo XII, en el *Misterio de los Reyes Magos*. En los comienzos del siglo XV quedan vencidas: solamente el verso del romance prolonga el conflicto hasta el siglo XVI.

El tipo acentual se halla en el arte mayor y en unos cuantos ejemplos de poesía lírica: tiene parentesco con la poesía galaicoportuguesa [1].

Las otras formas buscan el tono silábico, pero al principio se las maneja con imperfección, mayor o menor, por influjo de las formas amétricas. Dentro de su irregularidad, todas tienden hacia una medida ideal, un paradigma: de catorce, en el alejandrino de la cuaderna vía; de ocho, siete, seis o cuatro, en los metros líricos, El eneasílabo, abundante hasta el siglo XV, no llega a a alcanzar vida propia en la poesía culta cuando hubiera podido libertarse de la fluctuación: desaparece arrollado por el octosílabo.

La evolución general hacia el isosilabismo, estimulada por el ejemplo de las lenguas vecinas, llega a su término en los trovadores del *Cancionero de Baena*, en quienes se define y aclara el principio. Las masas anónimas lo adoptan a su vez, pero no de modo exclusivo: en la poesía popular, desde el siglo XV hasta nuestros días, el verso acentual subsiste junto al silábico, y el único que desaparece es el amétrico.

---

[1] Los versos de carácter acentual mencionados en este capítulo (*Cántica de velador*, de Berceo —muy acentual—; *cossante* de Mendoza; obras de arte mayor) se enlazan con la poesía galaicoportuguesa; sólo podría exceptuarse de esta relación el cantar de Berceo. En el capítulo siguiente se verá la probable contribución castellana al caudal de la versificación acentual de la Península Ibérica.

36

COMIENZOS DE LA VERSIFICACIÓN ACENTUAL EN CASTELLANO

(1350-1475)

§ 1. EL FINAL DEL SIGLO XIV, MOMENTO DE TRANSICIÓN. — Los años últimos del siglo XIV representan cambios trascendentales en la poesía española. La versificación amétrica va quedando vencida, tanto en los versos largos como en los cortos. Desaparece la cuaderna vía, que en vano luchó por imponer en castellano una estabilidad silábica semejante a la del alejandrino medieval francés. Quedan en pie los versos de cuatro, seis y ocho sílabas, regulares ya en manos de los poetas cultos, y cada vez más cercanos a la regularidad en la poesía del pueblo. Al mismo tiempo, surge a reinar en la literatura de las cortes la combinación acentual del arte mayor. Hay otros tipos de versificación irregular, conservados o adoptados por el pueblo, especialmente los versos acentuales, que no alcanzan plena vida sino ya cerca de 1500. El isosilabismo se erige en norma de la versificación castellana, pero no en norma absoluta: el principio de la versificación acentual, con grandes libertades respecto de las sílabas, se impone precisamente cuando las formas amétricas desaparecen. Ahora la irregularidad no afectará a toda la poesía, sino a manifestaciones especiales, de carácter lírico, ligadas a menudo con el canto y aun con la danza.

§ 2. FORMAS PRECURSORAS DE LA ESTROFA. — Otra gran transformación se efectúa a partir de 1350. Hasta entonces, es decir, hasta el momento en que la poesía trovadoresca comienza a convertirse de galaicoportuguesa en española, el verso castellano, en las obras extensas, no se organizaba en verdaderas estrofas: faltaba la estrofa como entidad, como grupo completo de versos, iguales o desiguales entre sí, con variedad en la distribución de las rimas. Las formas en que se agrupan los renglones son todavía simples, elementales, meras series sin variedad, sin alter-

nancia en las rimas: las *laisses* de la epopeya, irregulares como
sus propios versos; los pareados del *Misterio de los Reyes Magos*,
de la *Razón de amor*, de *Elena y María*, de la *Vida de Santa María
Egipcíaca*, de *Los tres reyes de Oriente* y de la mayoría de los *ensiemplos* en *El Conde Lucanor;* los monótonos cuartetos monorrimos de la cuaderna vía. Ni hay mayor complejidad en los romances viejos: forman series indefinidas como los poemas heroicos;
sólo después que el verso de diez y seis sílabas queda definitivamente partido en dos octosílabos apunta la tendencia a la cuarteta octosilábica, que se generaliza a fines del siglo xvi [1].

§ 3. Orígenes de la estrofa castellana. — En la poesía
lírica existió, desde tiempos lejanos, el *zéjel* o *estribote*, especie ru-
dimentaria de estrofa, «la forma más arcaica de la glosa», que Menéndez Pidal considera típica del idioma castellano. Desde la Edad
Media, el zéjel se perpetúa hasta el siglo xvii en canciones corales. Después de un villancico inicial, en dos o tres versos, que servía de estribillo, la estrofa se organizaba con tres versos monorrimos, seguidos de un cuarto verso que tomaba su rima del villancico:

> Señores, dad al escolar
> que vos viene a demandar.
>
> Dad limosna e ración:
> faré por vos oración
> que Dios vos dé salvación;
> quered por Dios a mí dar.
>
> El bien que por Dios fiziéredes,
> la limosna que a mí diéredes,
> quando deste mundo saliéredes,
> esto vos abrá a ayudar...

(Arcipreste [2]).

[1] No cabe atribuir el principio de la rima alterna a los romances antes de
que pueda considerárselos definitivamente como baladas de versos cortos.
La división de los romances en estrofas de cuatro renglones (así, generalmente, los oí cantar durante mi infancia en Santo Domingo, y después en España, Méjico, Cuba y la Argentina) data del siglo xvi, como presumió Bello
(Ortología y Métrica, § 9 de la sección *Arte métrica)* y ha probado Morley en
su importante estudio *Are the Spanish romances written in quatrains?* (en la
Romanic Review, 1916, págs. 65-66).
Son interesantes, además, los puntos de vista que expone Cirot en *Le mouvement quaternaire dans les romances:* su tesis principal es que, si bien el octosílabo es el elemento irreductible del romance, no es su unidad orgánica;
la unidad es el verso constituído por dos hemistiquios octosilábicos (véase
Bulletin Hispanique, 1919, págs. 121-122).
[2] Sobre este tipo estrófico, probablemente castellano por su origen, pero
muy usado entre los árabes —según parece, desde Mocádem de Cabra, el poeta ciego, muerto en 912, que a veces escribía en lengua romance—, véanse
Ramón Menéndez Pidal, *La primitiva poesía lírica española*, Madrid, 1919,
reimpreso en el tomo de *Estudios literarios*, Madrid, 1920 (págs. 310-312 y
332-333); Julián Ribera, *El cancionero de Aben Cuzmán*, discurso de entrada
en la Academia Española, Madrid, 1912; *La épica entre los musulmanes espa-*

El zéjel es todavía excesivamente sencillo: serie monorrima, cortada por la rima del villancico. El uso de estrofas, en toda su amplitud y variedad, no se difunde y fija sino después que se ha desarrollado la poesía galaicoportuguesa y ha influído sobre la castellana. Si el zéjel es el núcleo inicial de la estrofa lírica de castellanos y andaluces, el desarrollo paralelístico es la célula generadora del cantar de Portugal y Galicia. Y ya en el «Eya velar», la cántica de veladores de Berceo —dísticos con estribillo coral—, cabría suponer influjo galaicoportugués, a juzgar por sus conatos o restos de paralelismo [1].

Después de Berceo, el influjo occidental se hace evidente: primero, muchos poetas líricos, del rey abajo, escriben en gallego; luego, transportan las formas líricas al idioma propio. De tarde en tarde, durante el siglo XIII y la primera parte del XIV, hallamos nuevas tentativas de estrofa en castellano. Los versos, en español híbrido, atribuídos a Alfonso el Sabio, «Senhora, por amor de Dios...», y a Alfonso XI, «En un tiempo cogí flores...», están en grupos octosilábicos con rima alterna (predomina la combinación *a b a b*), y el tipo de cuarteta que se define imperfectamente en Alfonso el del Salado continúa apareciendo, ora en octosílabos, ora en heptasílabos, en unos cuantos *ensiemplos* de D. Juan Manuel, en los *Proverbios* del Rabí Santob, en el *Poema de Alfonso XI*: combinación que probablemente deba su origen a la rima interior en los pareados de versos largos [2].

ñoles, discurso de entrada en la Academia de la Historia, Madrid, 1915; *La música de las Cantigas*, Madrid, 1922 (págs. 5-9, 63-75; 80-82, 86-90, 101-109); H. R. LANG, *The original meaning of the metrical forms «estrabot», «strambotto», «estribote», «estrambote»* en los *Scritti... in onore di Rodolfo Renier*, Turín, 1912; *The Spanish «estribote» «estrambote» and related poetics forms*, en *Romania*, 1919, XLV, págs. 397-421; y ANGEL GONZÁLEZ PALENCIA, *Historia de la literatura arábigoespañola*, Barcelona, 1928 (págs. 11, 30, 104-112, 329-336). Los más antiguos zéjeles que conservamos en español están en el Arcipreste y en la *Doctrina* de Pedro de Veragüe (siglo XIV); pero antes se encuentran en la poesía galaicoportuguesa, inclusas las *Cántigas* de Alfonso el Sabio, y hasta en los comienzos de la provenzal, en Guillaume de Poitiers. Es admisible que la forma del zéjel la recibiesen de España los provenzales; pero no creo, como Ribera, que la versificación trovadoresca haya de explicarse toda como adopción de formas arábigoespañolas, por más que el zéjel, y su derivación culta, la *moaxaha*, se hayan multiplicado en formas complejas. En el siglo XIX, cultiva el zéjel en francés Víctor Hugo; de él deben de tomarlo Díaz Mirón («Sé que la humana fibra...») y Rubén Darío.

[1] Véase CAROLINA MICHAËLIS DE VASCONCELLOS, *Cancioneiro da Ajuda*, Halle, 1904 (tomo II, págs. 72, 822, 873, 929).

[2] Sobre la evolución de la serie poética en las lenguas romances, hasta llegar a la complejidad de la estrofa, ofrece buenas ideas STENGEL en su *Romanische Verslehre* (caps. XIII-XV). Concentra su atención sobre la poesía francesa y provenzal.

Sobre las obras mencionadas en el texto, véase MENÉNDEZ Y PELAYO, *Antología*, vol. III, págs. XLIII, CXVI-CXX, CXXIV; HANSSEN, *Notas a la versificación de D. Juan Manuel*.

Los versos que escribió el trovador provenzal Raimbaut de Vaqueiras (1180-1207) en español híbrido —aragonés con galleguismos— «Mas tan temo vues-

§ 4. DEL ARCIPRESTE AL SIGLO XVI. — Combinaciones iguales o semejantes, a veces nacidas del elemental recurso de la rima interna, que tiende a convertir los hemistiquios en versos independientes, se encuentran todavía en el siglo XIV: así en López de Ayala; de ellas surgen, para perpetuarse hasta nuestros días, las formas de cuarteta y redondilla *(a b a b,* y más tarde *a b b a).* El Arcipreste de Hita, que las emplea, usa también combinaciones complejas e ingeniosas; él es quien trae variedad y riqueza a nuestra versificación, tanto en los tipos de verso como en los de estrofa [1]. Contemporáneo suyo, o poco posterior, el autor de la versión mixta de la *Crónica Troyana* ofrece también interesante variedad de formas.

Del Arcipreste al *Cancionero de Baena* el tránsito es fácil. Los poetas del período de los cancioneros castellanos (1400-1550) conocen y emplean diversas formas de estancia, tanto en el arte mayor como en el arte menor o común [2]; pero el número de ellas se limita pronto, y nunca llega a igualar la variedad galaicoportuguesa. En la primera mitad del siglo XVI, el empobrecimiento de la poesía cortesana en Castilla estimuló la adopción de los metros italianos.

De la poesía cortesana, he dicho. En la poesía popular, y en la semipopular, junto a los moldes silábicos, circulaba la caudalosa corriente del verso acentual. De ella recibimos, junto con la versificación libre, acentual, estrofas regulares e irregulares: sólo la de arte mayor había logrado aclimatarse en los palacios; el pueblo acogió y desarrolló las otras.

tro pleyto....», podrían citarse también como ejemplo de rima alterna *(a b a b):* véase MILÁ Y FONTANALS, *De los trovadores en España,* 1861, reimpreso como vol. II de las *Obras completas* (consúltense págs. 35-36, 42, 131-132 y 532), y MENÉNDEZ PIDAL, *Poesía juglaresca y juglares,* pág. 154. Todavía son anteriores los versos «Tal dona no quiero servir...», de trovador castellano desconocido, hacia 1190, citados por Ramón Vidal de Besalú: véase *Poesía juglaresca y juglares,* págs. 185 y 255.

[1] El Arcipreste dice, en el prólogo en prosa a su libro, hablando de los motivos que le guiaron a escribirlo: «E compóselo otrosí a dar algunos leçión e muestra de metrificar e rrimar e de trobar; ca trobas e notas e rrimas e ditados e uersos, que fiz complidamente, segund que esta çiençia requiere». Sobre el Arcipreste, véanse los trabajos de PUYOL y de HANSSEN, especialmente *Los metros de los cantares de Juan Ruiz:* además, MENÉNDEZ Y PELAYO, *Antología,* vol. III, págs. VII, LXXIII, XCIX y C (y sobre Ayala, vol. IV, págs. XXXIII y siguientes), y MENÉNDEZ PIDAL, *Poesía juglaresca y juglares,* págs. 272-278.

[2] Varias formas mencioné en el capítulo anterior: la copla de pie quebrado (formas típicas: *ABc ABc; Ab Ab;* pero hay más); las estrofas de arte mayor (generalmente octavas con las rimas *ABBA ACCA,* o bien *ABAB BCCB,* o bien *ABBA ACAC);* y otras he mencionado en el texto de este capítulo (las redondillas *abab* o *abba).* Las octavas de octosílabos y hexasílabos se parecen a las de arte mayor; hay también estrofa de cinco, seis, siete, nueve y diez versos. Véase MILÁ, *Trovadores en España* (págs. 532-533 bis del vol. II de las *Obras)* y artículo sobre el *Cancionero de Baena* (vol. IV); MENÉNDEZ Y PELAYO, *Antología,* vol. IV, pág. XCIV.

A) GALICIA Y PORTUGAL

§ 5. LA POESÍA TROVADORESCA EN TODA ESPAÑA. — La poesía trovadoresca florece en Cataluña y Aragón durante los siglos XII y XIII; la galaicoportuguesa, desde el final del siglo XII hasta mediados del XIV: durante este período, no sólo la poesía de Galicia y Portugal, sino también gran parte de la lírica de las regiones donde imperaba el castellano, se escriben generalmente en la lengua occidental de la Península, si bien llenándola de castellanismos; en Castilla, Alfonso X (c. 1220-1284) autoriza la práctica con su ejemplo[1].

En el período que se extiende de mediados del siglo XIV a mediados del siglo XV, el castellano va imponiéndose rápidamente sobre el gallego. El último poeta culto de Castilla que emplea el idioma de Galicia en una composición original es Gómez Manrique (c. 1415-1490)[2].

---

[1] La antigua poesía galaicoportuguesa se contiene, como es sabido, en cuatro colecciones: I, el *Cancionero del Vaticano*, publicado en edición paleográfica por Monaci (Halle, 1875) y en edición crítica (discutida) por Theophilo Braga (Lisboa, 1878); II, el *Cancionero Colocci-Brancuti*, edición paleográfica de Molteni (Halle, 1880); III, el *Cancionero de Ajuda*, edición crítica de Carolina Michaëlis de Vasconcellos (Halle, 1904, en 2 volúmenes: el primero contiene los textos, con indicación de cuáles se hallan repetidos en las otras colecciones, y la reimpresión de ciento cincuenta y siete piezas más, procedentes de aquéllas, con lo cual el volumen sirve también como edición crítica de la mayor parte del *Colocci-Brancuti*, que bien la necesitaba; el volumen segundo contiene el riquísimo comentario); finalmente, IV, las *Cántigas de Santa María*, de Alfonso X el Sabio, impresas por la Academia Española (2 vols., Madrid, 1889), con introducción de Leopoldo Augusto de Cueto, Marqués de Valmar; después (1922) se ha agregado, como tercer tomo, *La música de las Cantigas*, estudio y transcripciones de Ribera. Véase, además, A. G. SOLALINDE, *El códice florentino de las «Cantigas»* (en la *Revista de Filología Española*, 1918, V, 143-179). Sobre las composiciones profanas del Rey de Castilla (en el *Cancionero del Vaticano*), véase CESARE DE LOLLIS, *Cantigas de amor e de maldizer di Alfonso el Sabio* (en los *Studi di filologia romanza*, de Roma, 1887).

De las dos primeras colecciones entresacó HENRY ROSEMAN LANG las poesías del rey Don Dionís de Portugal (1261-1325) para formar un cancionero, al que ha puesto introducción y notas muy importantes *(Das Liederbuch des Königs Denis von Portugal*, Halle, 1894); véase la reseña de Carolina Michaëlis de Vasconcellos en la *Zeitschrift für romanische Philologie*, de Halle, 1895, tomo XIX, págs. 641-719. De idéntica manera, JOSÉ JOAQUIM NUNES ha formado su colección de *Cantigas d'amigo dos trovadores galego-portugueses*, edición crítica —no muy perfecta—, con introducción muy extensa, 3 vols., Coimbra, 1926-1928; véase la reseña de Silvio Pellegrini en el *Archivum Romanicum*, de Ginebra, 1930, págs. 275-322. Consúltese también SILVIO PELLEGRINI: *Don Denis*, Belluno, 1927, *Auswahl altportugiesische Lieder*, Halle-Saal, 1928, *Studi su trove e trovatori della prima lirica ispano-portoghese*, Torino, 1937 y *Repertorio bibliografico della prima lirica portoghese*, Modena, 1939, 85 págs.

[2] LANG ha formado otra colección de poesía gallega, perteneciente a este segundo período, entresacándola del *Cancionero de Baena* y de otros: *Cancioneiro gallego-castelhano* (Nueva York, 1902; sólo ha aparecido el primer volumen, que contiene texto, glosario y notas).

El catalán, que desde el siglo XII hasta el XIV se mantuvo sometido al provenzal y alejado del castellano, ahora empieza a unírsele: los poetas de Cataluña y de Valencia se comunican activamente con los de Castilla durante el movimiento de unificación característico del siglo XV, y, a pesar del florecimiento que producen entonces, acaban por renunciar a su idioma en el XVI. Galicia, entre tanto, va desapareciendo del mapa literario; ni ella ni Cataluña habían de reaparecer, con vida vernácula, hasta mediados del siglo XIX [1]. El portugués sí vuelve a levantarse pronto, a principios del siglo XVI, con Bernardim Ribeiro, Christovam Falcão, Gil Vicente y Sã de Miranda.

El período final de esta literatura trovadoresca, que va de mediados del siglo XV a principios del XVI, comprende producciones de los poetas de toda la Península. El idioma castellano es el que predomina [2].

§ 6. La versificación galaicoportuguesa. — Los tipos de verso y estrofa de la lírica galaicoportuguesa, derivados unos de Provenza y quizá también de Francia, otros de fuentes nativas, pero influídos a veces por los modelos trovadorescos, se hallan definidos en el primero de aquellos tres períodos, el galaicoportugués (1175-1350). También allí, como en la antigua poesía castellana, se divide la producción *oficialmente* en dos clases: una culta, otra más cercana a todo el pueblo. La distinción es más técnica que intrínseca: se considera poesía más culta la artificiosa *cantiga de meestria* y poesía más popular la *cantiga de refram*, la canción con retornelo o estribillo, en que se reproduce a menudo el tono ingenuo y fácil de las alegrías y las *saudades* del pueblo, y particularmente de las mujeres, con el acento sentimental y la sugestión de misterio peculiares de Portugal y Galicia. Los dos tipos de canción se presentan en los cancioneros, con frecuencia,

---

[1] Véase Milá, *Resenya histórica y crítica dels antichs poetas catalans*, especialmente las páginas finales (vol. III de las *Obras*), *Trovadores de España* (vol. II de las *Obras*, págs. 509-521 y 536 bis) y *Observaciones sobre la poesía popular*, que sirven de introducción al *Romancerillo catalán* (vol. VI, especialmente pág. 49). Milá atribuye importancia al influjo de la escuela trovadoresca catalana en Castilla, pero las pruebas que aduce son escasas, y no puede decirse que la tesis haya sido confirmada por las investigaciones posteriores. Véase, además, Menéndez y Pelayo, *Antología*, vol. V, págs. XXI, XXII, CCLXXVIII, CCLXXXV, CCLXXXVIII; vol. VII, págs. CCXXVI y siguientes; pero, sobre todo, Menéndez Pidal, *Poesía juglaresca y juglares*, págs. 180-181 (y sobre el flujo y reflujo de los idiomas en el uso literario de la Península, véase pág. 142).

[2] Los lusitanos del período tercero, castellano-portugués (1449-1521, según Lang), se hallan representados, en ambas lenguas, en el *Cancioneiro geral*, de García de Resende, que apareció en 1516 (reimpresiones: la de Kausler, 3 volúmenes, Stuttgart, 1846-1852; la facsimilar de Huntington, Nueva York, 1904). Véase Menéndez y Pelayo, *Antología*, vol. III, págs. XLIII-LII, y vol. VII, págs. CI-CVI y CL-CLXIV.

como obra de unos mismos poetas: el rey Don Dionís entre otros [1].

§ 7. EL VERSO NATIVO. — La versificación predominante es silábica. En las canciones de estribillo, de *refram*, es acentual a veces, pero generalmente dentro de límites silábicos, con pocas libertades. La licencia más conocida (ley de Mussafia) es la equi-

[1] Los tratados de historia de la literatura portuguesa, que ciertamente no abundan, prestan poco auxilio para el estudio de la antigua poesía; por eso creo útil dar aquí breves indicaciones bibliográficas. Hay que hacer excepción en favor de la *Geschichte der portugiesischen Litteratur*, de CAROLINA MICHAËLIS DE VASCONCELLOS y THEOPHILO BRAGA, publicada en el *Grundriss*, de Gröber, con capítulos muy interesantes sobre la literatura popular y sobre la lírica trovadoresca. En la gran *Historia de literatura portuguesa*, dirigida por A. FORJAZ DE SAMPAIO, y comenzada en 1928, José Joaquim Nunes trata de la poesía medieval. Sobre relaciones con Provenza y con Francia —cuyo influjo probablemente exagera el autor—, véase el libro de ALFRED JEANROY, *Les origines de la poésie lyrique en France au moyen âge*, París, 1889, segunda parte, cap. V, y H. R. LANG, *The relations of the earliest Portuguese lyric school with the troubadours and trouvères*, en la revista *Modern Language Notes*, de Baltimore, 1895, tomo X, cols. 207-231. No conozco la obra de RODRIGUES LAPA, *Das origens da poesia lírica em Portugal na Idade Media*, Lisboa, 1929.

Sobre la versificación, el fragmento de Poética con que se abre el manuscrito de *Colocci-Brancuti* es muy incompleto y no arroja mucha luz; a veces hace lo contrario. Deben consultarse los estudios de Carolina Michaëlis de Vasconcellos en el *Cancionero de Ajuda* y de Lang en el de Don Dionís; luego, el de ADOLFO MUSSAFIA, *Sull'antica metrica portoghese* (en los *Sitzungsberichte... der Kaiserlichen Akademie der Wissenschaften*, Viena, 1896, fascículo X), que establece dos leyes: la isometría de las estrofas, en cuanto a la colocación de rimas graves y agudas, y la equivalencia de versos de igual longitud aritmética, pero métricamente distintos, según que los finales sean graves o agudos. La segunda, llamada comúnmente ley de Mussafia, no impide, en otras composiciones, la alternancia de rimas llanas y agudas en versos métricamente iguales: los dos sistemas coexisten. Véase Carolina Michaëlis de Vasconcellos, reseña del trabajo de Mussafia, en la revista *Literaturblatt für germanische und romanische Philologie*, de Leipzig, 1896, XVII, págs. 308-318.

HANSSEN, en su trabajo *Zur spanischen und portugiesischen Metrik*, explica diversos fenómenos y establece la relación entre el arte mayor español y metros gallegoportugueses antiguos y modernos, cultos y populares. En *Los versos de las Cantigas de Santa María* presenta un análisis minucioso y muy útil, aunque sus resultados son a veces discutibles (por ejemplo, el ritmo de la cántiga 275 sugiere el del endecasílabo épico con sílaba adicional después del acento en la cuarta: «A que nos guarda ¦ do gran fogo infernal...»; para asimilarlo al arte mayor hay que trastornar los acentos demasiado). Hanssen aplica el principio de la catalexis muy extensamente, sugiriendo que a él obedecen la ley de Mussafia y la contraria, viva todavía en la versificación romance, que equipara al verso llano el agudo con una sílaba adicional. Véanse, además, *Los endecasílabos de Alfonso X*, *Los alejandrinos de Alfonso X* y *Die jambischen Metra Alfons des X;* el trabajo de HENRI COLLET y LUIS VILLALBA, *Contribution à l'étude des Cantigas d'Alphonse le Savant*, donde se explica la relación entre la música y el verso de varias composiciones (en el *Bulletin Hispanique*, 1911), y *La música de las Cantigas*, de RIBERA, quien establece con acierto estas normas (págs. 105-108): «La rima es esencial al verso...; donde no haya rima podrá verse cesura que señale fracción de verso, pero no verso entero; en cambio, puede haber rimas interiores; el mayor número de las composiciones tiene forma estrófica de zéjel; admite, sin embargo, que influyen, «en unas veinticinco, la tradición popular gallega o la erudita provenzal».

Todavía se hace necesario consultar, cotejándolos en lo posible con las in-

valencia de versos de igual longitud numérica, pero no métrica,
sean llanas o agudas las palabras, como ocurre en los del rey Don
Dionís que comienzan:

> Pois mha ventura tal é ja
> que sodes tan poderosa
> de mim, mha senhor fremosa,
> por mesura que em vós a,
> é por bem que vos estará...

Esta licencia debe estimarse como caso de aplicación excesiva del principio silábico, y no del acentual: existió en Provenza,
y de allí pudo tomarse, aunque no es desconocida en la poesía popular de España (así, en la seguidilla).

En cambio, otras aplicaciones de la catalexis y de la anacrusis, supresión y adición de una o dos sílabas, sí pertenecen al sistema acentual; pero no van muy lejos.

El sistema rítmico de Portugal y Galicia, que probablemente
se extendía a León y Asturias, hubo de ser, en la poesía estrictamente popular, cantada y bailada, más rico, más libre que el de
los *Cancioneros*. No sería excesivo suponerle una variedad potencial comparable a la fluctuación del verso amétrico castellano,
pero gobernada por los acentos fijos del canto y la danza; en siglos posteriores encontraremos mucha variedad rítmica dentro
de la poesía española, y, en menor escala, dentro de la poesía popular de nuestros días en Galicia y Asturias. El verso nativo cabe
imaginarlo así. El verso escrito, aun en el caso de las canciones
de sabor popular, tendió a regularizarse, bajo la influencia de modelos cortesanos traídos del otro lado de los Pirineos, y a prestar
más atención a las sílabas que a los acentos [1].

§ 8. TIPOS DE VERSOS. — Los principales tipos de verso
empleados en los *Cancioneiros* son los siguientes [2]: de acentuación
yámbica, el pentasílabo, el heptasílabo, el de nueve sílabas con
acento interior en la cuarta (acento que en tiempos posteriores
suele pasar a la tercera, deshaciendo el esquema yámbico), el endecasílabo con acento en la cuarta (o bien en la sexta, o aun en
la quinta, destruyéndose también el esquema primitivo), el ale-

---

vestigaciones posteriores, los trabajos antiguos, que hicieron época, de FER-
DINAND WOLF (*Studien zur Geschichte der spanischen und portugiesischen Na-
tional-Litteratur*, 1859; hay traducción castellana de Unamuno: véase la sección IV), de FRIEDRICH DIEZ (*Über die erste portugiesische Kunst- und Hof-
poesie*, 1863) y de MILÁ Y FONTANALS (*Del decasílabo y endecasílabo anapésticos*, 1875, y *De la poesía popular gallega*, 1877; uno y otro, en el tomo V de las
Obras; Trovadores en España, 1861: consúltese el vol. II de las *Obras*, págs.
521-536).

[1] Véase MENÉNDEZ PIDAL, *Poesía juglaresca y juglares*, páginas 214-222.

[2] Sigo la clasificación de LANG en su *Liederbuch des Königs Denis von Portugal* (págs. CIX-CXX). Nombro los versos según el sistema italocastellano a
fin de conservar la uniformidad. Consúltense, además, los párrafos 19, 20 y 42
en la *Literatura portuguesa*, de BRAGA y CAROLINA MICHAËLIS (*Grundriss*).

jandrino, el verso de diez y ocho sílabas (once y siete, o nueve y nueve). Los versos de acentuación distinta, con base trisílaba, o trocaica cuando la cláusula fundamental es disílaba, son: versos de redondilla mayor y de redondilla menor, o sean octosílabo y hexasílabo; decasílabo bipartito con acento en la cuarta [1] (o bien en la quinta, o en la tercera, con tendencia anapéstica); endecasílabo con ritmo cadente, no yámbico, sino a veces anapéstico; dodecasílabo, como el nuestro de arte mayor; dodecasílabo trocaico, cuya acentuación, al hacerse variable, tendió a confundirse con la del otro verso de doce. Hay todavía otros tipos en las *Cántigas de Santa María*, del rey Alfonso el Sabio, que llegan hasta longitudes excesivas; el carácter de ensayo artificial se revela en la tendencia, meramente silábica, no acentual, de larguísimos versos descoyuntados, como los de diez y seis y quince sílabas [2].

§ 9. LA TEORÍA DE CAROLINA MICHAËLIS. — Los versos del grupo yámbico tienen cercano parentesco con los provenzales y franceses; los del otro grupo tienen más rasgos de fisonomía peninsular. Unos y otros han sufrido el influjo de la versificación de allende los Pirineos, donde las sílabas eran el elemento fundamental y el acento perdía gradualmente su valor [3]. En cambio, algunos, aunque de origen extranjero, se modificarían bajo influencias musicales. En ocasiones, cuando los moldes silábicos se rompen, los acentos recobran su importancia.

Carolina Michaëlis de Vasconcellos busca la base de la acentuación rítmica principalmente en torno a la distribución de cuatro *golpes* que se descubre en la música popular y en metros portugueses y españoles. «... Creo —dice— que, colocándonos inmóviles en el punto de vista francés, el del simple cuento de sílabas, nunca conseguiremos resultados satisfactorios respecto de la parte popular de la poesía hispánica, y peculiarmente el verso de arte mayor. Cuanto más veo y oigo de las danzas y la música peninsulares —donde el ritmo es todo—, tanto más me persuado de que los gallegos, astures, cántabros y lusitanos, de antaño y de hoy, no cuentan las sílabas, contentándose con un número fijo de *altas* o *levas* (cuatro en el verso de arte mayor)... El *trástalastrás*

---

[1] No sé que nadie haya aducido, para la dilucidación de estos problemas, los versos en lengua vulgar intercalados por Judá Leví en sus poesías hebraicas (siglo XII). Sólo conozco dos, restaurados por MENÉNDEZ Y PELAYO, que corresponden con singular exactitud al decasílabo de acento en cuarta de los poetas gallegos:

Venit, la fesca juvencenrillo.
¿Quem conde meu coragión feryllo?

Véase *De las influencias semíticas en la literatura española*, en los *Estudios de crítica literaria*, vol. II.

[2] Véase MILÁ, *Trovadores en España*, pág. 525; HANSSEN, trabajos sobre Alfonso el Sabio; RIBERA, *La música de las Cantigas*, pág. 108.

[3] Sobre la tendencia románica a conceder mayor importancia al cuento de sílabas que a los acentos, véase STENGEL, *Romanische Verslehre*, § 14.

de las castañuelas, el *trintilintrín* de los *ferrinhos*, el *cháscarras-chás* de las conchas, el *dóngolondrón* de los panderos, el *répinicár* de las guitarras, el *bírbirinchín* de la gaita, ruidos que, por el ritmo y el son, se adaptan completamente al *li ailí alí ailí* de la flauta, recuerdan a menudo el verso de arte mayor y señalan la necesidad de estudiar las cántigas coreográficas del pueblo. ¡Si ni aun de los compases y evoluciones de la *muiñeira* nos formamos idea cabal!» [1].

§ 10. Los versos de gaita gallega. — El ritmo de cuatro *altas* señalado por Carolina Michaëlis se descubre, según su indicación, en los versos de once y de doce sílabas; suele insinuarse en los de nueve, a pesar del origen o al menos influjo extranjero («De quánto mál por vós levéi...») [2]. Precisamente en los dodecasílabos y endecasílabos es donde con más amplitud se emplean los recursos de la catalexis: el resultado es, a veces, la combinación, dentro de la estrofa, de hasta tres versos diferentes, gobernados por afinidades y contrastes rítmicos.

El verso moderno de la muiñeira, acompañado por la música de la gaita gallega y difundido con ella, fuera de Galicia, a través de la España castellana y de la catalana, en su forma típica consta de once sílabas y lleva el acento principal en la cuarta («Tanto bailéi que me namoricara...»), con la posibilidad de convertirse en anapéstico o en dactílico, según que caiga otro acento en la séptima («E no camíno topóu unha filla...»), o dos más, uno en la séptima y otro en la primera («Ísca d'ahí, non me máte-la pita...»). El endecasílabo de esta acentuación es el centro de un grupo que abarca el decasílabo anapéstico y el dodecasílabo de arte mayor, los cuales pueden considerarse como variantes suyas, según se suprima o se añada una sílaba al principio; mediante estas alteraciones catalécticas los tres versos se equivalen, y así lo demuestra la poesía popular gallega de nuestros días en las muiñeiras:

> Cando te vexo d'o monte n'altura
> a todo mon corpo lle da calentura...

> Lagartiño vai ô foradiño
> que ven tua nai co'a cunca de viño... [3].

> Has de cantar á veira do rio,
> ó son d'as oliñas de campo frolido...

> Panadeira d'aquesta ribeira
> de dia móe e de noite peneira.

> ¡Válgate xuncras! ô estilo d'a terra
> de peneirar pol-a noite sin vela...

[1] *Cancioneiro da Ajuda*, vol. II, pág. 93.
[2] Lang, *Liederbuch des Königs Denis*, págs. cxv y cxvi; Milá, *Trovadores en España*, págs. 531, 532, 536.
[3] Milá, *De la poesía popular gallega*, coplas 115 y 127.

> Si queredes armar foliada,
> tornar Merexildo que non se nos vaya... [1].

Los decasílabos pueden abandonar el ritmo anapéstico y adoptar la fórmula bipartita, que consiste en dos pentasílabos:

> Meu maridiño | foise por probe,
> deixou un fillo, topou dezanove...
> Manga rachada | foy a Castilla...

En ocasiones, se mezclan los versos largos con sus quebrados de cinco o seis sílabas:

> Tantarantán por onde van a Noya,
> tantarantán po-la Corredoira,
> tantarantán [2].

La semejanza entre el metro de arte mayor y el de la muiñeira es evidente; pero también lo son las diferencias: mientras en el arte mayor sirve de paradigma el dodecasílabo propiamente dicho, en la muiñeira sirve de paradigma el verso de once, y cabe el de diez, en dos de sus formas.

§ 11. VERSOS ACENTUALES ANTIGUOS. —- No es difícil encontrar en la poesía galaicoportuguesa medieval composiciones en que se anuncian las modernas muiñeiras [3]. El principio acentual logra, a ratos, vencer la tiranía silábica y producir efectos parecidos a los de la lírica popular. Así en la cántiga X de Alfonso el Sabio, zéjel donde se mezclan versos de diez y de once sílabas:

> Rosa das rosas et Fror das frores,
> Dona nas donas, Sennor das Sennores.

> Rosa de beldad e de parecer,
> et Fror d'alegria et de prazer;
> Dona en mui pïadosa seer,
> Sennor en toller coitas e dolores.
> Rosa das rosas...

---

[1] *Cancionero popular gallego*, recogido por JOSÉ PÉREZ BALLESTEROS (vol. I, Madrid, 1885, págs. 136-141, y XIII-XXXIII del prólogo de Theophilo Braga; vol. II, 1886, págs. 200-211; vol. III, 1886, págs. 199-209); contiene otros tipos de versificación irregular, además de la muiñeira.

[2] *Cancionero popular gallego*, vol. I, pág. XIV; MILÁ, *De la poesía popular gallega*, coplas 119 y 124. En la poesía culta la admirable Rosalía de Castro (1837-1885) acoge los ritmos populares:

> As de cantar,   Vente, rapasa,
> meniña gaitera,   vente, meniña,
> as de cantar,   vent'a lavar
> que me moiro de pena...   no pilón d'a fontiña...

[3] Véase BRAGA, prólogo al *Cancionero popular*, de Pérez Ballesteros, págs. XIII-XXXIII; C. MICHAËLIS DE VASCONCELLOS, *Cancioneiro da Ajuda*, vol. II, págs. 56-58 y 925-934; MENÉNDEZ Y PELAYO, *Antología*, vol. III, pág. XXIV.

Atal Sennor deu'ome muit'amar
que de todo mal o pode guardar
e pode-ll'os pecados perdõar
que daz no mundo per máos sabores.
Rosa das rosas...

Deuémol'a muit'amar e seruir,
ca punna de nos guardar de falir;
desí dos erros nos faz repentir
que nós facemos come pecadores.
Rosa das rosas...

Esta Dona que tenno por Sennor
e de que quero seer trobador,
se eu per ren poss'auer seu amor,
dou ao demo os outros amores.
Rosa das rosas...

O en la cántiga de João Zorro, del siglo XIV (número 760ₐ del *Cancionero del Vaticano:*

Pela ribeira do rio salido
trebelhey, madre, con meu amigo;
amor ey migo
que nom ouvesse;
fiz por amigo
que nom fezesse.

Pela ribeira do rio levado
trebelhey, madre, con meu amado,
amor ey migo...

Como punto intermedio entre la versificación acentual de los *Cancioneiros* antiguos y la de las muiñeiras actuales, se encuentran interesantes trozos recogidos en el siglo XVII por Lope de Vega y Tirso de Molina. Preciosa muiñeira dialogada, más irregular que las modernas, es la que inserta Lope en el acto segundo de *La mayor virtud de un rey* (conservo la curiosa ortografía de la Biblioteca Rivadeneyra):

— Barqueriña fermosa, passaime,
da banda d'alem do rio Tejo,
nome de Jesu.
— Si trazeis dinheiro, eu vos passarei.
— ¿E si non le tenho? — Non vos passarei,
nome de Jesu.
¿Não? — Não.
— Y então ¿que farei?
Em la praya vos ficareis.

— Passaime, miñ'alma, que por vos morro.
— Non se move o barco sen prata ou oro.
— Ollai, meos ollos, que não le tenho.

— Ollai, que non queiro.
— Y então ¿que farei?
— Em la praya vos ficareis.

— Dexaime chegar a vossa falua.
— Quem entra e non paga, em passado zumba.
— Non seais tan crua, que eu vos pagarei.
— Em la praya vos ficareis.

Otra muiñeira es la danza de serranos que trae Tirso en *La gallega Mari Hernández* (acto II):

> Cando o crego andaba no forno
> ardèra lo bonetiño e toudo.

> Vos si me habés de levar, mancebo,
> ¡ay! non me habedes de pedir celos.

> Hum galan traye da cinta na gorra,
> diz que lla deu la sua señora.

> Quérole bem a lo fillo do crego.
> quérole bem por lo bem que le quero.

> ¡Ay miña mai! Passaime no rio,
> que se levam as agoas os lirios.

> Assenteime en hum formigueiro.
> docho a o demo lo assentadeiro.

§ 12. **La repetición de las estrofas.** — El principio del isosilabismo fué reforzado en la poesía galaicoportuguesa por otro principio regularizador, en boga al otro lado de los Pirineos: la isometría de las estrofas dentro de cada composición, o sea la repetición exacta de la forma de la primera estrofa en todas las demás: igual número de versos, igual distribución de los tipos de verso (si hay más de uno) y de las rimas graves y agudas.

Hay en los antiguos *Cancioneiros* buen número de combinaciones estróficas, de interesante variedad en la distribución de las rimas, pero limitadas en el empleo de diferentes tipos de verso: pocas veces más de dos.

§ 13. **Los discores.** — El isosilabismo y la isometría, sin embargo, sufren excepciones, autorizadas por el ejemplo de los *descorts* provenzales. De ahí los *discores* galaicoportugueses, que pueden ser regulares o irregulares:

> Quen' oj' ouvesse
> guisad' e podesse
> un cantar fezesse
> a quem mi-ora eu sei,
> e lhi dissesse:
> e pois pouco valvesse,
> non desse

49

ren que non trouxesse,
sei-t' en cas d'el rei.

(*Cancionero del Vaticano*, poesía 963). [1]

§ 14. CASOS ANÓMALOS. — Junto a los discores hay otros pocos ejemplos de irregularidad métrica en los cancioneros galaicoportugueses. Así, la canción que empieza «Non me posso pagar tanto...» (núm. 63 del *Vaticano*):

> ... E juro par Deus lo santo
> que manto | non tragerey, nem granhom,
> nem terrey d'amor razom
> nem d'armas porque quebranto | e chanto,
> nem d'elas ced'a sazom:
> mays tragerey hum d'ormão,
> e hirey pela marinha
> venden'a cebo e farinha
> e fugirey do passo do alazão,
> ca eu nom hy sey outra meezinha.
>
> Nem de lançar a tavolado,
> pagado | nom son, se deus m'amparo ha,
> e nem de bafordar | e andar de noite armado
> sem grad'o | faço, et a rolda ca:
> mais me pago do mar | que de ser cavalleyro
> ca eu fuy já marinheiro,
> e quero-me oy guardar do alacrá
> e coronar quem me foir primeiro...

15. LOS RETORNELOS IRREGULARES. — Si la ley de la isometría de las estrofas contribuyó grandemente a regularizar sobre moldes silábicos la versificación galaicoportuguesa, otros elementos, surgidos principalmente de la poesía nativa, ayudaban a conservarle libertad y variedad: el *refram*, retornelo o estribillo, interior o final, forjado a veces por renglones irregulares, y el paralelismo. Ejemplos de retornelos irregulares:

> Ao demo comend' Amor
> e min, se d'amar ei sabor!

(*Cancionero de Ajuda*, núm. 274).

> ...Vos vi, desy
> nunca coyta perdi.

(*Cancionero del Vaticano*, núm. 126).

[1] Sobre el *descort* en general, véase CARL APPEL, *Vom Descort*, en la *Zeitschrift für romanische Philologie*, 1888; sobre su empleo en la Península, véase LANG, *The Descort in Old Portuguese and Spanish Poetry*, en los *Beiträge zur romanischen Philologie*, Halle, 1899.

..E vam ss'as frores
d'aqui bem com meus amores!

(Vaticano, núm. 401). [1]

§ 16. LOS CANTARES PARALELÍSTICOS Y ENCADENADOS.—
Las estrofas de las canciones paralelísticas y encadenadas con
retornelo (las más lo tienen) combinan varias clases de versos y
adquieren a menudo aspecto abigarrado, asimétrico; pero cada
estrofa, con su propia asimetría, se repite rigurosamente, asimé-
tricamente, a través de toda la composición [2]:

Levantou-s' a velida,
levantou-s' alva,
e vai lavar camisas
e-no alto.
Vai-las lavar alva.

Levantou-s' a louçana,
levantou-s' alva,
e vai lavar delgadas
e-no alto.
Vai-las lavar alva.

E vai lavar camisas,
levantou-s' alva;
o vento lh' as desvia
e-no alto.
Vai-las lavar alva.

E vai lavar delgadas,
levantou-s' alva;
o vento lh' as levava
e-no alto.
Vai-las lavar alva...

(Canción del rey Don Dionís; núm. 172
en el *Vaticano*).[3]

Fui eu, madre, lavar meus cabellos
a la fonte, e paguey-m'eu d'elos
e de mi,
louçana e...

[1] Sobre los retornelos, véase CAROLINA MICHAËLIS DE VASCONCELLOS, *Cancioneiro da Ajuda*, vol. II, págs. 26, 174, 597, 924-926.
[2] Sobre los cantares paralelísticos, véase BRAGA y CAROLINA MICHAËLIS,
en la *Literatura portuguesa (Grundriss)*, § 20; *Cancioneiro da Ajuda*, vol. II,
págs. 920-936; LANG, *Liederbuch des Königs Denis*, págs. CXXXVIII y siguientes.
Carolina Michaëlis de Vasconcellos señala formas primitivas de paralelismo
en Martín Codax (ver *A propósito de Martín Codax e das suas cantigas de amor*,
en la *Revista de Filología Española*, 1915, II, pág. 262).
[3] Núm. 93 en el *Liederbuch*, ed. Lang. — Esquema: siete sílabas-cinco-
siete-cuatro-seis; los versos segundo, cuarto y quinto de cada estrofa forman
el retornelo invariable; los versos primero y tercero forman el tejido paralelístico y encadenado.

Fui eu, madre, lavar mhas garceras
a la fonte, e paguey-m'eu d'elas,
e de mi,
louçana, e...

(Núm. 291 del *Vaticano*).

Eu velida non dormia,
lelia doura!
E meu amigo venia
e doy, lelia doura!...

(Núm. 415 del *Vaticano*).

Baylemos nós já todas, todas, ay amigas,
só aquestas avelaneyras frolidas;
e quem for velida como nós velidas,
se amigo amar,
só aquestas avelaneyras frolidas
verrá baylar...

(Núm. 462 del *Vaticano*, atribuído al clérigo
Ayras Nunes)[1].

B) Castilla

§ 17. Orígenes de la versificación acentual. — En Castilla encontraremos, sobre todo desde 1500 en adelante, versificación acentual de mayor variedad y soltura que la de Portugal y Galicia. La versificación galaicoportuguesa hubo de poseer el principio acentual como propio y espontáneo; pero, en las obras de poetas cultos, los principios de la uniformidad silábica y la isometría estrófica —debidos en parte a influencias extrañas— tendieron a suprimir los ritmos libres. En Castilla veremos ahora versificación irregular, donde el valor de los acentos se percibe de modo claro, y versificación que, si bien cantada o cantable, se halla a medio camino entre la amétrica y la acentual, pues su distribución de acentos es caprichosa. Podríamos escoger entre dos hipótesis: o bien la versificación acentual castellana que conocemos se deriva de la galaicoportugesa, o bien es combinación de elementos del Oeste y del Norte con elementos del Centro. Habría que suponer que la versificación acentual pasó a Castilla, principalmente por vías populares, con toda la riqueza y variedad potencial que quiera suponérsele, y luego, una vez arraigada en suelo castellano, subió hacia la poesía culta durante la época de los Reyes Católicos y continuó penetrando en ella durante cien años. O, si no, podría aceptarse que la poesía galaicoportuguesa

---

[1] Hay otra versión más corta y más popular, atribuída al juglar João Zorro (núm. 761).

nunca haya sido mucho más libre ni muy distinta de la que conocemos gracias a los *Cancioneiros*, y suponerse que se combinó en
Castilla con tipos de versificación más irregulares: las formas amétricas no habían muerto aún en 1400. Y Castilla, junto al verso
heroico, hubo de poseer versos de canto y danza, con el ritmo acentual exigido por la música. Después del estudio de Menéndez Pidal sobre *La primitiva poesía lírica española* —maravillosa reconstrucción de la primavera sumergida, con ayuda de las flores
tardías—, no cabe dudar: serranillas, canciones de viaje, canciones de mayo, cánticas de velador, cánticas de segar y espigar, villancicos pastoriles, canciones de Nochebuena y de San Juan, de
verbena y de trébol, de banquetes, de romería, de ronda, que guar-
damos escritas desde el siglo xv, tienen hondas raíces en la Edad
Media de Castilla[1].

[1] Véase MENÉNDEZ PIDAL, *La primitiva poesía lírica española*, en *Estudios literarios*, págs. 280-336, y *Poesía juglaresca y juglares*, págs. 183-186 y
255-277. La cántica de velador de Berceo suscita diversas cuestiones. Es irregular, como piensan Menéndez Pidal y Baist, y no isosilábica como creía Hanssen. Menéndez Pidal (notas sobre *Elena y María*) dice: «está en pareados
de base eneasilábica, con alternativas cuya fórmula es 9, 8, 10... La falta de
regularidad métrica de la Cántica nos indica que Berceo imitaba en ella un
metro popular, sea de origen independiente de los pareados eneasílabos franceses, sea procedente de ellos, pero ya popularizado en tiempo de Berceo».
Obsérvese, además, que el primer verso de cada dístico es varias veces
menor que el segundo —tendencia frecuente en castellano, que se observa en
muchos proverbios y estribillos populares, no menos que en el verso épico,
donde el primer hemistiquio es generalmente el más corto—. De esta tendencia,
sin embargo, no faltan ejemplos en otras lenguas romances:

> Velat, aljama de los iudíos,
> que non vos furten el Fijo de Díos.

> Ca furtárvoslo querrán
> Andrés e Peidro et Iohán...

> Todos son ladroncielios
> que assechan por los pestiellos...

> Vuestra lengua sin recabdo
> por mal cabo vos ha echado...

> Tomaseio e Matheo
> de furtarlo han grant deseo...

Para reforzar la posibilidad de que haya relación entre la cántica de Berceo
y la poesía galaicoportuguesa (donde el verso de nueve sílabas era común),
podría recordarse el ritmo del cantar recogido por D. Juan Manuel en su *Tratado de las armas:*

> Rey velho que Deus confonda,
> tres son estas con a de Malonda.

Pero ritmos semejantes pueden encontrarse sin dificultad en castellano en
canciones populares. Así, la cántica de velador —precisamente— que Lope de
Vega recoge en *Las almenas de Toro* y en *El Nacimiento de Cristo:*

> Velador que el castillo velas,
> vélale bien, y mira por ti,
> que velando en él me perdí.

De todos modos, el campo donde creció y floreció la versificación acentual castellana fué el popular. Y no podía ser de otro modo: durante el siglo xv la escuela trovadoresca de Castilla se dedicaba con ardor de neófito a la versificación silábica, y son muy contados, como se verá, los poetas cortesanos que conceden atención a la acentual.

§ 18. IMPORTANCIA DEL PRINCIPIO SILÁBICO PARA LOS TROVADORES. — Los trovadores españoles de 1400 en adelante aplican como maestros —salvo excepciones— los principios del isosilabismo y la isometría; aplican otros principios secundarios y artificios curiosos, y se pagan mucho de ellos. A Juan Alfonso de Baena, por ejemplo, le interesan todas las cuestiones de versificación, como se ve por el prólogo del libro que formó y las notas con que encabezó las poesías; igual interés se advierte en Ferrán Manuel de Lando o en Alfonso Álvarez de Villasandino, que cifraba su orgullo en su pericia métrica, aunque se confesaba ignorante en otras materias. Estos poetas, y otros contemporáneos

O bien estos versos encadenados de danza coral que oí cantar en mi infancia en Santo Domingo (indico los acentos del canto):

Abejón del ábejón,
muérto lo llévan en ún serón.

El serón erá de pája;
muérto lo llévan en úna cája.

La cája erá de píno;
muérto lo llévan en ún pepíno.

El pepíno estabá mocáto;
muérto lo llévan en ún zapáto.

El zapáto erá de hiérro;
muérto lo llévan a lós infiérnos.

Los infiérnos 'tabán caliéntes;
muérto lo llévan a Sán Vicénte.

San Vicénte se arránc'un diénte,
y se ló pegó en la frénte.

Espinosa recoge otras versiones en el Suroeste de los Estados Unidos (la región que perteneció a Méjico):

Periquillo el labrador
muerto lo llevan en un colchón.
El colchón era de lana.
Muerto lo llevan en una rana.
Y la rana tenía su pico.
Muerto lo llevan en un burrico...
El pellejo era colorado.
Muerto lo llevan amortajado...

Véase ESPINOSA, *New-Mexican Spanish Folk-Lore*, en el *Journal of American Folk-Lore*, 1916, págs. 520-521, y *Romancero nuevomejicano*, en la *Revue Hispanique*, 1915, páginas 545-546.

El cantar proviene, naturalmente, de España: véase el cantar núm. 180 en los *Cantos populares españoles*, recogidos por D. FRANCISCO RODRÍGUEZ MARÍN, 5 vols., Sevilla, 1882-1883.

y sucesores suyos —entre ellos D. Enrique de Villena y el Marqués de Santillana, en lo que escribieron sobre arte poética—, hacen singular hincapié en el cuento de sílabas y en la acentuación, insistiendo en pormenores como los relativos a concurrencia de vocales. Es evidente que contraponían tales habilidades métricas a la tendencia, tradicional y popular, frecuente aún, hacia la irregularidad [1].

[1] Después que en el *Libro de Alejandro* se formula el principio de las «sílavas cuntadas», creo que no vuelve a mencionarse hasta fines del siglo xiv, cuando los poetas cultos realmente lo dominan.

Hay referencias a la técnica de la versificación en multitud de notas puestas por Baena a las composiciones de su *Cancionero:* véanse números 2, 34, 35, 37, 42, 57, 80, 81, 99, 123, 124, 125, 126, 139, 143, 144, 145, 146, 180, 184, 188, 195 y tantos más. A veces las cuestiones técnicas se discuten en el cuerpo de las poesías mismas: así, por ejemplo, en las que llevan los números 90, 96, 106, 124, 139, 190, 209, 225, 255, 257, 261, 263, 274, 341, 377, 401, 408, 429, 439, 452, 473, 476. La profesión de poeta ha suscitado ya toda suerte de disputas. La importancia dada al cuento de sílabas puede colegirse de los ejemplos que van a continuación:

En el prólogo al *Cancionero*, Baena dice: «el arte de la poetrya e gaya çiençia es una escryptura e compusiçión muy sotil e byen graçiosa, e es dulce e muy agradable a todos los oponientes e rrespondientes della e componedores e oyentes: la qual çiençia e avisaçión e dotrina que della depende e es avida e rreçebida e alcançada por graçia infusa del señor Dios que la da e la enbya e influye en aquel o aquellos que byen e sabya e sotyl e derechamente la saben fazer e ordenar e conponer e limar e escandir e medir por sus pies e pausas, e por sus consonantes e sylabas e acentos, e por artes sotiles e de muy diversas e syngulares nombranças...»

Villasandino, en la poesía «O criaturas tan organizadas...» (núm. 90 del *Cancionero):*

> ...En la poetría tan muy esmerado,
> segun lo demuestran sus compusyçiones
> de sylabas, tiempos e pies e diçiones
> que le doctan a ser profundo letrado.

En su poesía «Non seré de los de Buedo...» (núm. 106):

> Pruevo luego sy rrefyerto
> ser tus sylabas menguadas,
> laydas e desconçertadas...

Burlándose del mal versificador Sánchez de Jahén, dice en la composición «Perlado que afana por ser omeçida...» (núm. 124):

> ...Que non estos vestros laydos e fallydos,
> que quien bien catare en cada rrenglón
> fallará ditongos e gaçafatón
> e los consonantes errados, perdidos.

O suplicando al rey, en la poesía «Muy poderoso varón...» (núm. 209):

> Noble Rrey, sy puse o pongo
> en esta pobre seguida,
> caçaffatón o ditongo,
> palabra layda o perdida...

§ 19. EL ARTE MAYOR Y EL ENDECASÍLABO. — Es natural, pues, que en poetas preocupados con los primores de la versificación silábica no abunden las muestras de poesía acentual, fuera del arte mayor. Hay unas cuantas, sin embargo.

Fray Diego de Valencia comienza así una *Pregunta* contra Villasandino (núm. 473):

> Señor muy envysso e sabio cortés
> en todos los modos de la poetría,
> e muy exçelente en altimitría
> por síllabas longas e breve de pies...

Contra él va también Ferrán Manuel en la recuesta «Alfonso Álvarez amigo...» (núm. 257):

> Mesclad artes entricadas
> de pies medyos e perdidos,
> e consonantes partydos
> con sotilesas juntadas...

Don Enrique de Villena, en los fragmentos de su *Arte de trobar*, dice: «Por la mengua de la Sciencia todos se atreven a hacer ditados solamente guardada la igualdad de las sílabas i concordancia de los bordones, según el compás tomado, cuidando que otra cosa no sea cumplidera a la Rethórica dotrina...»

El Marqués de Santillana, en su famoso Proemio o carta al Condestable de Portugal: «E ¿qué cosa es la poesía (que en nuestro vulgar gaya sçiençia llamamos) si non un fingimiento de cosas útiles, cubiertas e veladas con muy fermosa cobertura, compuestas, distinguidas e scandidas por cierto cuento, pesso e medida?» Más adelante viene el conocido pasaje donde habla de la tercera y más baja clase de producciones poéticas: «Ínfimos son aquellos que sin ningún orden, regla ni cuento façen estos romances e cantares, de que las gentes de baxa e servil condición se alegran.» En otros lugares de su Proemio, refiriéndose a la poesía de las lenguas vulgares, el Marqués insiste constantemente en el «pesso e cuento de las síllabas» y demás reglas conexas.

A estos principios se refiere también en el prológo que puso a sus *Proverbios:*«...guardando el cuento de las síllabas e las últimas e penúltimas e en algunos logares las antepenúltimas, los yerros de los dipthongos e las vocales en aquellos logares donde se pertenesçen».

Y en la *Comedieta de Ponza* dice en elogio del rey Alfonso V de Aragón (refiriéndose a su habilidad en la métrica latina, pero aplicándole las nociones, o al menos las palabras, de la trovadoresca):

> Las síllabas cuenta e guarda el acento
> produeto e correto...

Luego, Gómez Manrique, en la poesía que comienza «Señor Marqués de Villena...», dice de Juan Poeta, versificador empírico:

> Él no sabe qué es acento,
> non ditongo nin mançobre...

El Dr. Pero Díaz, en su introducción al Decir de Gómez Manrique, *Exclamación y querella de la gobernación*, dice que hay «dos maneras de escreuir: una en prosa y oración soluta, e otra en metro e mesura de sylavas».

A fines del siglo xv, el principio silábico aparece definido con absoluta precisión en el *Arte de poesía castellana*, de Juan del Encina (el cual cree todavía necesario, sin embargo, aludir a los «que non se les da más echar una síllaba e dos demasiadas, que de menos»), y en la *Gramática castellana* de Antonio de Nebrija.

Desgraciadamente, las ideas grecolatinas comienzan a mezclarse con las

El arte mayor probablemente tuvo antecedentes rítmicos libres y amplios como los de las modernas muiñeiras. En sus comienzos, tratando de desarrollarse en Castilla, entre otros metros carentes de regularidad, fluctúa; los poetas del *Cancionero de Baena* lo perfeccionan, y entonces, por la influencia de los metros silábicos, se limita a los dodecasílabos con dos variantes catalécticas, una muy frecuente, el verso de once (a veces de diez) con pausa fuerte después del segundo acento («Es a saber / de presto tan braua...»), y otra rarísima, el de trece («Aristótiles cerca / del padre Platón...»). Se halla, pues, muy cercano ya al molde silábico.

Entre tanto, el endecasílabo, que había asomado la cabeza en los poemas heroicos, hace esfuerzos por adquirir vida propia, independiente, pero no la alcanza: así como el eneasílabo se sumerge bajo el octosílabo, así en la poesía culta el verso de once sobrevive, hasta 1526, sólo como auxiliar del de doce en el arte mayor, y pocas veces se escribe separado. Después de los ensayos de D. Juan Manuel y del Arcipreste, Micer Francisco Imperial, y sus copistas, enmarañan confusamente el endecasílabo dantesco con el arte mayor:

> ...Qual el desir atal será agora.
> Non era el fondo turbio nin lodoso,
> mas era diamante muy illuminoso...
> e las paredes de esmeralda fina... [1].

Santillana copia el endecasílabo italiano, con sus dos formas estrictas: la de acento en sexta sílaba y la de acento en cuarta; pero sus sonetos no tienen imitadores [2]. Y, finalmente, Fernán Pérez de Guzmán ensaya el endecasílabo semejante al épico primitivo de los franceses, con acento en la cuarta, y a veces con una sílaba de exceso después del acento interior:

> Yo digo assí | que la buena criança
> da más virtud | que la naturaleza,
> mas non lo digo | con tan vltra cuydança
> que non someta | mi grossera rodeza...

Pérez de Guzmán no confunde estos endecasílabos con los anapésticos que acompañan al dodecasílabo de arte mayor [3].

---

ideas fundadas en la observación directa de la práctica usual en las lenguas romances, y la confusión comienza desde que Nebrija se empeña en demostrar la conveniencia de introducir el sistema cuantitativo en la versificación española.

[1] *Cancionero de Baena*, núm. 250. Véanse también los números 226, 231, 238, 239, 521 y 548.

[2] Salvo el glosador que cita GALLARDO en el *Ensayo de una biblioteca española...*, tomo I, col. 585. Es Mosén Juan de Villalpando: los sonetos están en versos de once y de doce sílabas, error de que está libre el modelo.

[3] Véase HANSSEN, *Los versos de las Cantigas de Santa María (Anales,* 1901, pág. 538).

Ninguno de estos ensayos goza de popularidad, y el endecasílabo no se hace metro español sino después. Boscán lo pide de nuevo a Italia en 1526 y Garcilaso lo apoya. Durante tres siglos, hasta los comienzos del XIX, el endecasílabo yámbico español tiene, como el italiano, dos acentuaciones interiores posibles: una en la sexta sílaba («Flérida para mí dulce y sabrosa...»), o una en la cuarta («Pienso remedios en mi fantasía...»). Los versos de acento en cuarta sílaba reforzaban muy a menudo su ritmo yámbico con otro acento en la octava («Más que la fruta del cercado ajeno...»): esta variedad llegó a hacerse usual en español y desterrar por fin a su generadora (hacia 1800), haciendo a los escritores españoles creer equivocadamente que era la fundamental también en italiano. En cambio, el verso de acento en cuarta sílaba permite otro en la séptima («Tus claros ojos ¿a quién los volviste?»), y así se halla con frecuencia en italiano; pero en España se evitó, después de Garcilaso, porque se confundía con el endecasílabo *auxiliar* del arte mayor [1].

Entre tanto, este endecasílabo anapéstico o dactílico sobrevivía separadamente, en boca del pueblo, entre los versos acentuales de parentesco galaicoportugués: se le ha solido llamar «endecasílabo de gaita gallega».

§ 20. LOS CANTARES PARALELÍSTICOS EN CASTELLANO. — Aquel *cossante* de D. Diego Hurtado de Mendoza el viejo, almirante de Castilla (descripción del árbol de amor, cuyo encanto hace pensar en el verso de Keats: «Dance, and Provençal song, and sun-burnt mirth...»), se inspira en modelos occidentales, tanto para los versos (acentuales irregulares, de nueve a doce sílabas, con quebrados de seis) como para la estrofa, isométricamente repetida (tipo paralelístico y encadenada con estribillo):

A aquel árbol que mueve la foxa
algo se le antoxa.

Aquel árbol del bel mirar
façe de manyera flores quiere dar:
algo se le antoxa.

[1] Sobre todas las cuestiones relativas al endecasílabo en castellano, antes y después de Boscán, véase MENÉNDEZ Y PELAYO, *Antología*, vol. XIII, págs. 161 a 239, y mi trabajo *El endecasílabo castellano*, páginas 271-347 de este volumen. Debo agregar ahora que también D. Enrique de Villena hizo endecasílabos —con acento fundamental en la sílaba cuarta— y cita dos de ellos en su *Arte de trobar*. Para el endecasílabo desde Boscán y Garcilaso, hay que rectificar el valor de unos pocos ejemplos que cito en mi trabajo, de acuerdo con el importante estudio de TOMÁS NAVARRO TOMÁS, *Palabras sin acento* (en la *Revista de Filología Española*, 1925, páginas 335 y sigs.). Como ejemplo de las posibilidades de confusión entre el endecasílabo y el arte mayor: Gonzalo Fernández de Oviedo, en sus *Quincuagenas de los... reyes, príncipes... e personas notables de España* (1.ª parte, est. 4), dice que la *Divina Comedia* «del Danthe» y los *Triunfos* de Petrarca están en versos «de arte mayor de once e doce sílabas».

Aquel árbol del bel veyer
façe de manyera quiere florecer:
algo se le antoxa.

Façe de manyera flores quiere dar;
ya se demuestra; salidlas mirar:
algo se le antoxa.

Façe de manyera quiere florecer;
ya se demuestra; salidlas a veer:
algo se le antoxa.

Ya se demuestra; salidlas mirar;
vengan las damas las frutas cortar:
algo se le antoxa.

Ya se demuestra: salidlas a veer:
vengan las damas las frutas coger:
algo se le antoxa [1].

El cantar paralelístico hubo de existir como forma popular,
no sólo en Portugal y Galicia, sino en León y en Asturias, donde
subsiste hoy en forma más elemental que la antigua, sin retornelo
como letra de las danzas rústicas:

—¡Ay Juana, cuerpo garrido!
¡Ay Juana, cuerpo lozano!
¿Dónde le dejas a tu buen amigo?
¿Dónde le dejas a tu buen amado?
— Muerto le dejo a la orilla del río;
déjole muerto a la orilla del vado.
— ¿Cuánto me das y volvértelo he vivo?
¿Cuánta me das y volvértelo he sano?
— Doyte las armas y doyte el rocino;
doyte las armas y doyte el caballo.
— No he menester armas ni rocino,
No he menester armas ni caballo [2].

---

[1] Este canto de danza sobre el árbol de amor lo extrajo AMADOR DE LOS
Ríos de uno de los Cancioneros manuscritos de la Biblioteca Real de Madrid
y lo publicó en su *Historia crítica de la literatura española* (vol. V, pág. 293).
CAROLINA MICHAËLIS DE VASCONCELLOS lo reconstruye según las reglas del
cantar paralelístico *(Cancioneiro da Ajuda,* vol. II, pág. 929) y añade la última estrofa, que faltaba en el original.

[2] MILÁ, *Del decasílabo y endecasílabo anapéstico (Obras,* volumen V, pág.
339). En su libro *Poesía popular: colección de los viejos romances que se cantan
por los asturianos...* (Madrid, 1885). JUAN MENÉNDEZ PIDAL recogió este
cantar (pág. 245) con los primeros versos ya en forma de decasílabos:

Ay probe Xuana de cuerpo garrido,
ay probe Xuana de cuerpo galano...

Así lo reproducen MENÉNDEZ Y PELAYO, *Antología,* vol. X, página 141;
C. MICHAËLIS DE VASCONCELLOS, *Cancioneiro da Ajuda,* vol. II, pág. 931.

59

Hay otra canción asturiana de paralelismo elemental, como
el de la anterior, en forma de doble romance; sirve para la *danza
prima.* Ya la mencionaba Jovellanos en el siglo XVIII. La versión
recogida por Juan Menéndez Pidal comienza así:

> ¡Ay! un galán d'esta villa
> ¡Ay! un galán d'esta casa
> ¡ay! él por aquí venía
> ¡ay! él por aquí llegaba.
> — ¡Ay! diga lo que él quería
> ¡ay! diga lo que él buscaba.
> — ¡Ay! busco la blanca niña
> ¡ay! busco la niña blanca,
> la que el cabello tejía,
> la que el cabello trenzaba... [1].

Al pasar a Castilla, el cantar paralelístico no alcanzó tanta
popularidad como en las tierras de su origen; pero se empleó con
relativa frecuencia durante el siglo XV. Así se ve en los que trae
el *Cancionero musical de los siglos XV y XVI*, publicado por Francisco Asenjo Barbieri (Madrid, 1890); ejemplo:

> Al alba venid, buen amigo,
> al alba venid.
>
> Amigo el que yo más quería,
> venid a la luz del día.
>
> Amigo el que yo más amaba,
> venid a la luz del alba.
>
> Venid a la luz del día,
> non traigáis compañía.
>
> Venid a la luz del alba,
> non traigáis gran compaña [2].

---

[1] JUAN MENÉNDEZ PIDAL, *Poesía popular*, pág. 147; MENÉNDEZ Y PELAYO,
Antología, vol. X, págs. 9-18 y 79-83; C. MICHAËLIS DE VASCONCELLOS, *Cancioneiro da Ajuda*, vol. II, pág. 932.

[2] LANG traduce al gallego este cantar, considerándolo como de origen occidental (véase *Cancioneiro gallegocastelhano*, número 70); pero R. MENÉNDEZ
PIDAL *(La primitiva poesía lírica*, páginas 327-328) estima que no hay motivo para declararlo gallego. CAROLINA MICHAËLIS, en el de *Ajuda*, lo reproduce en castellano (vol. II, pág. 930). Lang recoge tres poesías en gallego, del
Cancionero musical de los siglos XV y XVI, transcrito y comentado por FRAN-
CISCO ASENJO BARBIERI, Madrid, 1890 (números 50, «Minno amor, dixestes
ay...»; 437, «Meu laranjedo no ten fruto...», y 458, «Meus ollos van por
lo mare...»): las tres son canciones paralelísticas, y prueban la difusión de
la poesía popular gallega en Castilla. Véase *Cancioneiro gallegocastelhano*, página 237; además, el villancico gallego «Si viniesse e me levasse», núm. 4 de
las *Diez canciones españolas de los siglos XV y XVI*, publicadas por el P. LUIS
VILLALBA, Madrid, s. a., c. 1920.
Hay otras canciones paralelísticas o encadenadas; en castellano, en el *Cancionero musical* (núms. 245, 259, 400, 415: la primera combina la fórmula pa-

Después del siglo xv la fórmula paralelística y la encadenada, ya en combinación, o ya separadamente, resurgen de tarde en tarve en la literatura española: más a menudo a través de los poetas portugueses —como Gil Vicente— que de los castellanos.

§ 21 AUSENCIA DE VERSIFICACIÓN ACENTUAL EN EL «CANCIONERO DE BAENA», FUERA DEL ARTE MAYOR. — A pesar de su vasto contenido y de sus numerosos elementos gallegos, en el *Cancionero de Baena* se nota la ausencia del elemento acentual en versificación irregular, fuera del arte mayor. Ejemplos de metro todavía fluctuante sí se hallan de tarde en tarde, como luego en los Cancioneros *Stúñiga* y *Herberay* [1]; pero son productos de vacilaciones ocasionales, y, fuera del arte mayor, todos los versos de la colección obedecen al principio silábico. Los discores que aparecen allí no son irregulares, sino al contrario [2]. Semejantes a esos discores, pero menos regulares que ellos, hay dos composiciones de movimiento estrófico curioso: la segunda pudiera tener lejana relación con algún metro acentual. La una es de Alfonso Álvarez de Villasandino (núm. 6), poeta todavía bilingüe, castellano y a ratos gallego:

> Amigos, tal | coyta mortal
> nunca pensé que avrya:
> por ser leal | rresçivo mal
> donde plaser atendya.
> Ya non me cal
> pensar en úl,
> salvo señal
> de omme carnal,
> e seguir por la triste vía
> d'este enxemplo natural:
> amansar deve su saña
> quien por sí mesmo se engaña...

La otra es de Juan Alfonso de Baena (núm. 452):

> Muy alto señor, | non visto aduay,
> nin visto color | de buen verdegay,
> nin trobo discor | ni fago deslay,
> pues tanto dolor | yo veo que ay:
> mas llanto

ralelística y la encadenada; la segunda y la tercera presentan simple paralelismo; la cuarta, simple encadenamiento). Se relacionan con el tipo paralelístico o con el encadenado las composiciones que llevan los números 17, 402, 423, 434, y probablemente también 48, 53, 61, 85, 98, 103, 115, 127, 131, 143, 236, 237, 263, 401, 403, 416, 427. Véase CAROLINA MICHAËLIS DE VASCONCELLOS, *Cancioneiro da Ajuda*, vol. II, págs. 925, 926, 935.

[1] Véanse §§ 7 y 11 del cap. I de este libro.
[2] Véase LANG, *The Descort in Old Portuguese and Spanish Poetry*.

> e quebranto
> en planto
> faré canto
> ¡ay, ay, ay! por el mal tanto.
>
> Omme pobre e ssyn dinero
> nunca bive plaçentero...

En ambas el modelo de la estrofa se repite, según la ley de la isometría [1].

Otra composición curiosa, de tipo semejante, se encuentra en el manuscrito de *Poesías del siglo XV* (segunda mitad) publicado por Bonilla. Su autor es Montoro (no Antón, el ropero de Córdoba, sino el cortesano contemporáneo suyo):

> Amor que yo vi
> por mi pesar,
> quiero oluidar.
>
> Mi coraçón se fué perder
> amando a quien no pudo aver.
> Si lo perdí
> por mi mal buscar
> ¿dó lo yré fallar?
>
> Por se perder cuytas le dan
> et puso a mí en tal afán.
> que biuo así
> sin le cobrar,
> por le contentar.
>
> Allí do piensa beuir
> ffaze a mí solo morir,
> mas pues allí
> piensa durar,
> déuolo dexar [2].

§ 22. EL VILLANCICO DE SANTILLANA A SUS HIJAS. — El Marqués de Santillana, desdeñoso como se manifiesta para los que escriben «sin ningún orden, regla ni cuento», recoge, sin embargo, trozos de cánticas populares en una de sus composiciones: el villancico a sus hijas, «Por una gentil floresta...» El primero y el tercero de los trozos, al menos, son irregulares:

---

[1] Sobre el carácter cortesano del *Cancionero de Baena*, véase MENÉNDEZ PIDAL, *La primitiva poesía lírica*, págs. 269-280.

[2] Véase *Anales de la literatura española*, publicados por Adolfo Bonilla y San Martín, Madrid, 1904, pág. 201; aparece también en el *Cancionero inédito del siglo XV*, publicado por Alfonso Pérez Gómez Nieva, Madrid, 1884, pág. 95, versión ligeramente distinta.

Aguardan a mí:
nunca tales guardas vi.

— La niña que amores ha,
sola, ¿cómo dormirá?

—Dejatlo al villano, pene,
véngueme Dios delle.

— Sospirando yva la niña
e non por mí,
que yo bien se lo entendí.

Todos tienen el sabor de la poesía castellana influída por las
cantigas de refram galaicoportuguesas. El parentesco con Galicia y Portugal puede probarse, al menos parcialmente: recuérdese la canción de Ayras Nunes, «Oy oj' eu hũa pastor cantar...»
(núm. 454 del *Cancionero del Vaticano*):

Pela ribeyra do rio
cantado ia la virgo
d'amor:

— Quem amores ha
como dom' or' ay,
bela frol? [1]

---

[1] Véase LANG, *Cancioneiro gallegocastelhano*, pág. 223. Cito el final de la
canción de Ayras Nunes en la forma en que aparece en el *Cancioneiro portu-
guez da Vaticana*, según la edición de Theophilo Braga. Lang, en su *Liederbuch des Königs Denis*, pág. cxiv, lo cita en endecasílabos:

Pela ribeyra do rio cantando
ia la virgo d'amor. Quem amores
ha, etc.

Lang se atiene a la forma en que aparece copiado el trozo en el manuscrito del Vaticano (véase la edición paleográfica de Monaci). Pero me parece
mejor el arreglo de Braga, que atiende a las rimas y a la unidad de las frases,
como «Quem amores ha». El manuscrito es guía poco seguro para la división
de los versos en los estribillos populares: en esa misma composición de Nunes
(núm. 454) transcribe el primer trozo popular cortando el primer verso en mitad de la palabra *avellanedo*. En la composición 757, por ejemplo, el manuscrito ofrece dos formas contradictorias:

Pela ribeyra do rio
cantando ia la dona virgo
d'amor...

Y luego:

Pela ribeyra do alto cantando
ia la dona dalgo d'amor.

La primera forma es la mejor, y permite restablecer la de la segunda:

Pela ribeyra do alto
cantando ia la dona dalgo
d'amor.

Véase C. MICHAËLIS DE VASCONCELLOS, *Cancioneiro da Ajuda*, vol. II,
págs. 920-921.

El motecillo conservó su popularidad hasta el siglo XVI. Juan Vásquez, maestro de música, lo recoge, alterado con ligero toque humorístico, entre sus *Villancicos y canciones* (1551):

> Quien amores tiene
> ¿cómo duerme?
>
> Quien amores tiene de la casada
> ¿cómo duerme la noche ni el alba?
>
> Duerme cada cual como puede[1].

El fragmento primero, sobre la niña a quien se quiere guardar, tiene antecedentes en la lírica galaicoportuguesa:

> Mha madre velida! e non me guardedes
> d'ir a San Servando; ca se o fazedes
> morrerey d'amores...
>
> ...Podem-m' agora guardar
> mays non me partiram de o amar.
>
> (*Cancionero del Vaticano*, núms. 741 y 742.)

Persiste el tema en la literatura española, hasta la seguidilla popular hacia 1600, que recogen Cervantes y Lope:

> Madre, la mi madre,
> guardas me ponéis...[2].

El tipo de composición a que corresponde el villancico del Marqués, donde se intercalan fragmentos de cantares y a veces cantares completos, tiene antecedentes trovadorescos, y probablemente pasa de Galicia y Portugal a Castilla. Continúa existiendo, y de 1500 en adelante suele hallarse bajo el nombre de *ensalada*, y luego de *ensaladilla*[3].

§ 23. LAS PRIMERAS SEGUIDILLAS. — El apego a las formas isosilábicas en la poesía escolástico-cortesana del siglo XV se revela de modo peculiar en la selección de motes o de estribillos populares para las composiciones que los llevan: son estribillos de versos iguales, salvo contadas excepciones. Después de Santillana, otra excepción es Juan Álvarez Gato (c. 1430-c. 1496), quien imita a lo divino la seguidilla popular:

---

[1] *Ensayo*, de Gallardo, col. IV, columnas 926 y 931.
[2] Sobre el villancico de Santillana, véase MENÉNDEZ PIDAL, *La primitiva poesía lírica*, págs. 317-319 y 330.
[3] En el *Arte poética*, de RENGIFO, se describe la ensalada: existía al publicarse la obra por primera vez (1592), pero la descripción pertenece a las adiciones hechas después.

> Quita allá, que no quiero,
> falso enemigo;
> quita allá, que no quiero
> que huelgues conmigo.

La imitación, que encabeza una poesía en hexasílabos, «Ya sé lo que quieres...», dice:

> Quita allá, que no quiero,
> mundo enemigo;
> quita allá, que no quiero
> pendencias contigo.

Al terminar la composición, el mote se repite con ligeras variantes: «falso enemigo...»; «quitallá».

El cantar originario conservó su popularidad hasta bien entrada la siguiente centuria. Dos de sus versos, bajo otra variante:

> Tir'allá, que non quiero,
> mozuelo Rodrigo...

reaparecen como estribo de una composición (núm. 397 del *Cancionero musical*), cuyas coplas están en hexasílabos, «Mi tiempo perdido...». Después, Luis Milán, en su *Cortesano* (Valencia, 1561), vuelve a citarla:

> Tirte allá, que no quiero
> mozuelo Rodrigo;
> tirte allá, que no quiero
> que burles conmigo.

Grande es la importancia de este cantar: se le considera como la primera seguidilla que aparece en la literatura castellana.

Antes de Álvarez Gato, que floreció entre 1453 y 1495, empleó la seguidilla, en portugués, el infante Don Pedro de Portugal (1429-1466):

> Eu tenno vountade
> d'Amor me partir
> e tal en verdade
> nunca o servir.
>
> De m'ir e razon
> sen aver galardon
> de minna sennor [1].

---

[1] El estudio de HANSSEN sobre *La seguidilla (Anales*, 1909) es importantísimo. En él analiza minuciosamente los diversos tipos y variantes que existen. Sobre el origen, véanse en particular las págs. 725 y siguientes.

Ya en 1626 describía bien las formas de la seguidilla el maestro GONZALO CORREAS, en su *Arte grande de la lengua castellana* (véase edición de Viñaza, Madrid, 1903, págs. 271-282).

§ 24. ORIGEN DE LA SEGUIDILLA: PROBABLEMENTE, CASTE-
LLANO. — El Infante ¿trasladaba un metro castellano al portugués, como hizo en otros casos, o simplemente escribía en un metro de su lengua nativa? Hay semejanzas de procedimientos entre
las seguidillas antiguas y la poesía galaicoportuguesa: el empleo
de la catalexis, la aplicación de la ley de Mussafia. Pero dado que
la seguidilla no se encuentra entre la multitud de tipos estróficos
de los antiguos *Cancioneiros*, debe pensarse que el tipo hubo de
formarse en Castilla, sobre elementos de versificación fluctuante.
Ya la *Serranilla de la Zarzuela*, a principios del siglo XV, parece
anunciarlo.

§ 25. FORMAS DE LA SEGUIDILLA. — La seguidilla es, en su
origen, esencialmente irregular, fluctuante. Consistía en la alternancia de dos versos breves, como en las baladas inglesas: más
largo el primero, de seis a ocho sílabas, y aun nueve, según el maestro Gonzalo Correas; más corto el segundo, de cuatro a seis. Pero
solían los dos versos, largo y corto, escribirse como uno solo: así
se imprimen todavía en el *Quijote* y en *Rinconete y Cortadillo*. Su
subdivisión es caso paralelo al de los versos de romance: como
en el romance, la rima —asonancia o consonancia— resulta entonces alterna, en los versos pares; pero, a diferencia del romance,
adquiere con el tiempo otra rima alterna, en los versos im-
pares.

Oscila entre dos extremos: el máximum de desigualdad entre
los dos versos fundamentales (8 + 4) la equipara momentáneamente a la copla de pie quebrado, pero esto se da raras veces; en
el extremo contrario, sus dos versos resultan iguales (6 + 6) y
se confunden con los de la endecha, metro hexasilábico de la época. La combinación paradigma es la alternancia de heptasílabos
y pentasílabos (7 + 5); pero el hexasílabo era muy frecuente antes como verso inicial. Lo más común es que, aun en las coplas
más fluctuantes, cualesquiera que sean las medidas iniciales, el
ritmo tienda a definirse al final (7 + 5).

La acentuación del final del verso es, generalmente, llana, pero
las formas más antiguas, y las populares de hoy, admiten libremente los versos de terminación aguda, ya sea como equivalente
de los versos graves de igual medida numérica (ley de Mussafia),
ya como equivalente de los graves de igual valor métrico.

Junto con la estrofa de cuatro versos existe, desde temprano, pero mucho menos frecuente, la de tres; a veces, la de cuatro
parece ser una de tres con repetición de algún verso (así la recogida por Álvarez Gato). Posteriormente, las dos se combinan en
una de siete renglones, como ya ocurría en el cantar del Infante
Don Pedro (7-5-7-5-5-7-5).

Con el tiempo, en la poesía culta la seguidilla llegará a convertirse en regular: versos de siete y de cinco sílabas obligatorias;
su evolución durará dos siglos.

§ 26. LA SEGUIDILLA EN EL «CANCIONERO HERBERAY». — Hay otra seguidilla del siglo XV que hasta ahora no se había traído a cuento para la historia del tipo. Figura en el *Cancionero Herberay*, cuyo contenido pertenece exclusivamente a aquella centuria, y puede estimársela contemporánea de la que imitó Álvarez Gato, o poco posterior:

> Ojos de la mi señora
> ¿y vos qué avedes?
> ¿por qué vos abaxades
> cuando me veedes? [1].

Las coplas, sin nombre de autor, que acompañan la seguidilla, son de pie quebrado: «Vuestro lindo parecer | y fermosura...» ¿Indica esta circunstancia alguna confusión entre los dos tipos estróficos en la mente del autor? Tal vez no; pero sí pudiera suponerse en otra composición del mismo *Cancionero*, escrita en coplas de pie quebrado, en que el octosílabo es siempre agudo y hace *enjambement* con el verso corto, obligándole a tener cuatro sílabas $(7 + 5 = 8 + 4)$:

> Pues que me queréys matar,
> tal es mi suerte,
> non me fagades más penar,
> datme la muerte [2].

Estos primeros cuatro versos, que sirven de cabeza o mote, hacen pensar en la influencia de la seguidilla.

Podría pensarse también que hay influencia de la seguidilla en otras composiciones anónimas, quizá populares, del *Cancionero Herberay:*

> Quiçá si pensáys
> que vos aya faltado,
> vos no lo creáys...
>
> — La yra de Dios
> agora me levasse...
> La causa soys vos,
> mas si me pesasse,
> agora me levasse
> la yra de Dios [3].

---

[1] El *Cancionero Herberay* perteneció al célebre traductor francés de los libros de caballería española, Herberay des Essarts. El manuscrito es del siglo XV; Gallardo lo describe y extracta en el tomo I de su *Ensayo*, cols. 451-567.

[2] *Ensayo*, de Gallardo, vol. I, cols. 457-458. En el cancionero inédito del siglo XVI, ms. 5.593 (antes P. supl. 279) de la Biblioteca Nacional de Madrid, hay un *chiste* con las mismas peculiaridades métricas:

> Robóme mi coraçón
> una donzella
> porque le di mi libertad
> por ser tan bella.

[3] *Ensayo*, de Gallardo, vol. I, col. 499.

—Quien biue sufriendo
continuo pesar...
 Pues muerte meior
ya darme sería,
que tanto dolor
no bastaría...

 — Quien gasta su vida
en vos servir...

 — Temiendo aquel día
que parta de vos,
aver alegría
no puedo por Dios.
Mas mis tristes enojos
ya tanto reçelo
que nunca mis ojos
leuanto del suelo.
Alegre sería
no ver por Dios
aquel triste día
que parta de vos [1].

§ 27. SEGUIDILLA Y ENDECHA. — La tendencia a la confusión entre la seguidilla y la copla de pie quebrado es muy débil, los casos pocos; pero la posibilidad de confundir la seguidilla con la endecha hexasilábica sí es frecuente cuando aquélla emplea versos agudos. La posibilidad se ve en los versos portugueses de D. Pedro, y probablemente a ella deberá atribuirse la fluctuación de los hexasílabos en la serie de composiciones del *Herberay*. La confusión se observa todavía a principios del siglo XVII (en *Rinconete y Cortadillo*, por ejemplo) y hay casos en que la distinción sería imposible si no hubiera declaración expresa en los textos.

Endecha es, al parecer, el *cantar viejo* sobre *Los Comendadores de Córdoba;* así lo hace pensar el tono doliente:

Los Comendadores,
por mi mal os vi;
yo vi a vosotros,
vosotros a mí.

El cantar resonará luego en la lírica y en el teatro durante doscientos años, bajo otra lección las más veces:

Tristes de vosotros,
cuitada de mí.

Sin embargo, su más antigua glosa, que pudiera remontar al final del siglo XV, según Menéndez y Pelayo (puesto que ya parece que se la imita en el cantar de *Sierra Bermeja*, poco posterior

---

[1] *Ensayo*, de Gallardo, vol. I, col. 544.

a 1501), está en versos que fluctúan entre endecha y seguidillas, combinados en estrofas isométricas en cuanto a la rima:

Al comienzo malo
de mis amores,
convidó Fernando
los Comendadores
a buenas gallinas,
capones mejores.
Púsome a la mesa
con los señores.
Jorge nunca tira
los ojos de mí.
¡Los Comendadores,
por mi mal os vi!

Turbó con la vista
mi conoscimiento:
de ver en mi cara
tal movimiento,
tomó de hablarme
atrevimiento.
Desque oí cuitada
su pedimiento,
de amores vencida
le dije que sí.
¡Los Comendadores,
por mi mal os vi!

Los Comendadores
de Calatrava
partieron de Sevilla
a hora menguada,
para la cibdad
de Córdoba la llana...

Por la Puerta del Rincón
hicieron su entrada,
y por Sancta Marina
la pasada.
Vieron sus amores
a una ventana... [1].

---

[1] Lope funda en este cantar su drama *Los Comendadores de Córdoba*. Véanse *Obras* de Lope de Vega, edición de la Academia Española, vol. XI, págs. LXI-LXIV (prólogo de Menéndez y Pelayo), y *Romancero*, ed. Agustín Durán (vol. XVI de la Biblioteca Rivadeneyra, pág. 697). Además, sobre el cantar, MENÉNDEZ Y PELAYO, *Antología*, X, págs. 230 y 369-375. GALLARDO, *(Ensayo*, vol. III, cols. 391-392) atribuye a Pedro de Lerma las coplas en que se glosa el cantar; la atribución es dudosa. Ya desde 1528, Francisco Delgado o Delicado, en *La Lozana Andaluza* (mamotreto XV), cita, en forma corrompida, versos de las coplas y les da el nombre de endecha:

Jueves era, jueves,
día de mercado,
convidó Hernando
los Comendadores...

69

Endecha semejante, tal vez coetánea con la de *Los Comendadores*, y de fortuna muy semejante en la poesía lírica y dramática, es la de *La niña de Gómez Arias;*

> Señor Gómez Arias,
> doléos de mí,
> soy mochacha y niña
> y nunca en tal me vi.

En los siglos XVI y XVII aparecerá glosada, como la de *Los Comendadores*, en metro que fluctúa entre la seguidilla y la endecha [1].

§ 28. VERSOS DE GAITA GALLEGA. — Los versos a estilo de gaita gallega, que ya encontramos en el *cossante* de D. Diego Hurtado de Mendoza [2], vuelven a surgir en las poesías anónimas, de sabor popular, del *Cancionero Herberay:*

> Soy garridilla e pierdo sazón
> por mal maridada;
> tengo marido en mi corazón
> que a mí agrada [3].

Aquí aparece por primera vez esta deliciosa canción de la Bella malmaridada, paralela a la octosilábica sobre igual tema [4]. La he encontrado luego en un cancionero manuscrito, de hacia 1600, de la Biblioteca Nacional de Madrid (núm. 5.593):

> Soy garridilla
> y biuo penada
> por ser mal casada.

La del *Cancionero Herberay* continúa en coplas de arte mayor, cuya forma estrófica es de zéjel, pero el copista cortó en dos cada verso:

Lope de Rueda, en el *Coloquio de Timbria*, parodia el cantar en lenguaje que pretende ser rústico y en metro que se aproxima a la seguidilla:

> Las Comendadoras
> de Casalava,
> salí de Sevilla
> enoramala...

---

[1] Se encuentra en Sebastián de Horozco, en el entremés *El viejo celoso*, de Cervantes, y en el drama de Calderón intitulado *La niña de Gómez Arias*. Es posible que sea alusión a este cantar la frase «que nunca en tal me vi», en el mamotreto XIX de *La Lozana Andaluza* (1528).

[2] Véase § 20 de este capítulo.

[3] *Ensayo*, de Gallardo, vol. I, col. 455.

[4] Véase el comentario de FRANCISCO ASENJO BARBIERI a la composición núm. 158 del *Cancionero musical* (y adiciones, páginas 607-610), y la nota de PUYOL en su edición de *La pícara Justina*, Madrid, 1912 (vol. III, págs. 322-324). Lope tiene una comedia de *La bella malmaridada* y otra de *La mal casada*.

Ha que soy suya bien cinquo o seys años,
que nunca dél huue camisa ni panyos... [1]

Otro cantar en que se discierne el ritmo anapéstico es humorístico:

Si desta scapo sabré qué contar,
non partiré dell'aldea
mientras viere nevar.

Una moçuela de vil semeiar
fízome ademán de conmigo folgar;
non partiré dell'aldea
mientras viere nevar [2].

De esta especie de versos debió nacer, por división, el tipo fluctuante entre cinco y seis sílabas que encontramos en Álvarez Gato:

Querésme perder
con pena y destierros
por nunca querer
de mí adoleceros.

Daisme fatiga,
dolor, desabrigo;
en nombre damiga
me sois enemigos;
echáisme a perder
sin culpa ni yerros
por nunca querer
de mí adoleceros.

Muero viviendo,
que sois al revés;
sirvo, y sirviendo
peor me querés.
Es vuestro plazer
doblarme los hierros
y nunca querer
de mí adoleceros [3].

---

[1] En el *Cancionero* del Museo Británico, perteneciente al siglo xv y publicado por Rennert *(Romanische Forschungen*, de Erlangen, vol. X, 1899), la
composición 116, *A Nuestra Señora*, presenta igual aspecto:

Antes del siglo,
vos, Virgen benigna...

Pero es sólo efecto de la escritura, que hace aparecer como cortos los versos cuando en realidad son de arte mayor (forma estrófica de zéjel: rimas *a a
a b — c c c b — d d d b — e e e b).*

[2] *Ensayo*, de Gallardo, vol. I, col. 456.

[3] Vuelve a encontrarse (véase capítulo siguiente) en Lucas Fernández y
en Fray Ambrosio Montesino.

71

§ 29. Versos eneasílabos. — El *Cancionero Herberay* contiene además otro cantarcillo anónimo, al que puede suponérsele pauta eneasilábica, o bien, suprimiéndole el *non*, tendencia a la seguidilla:

> Que non es valedero, non,
> el falso del amor,
> que non es valedero, non [1].

Así aparecerán más adelante muchos trozos de poesía popular en castellano, cuyo ritmo es difícil de fijar y cuya característica no es sino la irregularidad con tendencias acentuales imprecisas.

En Álvarez Gato se encuentra, sin embargo, bien definido el eneasílabo. Dentro de la poesía castellana culta, el eneasílabo desaparece desde principios del siglo xiv, y no resurge sino ya cercano el xx, exceptuando los casos en que los poetas de la época áurea escriben en ritmos populares: el eneasílabo será, desde el siglo xv hasta el xviii, característico de la poesía popular, y generalmente se presentará como elemento dominante en cantares de versificación irregular; con frecuencia, también, se combinará con endecasílabos y decasílabos a estilo de gaita gallega [2]. La

---

[1] *Ensayo*, de Gallardo, vol. I, col. 458.

[2] El eneasílabo, como metro regular, hace su aparición en el siglo xviii. Ejemplos: Tomás de Iriarte (1740-1791), fábula *El manguito, el abanico y el quitasol* («Si querer entender de todo...»: acento interior fijo en la sílaba tercera); Francisco Sánchez Barbero (1764-1819), en la cantata *La Venus de Melilla*, 1816 («¡Melilla, tu Venus adora!»: acentos interiores fijos en la segunda y la quinta sílabas); Juan María Maury (1772-1845), en *El festín de Alejandro* («Suene otra vez la lira de oro...»: acento interior fijo en la sílaba cuarta); Dionisio Solís (1774-1834), en *Cánticos sagrados*, I («Al pie del leño de que pende...»), y *Filis llorosa* («A las orillas de este río...»: en ambos casos, acentuación como la de Maury); Andrés Bello (1781-1865), en su versión de *Los duendes* de Hugo («San Antón, no soy tu devoto... O hinchado torrente que ha roto...» y «¡Partieron! La sonante nota...»: acentuación libre); el mejicano Joaquín María del Castillo y Lanzas (1781-1878), soneto *El recuerdo* («Pronto a partir de occidente...»: acentuación como la de Maury; caso singular de soneto en eneasílabos y, con el de Pedro Espinosa en alejandrinos, uno de los pocos sonetos castellanos escritos en versos que no fuesen endecasílabos antes de Rubén Darío, si se exceptúan los sonetos en versos de arte mayor anteriores a Boscán); José María Heredia (1803-1839), *La desesperación*, traducida de Lamartine («Cuando el Creador en hora infausta...»), y *Dios al hombre*, traducida igualmente de Lamartine («El hijo imbécil de la nada...»: con acentuación libre, como en Bello); Espronceda (1808-1842), en *El estudiante de Salamanca* («Y luego el estrépito crece...»: acentuación como la de Sánchez Barbero); Gertrudis Gómez de Avellaneda (1814-1873), en el canto a *La Cruz* («¡Tú elevas el hombre hasta Dios!»), *La pesca en el mar* y *La noche de insomnio y el alba* (todos acentuados en segunda y quinta, como en Sánchez Barbero); Juan Valera (1824-1905), en su *Fábula de Euforión* («Diosa fatal del desaliento...»: acentuación como Maury;) Rafael Pombo (1833-1912), fábula *El pudor y el abanico* («Te debo yo más de un favor...»), *El niño veraz* («Érase un niño de ojos negros...»), *La fragua* («El hierro, amigos, y el vapor...»), *Dejémoslo para mañana* (comienza así), *El niño grande*,

composición «Viniedes enamorado...», de Álvarez Gato, en versos hexasílabos, lleva como mote, tomado de un cantar popular, el dístico eneasilábico

> Solíades venir, amor,
> agora non venides, non [1].

§ 30. LOS PROVERBIOS Y REFRANES; LOS CHISTES Y LOS JUEGOS. — Finalmente, aun podrían tomarse en consideración los proverbios y refranes como motes de poesías; de por sí, muchos de ellos debieron de formar parte de la primitiva poesía en versificación amétrica: así parece confirmarlo el manuscrito del juglar cazurro del siglo XV que Menéndez Pidal cita y comenta en *Poesía juglaresca y juglares*, con máximas como

> Necio es en porfía
> quien del necio mucho fía [2].

Muchos de los viejos adagios españoles (así, los de la colección, publicada a principios del siglo XVI, que se atribuyó al Mar-

---

El puntero de reloj y *Los relojes* (en todos, acentuación como la de Maury); Gumersindo Laverde Ruiz (1840-1890), eneasílabo que él inventó y que Menéndez y Pelayo llamó *laverdaico*, en muchas composiciones, solo o combinado con otro tipo de verso; así, *Madrigal* («¿No ves en la estación de amores. . .?»), *Plegaria a la virgen* («Da oídos al clamor ferviente...») y *A mi inmortal amiga* («Sonrisa de inefable amor...»: combinado con endecasílabos): lleva acentos interiores fijos en la segunda y en la sexta sílabas; Miguel Antonio Caro (1843-1909), *La flecha de oro* («Yo busco una flecha de oro...») y *Soñando* («Recuerdos, ¿a dónde sois idos?...»: como Sánchez Barbero en ambas poesías). CARO escribió sobre el eneasílabo en el *Repertorio Colombiano*, revista de Bogotá, noviembre de 1882 (el artículo está recogido en el tomo V de sus *Obras completas*). D. Baldomero Sanín Cano me comunica que este tipo de verso se usó en canciones políticas de la América del Sur durante la primera mitad del siglo XIX: «Hijos de Chile, antes morir», decía un himno chileno; «Honor, virtud, amor, placer», uno de Colombia hacia 1840.

Consúltese además el trabajo juvenil de MENÉNDEZ Y PELAYO, *Noticias para la historia de nuestra métrica*, de 1876, incluído en el tomo XI de la nueva edición de sus *Obras completas* y VI de sus *Estudios y discursos:* allí indica que usaron el eneasílabo Juan Gualberto González (1777-1859), José Musso Valiente (1785-1838) en *La cierva herida* (eneasílabo iriartino combinado con heptasílabos), Sinibaldo de Mas (1809-1868) en su *Himno* «¡Al arma, hijos del Cid, al arma!», y Zorrilla (1817-1893) en *La leyenda de Alhamar*.

El eneasílabo sólo vuelve a adquirir vitalidad en la poesía culta a partir de Rubén Darío y su *Canción de otoño en primavera:* «Juventud, divino tesoro...» Hoy es frecuente, tanto en América como en España.

[1] Bajo la forma «Solías venir amor...», reaparece en el portugués Pedro de Andrade Caminha (muerto en 1589): véase CAROLINA MICHAËLIS DE VASCONCELLOS, estudio sobre este poeta, en la *Revue Hispanique*, 1901 (vol. VIII, págs. 373 y 424). Salinas *(De musica*, Salamanca, 1577, págs. 343 y 344) lo cita así:

> Solíades venir, amor,
> mas agora non venides, non.

[2] *Poesía juglaresca y juglares*, págs. 300-307 y 462-467.

qués de Santillana) son dísticos en metro regular o irregular, con rima consonante o asonante:

> El fijo sabio alegra al padre,
> mas el loco tristeza es de la madre.

> — Non podemos seer meiores
> de nuessos anteçesores.

> — El encantador malo
> saca la culebra del forado.

> — Cuando te dan la cabliella,
> acorre con la soguiella [1].

Durante el siglo xiv, la poesía gnómica alcarza lozano florecimiento en manos de los versificadores cultos, como D. Juan Manuel y el Rabí Santob, que la enriquece con aportaciones de la sabiduría hebraica. Todavía en el siglo xv son poetas gnómicos, a veces, los mejores: Santillana, Pérez de Guzmán, Gómez Manrique, y sólo en la época áurea pasa el género a poetas medianos, como Alonso de Barros y Cristóbal Pérez de Herrera.

Si el proverbio, como género, parecía a los poetas cultos digno del verso, es probable que en los proverbios populares se creyese ver trozos de poesía arcaica. Así, no es extraño que se les empleara como retornelos o estribillos en poesías, ni que la palabra *refrán* haya llegado a significar en Castilla proverbio o adagio, perdiendo su significación originaria de retornelo y desterrando el antiguo nombre de *retraheres*.

El *Cancionero Herberay* contiene una colección, sin nombre de autor, de poesías que terminan en refranes, dispuestos en serie alfabética; unos pocos no tienen forma de verso, los más sí:

> Gran mal tiene
> quien amores atiende.

> — Si la locura fuese dolores,
> en cada casa darían voces.

Pero desde el siglo xv diríase que el proverbio se *despoetiza:* los más nuevos no tienden tanto a sugerir el dístico, o bien son, aunque escritos en verso, creaciones artificiales que no se popularizan [2]. Desde 1500, el refrán atrae la atención, más que de los poetas, de hombres de estudio, como Pedro Vallés, Hernán Núñez Pinciano, Lorenzo Palmireno, Juan de Mal Lara y Gonzalo Correas; también de novelistas como Cervantes y Quevedo, precedidos

---

[1] Véase AMADOR DE LOS RÍOS, *Historia crítica de la literatura española*, vol. II, págs. 524 y siguientes.

[2] Compárense los refranes recogidos hasta el siglo xv con los característicos del *Quijote* y se verá que la forma versificada va en decadencia o cayendo en olvido.

en este camino por el Arcipreste de Talavera y Fernando de Rojas. Sin embargo, se dan casos como el de Sebastián de Horozco, que compuso hacia 1550 sus voluminosos *Refranes glosados en verso* [1].

Parecidos a los refranes, los chistes y juegos adoptan también fórmulas versificadas. Si los refranes se asemejan a la poesía de verso amétrico, los chistes, las adivinanzas y los juegos se inclinan a las formas de la acentual; los juegos son a menudo bailes, en cuya letra es primordial el principio rítmico. En la época áurea, los chistes y juegos se hallarán utilizados por poetas como Horozco, Ledesma, Lope y Valdivielso [2].

§ 31. RESUMEN. — La versificación irregular de tipo acentual, en castellano, es probablemente combinación de elementos nativos de Castilla con influencias de la poesía galaicoportuguesa cuyo dominio debió de extenderse a León y Asturias. En la lengua castellana, esta versificación nos ofrecerá ejemplos de libertad y soltura, en el verso y en la estrofa, mayores que en la antigua literatura de Portugal y Galicia.

Los tipos de versificación acentual que se propagan en Castilla son, junto al *arte mayor*, favorito de los poetas cultos [3], el metro de *muiñeira* o versos de gaita gallega (de diez a doce sílabas con ritmo cadente, acompañados a veces por quebrados de cinco o seis sílabas) [4], y el que tiene como verso central el *eneasílabo*, relacionado estrechamente con el de muiñeira en los cantos del pueblo [5]. Esos tres tipos tienen conexión con la poesía galaicopor-

---

[1] En el *Boletín de la Academia Española*, de Madrid, 1915-1917 (incompletos).

[2] Entre las principales fuentes sobre el refrán español, mencionaré la colección atribuída a Santillana (reimpresa en los *Orígenes de la lengua española*, de GREGORIO MAYÁNS Y SICAR, Madrid, 1737; segunda edición, 1873); los *Refranes o proverbios* de HERNÁN NÚÑEZ PINCIANO (1555, reimpresa en cuatro volúmenes en Madrid, 1804); el *Vocabulario de refranes y frases proverbiales* del maestro GONZALO CORREAS (impreso sobre el manuscrito del siglo XVII, Madrid, 1906); los diez volúmenes del *Refranero general español* de JOSÉ MARÍA SBARBI (Madrid, 1874-1878: véase especialmente la introducción al tomo IV) y su catálogo, incluso en la *Monografía sobre los refranes, adagios y proverbios castellanos* (Madrid, 1891). A estas obras hay que agregar el *Catálogo Paremiológico* de M. GARCÍA MORENO, Madrid, 1918, y las colecciones de FRANCISCO RODRÍGUEZ MARÍN, *Más de 21.000 refranes castellanos no contenidos en la copiosa colección del Maestro Gonzalo Correas*, Madrid, 1926, y *12.600 refranes más...*, Madrid, 1930. Para Portugal, véase el *Adagiario portugués* que publicó THEOPHILO BRAGA en la *Revista Lusitana* de Lisboa.

Apunta opiniones interesantes sobre los refranes españoles como fórmulas poéticas GARCÍA GUTIÉRREZ en su discurso de entrada a la Academia Española, 1862 (reproducido por Sbarbi en su *Refranero*). Extensamente trata de ellos y su versificación AMADOR DE LOS RÍOS, *Historia crítica de la literatura española*, vol. II, págs. 503-538; sobre los juegos y otros versos populares hace breves indicaciones en el vol. IV, págs. 538-542.

[3] Véase § 5 del cap. I y § 19 del cap. II de este libro.

[4] Véase § 7 del cap. I y §§ 8, 10, 11, 20, 22 y 28 de este capítulo.

[5] Véase § 7 del cap. I y §§ 8, 17 y 29 de este capítulo.

tuguesa. En compañía de ellos, se propaga durante algún tiempo la *estrofa paralelística* [1].

De origen castellano parece la *seguidilla* [2], y quizá lo son también otros tipos de ritmo más vago, que han de considerarse meramente irregulares con tendencia a formas acentuales [3]. Debe advertirse que, mientras en los versos a que puede atribuirse origen occidental el ritmo tiende a definirse en altas o golpes (así en el arte mayor y el metro de gaita gallega), en los versos de probable origen castellano el ritmo es menos preciso: en la seguidilla no se definen bien altas o golpes, sino la alternancia de renglón largo y renglón corto.

Las formas acentuales alcanzan difusión y desarrollo en Castilla cuando la simple ametría se va extinguiendo (hacia 1400). Durante cien años, hasta el comienzo del reinado de los Reyes Católicos, parecen llevar vida lánguida. Entonces adquieren nueva vida, según lo atestigua el riquísimo *Cancionero musical de los siglos XV y XVI*.

[1] Véanse §§ 3, 16, 20 y 22 de este capítulo.
[2] Véanse § 10 del cap. I y §§ 23 a 27 de este capítulo.
[3] Véanse § 12 del cap. I y §§ 22, 26, 27, 28 y 30 de este capítulo.

CAPÍTULO III

DESENVOLVIMIENTO DE LA VERSIFICACIÓN ACENTUAL

(1475-1600)

§ 1. La versificación acentual en los cantos del pueblo y en la poesía cortesana. — Durante doscientos años, desde que puede comprobarse su existencia en la literatura castellana, la versificación irregular de tipo acentual, o con vaga tendencia acentual, imperfectamente definida, sale a la superficie pocas veces; pero a fines del siglo xv sube a gozar de prestigio y sigue disfrutándolo desde entonces: primero, entre el pueblo mucho más que entre los poetas cortesanos y ciudadanos; luego, difundiéndose por igual entre uno y otros.

Su evolución, ligada a la de la música, y en buena parte a la del baile, cae bajo la influencia de fenómenos de la vida general española. El primer período en que abunda la versificación acentual, compañera del canto y la danza, corresponde a la plenitud de vida de España bajo los Reyes Católicos. Hay una ligerísima disminución, bajo Carlos V, debida acaso a la importancia que adquirieron los nuevos metros silábicos traídos de Italia y usados a veces en el canto (así, los estribillos de las canciones, que solían tomarse de la poesía popular, o al menos imitarla, empiezan a componerse en endecasílabos y heptasílabos): con todo abundan los cantares de verso irregular a mediados del siglo. Bajo Felipe II, a medida que la nación se ensombrece, la versificación acentual florece menos que antes: las colecciones de música se hacen menos comunes a partir de 1560. Pero en 1598, al morir el rey, con la reapertura de los teatros y el retorno a mayor alegría, aparecen nuevos cantares, nuevas danzas, y con ellos cobran nueva vida los versos de tipo acentual: así sabemos que de entonces data el apogeo de la seguidilla como baile, confirmado por su divulgación como tipo métrico. La aristocrática vihuela —que no desdeñaba ejecutar los sones y danzas del pueblo— cede el puesto a la popular guitarra; y en literatura, como en música, crece la libre mezcla de la inspiración popular y la técnica artística [1].

Hasta 1600, la versificación acentual está comúnmente en manos populares y vulgares, y recibe poca atención de los hombres de letras; desde 1600, los poetas cultos se apoderan de ella, y acaban por transformarla, regularizándola.

§ 2. FUENTES. — Las fuentes para el estudio de la versificación acentual son, para el reinado de los Reyes Católicos y primeros años de Carlos V, el *Cancionero musical de los siglos XV y XVI*, o *Cancionero de Palacio*, publicado por Francisco Asenjo Barbieri (su contenido podría fecharse en torno a 1500), y los cancioneros individuales de Juan del Encina, Fray Íñigo de Mendoza, Fray Ambrosio Montesino.

Para el reinado del Emperador, las obras poéticas de Gil Vicente, Diego Sánchez de Badajoz, Cristóbal de Castillejo, Francisco de Sâ de Miranda y otros —pocos— poetas líricos y dramáticos, castellanos y portugueses; mejor aún, las obras de los maestros de música, cuya abundancia es notable a mediados del siglo XVI: *El maestro*, libro de música de vihuela (Valencia, 1535), y *El cortesano*, libro de educación social a la manera del Renacimiento (Valencia, 1561), de Luis Milán; *El Delfín de música*, de Luis Narváez (Valladolid, 1538); los *Tres libros de música en cifras para vihuela*, de Alonso Mudarra (Sevilla, 1546); *Silva de sirenas*, de Anríquez de Valderrábano (Valladolid, 1547); *Villancicos y canciones a tres y a cuatro* (Osuna, 1551), *Recopilación de sonetos y villancicos a cuatro y a cinco* (Sevilla, 1559) y *Recopilación de sonetos y villancicos a cuatro y a cinco* (Sevilla, 1560), de Juan Vásquez; *Libro de música de vihuela*, de Diego Pisador (Salamanca, 1552); *Orphénica Lira*, de Miguel de Fuenllana (Sevilla, 1554); el *Cancionero de Upsala*, reproducción moderna, hecha por Rafael Mitjana, del libro *Villancicos de diversos autores, a dos y a tres y a cuatro y a cinco voces* (Venecia, 1556), y el *Libro de cifra nueva para tecla, arpa y vihuela*, de Luis Venegas de Henestrosa (Alcalá, 1557). Aunque estos libros estaban destinados a

---

[1] Véase HANSSEN, *La seguidilla*. Cita el testimonio de Mateo Alemán en la primera parte del *Guzmán de Alfarache*, impresa en 1599 (libro II, cap. VII): «Las seguidillas arrinconaron a la zarabanda» (que había sido muy popular diez años antes), y el testimonio del maestro Gonzalo Correas, en el *Arte grande de la lengua castellana*, compuesto en 1626: «son las seguidillas poesía muy antigua y tan manual y fácil que las compone la gente vulgar y las canta, con que admiro de que las olvidasen las *Artes Poéticas;* quizá como tan triviales y que no pasan de una copla, no repararon o no hicieron caso de ellas... Mas desde el año 1600 a esta parte han revivido y han sido tan usadas y se han hecho con tanta elegancia y primor, que exceden a los epigramas y dísticos en ceñir en dos versillos (en dos las escriben muchos) una muy graciosa y aguda sentencia; y se les ha dado tanta perfección, siguiendo siempre una conformidad, que parece poesía nueva».

las cortes, recogían, no sólo la canción artística, sino también la popular [1]. A ellos deben agregarse los cancioneros manuscritos, que existen en buen número en las bibliotecas de España, particularmente en la Nacional de Madrid [2].

Para el reinado de Felipe II, las obras de unos cuantos poetas líricos como Baltasar del Alcázar y San Juan de la Cruz; las de los poetas dramáticos, como Lope de Rueda, Cervantes, los valencianos, con especial atención al teatro religioso [3]; los tratados y colecciones de los músicos: así el libro del famoso Francisco Salinas, en latín, *De musica*, 1577; la recopilación *El Parnaso*, de Esteban Daza, Valladolid, 1576, y las *Ensaladas* de Mateo Flecha, Praga, 1581 [4]; y las colecciones manuscritas de poesías, de

[1] La descripción de la mayor parte de estas obras puede verse en GALLARDO, *Ensayo de una biblioteca de libros españoles raros y curiosos* (vol. II, cols. 919 y 1.098; vol. III, cols. 806, 807, 935, 947, 950, 1.233; vol. IV, cols. 921, 926, 929, 1.018 y 1.552); de las obras de Vásquez y Pisador, Gallardo da extensos extractos. De las de Fuenllana y Valderrábano hay extractos en el *Catálogo de la biblioteca de Salvá* (2 vols., Valencia, 1872). Las obras originales existen en pocas bibliotecas. Y EDUARDO MARTÍNEZ TORNER ha comenzado a publicar una *Colección de vihuelistas españoles:* ha reimpreso *El Delfín*, de Narváez, Madrid, 1923. Véanse, además, M. MENÉNDEZ Y PELAYO, *Historia de las ideas estéticas en España* (9 vols., Madrid, 1883-1891), vol. IV, págs. 667-672, y las frecuentes referencias de ASENJO BARBIERI en el *Cancionero musical de los siglos XV y XVI* (consúltese el índice de personas).

La colección veneciana de 1556 la reprodujo RAFAEL MITJANA bajo el título de *Cincuenta y cuatro canciones españolas del siglo XVI: Cancionero de Upsala* (Upsala, 1909); no reimprimió la música, como Barbieri, sino solamente la letra. Menciona con frecuencia, en sus notas, las obras de Milán, Valderrábano, Vásquez, Pisador y Fuenllana (véanse págs. 43, 47, 48, 51, 52, 53, 54, 56 y 57).

El cortesano, de Luis Milán, fué reimpreso en Madrid, 1872, vol. VII de la *Colección de libros españoles raros y curiosos*.

En la *Revista de Filología Española*, 1919, publicó MITJANA unos importantes *Comentarios y apostillas al Cancionero musical y poético del siglo XVII* (de Sablonara), que comienzan por una sucinta historia de la evolución de las características nacionales en la música española, donde se ve el papel de aquellos músicos. De ellos tratan también J. B. TREND, *Luis Milán and the vihuelistas*, Oxford, 1925, y *The music of Spanish history*, Oxford, 1925.

[2] He hecho extractos de varias colecciones existentes en la Biblioteca Nacional de Madrid. La mayor parte de las que vi contienen materiales de fines del siglo XVI y de todo el XVII. De una de ellas (ms. 3.913) proceden las *Poesías de antaño*, publicadas por Antonio Guzmán e Higueros, sin nota ni explicación alguna, en la *Revue Hispanique*, 1914.

[3] Véanse el volumen de los *Autos sacramentales* de la Biblioteca de Rivadeneyra y la *Colección de autos, farsas y coloquios del siglo XVI*, publicada por LÉO ROUANET (4 vols., *Biblioteca Hispánica*, Barcelona y Madrid, 1901; los materiales datan generalmente, según calcula el coleccionador, de 1550 a 1575). Mucho menos material se encuentra en el *Teatro español del siglo XVI*, publicado por URBAN CRONAN (obras cuyas fechas oscilan entre 1525 y 1560), Madrid, Sociedad de Bibliófilos Madrileños, 1913.

[4] Del tratado de Salinas *(De musica libri septem*, Salamanca, 1577) se obtienen las ideas de la época sobre el canto, y a veces referencias a determinados tipos musicales, así como textos de las letras. Véase el *Cancionero musical*, págs. 21, 97, 108 y 205.

carácter más o menos popular o vulgar, con música o sin ella, existentes en bibliotecas españolas y extractadas a veces por Gallardo o por otros investigadores[1]. Los cancioneros cortesanos impresos durante el siglo XVI ofrecen escasísimo material: la primera colección entre vulgar y cortesana de la cual se obtiene alguna ayuda es el *Romancero general,* cuya primera parte sale a luz en 1600[2].

A) LOS POETAS CULTOS

§ 3. LOS POETAS CULTOS BAJO LOS REYES CATÓLICOS Y POCO DESPUÉS. — La versificación irregular, en los poetas cultos de 1475 a 1600, se halla en estribillos populares que ellos acogen; como excepción, hay composiciones originales donde la emplean, con versos que fluctúan libremente y estrofas que se repiten isométricamente en la distribución de las rimas.

Si a Juan del Encina (c. 1469-c. 1529) debe estudiársele en relación con el desarrollo de la versificación acentual, es sólo como manera de inferir los caminos que ella seguía. Encina, poeta y músico de la ciudad y de la corte, es en tiempo de los Reyes Católicos el que más se distingue por su afición a introducir y apro-

---

Sobre el *Libro de música en cifras para vihuela, intitulado el Parnaso,* de Esteban Daza, véanse GALLARDO, *Ensayo,* vol. II, col. 754; el *Cancionero musical,* págs. 132 y 183, y el *Cancionero de Upsala,* pág. 53.

Hay otros libros de música, como el *Arte de tañer fantasía,* de Fray Tomás de Santa María, Valladolid, 1565 —uno de los últimos de vihuela—, y la *Guitarra española,* de Juan Carlos Amat, el primero de su especie, Barcelona, 1572 (aunque generalmente se dice que data de 1586); pero no me referiré a ellos, porque no tengo noticia de su contenido, y no sé qué materiales contengan que puedan relacionarse con este trabajo.

[1] He hecho extractos de los manuscritos musicales existentes en la Biblioteca Nacional de Madrid. Pertenecen principalmente al siglo XVII. De colecciones semejantes hizo extractos GALLARDO: al final del siglo XVI pertenecen los manuscritos de *Tonos castellanos* y *Tonos antiguos,* cuyo contenido literario describe (vol. I, cols. 1.193 y 1.203). FELIPE PEDRELL publicó en Leipzig, 1900, su *Folklore musical castillan du XVIᵉ siècle.* El *Boletín de la Academia Española* ha publicado el *Cancionero musical y poético del siglo XVII,* recogido por Claudio de la Sablonara; después apareció en volumen, Madrid, 1918.

[2] Además del *Cancionero castellanoportugués,* de García de Resende (véase nota del § 5 del cap. II), de 1516, son bien conocidos, como grandes colecciones de obras de muchos poetas, el *general* de Hernando del Castillo, impreso por primera vez en Valencia en 1511 y reimpreso con adiciones durante muchos años, y el posterior, impreso sin fecha, de Juan Fernández de Constantina. Otros varios aparecen a lo largo del siglo XVI.

Hacia 1550 comienzan los romanceros; tienen interés para este estudio sólo el *Romancero general* (primera parte, 1600; segunda, 1605; reimpresiones de la primera, 1602, 1604 y 1614; reimpresión moderna: la de la Sociedad Hispánica de América, Nueva York, 1904) y los *Romancerillos de la Biblioteca Ambrosiana,* que en gran parte le sirvieron de base, impresos entre 1589 y 1594: los reimprimió FOULCHÉ-DELBOSC en su *Revue Hispanique,* 1919, vol. XLV.

vechar elementos populares en su obra. Entre tales elementos, no habían de faltar en los villancicos, líricos o dramáticos, los motes o estribillos tomados o imitados del pueblo. Y, sin embargo, en ellos Encina huye deliberadamente de las combinaciones irregulares de versos; pocas veces las acepta, en estribillos muy breves

> Ya soy desposado,
> nuestr'amo,
> ya soy desposado.

> — Vuestros amores he, señora,
> vuestros amores he.

> — Ojos garzos ha la niña.
> ¿Quién se los enamoraría? [1]

Se desliza con más frecuencia hacia la versificación acentual en las poesías burlescas: véanse las que llevan los núms. 406, 415 y 455 del *Cancionero musical*, la segunda de las cuales tiene forma encadenada [2].

De los contemporáneos de Encina, Garci-Sánchez de Badajoz (c. 1460-c. 1526) ofrece dos estribillos de versificación acentual en su composición «Caminando por mis males»:

> Hagadesmé, hagadesmé,
> monumento d'amores he [3].

---

[1] Es posible que Encina escribiera dos octosílabos, poniendo «namoraría», según aparece en diversas impresiones del villancico, pero no en GALLARDO, *Ensayo*, I, col. 698, ni en el *Cancionero de Upsala*. Alonso de Villegas Selvago, en su *Comedia Selvagia* (1554), trae «enamoraría». Véanse *Cancionero de Upsala*, composición núm. 25 y nota respectiva, la *Recopilación* de Juan Vásquez, 1560, y CAROLINA MICHAËLIS DE VASCONCELLOS, *Notulas sobre cantares e vilhancicos*, en la *Revista de Filología Española*, 1918.
De una vez por todas advierto que, al indicar la reaparición de los cantares en diversas colecciones u obras y las relaciones de unos con otros, no pretendo agotar el material, que es inagotable, sobre todo al llegar al siglo XVII.

[2] Véase también la composición, de sabor rústico, que lleva el núm. 33 en el *Cancionero de Upsala:*

> Falalalanlera,
> de la guarda riera.

> Quando yo me vengo
> de guardar ganado...

Mitjana la atribuye a Encina. Compárese con la composición anónima núm. 46:

> Riu, riu, chiu,
> la guarda riera...

Luego se verá que Encina recogió versos populares que acaso sean de seguidilla (§ 18 de este capítulo).

[3] Sobre el cambio de acentuación de las palabras en el verso, véanse § 5 del cap. I (nota) y § 5 de este capítulo.

— ¿Adónde iré? ¿Adónde iré?
¡Qué mal vecino amor es! [1].

Entre los poetas que siguen a Encina en el teatro, como Lucas Fernández, se halla con frecuencia el estribillo de sabor popular; solamente una vez la irregularidad del verso, en el villancico «Quien sirve al amor», al final de la *Farsa o cuasi comedia* que principia «¡Ay de mí, triste, cuitado!» (el metro fluctúa entre cinco y seis sílabas):

Ninguno desvíe
do puso su fe,
y no desconfíe
de ser cúyo fué.

Y aunque el dolor
le quite esperanza
con su confianza
podrá haber favor.

Y aunque no halle
remedio en su amiga,
súfrase y calle,
y a nadie lo diga.

Y aunqu'el amor
le ponga en balanza,
tenga esperanza
de haber d'él favor...

...Y el disfavor,
con fe y esperanza
hace mudanza
volviéndose amor.

La fruta más dura
viene a sazón... [2].

En Bartolomé de Torres Naharro († c. 1531) no hay irregularidades.

Ni nos ofrecen más material los poetas líricos. Las grandes

---

[1] Este cantarcillo reaparece en el *Sermón de amores* de Cristóbal de Castillejo:

¿Adónde iré? ¿Qué haré?
¡Qué mal vecino es el amor!

Y Salinas lo cita en *De musica* (pág. 435):

¡Qué mal vecino es el amor!

[2] Véanse cap. II, § 28, y en este capítulo, § 4, los versos de Montesino:

Reina del cielo...

colecciones típicas de la época, como el *Cancionero* de Juan Fernández de Constantina, y el *Cancionero general*, de Hernando del Castillo, nada contienen. Como excepción podría citarse, apenas, la canción en que el marqués de Astorga hace recuerdo fugaz de una popular:

> ¿A quién contaré mis quejas
> si a ti no?

Salinas la recoge en versificación irregular:

> ¿A quién contaré yo mis quejas,
> mi lindo amor,
> a quién contaré yo mis quejas
> si a vos no? [1].

§ 4. POETAS CULTOS AFICIONADOS A LA VERSIFICACIÓN ACENTUAL. — Hay que volver atrás, a los frailes Mendoza y Montesino, en busca de referencias a la versificación de las danzas populares [2].

Uno y otro, Fray Íñigo y Fray Ambrosio, recogen los versos del baile de la zorrilla, para cuya música escriben versos a lo divino:

> La zorrilla con el gallo
> mal han barajado [3].

Montesino escribió tres composiciones para cantarse al son de otra cántica popular, cuyo corte oscila entre la copla de pie quebrado, metro de las tres poesías, y la seguidilla:

---

[1] Salinas, *De musica*, pág. 326. Véase MENÉNDEZ PIDAL, *La primitiva poesía lírica española*, págs. 258-260.

[2] Fray Íñigo de Mendoza florece en 1482, fecha de su *Vita Christi;* Fray Ambrosio Montesino, entre 1502 *(Vita Christi)* y 1512 (versión de la misa), año en que probablemente muere.

[3] Fray Íñigo de Mendoza imita así el cantar (véase GALLARDO, *Ensayo*, vol. III, col. 764):

> La zorrilla con el gallo,
> el infante y el pecado,
> mal han barajado.

La composición sigue

> Al sereno está el cordero...

Para Fray Ambrosio Montesino, véanse *Romancero y canciones sagrados*, vol. XXXV de la Biblioteca de Rivadeneyra, página 444, y GALLARDO, *Ensayo*, vol. III, col. 880.

El *Cancionero musical* trae el estribillo bajo otra forma al frente de una canción anónima (núm. 442):

> La zorrilla con el gallo
> zangorromango.

> Aquel pastorcico, madre,
> que no viene,
> algo tiene en el campo
> que le duele,

la cual aparece en el contemporáneo *Cancionero musical de los siglos XV y XVI* (núm. 438), en la más antigua de las *ensaladas*, con música de Francisco Peñalosa (c. 1470-c. 1538), y vuelve a encontrarse después en idéntica forma o en imitaciones (por ejemplo, en el *Coloquio de Timbria*, de Lope de Rueda) [1].

> Toca la queda, mi amor no viene;
> algo tiene en el campo que le detiene...

es la versión (seguidilla) que trae Luis Vélez de Guevara en el acto segundo de *La luna de la sierra* [2].

---

[1] Me llamó la atención sobre esta reminiscencia el escritor argentino RAÚL MOGLIA, en la revista *Nosotros*, de Buenos Aires, 1925; indica, además, que el cantar sobrevive en el interior de la Argentina.

[2] Véanse el *Cancionero* de Fray Ambrosio en el vol. XXXV de la Biblioteca de Rivadeneyra, págs. 441, 459 y 461, y en el *Ensayo* de Gallardo, vol. III, cols. 871 y 881.

Es probable que la versión de Vélez de Guevara sea producto de contaminación entre dos cantares del siglo XV: uno, el que recogen Montesino y Peñalosa; otro, el que menciona el índice de obras que faltan en el *Cancionero musical*: «Que la noche hace escura», y que recogen después, en dos versiones distintas, octosilábicas, Diego Pisador y el *Cancionero de Upsala* (núm. 14):

> Si la noche hace escura
> y tan corto es el camino,
> ¿cómo no venís, amigo?

> La media noche es pasada
> y el que me pena no viene;
> mi desdicha lo detiene...

Este segundo cantar es el que imitan Fernando de Rojas en el incomparable acto décimonono de la *Celestina* (edición de 1502):

> ...La media noche es pasada
> y no viene;
> sabedme si hay otra amada
> que lo detiene...

el poeta anónimo del *Cancionero espiritual*, impreso en Valladolid, 1549, y reimpreso en la *Revue Hispanique*, 1916, donde aparece un «villancico... contrahecho a otro que dice: *Si la noche hace escura y corto es el camino*». Comienza:

> Si con extrema tristura
> cien mil suspiros te envío,
> ¿cómo no vienes, Dios mío?

Santa Rosa de Lima (1586-1617) —nótese ya el paso al metro de seguidilla—:

> Las doce son dadas,
> mi Esposo no viene:
> ¿quién será la dichosa
> que lo entretiene?

Montesino escribió, además, dos composiciones originales en metro irregular. Una se acerca por momentos a la seguidilla:

> Todos vienen de la cena
> y no mi vista buena [1].

> Yo soy la Virgen María
> que oístes decir
> que de cruel agonía
> me quiero morir,
> porque no veo venir
> a mi vista-buena.

> Todos vienen de la cena
> de Hierusalem,
> mas no la rica vena
> que es todo mi bien...

La otra composición, *Coplas a la Virgen*, tiene efectos, ya semejantes a los de la seguidilla, ya contrarios a ésos y semejantes a los del arte mayor:

> Reina del cielo,
> del mundo señora,
> sey mi valedora...

Quiñones de Benavente introduce esta ingeniosa parodia en el entremés *La puente segoviana*, primera parte:

> ¿Dónde está Manzanares?
> ¿Cómo no viene?
> Algo tiene en agosto
> que lo detiene.

Finalmente, aun hoy se canta esta seguidilla en Andalucía, según Rodríguez Marín:

> Las ánimas han dado,
> mi amor no viene;
> alguna picarona
> me lo entretiene.

Véanse RAFAEL MITJANA, nota a la composición núm. 14 del *Cancionero de Upsala;* FRANCISCO RODRÍGUEZ MARÍN, *La copla* (Madrid, 1910), págs. 42-44; VENTURA GARCÍA CALDERÓN, *La literatura peruana (1535-1914),* en la *Revue Hispanique,* 1914 (vol. XXXI, pág. 313). Para otras conexiones todavía, véanse CAROLINA MICHAËLIS DE VASCONCELLOS, *Notulas sobre cantares e vilhancicos,* en la *Revista de Filología Española,* 1918, y *Cartapacios literarios salmantinos del siglo XVI,* extractados por D. RAMÓN MENÉNDEZ PIDAL, en el *Boletín de la Academia Española,* 1914 (vol. I, pág. 304).

[1] Francisco de Sâ de Miranda y Pedro de Andrade Caminha, poeta portugués muerto en 1589, traen:

> Todos vienen de la vela...

Antonio Prestes imita, en el *Auto do Ave María:* «Todos vienen de la Eva». Véase CAROLINA MICHAËLIS DE VASCONCELLOS, estudios sobre *Pedro de Andrade Caminha,* en la *Revue Hispanique,* 1901, vol. VIII, pág. 375.

Si el mar oceano
fuese la tinta
y el sol escribano
que el verano pinta...

El que te puede
loar de contino,
del Padre procede
y en tu vientre vino
por que te quede
por nombre más dino
de paz inventora...[1].

§ 5. PORTUGUÉS Y CASTELLANO: GIL VICENTE. — Al celoso cuidado que ponen Encina y su escuela en evitar el empleo de trozos irregulares, como estribos, cabezas o motes, sucede, con Gil Vicente, otro modo más amplio de utilizar los elementos populares. Ya en portugués, ya en castellano, Gil Vicente introduce en sus obras dramáticas, canciones en diversos tipos de versificación irregular, tomándolas de la tradición popular muy a menudo. La transcripción y la imitación se mezclan en él a tal punto que se dificulta distinguirlas[2].

Así, en su lengua nativa

Sem mais mando nem mais rogo
aquí me tendes, levae-me logo...

(Cortes de Júpiter)

Apartarme-hão de vos,
garrido amor.

(Quem tem farelos)

A mi seguem dous açores:
hum delles morirá d'amores.
Dous açores qu'eu havia
aqui andão nesta bailia.
Hum delles morirá d'amores.

---

[1] Véanse los versos de Lucas Fernández, § 3 de este capítulo, y el § 28 del cap. II.

[2] Sobre las aficiones de Gil Vicente a la musa del pueblo, véase THEOPHILO BRAGA, *Historia da literatura portuguesa*, volumen VIII; M. MENÉNDEZ Y PELAYO, *Antología de poetas líricos castellanos*, vol. VII, cap. III; CAROLINA MICHAËLIS DE VASCONCELLOS, *Cancioneiro da Ajuda*, vol. II (pasajes sobre Gil Vicente, señalados en el índice alfabético), y el índice de personas del *Cancionero musical de los siglos XV y XVI*.

— Quando aqui chove e neva,
que fará na serra [1].
Na serra de Coimbra
nevava e chovia.
Que fará na serra.

(A Serra da Estrella)

En castellano:

Mal herido me ha la niña,
no me hacen justicia.

(Comedia do Viuvo)

Estánse dos hermanas
doliéndose de sí;
hermosas son entrambas
lo más que yo nunca vi.
¡Hufa, hufa!
A la fiesta, a la fiesta,
que las bodas son aquí.
  Namorado se había dellas
Don Rosvel Tenorí;
nunca tan lindos amores
yo jamás contar oí.
¡Hufa, hufa!
A la fiesta, a la fiesta,
que las bodas son aquí.

(Comedia do Viuvo)

Aquel caballero, madre, si me habrá,
con tanta mala vida como ha.

(Cortes de Júpiter) [2]

Por el río me llevad, amigo,
y llevadme por el río.

(Cortes de Júpiter) [3]

---

[1] Se canta aun hoy, en Asturias, en castellano.

[2] Véase la canción anónima del *Cancionero musical* (número 227):

> Aquel caballero, madre,
> si morirá
> con tanta mala vida como ha.

Son muchas las canciones populares de los siglos xv a xvii que comienzan: «Aquel caballero, madre» y continúan de diversos modos (véase *Cancionero musical*, núm. 209); por ejemplo, en Alonso de Alcaudete *(Ensayo*, de Gallardo, I, col. 72):

> Aquel caballero, madre,
> tres besicos le mandé:
> cresceré y dárselos he.

[3] Gil Vicente lo recuerda, además, en la lista de cantares mencionados en la *Rubena*.

A veces mezcla ambos idiomas (si no es culpa de las imprentas primitivas):

> — Niña, erguedme los ojos
> que a mi namorado mão [1],
>
> — Estos meus cabellos, madre,
> dos a dos me los lleva el aire [2].

(Cortes de Júpiter)

> Palombas, se amigos amades,
> no riñades,
> paz in celis, paz in terra,
> e paz no mar:
> tau garredica la vi cantar,
> ficade, amor, ficade;
> ficade, amor.

(Farsa dos Fisicos)

Las canciones paralelísticas y las encadenadas abundan: se relacionan con esos tipos el cantar que aparece en el *Auto da fe:*

> Que no quiero estar en casa,
> no me pagan mi soldada...,

los dos del *Auto dos quatro tempos:*

> Mal haya quien los envuelve,
> los mis amores...,

y el que se intercala entre coplas octosilábicas:

> En la huerta nace la rosa:
> quiérome ir allá,
> por mirar al ruiseñor
> cómo cantabá.
>
> Por las riberas del río
> limones coge la virgo:
> quiérome ir allá,
> por mirar al ruiseñor
> cómo cantabá.

---

[1] Véase *Cancionero musical*, núms. 58, 59 y 60.

[2] El cantar de los cabellicos es conocido a través de otras muchas fuentes. Según López de Gómara, Francisco de Carabajal, el *Demonio de los Andes*, lo cantaba:

> Estos mis cabellicos, madre,
> dos a dos me los lleva el aire.

Luis Milán, al principio de la jornada IV de su *Cortesano*, también lo cita: «Estos mis cabellos...»; y otra vez con «cabellicos», como ejemplo de versos de nueve sílabas, el maestro Gonzalo Correas en su *Arte grande de la lengua castellana* (pág. 287) y *Vocabulario de refranes* (pág. 139).

Limones cogía la virgo
para dar al su amigo.
Quiérome ir allá,
para ver al ruiseñor
cómo cantabá.

Para dar al su amigo
en su sombrero de sirgo.
Quiérome ir allá,
por mirar al ruiseñor
cómo cantabá [1].

---

[1] Uno de los elementos utilizados por Gil Vicente en este cantar procede del siglo XIII, y quedó citado en el cap. II (§ 22 y nota 1 de la pág. 63), a propósito de Santillana:

Pela ribeyra do rio...

Véase CAROLINA MICHAËLIS DE VASCONCELLOS, *Cancioneiro da Ajuda*, vol. II, págs. 920, 921, 925.

La alteración del acento de las palabras es frecuente en la poesía popular española, antigua y moderna, unas veces para adaptar la letra a los acentos de la música (desde ejemplos como «Ábejón del ábejón»: véase § 17 del cap. II, nota), otras veces como simple licencia del poeta, pero siempre en versos para cantar y de preferencia para bailar, como en el «Polvó menudó», que imitan o mencionan Cervantes, Góngora, Quevedo, entre otros (véase § 11 de este capítulo).

Para estos ejemplos, véase *Cancionero musical*, núm. 85:

¡Quién vos había de llevar!
¡Oxalá!
¡Ay Fátima, Fatimá!

Estribillo recogido por Valdivielso, *Romancero espiritual*, pág. 105:

La malva morenica, y va,
la malva morená.

Francisco de Trillo y Figueroa, *Letrilla:*

Solía que andaba
el mi molinó,
solía que andaba
y ahora no.

(Véase GALLARDO, *Ensayo*, vol. IV, col. 1.246, donde aparece en una letrilla atribuída a Góngora: «Molino de viento»).

Quiñones de Benavente, *Entremés de los órganos* y *Entremés de Juan Francés:*

Dios me libre, madre,
de las mozuelás,
que a mí preso me tienen
y a mí muerto me han.

Quiñones de Benavente, entremés de *La puente segoviana*, segunda parte:

— Responded, vino zupia:
¿queréis ser puró?
— Sí quisiera, si el agua
viniera en elló.

Luego, en el *Auto da Feira:*

> Blanca estáis colorada,
> Virgem sagrada...,

en el *Auto da Serra da Estrella:*

> E se ponerei la mano em vos,
> garrido amor...,

en la *Farsa dos Almocreves:*

> A serra he alta, fria e nevosa:
> vi venir serrana gentil, graciosa...,

Como se ve, es en metro de seguidilla, o parecido, donde con más frecuencia se hace esta alteración; QUIÑONES DE BENAVENTE la presenta otra vez en seguidillas escritas en renglones dobles, en el entremés *La visita de la cárcel:*

> — Pulí, pulidí, pulido Alcaldé,
> ¿por qué galericas, si no hay por qué?
> — Pulí, pulidí, pulido presó,
> que no hay galeritas sin delitó.
> — Yo vivo remando con mi esposá.
> — Pues no se casara, y no remará.
> — Mi remo es la guarda del dineró.
> — Quien presta y socorre suelta el remó.
> — El naipe y el dado es mi galerá.
> — El juego da gritos: ¡ropa fuerá!
> — ¿Qué manda el Alcalde a las que pidén?
> — Que callen y remen en los bailés.
> — Pulí, pulidí...

En el siglo XVIII, Diego de Torres Villarroel, villancico de *La gaita zamorana:*

> Tumbailá, mi Marianita;
> tumbailá, mi Marianá.

En tiempos recientes, la dislocación se observa en cantares de Asturias y León: «Verdes, azules y coloradós»; «Pandereterita mía — pandereterá... sigue cantandó»; «Tres hojitas tiene, — madre, el arbolé...» En Castilla sólo se halla probablemente en cantares que proceden de Asturias y León.

Hay que distinguir entre esta alteración artificial y la mera acentuación del pronombre enclítico, como «Hagadesmé» en Garci Sánchez de Badajoz (§ 3 de este capítulo) o «Déjalá», de la canción madrileña, muy popular en 1919, «Agua que no has de beber». Esta acentuación del enclítico es fenómeno conocido en el habla popular de España y frecuente en gran parte de la América del Sur: naturalmente, ha pasado a los poetas gauchescos (véase ELEUTERIO F. TISCORNIA, *La lengua de Martín Fierro,* Buenos Aires, 1930, § 4) y hasta a poetas que son a la vez gramáticos, como Bello: «Acaba, dímeló». Véase *Palabras sin acento,* de TOMÁS NAVARRO TOMÁS, en la *Revista de Filología Española,* 1925, pág. 359.

S. GRISWOLD MORLEY dedica detenido estudio a *La modificación del acento de la palabra en el verso castellano,* en la *Revista de Filología Española,* 1927, págs. 256-272. Véase también MENÉNDEZ PIDAL, ed. crítica del *Cantar de Mio Cid,* págs. 169 y 1.177.

en el *Triumpho do Inverno:*

> Del rosal vengo, mi madre,
> vengo del rosale...

> El mozo y la moza
> van en romaria...,

en el *Auto da Lusitania:*

> ¿Donde vindes, filha,
> branca e colorida?...

Y no son las únicas.

Como composición original en versos irregulares, Gil Vicente produjo una, exquisita, en alabanza de la Virgen María, que insertó en el *Auto da Sibilla Cassandra.* En ella parece aplicar, modificándolos con nuevo gusto, la versificación irregular y el esquema paralelístico:

> Muy graciosa es la doncella:
> ¡cómo es bella y hermosa!

> Digas tú, el marinero,
> que en las naves vivías,
> si la nave, o la vela, o la estrella,
> es tan bella.

> Digas tú, el caballero,
> que las armas vestías,
> si el caballo, o las armas, o la guerra,
> es tan bella.

> Digas tú, el pastorcico,
> que el ganadico guardas,
> si el ganado, o las valles, o la sierra,
> es tan bella.

§ 6. LOS POETAS CULTOS BAJO CARLOS V. — Entre los poetas conocidos, bajo Carlos V, sólo Gil Vicente hace uso franco del verso irregular; en los demás aparece rara vez fuera de los ocasionales estribillos.

Francisco de Sâ de Miranda (c. 1489-c. 1558) glosa muchos trozos de *cantares velhos*, en portugués:

> — Suidade minha
> ¿quando vos veria? [1]

---

[1] Mejor conocido bajo la forma:

> Saudade minha
> ¿quando vos veria?

— Naquela serra
quero ir a morar:
quem me bem quiser,
la me irá buscar [1].

En castellano, unos pocos:

— Sola me dejaste
en aquel iermo,
villano, malo, gallego [2].

— Todas vienen de la vela
y non viene Domenga [3].

— ¡Quién viese aquel día
quando, quando, quando
saliese mi vida
de tanto bando! [1]

Los dos versos de la última tienen el ritmo de la seguidilla.
En Diego Hurtado de Mendoza (1503-1575) no encontramos

Así lo traen Luis Vélez de Guevara en el acto primero de *Reinar después
de morir*, y antes que él lo emplean Camoens, Pedro de Andrade Caminha
(véase *Revue Hispanique*, vol. VIII, págs. 387, 388, 423), Fray Agostinho da
Cruz, Miguel Leitão de Andrade y D. Francisco de Portugal. Todavía lo canta
el pueblo portugués:

Saudade minha
¿quando te veria?

Consúltese el interesante libro de CAROLINA MICHAËLIS DE VASCONCE-
LLOS, *A saudade portuguesa*, Porto, 1919 (especialmente págs. 7-9, 87-98 y
142-143).

[1] CAROLINA MICHAËLIS DE VASCONCELLOS *(Cancioneiro da Ajuda*, vol. II,
pág. 916) indica que «N'aquela serra...» (que cita allí en dos versos largos,
en vez de cuatro cortos) fué utilizado posteriormente por Fray Agostinho da
Cruz y por Jorge Ferreira de Vasconcellos. De estos y de otros poetas portugueses indica que utilizaron trozos de cantares populares del occidente o del
centro: principalmente, Diego Bernardes, Francisco Rodrigues Lobo, Pedro
de Andrade Caminha, Camoens. Para referencias, véase el *Catálogo... de los
autores portugueses que escribieron en castellano*, de Domingo García Peres,
Madrid, 1890.

Para las citas en portugués, tomadas a Sâ de Miranda, véanse sus *Poesías*, edición de Carolina Michaëlis de Vasconcellos (Halle, 1885); composiciones núm. 59 (vilancete XVIII) y número 54 (cántiga XXVI). Para las citas en castellano que van a continuación, véanse núms. 60 (vilancete XIX),
26 (vilancete IV) y 136 (vilancete XXX).

[2] Usado también en dos canciones anónimas del *Cancionero musical* (núms.
420 y 421) y por Rodrigo de Reinosa (véase GALLARDO, *Ensayo*, vol. IV, cols·
1.413, 1.415 y 1.417).

[3] Véase § 4, pág. 85 nota.

[4] Véase CAROLINA MICHAËLIS DE VASCONCELLOS, *Pedro de Andrade Caminha* (poeta que emplea el mismo cantarcillo), *Revue Hispanique*, vol. VIII,
pág. 366.

composiciones en métrica irregular; pero es interesante recoger de su obra dos versos eneasílabos de cantar pastoril:

> — Carillo ¿quieres bien a Juana?
> — Como a mi vida y a mi alma [1].

Carillo —diminutivo afectuoso que se vuelve personaje pastoril, compañero de Blas—, reaparece en el cantar popularísimo que recoge el castizo Cristóbal de Castillejo (c. 1490-c. 1550):

> Guárdame las vacas,
> Carillejo, y besarte he;
> si no, bésame tú a mí,
> que yo te las guardaré [2].

Lo recoge también, ligeramente diverso, Sebastián de Horozco, como *canción vieja:*

> Guárdame las vacas,
> Carillo, y besarte he:
> bésame tú a mí,
> que yo te las guardaré [3].

En la composición *A un amigo suyo, pidiéndole consejo en unos amores aldeanos*, Castillejo incluye este cantar de bodas en versos irregulares, bajo esquema paralelístico simple:

[1] Biblioteca de Rivadeneyra, vol. XXXII, pág. 90. Hay formas con variantes: «...como la mi vida, como la mi alma...», en el *Cancionero de Évora* publicado por Victor Eugène Hardung, Lisboa, 1875 (parece compilado hacia 1590-1600); «...como a mi vida y como a mi alma...» en los manuscritos 4256 y 4268 de la Biblioteca Nacional de Madrid.

[2] Biblioteca de Rivadeneyra, vol. XXXII, pág. 129; GALLARDO, *Ensayo*, vol. II, col. 288: variante, «Carillo, y besarte he...»; en la nueva edición de CASTILLEJO, en los *Clásicos de «La Lectura»*, 4 vols., Madrid, 1926-1929, J. Domínguez Bordona escribe en dos renglones los cuatro versos del cantar: oscilación frecuente en la escritura de la poesía popular.

[3] Sebastián de Horozco, *Cancionero*, edición de 1874, páginas 109 y 134. Su hijo Sebastián de Covarrubias Orozco, en el *Tesoro de la lengua castellana*, 1611, artículo *Vacas*, se refiere a esta canción, y la cita:

> Guárdame las vacas,
> Carillo, por tu fe.

Reaparece en Pisador *(Libro de música de vihuela*, fols. 2-3), Salinas *(De musica*, pág. 348), y Francisco de Ocaña *(Cancionero para cantar la noche de Navidad*, Alcalá, 1603, núm. 28).

Sobre el baile que nació de este cantar (en el siglo XVII lo mencionan todavía Lope, Quevedo y Moreto), véase EMILIO COTARELO Y MORI, Introducción a los *Entremeses, loas, bailes, jácaras y mojigangas*, en la nueva Biblioteca de Autores Españoles, XVII, pág. CCLXIII. Véanse, además, GALLARDO, *Ensayo*, vol. III, col. 1.009, y vol. IV, cols. 1 (en pliego volante, autor desconocido, tal vez Quesada) y 498 (en pliego volante, glosa de Bartolomé de Santiago), y MENÉNDEZ PIDAL, *La primitiva poesía lírica española*, pág. 312.

Aquí no hay
sino ver y desear;
aquí no veo
sino morir con deseo.

Madre, un caballero
que estaba en este corro
a cada vuelta
hacíame del ojo.
Yo, como era bonica,
teníaselo en poco.

Madre, un escudero
que estaba en esta baila
a cada vuelta
asíame de la manga.
Yo, como soy bonica,
teníaselo en nada [1].

Otra composición en versos irregulares (pero cabe suponer que la irregularidad ha sido aumentada por errores de copia):

Si tantos monteros la garça combaten,
por altos oteros los perros le llaten,
neblís muy ligeros contra ella se abaten,
no es mucho la maten.

Si la dama es servida de los escuderos
y mucho seguida de los caballeros,
de grandes señores con sus mensajeros,

---

[1] Véanse CLARA LEONORA NICOLAY, *The life and works of Cristóbal de Castillejo*, Filadelfia, 1910, págs. 110 y 111; CAROLINA MICHAËLIS DE VASCONCELLOS, *Cancioneiro da Ajuda*, vol. II, páginas 58 y 851. Es interesante notar que Castillejo todavía escribió en portugués:

O erro meu dano tein...

(pág. 131, vol. XXXII de la Biblioteca de Rivadeneyra).
Otros trozos irregulares en Castillejo:

Non pueden dormir mis ojos,
non pueden dormir...

que se halla también en el *Cancionero musical* (núm. 408) y, en portugués, en Pedro de Andrade Caminha (véase *Revue Hispanique*, vol. VIII, pág. 364):

Vi los barcos, madre,
vilos y no me vale,

al final del *Diálogo entre el autor y su pluma* (véase *Cancionero de Upsala*, núm. 28):

¿Adónde iré? ¿Qué haré?...,

en el *Sermón de amores*, citado ya a propósito de Garci Sánchez de Badajoz.

que sea vencida
siendo hermosa
en esta partida,
no digo cosa,
mas si es virtuosa [1].

Boscán (c. 1500-c. 1542) glosa un cantar burlesco, donde aparece de paso el verso eneasílabo:

Halagóle y pellizcóle
la moçuela al asnejón;
allególe y enamoróle,
y él estávase al rincón [2].

Bajo forma bastante diversa, más danzante, lo trae Sebastián de Horozco:

Besábale y enamorábale
la donzella al villanchón;
besábale y enamorábale,
y él metido en un rincón.

Jaime de Huete trae dos canciones en la jornada segunda de la *Comedia Vidriana;* una de ellas con buen sabor campestre, conocida ya de los coleccionadores del *Cancionero musical:*

Llueve menudico
y haze la noche oscura;
el pastorcillo es nuevo,
non yré segura [3].

Sebastián Fernández, en el acto XXIII de la *Tragedia Policiana* (1547), introduce la seguidilla:

[1] Estuvo inédita hasta que la publicó J. Domínguez Bordona en su edición de Castillejo, tomo II, pág. 164. Cotéjese con el *Vocabulario de refranes*, de Correas, pág. 259, «Si tantos monteros...», y *El Delfín*, de Narváez, folio 67:

Si tantos halcones
la garza combaten,
por Dios, que la maten.

[2] La composición de Boscán, que pertenece al tipo de «obras de burlas provocantes a risa», figura (pág. 531) en el *Cancionero general de obras nuevas*, publicado por Esteban de Nájera, Zaragoza, 1554, y reproducido por M. Alfred Morel-Fatio en *L'Espagne au XVIe et au XVIIe siècle* (Heilbron, 1878).
MENÉNDEZ Y PELAYO cita el cantar *(Antología*, vol. XIII, pág. 265), alterándolo: escribe «namoróle», en vez de «enamoróle», con lo cual todos los versos resultan octosilábicos.

[3] De «Llueve menudico» quedó sólo el primer verso en el *Cancionero musical* (núm. 456). En el *Teatro español del siglo XVI*, de Cronan, donde aparece la comedia de Huete, véase también la *Tragicomedia alegórica del paraíso y del infierno*, anónima, de 1539 (págs. 280, 287, 290, 317).

> Páreste a la ventana, niña en cabello,
> que otro parayso yo no le tengo.

Diego Sánchez de Badajoz introduce en su *Farsa del juego de cañas* este cantar picante, cuyo estribillo se conocía ya también en los tiempos del *Cancionero musical:*

> No me las enseñes más,
> que me matarás;
> no me las enseñes más,
> que me matarás.
>
> Estábase la monja
> en el monesterio,
> sus teticas blancas
> de so el velo negro, más
> que me matarás... [1]

y luego:

> Mal amiga, en buena fe,
> por que no me mates yo te mataré [2].

Antonio de Villegas († c. 1551), en su *Inventario* (publicado en 1565):

> En la peña y sobre la peña
> duerme la niña y sueña.

Francisco de Lora, en *Coplas* (pliego suelto):

> Mariquita fué a la plaza
> más ha de un hora:
> no puede más la pecadora.

---

[1] Véase el *Cancionero musical*, índice de obras que faltan:

> No me las enseñes más...

En el *Cancionero de Upsala* (composición núm. 5) aparece el estribillo ligeramente variado:

> No me las amuestres más,
> que me matarás.

La copla que sigue es octosilábica.

[2] Diego Sánchez de Badajoz, *Recopilación en metro*, obras líricas y dramáticas, c. 1554, reimpresa entre los *Libros de antaño*, Madrid, 2 vols., 1882-1886: véase I, págs. 268, 296, 418 y 438; II, pág. 284. Con «Mal amiga, en buena fe», de Diego Sánchez de Badajoz, compárese «Vos, señora, en buena fe», del índice de omisiones en el *Cancionero musical de los siglos XV y XVI*. Otros estribillos populares: «Dáme el camisón...»; «Ande, ande la cotufada...».

§ 7. Sebastián de Horozco. — Grande amante del folklore, Sebastián de Horozco, hacia 1550, introduce en sus canciones, además de los refranes, juegos y chistes en verso, trozos como los citados a propósito de Castillejo y Boscán:

> — Pídeme, Carillo,
> que a ti darte me han;
> que en casa del mi padre
> mal aborrecido me han.

> — Madrugábalo el aldeana,
> cómo lo madrugaba [1].

> — No puedo apartarme
> de los amores, madre;
> no puedo apartarme [2].

> — Lo que demanda el romero, madre,
> lo que demanda no se lo dan [3].

Las dos últimas, con sus invocaciones de mujer joven a la madre, recuerdan inmediatamente la tradición galaicoportuguesa. También hacen pensar en ella estos dísticos caracterizados por la cadencia anapéstica:

> — Esta cinta, de amor toda,
> quien me la dió ¿para qué me la toma?

> — Toledano, alzo berenjena.
> — Yo no las como, que soy de Llerena.

(Chiste viejo)

> — Toma, vivo te lo do.
> ¿Para qué? ¿para qué? ¿para dó?

(Juego [4])

---

[1] Véase Tirso de Molina, acto primero de *Antona García:*

> Rastrillábalo el aldeana
> ¡y cómo lo rastrillaba!

[2] Véanse el *Cancionero musical* (núm. 234), la *Recopilación* de Juan Vásquez, 1560 (véase Gallardo, *Ensayo*, vol. IV, col. 931), y Pedro de Andrade Caminha (véase *Revue Hispanique*, vol. VIII, pág. 374).

[3] Aparece también en el *Cancionero musical* (núm. 236, composición anónima), en dos versos largos —que es la escritura adecuada— y no en cuatro breves, como lo trae Horozco.

[4] Lo citan también Luis Hurtado de Toledo, adición a la *Comedia Tibalda:* «Toma el amor, biuo te lo do», y Alonso de Ledesma en sus *Juegos de Nochesbuenas* (1605): «Sopla, vivo te lo do», forma en que sobrevive todavía en Méjico y en la Argentina.

Aún tienen más interés sus seguidillas, tipo métrico no bien definido en la mente de Horozco, puesto que lo mezcla con la endecha, glosando la *canción vieja*, popularísima, de *La niña de Gómez Arias:*

> Señor Gómez Arias,
> doléos de mí,
> soy mochacha y niña
> y nunca en tal me vi.
>
> Señor Gómez Arias,
> vos me traxistes,
> y en tierra de moros
> mal me vendistes.
> Yo no sé la causa
> por que lo hezistes,
> que yo sin ventura
> no os lo merecí.
>
> Señor Gómez Arias,
> doléos de mí,
> soy mochacha y niña
> y nunca en tal me vi.

La composición continúa en hexasílabos:

> Si mi triste madre
> tal cosa supiese...

y sólo al final vuelve a caer en parte en el metro de seguidilla:

> Señor Gómez Arias,
> si a Córdoba fuerdes,
> a mi padre y mi madre
> me encomendedes;
> y de mis hermanos
> vos os guardedes,
> que no os den la muerte
> por amor de mí [1].

---

[1] En el entremés *El viejo celoso* trae Cervantes así la canción:

> Señor Gómez Arias,
> doléos de mí;
> soy niña y muchacha,
> nunca en tal me vi.

Y Calderón, en *La niña de Gómez Arias*, acto tercero, como sigue:

> Señor Gómez Arias,
> duélete de mí,
> no me dejes presa
> en Benamejí.

Recuérdese lo dicho sobre esta canción en el cap. II, § 27 y nota final.

Otra composición de Horozco se atiene más a la fórmula del tipo seguidilla, con la libertad de las rimas agudas, según la ley de Mussafia: es la *Canción contrahecha al cantar viejo que dice: ¿Cómo le llamaremos al amor nuevo? Servidor de damas, buen caballero.*

> ¿Cómo le llamaremos
> al niño nuevo?
> Salvador de almas,
> Dios verdadero.
>
> ¿Cómo será el nombre
> desde chiquito?
> Este es Dios y hombre,
> sumo, infinito;
> cumple lo escrito
> deste cordero,
> Salvador de almas,
> Dios verdadero.
>
> ¿Qué nombre es bastante
> o quál puede ser
> deste nuestro infante
> qu'oy quiso nacer
> por nos guarecer
> del cancerbero?
> Salvador de almas,
> Dios verdadero.
>
> El sumo señor
> de lo criado,
> por el pecador
> se ha humanado:
> ¡bendito y loado
> tal compañero,
> Salvador de almas,
> Dios verdadero!
>
> Razón es gozarnos
> con su venida,
> pues viene a salvarnos
> y darnos la vida,
> y en nuestra partida
> ser buen tercero,
> Salvador de almas,
> Dios verdadero.

§ 8. Los poetas líricos bajo Felipe II. — Bajo Felipe II, los trozos de versificación irregular o acentual se hacen más raros que antes entre los poetas cultos. Sólo se exceptúan los dramáticos, los cuales se hallaban entonces, a la verdad, a medio camino entre los líricos cortesanos y los populares. La novela pastoril, como género de abolengo grecolatino e italiano, nada contiene; al contrario de lo que ocurre con el teatro pastoril, hijo de la tradición nacional.

En las poesías atribuídas a Santa Teresa de Jesús (1515-1582) se encuentran varios ejemplos de versificación irregular.

Hay una composición en metro fluctuante como las de Fray Ambrosio Montesino y Lucas Fernández:

> Pues el amor
> nos ha dado Dios,
> no hay que temer,
> muramos los dos.
>
> Danos el Padre
> a su único Hijo:
> hoy viene al mundo
> en un pobre cortijo...

En otra, el estribillo es de seguidilla y en las coplas no falta fluctuación:

> Pero la estrella
> es ya llegada,
> vaya con los Reyes
> la mi manada...
> Pues en nuestros días
> es ya llegada...

En otras composiciones hay estribillos de tono popular con versos eneasilábicos:

> Este niño viene llorando:
> mírale, Gil, que te está llamando.
>
> Mi gallejo, mira quién llama.
> — Ángeles son, que ya viene el alba.
>
> Vuestro soy, para Vos nací:
> ¿qué mandáis hacer de mí?

Baltasar del Alcázar (1530-1606) ofrece hasta cuatro muestras de seguidilla:

> — No quiero, mi madre,
> los montes de oro,
> sino sólo holgarme
> con quien adoro.
>
> — Morena bella,
> tóquete de mi fuego
> una centella.

— Di mi cuerpo y mi sangre
por el pecador:
decid, mi dulce madre
si le tengo amor.

— Norabuena Amarilis al valle venga,
que en faltando del valle no hay hora buena [1].

Las tres primeras se combinan, como estribillos, con coplas
hexasílabas; la última con octosílabos, a manera de remate [2].
La seguidilla aparece, pero más fluctuante, en el cantar recogido por Baptista Montidea en su cancionero *Billete de amor:*

Doy al diablo
mi Diego Moreno,
que ya se me ha vuelto
malo de bueno [3],

y en San Juan de la Cruz (1542-1591), *Cantar del alma:*

Que bien sé yo la fuente que mana y corre
aunque es de noche.

. Aquella eterna fuente que está escondida,
que bien sé yo dó tiene su manida;
aunque es de noche.

Sé que no puede ser cosa tan bella
y que cielos y tierra beben en ella,
aunque es de noche... [4]

En Diego Cortés se presenta menos fluctuante, en sucesión
de grupos de tres versos, 5-7-5 *(Discurso del varón justo,* 1592;
véase el tomo XXXV de la Biblioteca de Rivadeneyra):

[1] Véase § 11 de este capítulo, nota sobre los cantares de enhorabuena.
[2] Véase Baltasar del Alcázar, *Poesías,* edición de la Academia Española,
Madrid, 1908, págs. 8, 11, 152 y 193.
[3] *Cancionero llamado Billete de Amor, compuesto por Baptista Montidea,*
publicado por Timoneda, sin año; reimpresión de la Sociedad Hispánica, Nueva York, 1903. Diego Moreno aparece citado por Quevedo al final de *La visita de los chistes.*
[4] Biblioteca de Rivadeneyra, vol. XXVII, pág. 263.
La composición continúa en dísticos endecasilábicos con el estribillo «Aunque es de noche...». Hay textos que reducen toda la composición a endecasílabos regulares; véase *Obras,* tomo III, Toledo, 1914, pág. 172:

Aquella eterna fonte está escondida...
Y que cielos y tierra beben de ella...

Consúltese CAROLINA MICHAËLIS DE VASCONCELLOS, *Cancioneiro da Ajuda,* vol. II, págs. 58 y 928, para la relación entre este trozo y la antigua poesía peninsular.

Son puras flores,
Pastor y Justo, a Dios,
vuestros dolores.

Que si sentistes
gran pena en el martirio
por do pasastes,
ya florecistes
cual fresco y tierno lirio,
y agradastes
a Dios que amastes
con fe tan clara, digna
de mil loores.
Son puras flores...

¡Oh almas duras,
que la corpórea vida,
que pasa en vuelo,
por las dulzuras
de la inmortal subida
de ese cielo,
acá en el suelo
trocastes porque Cristo
os dió favores!
Son puras flores...

Juan de Valverde Arrieta, *Despertador*... (Madrid, 1581):

Las vacas de la virgo
no quieren beber en el río
sino en bacín de oro fino.

— Marido, vendamos los bueyes,
que otros nos dará Dios después.
— Mujer, no seas loca:
vendamos esa tu toca [1].

Eugenio de Salazar, que en su *Romance de Catalina* introduce
reminiscencias de los cantares paralelísticos («¡Ay, cómo tardas,
amigo! ¡Ay, cómo tardas, amado!»), debe de tener en sus obras
todavía inéditas trozos de versificación irregular, como éste que
extractó Cejador de su *Silva de poesía*, manuscrita en la Academia
de la Historia, de Madrid:

Llorad, mis ojos, llorad,
llorad, llorad, y no os canséis,
pues tanta razón tenéis.

---

[1] ¿Deberá acentuarse *bueyés* para rimar con *después*? Consúltese la nota
final del § 5 de este capítulo, págs. 89-90.

Entre los poetas portugueses, los cantares populares continúan en auge durante este período, pero más bien en su lengua nativa que en la nuestra. Así sucede con Camoens (1525-1580), que utiliza breves dichos o cantares, a menudo como *mote alheio* o *cantiga velha* (p. ejemplo, el refrán conocido de «Amor loco, amor loco, yo por vos y vos por otro») [1]. Pero en Pedro de Andrade Caminha predominan los castellanos en la larga serie de trozos populares que recoge. En él se hallan, junto a los ya citados [2], éstos de seguidilla, que luego reaparecen en el romance «Hermana Marica...», de Góngora (1580), en la comedia *Lo que pasa en una tarde*, de Lope, y en Francisco de Trillo y Figueroa:

No me aprovecharon,
madre, las yerbas;
no me aprovecharon
y derramélas [3].

Jorge de Montemayor (c. 1520-c. 1561), también recoge al menos o imita el cantar popular que inspira una de las poesías atribuídas a Santa Teresa («Véante mis ojos, dulce Jesús bueno...»):

Véante mis ojos
y muérame luego,
dulce amor mío,
y lo que yo más quiero.

Fray Pedro de Padilla, que como Montemayor escribía sólo en castellano, trae estos versos en su *Jardín espiritual* (1585):

Al Niño sagrado
que es mi salvador,
cada vez que le miro
me parece mejor.

§ 9. LOS DRAMATURGOS. — Los poetas dramáticos ofrecen mejores materiales que los líricos. Lope de Rueda (¿1510?-1565) trae dos versos a estilo de gaita gallega en el *Coloquio de Camila:*

— Mi gallejo está so la rama;
su carilleja Menga le llama...

---

[1] Véase el índice alfabético del *Cancioneiro da Ajuda*, vol. II, y las *Obras de Luiz de Camões* (6 vols., Lisboa, 1860-1869), vol. IV, donde hay motes irregulares como «Sois formosa, e tudo tendes | Senão que tendes os olhos verdes». Su letrilla «Irme quiero, madre...», en versos regulares, compárese con el *Romancero de Barcelona:* «Irme quiero, madre, a la galera nueva...»

[2] Véase cap. II, § 29, y cap. III, §§ 4, 6 (cuatro notas) y 7.

[3] Véase CAROLINA MICHAËLIS DE VASCONCELLOS, *Pedro de Andrade Caminha*, en la *Revue Hispanique*, vol. VIII, págs. 364 a 375, 387 y 419 a 426.

— ¡Ay, señora, queráisme dejar,
no me tratéis mal... [1]

y se aproxima a la seguidilla en el *Coloquio de Timbria*, parodiando el cantar de *Los comendadores de Córdoba* [2]. El *Coloquio de Timbria* recuerda, además, el cantar de «Aquel pastorcico, madre...» [3].

Oscilan entre la endecha y la seguidilla los trozos siguientes, de dos obras atribuídas a Rueda, la *Discordia y cuestión de amor:*

Buscando venimos
remedio de amores,
volvemos peores.
Soltad, pastores,
soltad al amor,
por haber favor...,

y el *Auto de Naval y Abigaíl:*

Mimbrera, amigo,
so la mimbrereta.
Y los dos amigos
idos se son, idos,
so los verdes pinos,
so la mimbrereta,
mimbrera, amigo [4].

En la copiosa producción de autos sacramentales y otras obras dramáticas de carácter religioso que llenan el teatro del siglo XVI, abundan fragmentos brevísimos de versificación irregular, colocados las más veces en el villancico que da fin a la representación. De entre ellos entresaco algunos:

— Ya viene el alba, la niña,
ya viene el día [5].

---

[1] Véase en el § 20 de este capítulo, la canción, recogida por Juan Vásquez, que imita Lope de Rueda. Y en la tragedia *Serafina*, de Alonso de la Vega:

¡Ay Amor, queráisme ayudar!

[2] Véase cap. II, § 27.
[3] Véase cap. III, § 4.
[4] Véase CAROLINA MICHAËLIS DE VASCONCELLOS, *Cancioneiro da Ajuda*, vol. II, pág. 923. Para Lope de Rueda y las obras atribuídas a él, véase la edición de sus *Obras*, hecha por la Academia Española, 2 vols., Madrid, 1908: vol. II, págs. 39, 47, 49 *(Coloquio de Camila)*, 105 *(Coloquio de Timbria)*, 353 *(Discordia y cuestión de amor)*, 359, 364 *(Auto de Naval y Abigaíl)*, 421 *(Farsa del Sordo*, atribuída a Rueda).
[5] Los cantares de alba son muchos en los siglos XVI y XVII. Véase Lope: en *Los pastores de Belén*, libro V; o el auto *La vuelta de Egipto;* o la comedia *El cardenal de Belén.*

— Est'es el camino del cielo,
este es camino de allá [1].

(Auto de *Los hierros de Adán*)

Trébol, florido trébol,
trébol florido [2].

(Primer auto de *La Resurrección de Cristo*)

A la gala de la panadera,
a la gala della,
a la gala della
y del pan que lleva [3].

(Premática del pan)

A la guerra van mis ojos:
quiérome ir con ellos,
no vayan solos.

(Desafío del hombre)

---

[1] Véase Valdivielso, auto *El peregrino* (vol. LVIII de la Biblioteca de Rivadeneyra).

[2] En el cap. IV se verá otra canción del trébol, que fué popularísima:

Trébole ¡ay, Jesús, cómo huele!

Sobre las canciones de trébol y de verbena, véase MENÉNDEZ PIDAL, *La primitiva poesía lírica española*, págs. 312-313.

[3] Estos cantares de la *gala* abundan, por ejemplo, en Lope de Vega. Véase en el auto *El pastor ingrato:*

A la gala del pastorcico...;

en el drama religioso *La madre de la mejor:*

A la gala del mercader
que vende, que fía, que causa placer...;

en la comedia *Amores de Albanio e Ismenia:*

A la gala de la madrina,
que nadie la iguala en toda la villa...;

sin contar otros cantares que tienen forma de seguidilla (como «Canten os la gala...» en los dos *Coloquios de la Concepción*).
Véanse también «Válame la gala de la menore», en Juan Vásquez (GALLARDO, *Ensayo*, vol. IV, col. 931); en Rodrigo de Reinosa (GALLARDO, *Ensayo*, vol. IV, col. 1.413):

Viva la gala de la pastorcilla
que al pastor hace penar...,

estribillo de una composición en coplas octosilábicas, y tambien (vol. IV, col. 1.411):

¡A la china gala,
la gala chinela!

— ¡Ah, gusano de mal hombre!
Dí a públicas voces
de dó vienes, hombre.

— De hoces.

— Y dínos: ¿qué pides?

— Coces.

— ¿Chicas, o grandes?
— Como mandardes [1].

(La Resurrección de Nuestro Señor)

[1] Véanse los brevísimos trozos a que aludo en la *Colección de autos, farsas y coloquios*, de Rouanet: vol. I, *El amor divino* (págs. 120, 122 y 125); *La residencia del hombre* (pág. 168: «A la gala del juez»); *El rey Asuero y Amán* (págs. 294 y 298); *La ungión de David* (pág. 325); *El sacrificio de Jeté* (pág. 422: «Vengáis norabuena»); *Sant Jorge* (pág. 450).
Vol. II: *Los hierros de Adán* (págs. 223 y 231); *La residencia del hombre*, versión más extensa (pág. 355); *La huída de Egipto* (pág. 378: «Caminad, chiquito...») imita el popularísimo cantar de viaje que cita Salinas, *De musica*, pág. 308, que se incluye en la ensaladilla anónima *Entre dos claros arroyos*, ms. 3.913 de la Biblioteca Nacional de Madrid, y que emplea Francisco de Ocaña en un romancillo núm. 440 del *Romancero y cancionero sagrados*, vol. XXXV de la Biblioteca de Rivadeneyra; véase además, MENÉNDEZ PIDAL: sobre cantares de viaje, en *La primitiva poesía lírica española* (págs. 288-291):

Caminad, señora,
si queréis caminar,
que los gallos cantan,
cerca está el lugar...

La Resurrección de Christo (págs. 155 y 641).
Vol. III: *La Resurrección de Christo*: no es nueva versión del anterior, sino otro auto (pág. 18); Auto incompleto y sin título (págs. 121, 122, 125 y 130); *Las cortes de la Iglesia* (pág. 143); *Peralforja* (pág. 200: véase «Teresica hermana, de la fararira» en el *Cancionero de Upsala*, núm. 36; aparece también en la *Silva de sirenas*, de Anríquez de Valderrábano, 1547):

Teresilla hermana,
de la farira rira,
hermana Teresa.

Periquillo hermano,
de la fariri runfo,
hermano Perico.

La esposa de los cantares (pág. 218); *Premática del pan* (págs. 251 y 256); *Farsa del engaño* (pág. 281); *Farsa de Moselina* (pág. 315); *Farsa de las coronas* (págs. 381, 384 y 393); *Farsa de la moneda* (pág. 426); *Farsa del Sacramento* (pág. 482); *La entrada del vino* (pág. 491), estribillo que reaparecerá en Lope, en el auto *El heredero del cielo*, con el segundo verso distinto:

A la viña, viñadores,
a la viña divinal.

Desafío del hombre (pág. 527).
Vol. IV: *Las bodas d'España* (pág. 28: el segundo verso es común en cantares de bodas:

España y el Divino Amor
para en uno son;

Juan de Timoneda (muerto en 1583), en su auto *La oveja perdida*, entre otros cantares, introduce los siguientes:

— Pasced a vuestro solaz,
la mi ovejica,
pues sois bonica.
Pasced a vuestro solaz
en la majada;
catad que no comaz
cosa vedada,
cosa no usada,
grande ni chica,
pues sois bonica.

— Que debajo del sayal pascual,
que debajo del sayal hay ál [1].

por ejemplo, en LOPE, *Peribáñez, Historia de Tobías, El nacimiento de Cristo, El vaso de elección, El tusón del rey del cielo). La Resurrección de Nuestro Señor* (págs. 96, 102 y 103).

Además, véase el volumen LVIII de la Biblioteca de Rivadeneyra, *La fuente de la gracia* (pág. 36):

Venid a la fuente,
venid, pecadores,
limpios de errores.

Luego, la farsa *Danza de la muerte*, de Juan de Pedraza (página 41), y la anónima *Parabola coenae* (pág. 132):

Ésta es la justicia
que mandan hacer
al que malo quiso ser,

canción cuyos dos primeros versos son conocidísimos, pero generalmente se continúan en metro regular como endecha (véase en Diego Hurtado de Mendoza y en el auto de Lope, *El hijo pródigo*).

Para Alonso de la Vega, véase *Tres comedias*, Madrid, 1905, págs. 23, 28, 29 *(Tolomea)*, 54, 55, 65 y 66 *(Serafina)*. Para Bartolomé Palau, *Santa Orosia:* «Aquí lo traigo, el santo dón...»

[1] Biblioteca de Rivadeneyra, vol. LVIII, págs. 78 y 88.
En el teatro profano de Timoneda pueden recogerse otros estribillos: véase el primer tomo de sus *Obras completas*, edición de la Sociedad de Bibliófilos Valencianos, Valencia, 1911 (págs. 13, 61, 103, 111 y 351). En el introito de la *Comedia de Anfitrión* hay una cántiga en versos de diez y de cinco sílabas, que bien pudiera tener relación con los versos de la danza llamada entonces *endechas de Canarias:*

Dinos, zagala, ¿quál de ios dos
es el tu amado?
Callad, carillos; andad, por Dios,
ya lo he mostrado.

Compárense con las que así se llaman en el *Libro de música de vihuela*, de Pisador (1552), y en la *Orfénica Lira*, de Fuenllana (1554):

¿Para qués, dama, tanto quereros?
Para perderme y a vos perderos.
Más valiera nunca veros
para perderme y a vos perderos;

Y en sus obras líricas *(Sarao de amor,* 1561):

> — Aba los tus ojos,
> linda morena,
> ábalos, ábalos,
> que me dan pena.
>   Ábalos, no miren
> con su bel mirar
> y no me retiren
> de te contemplar:
> déjenme gozar
> vista tan buena,
> ábalos, ábalos,
> que me dan pena... [1]
> — Fuera, fuera, fuera,
> el pastorcico!
> Que en el campo dormirás
> y no conmigo.
>   Casóme mi padre
> en signo menguado
> con un pastorcico
> de guardar ganado;
> la primera noche
> que me vino a ver
> zurrón y cayado
> trujo consigo... [2]

y las que incluye el P. Luis Villalba en sus *Diez canciones españolas de los siglos XV y XVI:*

> Si los delfines
> mueren de amores,
> ¡triste de mí!
> ¿qué harán los hombres
> que tienen tiernos
> los corazones?

Realmente canarias, del siglo xv, son las que cita Menéndez y Pelayo *(Antología,* vol. X, págs. 229-230, y vol. XI, pág. 103: «romancillo pentasilábico...», de cuatro series asonantadas de seis versos cada una, siendo patente su analogía con los versos fúnebres vascongados que cita Garibay):

> Llorad las damas,
> si Dios os vala.
> Guillén Peraza
> quedó en La Palma,
> la flor marchita
> de la su cara...

[1] En todas las coplas, los versos sexto, séptimo y octavo tienen cinco sílabas, en vez de las seis de los versos anteriores.

[2] Son siete coplas: el último verso tiene, en todas, cinco sílabas.

§ 10. El teatro hacia 1600. — Al siglo xvi pertenece todavía el canónigo Tárrega (c. 1554-c. 1602), cuyos dramas tienen importancia dentro de la escuela de Valencia. En *Los moriscos de Hornachos* (acto I) introduce una canción en versos octosilábicos alargados para ajustarse a música de baile, convirtiéndolos así en metro irregular, como sucede a menudo en el canto:

> Dança morica, dança morica, dança
> al són de la guitarra, guitarra;
> dança morica a este són, morica a este són.

> No temáis tener passión,
> pues con moricos dançáis, moricos dançáis,
> muy gallardas bueltas days, bueltas days,
> aquel por dar onor, dar onor
> mejor que las dió Almançor, Almançor,
> a los moros otomanos, otomanos,
> y burlar de los christianos, christianos,
> y con esta dança morica, dança morica,
> al són de la guitarra, la guitarra [1].

En el *Baile de Leganitos*, que precede a la comedia *La enemiga favorable*, de Tárrega, se introducen seguidillas:

> Sol de Leganitos,
> luna del Prado,
> bailes del Sotillo,
> vino del Santo [2].

> Dije yo guifero,
> dijo él cuchillo,
> anduvimos al pelo,
> quedó vencido.

[1] La comedia ha sido publicada por Caroline B. Bourland en la revista *Modern Philology*, de Chicago, en abril y junio de 1904.

[2] Bajo otra forma la cita el maestro Gonzalo Correas en su *Arte grande de la lengua castellana* (pág. 276), como ejemplo de seguidilla, todavía *moderna* hacia 1625:

> Viento del Sotillo
> luna del Prado,
> agua de Leganitos
> vino del Santo.

Véase Luis Vélez de Guevara, Romance «Murmuraba entre unas peñas»:

> En las Fuentes del Prado,
> madre, de Madrid,
> lloraré soledades
> del Guadalquivir.

> ¡Ay, que me abraso,
> me fino y me muero!
> ¿Cómo no tocan y tañen
> y tañen a fuego?
>
> Calle de Leganitos,
> dichosa fuiste,
> pues que dentro tienes
> a mi Rodríguez...

y versos anapésticos:

> En los álamos duerme la niña,
> y un arroyuelo que pasa veloz
> saltando y bailando la despertó [1].

También cabe colocar en el siglo XVI los dramas de Miguel Sánchez (muerto antes de 1609). Se introducen diversos cantares de primavera en el *Baile de la Maya* (probablemente suyo), que precede a su comedia *La guarda cuidadosa* en todas las ediciones desde 1615. Excepto el primer cantar, todos pertenecen a la fiesta de la Maya, y Lope los introduce también en su auto, anterior a 1604, de igual título que el baile del *divino Sánchez:*

> — Entra Mayo y sale Abril:
> ¡cuán garridico le vi venir! [2].
>
> — Esta Maya se lleva la flor,
> que las otras no [3].

---

[1] Biblioteca de Rivadeneyra, vol. XLIII, págs. 98 y 99. Véase también MILÁ, *Del decasílabo y endecasílabo anapésticos (Obras,* vol. V, pág. 330).

[2] Véanse también el *Cancionero musical,* núm. 61, y el *Romancero espiritual,* de Fray José de Valdivielso, edición de Madrid, 1880, pág. 227. Sobrevive el cantar, modificado, en Castilla: véase el *Cancionero popular de Burgos,* recogido por Olmeda (Sevilla, 1903).

[3] Además del auto *La Maya,* de Lope, donde aparece la versión «Esta Maya...», véase su comedia *El molino* y la de Vélez de Guevara *La serrana de la Vera* (lo cita, además, Gonzalo Correas en su *Vocabulario de refranes:* véase J. F. MONTESINOS, tomo I de *Poesías líricas* de Lope, Madrid, 1925, nota a la página 142):

> Esta novia se lleva la flor,
> que las otras no.

Véanse entre otros ejemplos, Trillo y Figueroa, Letrilla:

> Esta niña se lleva la flor,
> que las otras no...

Tirso, *La mejor espigadera:*

> Esta sí que se lleva la gala...
> que las otras que espigan non.

— Den para la Maya,
que es bonita y galana.

— Echad mano a la bolsa,
cara de rosa;

echad mano al esquero,
caballero [1].

Lope, auto *La isla del sol:*

Éste es rey y éste es señor,
que los otros no.

Lope, *La esclava de su hijo:*

Éste sí que es mayo famoso,
que los otros mayos no.

Rojas Zorrilla, *García del Castañar:*

Ésta es blanca como el sol,
que la nieve no.

Sor Juana Inés de la Cruz, *Letras en la profesión de una religiosa;*

Éste sí que es enamorado
como lo he menester yo,
éste sí, que los otros no.

Quevedo, letrilla:

Éste sí que es corredor,
que los otros no.

Moreto, auto *La gran casa de Austria:*

Éste sí que es pan de los cielos,
que no lo encarecen los panaderos.

Hay otros cantares con «Éste (o ésta, o esto) sí», sin «que los otros no»; ejemplos:

Ésta sí que es siega de vida,
ésta sí que es siega de amor.

(Lope, auto *La siega:* la glosa, en zéjel).

Esto sí, esto sí,
esto sí que es lucir.

(Sor Juana Inés de la Cruz, *Villancicos de Santa Catalina,* 1691).

[1] Los cuatro últimos versos tienen metro de seguidilla, y hacen pensar en el esquema paralelístico. Los cita también Sebastián de Covarrubias Orozco, escritos en renglones dobles, en su *Tesoro de la lengua castellana,* 1611, artículo *Cara.* Véase, además, el auto *El hijo pródigo,* de Valdivielso. En *El truhán del cielo,* Lope recoge solamente el trozo:

Den para la Maya
que es bonita y galana.

Luis Quiñones de Benavente, entremés de *La Maya:*

¡Para la Maya, que es linda y galana!

Entremés anónimo de *La Maya,* segunda mitad del siglo XVII:

Den para la Maya,
que es hermosa, pulida, bonita y gaiana.

111

— Pase, pase el pelado,
que no lleva blanca ni cornado [1].

§ 11. CERVANTES (1547-1616). — Cervantes, cuyas obras principales se publican después de 1600, pero pueden considerarse, en general, como elaboradas con materiales procedentes del siglo XVI, introduce no pocos cantares de origen popular en sus dramas y cita otros en sus novelas. Así, en *Don Quijote* (segunda parte, capítulo XXIV), el mancebito que iba a la guerra, muy apropiadamente «iba cantando seguidillas para entretener el trabajo del camino»:

A la guerra me lleva mi necesidad;
si tuviera dineros no fuera en verdad [2].

En *Rinconete y Cortadillo* hay toda una serie de seguidillas:

Por un sevillano rufo a lo valón
tengo socarrado todo el corazón.

— Por un morenico de color verde
¿quién es la fogosa que no se pierde?

— Riñen dos amantes, hácese la paz,
si el enojo es grande, es el gusto más.

— Detente, enojado, no me azotes más;
que si bien lo miras, a tus carnes das.

Tres parecen endechas, por el uso de hexasílabos agudos en lugar de pentasílabos graves; no sabríamos que son seguidillas si Cervantes no lo dijese, y no lo confirmara la segunda. Tampoco, sin su testimonio y el del maestro Gonzalo Correas, sabríamos

___

[1] Fórmula de juego, más bien que cantar. Véase Lope, *El laberinto de Creta;* Valdivielso, auto *El hijo pródigo.* Sobre el tema de la Maya hay el baile atribuíble a Miguel Sánchez, un auto de Lope, un entremés de Quiñones de Benavente, uno anónimo y un baile de Antonio de Zamora: véase COTARELO, Introducción a los *Entremeses, loas, bailes, jácaras y mojigangas,* págs. CXXXIII, CXXXIV, CCIII y CCIV. Véase, para las citas de Sánchez, Biblioteca de Rivadeneyra, vol. XLIII, o la edición de *La Isla Bárbara y La guarda cuidadosa,* de Rennert. Cotarelo reproduce el baile como anónimo, pág. 484. Sobre los cantares de mayo, véanse HANSSEN, *Las coplas 1.788-1.792 del «Libro de Alexandre»,* en la *Revista de Filología Española,* 1915, y MENÉNDEZ PIDAL, *La primitiva poesía lírica española,* págs. 301-303; además, el núm. 69 del *Cancionero musical de los siglos XV y XVI.*

[2] Sobre las seguidillas de Cervantes, véanse las anotaciones de D. FRANCISCO RODRÍGUEZ MARÍN al *Quijote* (segunda parte, cap. XXIV) y a *Rinconete y Cortadillo,* su conferencia *La copla* (Madrid, 1910), reproducida en su libro *El alma de Andalucía* (Madrid, 1929), y especialmente su estudio *El Loaysa de «El celoso extremeño»* (Sevilla, 1901), págs. 276 a 288. Consúltese, además, el estudio de HANSSEN, *La seguidilla,* §§ 2, 3, 7 y 17.

que era seguidilla y no endecha, el conocido cantar, seguramente muy antiguo, que Cervantes cita en la novela *El celoso extremeño* (donde Loaysa está descrito como hábil en cantar *coplas de la seguida* y en la comedia *La entretenida* (jornada tercera, donde se dice: «toquen unas seguidillas»):

> Madre, la mi madre,
> guardas me ponéis;
> que si yo no me guardo
> no me guardaréis [1].

Trae otros cantarcillos Cervantes. En la comedia *La casa de los celos:*

> Derramastes el agua, la niña,
> y no dijiste ¡agua va!
> La justicia os prenderá.
> Cautivásteme el alma, la niña,
> y tenéisla siempre allá.
> El amor me vengará [2].

> — Bien haya quien hizo
> cadenitas, cadenas;
> bien haya quien hizo
> cadenas de amor [3].

[1] Véase Correas, *Arte grande*, pág. 280. Lope de Vega la trae también en su comedia *Los melindres de Belisa*, en versos hexasilábicos; con el tercer verso como heptasílabo, en *El mayor imposible* (1615) y en *El aldehuela;* en la última, además, la seguidilla está escrita en versos largos dobles. También la trae Calderón, con el tercer verso como heptasílabo, en su comedia burlesca *Céfalo y Procris*. Para antecedentes, véase capítulo II, § 22, de este libro.

Alonso Álvarez de Soria (1573-1603), a quien Rodríguez Marín nos presenta como original del Loaysa de Cervantes, empleaba realmente la seguidilla, como se ve en el romance, escrito probablemente entre 1590 y 1593, que comienza: «Otra vez, Sierra Morena»; allí introduce este cantarcillo:

> Nunca viera, Tajo,
> tu clara orilla,
> pues de verla nacieron
> tantas desdichas.

Véanse las páginas 106-108 de *El Loaysa de «El celoso extremeño»*.

[2] Combinación de endecasílabos anapésticos con octosílabos.

[3] Lope, en la comedia *El nacimiento de Cristo* (acto I), lo trae en renglones largos. Así, también, Fray Pedro de Padilla (véase Biblioteca de Rivadeneyra, vol. CXXXV, pág. 186).

— Venga norabuena
Cupido a nuestras selvas,
norabuena venga [1].

En la comedia *Pedro de Urdemalas* (acto I), seguidillas:

A la puerta puestos
de mis amores,
espinas y zarzas
se vuelven flores.

Otra, en la comedia *La gran sultana* (acto III):

Escuchaba la niña
los dulces requiebros
y está de su alma
su gusto lejos.

Otras, en el entremés *La guarda cuidadosa:*

Sacristán de mi vida, tenme por tuya,
y fiado en mi fe canta aleluya.

Y en *La elección de los alcaldes de Doganzo*, donde las bailan, y la última, que constituye un cantar paralelístico, presenta en el estribillo la alteración de las palabras finales del verso:

Pisaré yo el polvico
atán menudico;
pisaré yo el polvó
atán menudó.

Pisaré yo la tierra
por más que esté dura,
puesto que me abra en ella
amor sepultura,

---

[1] Estos cantares de enhorabuena son antiguos. Ya en el *Cancionero musical* (núms. 369 y 370) y en *As matinas de Natal*, de Gil Vicente, se halla «Norabuena vengas, Menga». Luego, «Vengáis norabuena», en *El sacrificio de Jeté* (colección de Rouanet), y multitud de ejemplos en el teatro de Lope *(Santa Casilda)*, Tirso (auto *El colmenero divino* y primera parte de *La Santa Juana*), Calderón (comedia burlesca *Céfalo y Procris*, auto *La primer flor del Carmelo)*, en *Los pastores de Belén* (libro III), de Lope, y en muchas obras más; véanse las citas de Baltasar del Alcázar, § 8 de este capítulo.

En *La casa de los celos* hay otro cantar, en forma isosilábica:

Corrido va el abad
por el cañaveral,
corrido va el abad...

del cual da otra versión Lope en el auto *La Maya.*

pues ya mi buena ventura
amor la pisó
atán menudó.

Pisaré yo lozana
el más duro suelo,
si en él acaso pisas
el mal que recelo;
mi bien se ha pasado en vuelo
y el polvo dejó
atán menudó [1].

Como se ve, Cervantes, situado en el punto medio entre las dos centurias, acoge con interés la seguidilla y se hace eco de su reciente popularidad.

Las hay en obras que se han querido atribuir, sin mucho fundamento, a Cervantes, como el entremés *La cárcel de Sevilla:*

Pues que ya está libre
mi sentenciado,
gástese mi saya
y lo que he ganado...

El entremés *El hospital de los podridos:*

Cuando sale Jesús a sus corredores
Bercebú no parece y Satán se esconde.

---

[1] Cervantes recuerda el baile del *Polvico* en *La gitanilla*, después de la primera canción de Preciosa, y en el entremés *El vizcaíno fingido*. Quevedo también, en *El entremetido y la dueña y el soplón*. Góngora da otra versión del estribillo (letrilla de 1615):

Pisaré yo el polvico
menudico,
pisaré yo el polvó
y el prado no.

Sobre el baile, véase RODRÍGUEZ MARÍN, *El Loaysa*, págs. 259 y 261, y COTARELO, Introducción a la *Colección de entremeses, loas, bailes, jácaras y mojigangas*, de la Nueva Biblioteca de Autores Españoles, XVII, págs. CCLVII y CCLVIII, donde cita otras versiones del cantar: una en el baile de *Pásate acá, compadre*, publicado con comedias de Lope en 1617:

Pisaré yo el polvillo
menudillo, menudillo;
pisaré yo el polvó
atán menudó...

y otra en la comedia *La Baltasara*, de tres ingenios, 1652:

Pisaba yo el polvillo
atán menudillo;
pisaba yo el polvó
atán menudó.

115

Y el *Entremés de los Romances:*

> Frescos ventecillos,
> favor os pido,
> que me anego en las olas
> del mar de olvido.

§ 12. Los villancicos de las iglesias. — A fines del siglo comienzan a escribirse los villancicos de Navidad y de otras festividades, que se convirtieron, durante la centuria siguiente, en fiestas obligatorias de las catedrales: Madrid, Toledo, Sevilla, Córdoba, Granada, Cádiz, Barcelona, Valencia, Zaragoza, especialmente; en América, Méjico y Puebla sobre todas. Para ellos se escriben y se imprimen letras en que abundan los elementos populares, imitados *a lo divino:* forman rudimentos de dramas líricos sacros, nacidos de la canción popular. Comenzaron las canciones por figurar como parte de las representaciones sacras, y acabaron por constituir género aparte, «especie de opereta sacra» [1].

Los primeros villancicos que se imprimen en Toledo (1595) son obra de Esteban de Zafra y están hechos para cantarse al son de tonos profanos del pueblo, tales como «Ojos morenicos..» [2], «Aserrojar serrojuelas...» y «Rezaremos, beatas, oír...». Las letras de Zafra están a menudo en versos irregulares, a juzgar por los comienzos que cita Gallardo:

> Digas, pastorcico,
> que gozas de amor,
> dó viste al redentor...
>
> Vamos, amigo, jugando,
> La Salve Regina cantando...
>
> ¡Rite, eh, eh!
> ¡Mas rite, eh, eh!
> La turulú turulé,
> turulú, turulá...
>
> Debajo de la peña nace
> la rosa que no quema el aire...

Los dos últimos versos forman el estribillo del último villancico, escrito en coplas octosilábicas [3].

---

[1] Véase Carolina Michaëlis de Vasconcellos, *Cancioneiro da Ajuda,* vol. II, págs. 787-790.

[2] Sobre la canción de los «Ojos morenos», véase § 19 de este capítulo.

[3] Véanse Biblioteca de Rivadeneyra, vol. XXXV, composición núm. 808; Gallardo, *Ensayo,* vol. IV, col. 1.093, y Cristóbal Pérez Pastor, *La imprenta en Toledo,* Madrid, 1887 (núm. 418). Pérez Pastor registra los villancicos posteriores que se escribieron en Toledo: el que sigue es de 1662, y de

§ 13. LOS PRIMEROS DRAMAS DE LOPE DE VEGA. — Ya para entonces, Lope de Vega (1562-1635) se apodera del teatro y adopta para él los diversos tipos de canto y baile, populares, vulgares y cortesanos. No cabe duda que comenzó su amplia práctica de aplicación y explotación de esos tipos desde antes de 1600: basta recorrer la lista de sus obras dramáticas contenidas en la primera edición de *El peregrino en su patria* (1604) para advertir que en muchas de ellas aprovecha aquellos elementos; igual cosa hace en los cuatro autos religiosos incluídos en el texto de *El peregrino* y en su comedia única en prosa, *La Dorotea*, escrita en la última década del siglo XVI y publicada en 1632.

La seguidilla se halla en *La Dorotea:*

> Que no quiero favores
> para mis penas,
> pues me basta la causa
> de padecellas...

En dos de los autos aludidos, *La Maya* («Echad mano a la bolsa») y *Las bodas entre el alma y el amor divino*, en comedias anteriores a 1604 mencionadas en la lista de *El Peregrino:* tales, *Adonis y Venus, El caballero de Illescas, El mármol de Felisardo* y *Pedro Carbonero*, donde hay una zambra bailada, con letra de rima aguda en los versos cortos:

> Riberitas hermosas
> de Darro y Genil,
> esforzad vuestros aires
> que me abraso aquí.

Junto a éstos puede mencionarse *El Caballero de Olmedo*, drama basado en el cantar viejo, de la misma familia que el de *Los Comendadores de Córdoba* y el de *La niña de Gómez Arias:*

---

ahí en adelante se hacen más frecuentes, con intervalos de pocos años entre unos y otros; de 1700 en adelante se suceden anualmente con raras interrupciones (en realidad, bien pocas otras cosas se imprimen entonces en Toledo), y cesan en 1833.

Otra serie semejante de villancicos registra J. M. VALDENEBRO Y CISNEROS en *La imprenta en Córdoba* (Madrid, 1900), desde 1628 a 1834. Estas colecciones de villancicos pertenecieron a Francisco Asenjo Barbieri y ahora se encuentran en la Biblioteca Nacional de Madrid. La de Toledo contiene 114 impresos; la de Córdoba, 74; la de Sevilla, 115 para el siglo XVII y 129 para el XVIII; la de Madrid, 98 para el XVII y 70 para el XVIII; la de Barcelona, 124; la de Cádiz, 98; la de Valencia, 93; la de Zaragoza, 90; la de Granada, 55; la de Ávila, 22, y la de Burgos, 17. Hay todavía otras colecciones pequeñas. Para el villancico en Portugal, véase CAROLINA MICHAËLIS DE VASCONCELLOS, *Cancioneiro da Ajuda*, vol. II, págs. 787-790 y 869.

> Que de noche le mataron
> al caballero,
> a la gala de Medina,
> la flor de Olmedo [1].

§ 14. RESUMEN. — La precedente excursión [2] indica cómo procedían los poetas cultos durante el siglo XVI respecto del arte popular: Encina y su escuela, tanto en la lírica como en el teatro, utilizan de preferencia las canciones en metro isosilábico y evitan las irregularidades. Así se continúa procediendo en la lírica cortesana, salvo excepciones, sobre todo las de personajes muy

---

[1] Lope recuerda el cantar del *Caballero de Olmedo*, no sólo en la obra así titulada, sino en otras, imitándolo o parodiándolo: el auto *Del pan y del palo*, el *De los cantares*, y las comedias *El truhán del cielo* y *El Santo Negro Rosambuco*. Probablemente es anterior a la de Lope otra comedia de tres ingenios, *El Caballero de Olmedo*, fechada en 1606; es posterior la burlesca de Francisco Antonio de Monteser, escrita en 1621. El episodio a que se refiere el cantar ocurrió en 1521 y es probable que los versos se escribieran poco después (véase Menéndez y Pelayo, introducción al tomo X de la edición académica de las *Obras* de Lope, págs. LXXV y LXXVI). El cantar continuaba, según parece, así:

> Sombras le avisaron
> que no saliese
> y le aconsejaron
> que no se fuese
> el caballero,
> la gala de Medina,
> la flor de Olmedo.

Cantar emparentado con el del *Caballero de Olmedo* es el que recoge Lope en *Las almenas de Toro*:

> Por aquí daréis la vuelta,
> el caballero,
> por aquí daréis la vuelta
> si no me muero.

Del cantar del *Caballero* surgió una danza, que ya aparece en el *Baile famoso del Caballero de Olmedo*, atribuído a Lope y publicado en la *séptima parte* de sus obras, 1617, donde se agrega a la copla inicial esta otra:

> ¡Ay, Don Alonso,
> mi noble señor,
> caro os ha costado
> el tenerme amor!

La danza reaparece, siempre con la letra favorita de Lope, en entremeses del siglo XVII y en la *Mojiganga de los sones*, de Cañizares: véase COTARELO, Introducción a los *Entremeses, loas, bailes, jácaras y mojigangas*, págs. CCXXXV y CCXXXVI.

Consúltense CORREAS, *Arte grande*, pág. 274; GALLARDO, *Ensayo*, vol. I, col. 1.275; Príncipe de Esquilache, romance «Enamorado en Medina...»

[2] Los resultados se clasificarán más adelante; véanse § 16 de este capítulo y el comienzo de los §§ 19, 20, 21, 22 y 23.

castizos, como Castillejo, Alcázar y Horozco, verdadero especialista en folk-lore.

En el teatro, la influencia de Gil Vicente favorece los metros irregulares; después de él disminuyen, o se reducen a trozos brevísimos, como ocurre en los autos religiosos; hacia el final del siglo aumentan de nuevo y Lope los lleva al drama sacro y al profano.

El origen popular de los trozos intercalados por los poetas es indiscutible: unas veces cabe comprobarlo por las declaraciones de los autores que los insertan, por medio del *Cancionero musical de los siglos XV y XVI*, donde aparecen anónimos, al igual que en el *Cancionero de Upsala* y demás libros de música, y de cuando en cuando, por testimonios de otro orden que suelen datar de épocas lejanas, como en el caso de «Quien amores ha...»; otras veces la prueba falta, pero el carácter de la composición no deja lugar a dudas, como sucede con los anónimos del *Cancionero Herberay*.

Además, por excepción —que en el siglo XVII dejará de serlo—, los poetas cultos una que otra vez componen cantares en verso libre: así, el cossante de Hurtado de Mendoza el Viejo, en el siglo XIV; o, en el XVI, la danza «Estánse dos hermanas...» y la canción «Muy graciosa es la doncella...», de Gil Vicente; el cantar de bodas de Castillejo; las dos composiciones en seguidillas de Sebastián de Horozco; el diálogo en versos libres del auto anónimo *La Resurrección de Nuestro Señor;* el *Cantar del alma*, de San Juan de la Cruz; las seguidillas a Santos Justo y Pastor, de Diego Cortés; las seguidillas de Cervantes en *La elección de los alcaldes de Daganzo*, y probablemente las de *Rinconete y Cortadillo*. En todas ellas, frente a la irregularidad de los versos, se aplica el principio de la isometría de las estrofas en la distribución de rimas; después, en el siglo XVII, no siempre se aplicó.

A partir de 1600 la situación cambiará; los metros irregulares, acentuales o meramente libres, se pondrán en boga entre los poetas cultos; el empleo de estribillos populares será menos necesario y se irá haciendo menos frecuente [1].

[1] He aquí la lista de los poetas en cuyas obras se encuentra versificación irregular; bajo los Reyes Católicos: Juan del Encina, Lucas Fernández, Garci Sánchez de Badajoz, el marqués de Astorga, Fray Íñigo de Mendoza, Fray Ambrosio Montesino; bajo Carlos V: Gil Vicente, Alonso de Alcaudete, Rodrigo de Reinosa, Francisco de Sâ de Miranda, Diego Hurtado de Mendoza, Cristóbal de Castillejo, Juan Boscán, Jaime de Huete, Sebastián Fernández, Diego Sánchez de Badajoz, Antonio de Villegas, Francisco de Lora, Alonso de Villegas Selvago (véase nota sobre Encina, § 3), Sebastián de Horozco; bajo Felipe II: los desconocidos autores de los autos, Juan de Pedraza, Alonso de la Vega, Bartolomé Palau, Santa Teresa, Baltasar del Alcázar, Baptista Montidea, San Juan de la Cruz, Diego Cortés, Juan de Valverde Arrieta, Eugenio de Salazar, Jorge de Montemayor, Luis de Camoens, Pedro de Andrade Caminha, Lope de Rueda, Juan de Timoneda, Francisco Tárrega, Miguel Sánchez, Esteban de Zafra, Fray Pedro de Padilla (§ 11, nota), Alonso Ál-

B) Los poetas populares y vulgares

(1475-1600)

§ 15. El «Cancionero musical de los siglos xv y xvi».
— Cuando se abandona la poesía cortesana y el teatro para ir
a las colecciones donde los maestros de música —aunque cortesanos también— hacen uso de los cantos y bailes del pueblo o del
vulgo y recogen las letras populares o vulgares, la versificación
irregular, ya imperfectamente, ya plenamente acentual, aparece
como normal, no como excepción, y en los estribillos figura con
igual frecuencia que la métrica silábica.

Nuestras fuentes principales para el cantar anónimo son, en
primer término, el *Cancionero musical de los siglos XV y XVI;*
en segundo término, las colecciones musicales dadas a luz entre
1530 y 1581; en tercer lugar, colecciones varias de poesías, con
música o sin ella, publicadas o inéditas, pertenecientes en su mayoría al final del siglo xvi. La publicación de otro libro de versos
sin música, la primera parte del *Romancero general,* el año de 1600,
cierra la serie de fuentes anónimas de la centuria.

El *Cancionero musical* contiene materiales anteriores a 1500;
pero, a menos que la anterioridad esté probada, es lo prudente
considerarlos todos como fechados hacia 1500 y los años inmediatamente posteriores, según lo sugieren la música y los nombres
que se conservan de los compositores y poetas [1]. Así, la contribución del siglo xv queda reducida, por ahora, a los ejemplos de

varez de Soria (§ 11, nota), Cervantes y Lope. Puede agregarse a Juan López de Úbeda, que en su *Cancionero y vergel de plantas divinas* (1588) imita
la *Serranilla de la Zarzuela* (véanse § 10 del cap. I y § 24 del cap. II); a poetas
como Francisco de Ocaña, Alonso de Ledesma y Francisco de Ávila, cuyos
cancioneros se publican muy a principios del siglo xvii, y a Góngora que en
poesías anteriores a 1601 emplea estribillos irregulares («Déjame en paz, amor
tirano...», 1580; «Dejadme llorar, orillas de la mar —o del mar—...», 1580;
«Ándeme yo caliente...», 1581; «Que se nos va la pascua, mozas...», 1582;
«Si en todo lo que hago...», 1585; «Clavellina se llama la perra...», 1591;
«Ya no más, ceguezuelo hermano...», 1592; «Mandadero era el arquero...»,
1593; «Barquero, barquero...», 1595; «Los dineros del sacristán...», 1600;
«¿Por qué llora la Isabelitica?...», 1600).

Sobre el interés que despierta el canto popular desde la época de los Reyes Católicos hasta la de Felipe II, véase MENÉNDEZ PIDAL, *La primitiva poesía lírica española,* págs. 333-340.

[1] Véanse RAFAEL MITJANA, *Nuevas notas al Cancionero musical de los siglos XV y XVI,* en la *Revista de Filología Española,* 1918, y JULIÁN RIBERA,
La música de las Cantigas, pág. 27. Del *Cancionero musical* he citado o indi-
cado ya muchos cantares: véanse cap. I, § 10, nota sobre la *Serranilla de la
Zarzuela,* y nota sobre el hexasílabo; cap. II, §§ 20 y 23; cap. III, §§ 2, nota
sobre Salinas; 3, 4, notas; 5, notas; 6, notas; 7, notas; 10, nota; y 11, notas.

fecha indudable [1], pero debe tenerse en cuenta que el *Cancionero* representa el lazo de unión entre el período de los orígenes y el siglo XVI. De las cuatrocientas sesenta canciones allí contenidas, en cerca de ciento hay versificación irregular.

§ 16. LOS TIPOS MÉTRICOS IRREGULARES Y SU EMPLEO EN VILLANCICOS Y ENSALADAS. — Los tipos de versificación que se descubren en el *Cancionero musical,* fuera de los silábicos, son los mismos que ya aparecían en el siglo XV y que continuaron apareciendo durante la excursión a través de las obras de poetas conocidos. Pueden clasificarse en cuatro: el cantar de cadencia anapéstica, al estilo de gaita gallega; el que tiene como elemento predominante el verso eneasílabo; la seguidilla; y los esquemas libres, en que se percibe con menos precisión el plan rítmico o se mezclan ritmos diversos. Los dos primeros tienen parentesco con la lírica galaicoportuguesa y ritmo acentual bien definido; los últimos son de probable origen castellano, como si en Castilla hubiese menos aptitud que en Occidente para la música verbal y los metros del canto tendieran a quedarse en simple estado de fluctuación, semejante a la del verso amétrico.

El género de composición poética donde más fácilmente se emplean es el villancico; la medida del verso de las coplas puede ser cualquiera, regular o variable, aunque las composiciones típicas son en octosílabos o en hexasílabos, con estribillo de dos, tres o cuatro versos, y coplas de seis, más el retornelo o repetición, enlazado con ellas:

> Más vale trocar
> placer por dolores
> qu'estar sin amores.
>
> Donde es gradecido
> es dulce morir;
> vivir en olvido,
> aquel no es vivir;
> mejor es sufrir
> passión y dolores
> qu'estar sin amores...

> (Juan del Encina)

Abunda también el zéjel, especialmente en la forma simple, la cuzmaní:

> Has tan bien bailado,
> corrido y luchado,
> que m'has namorado,
> y d'amores muero...

[1] Véase cap. II, sobre orígenes.

No sé qué te diga:
tu amor me fatiga;
tenme por amiga,
sey mi compañero...

(Juan del Encina)

Rengifo, en su *Arte poética* (1592), consagra el principio de la libertad en la versificación de los villancicos: «...Villancicos hay que se conforman en la cantidad y el número de las sílabas con el punto de la música en que se cantan; y llevan más o menos largos los versos, según lo piden las fugas que se hacen en las sonadas. De éstos no se puede dar regla cierta, porque penden de la música; de suerte que el que hubiere de componer, o ha de ser músico, o a lo menos tener buen oído, para que, oyendo la sonada, la sepa acomodar al metro» [1].

Correas, hacia 1625, también habla de «cantares y villancicos y coplillas sueltas y desiguales de número de versos y sílabas dellos, y... *seguidillas*, que son los más iguales y regulares, pero todos dulces y suaves para cantar»; y, más adelante, de «coplas desiguales de tres y cuatro versos, de más y menos sílabas, dispuestas a cantar con guitarra, sonajas y pandero, que hacen perfecto sentido y andan solas» (Correas quiere que se les aplique a todos el nombre de *folías*) [2].

Los antiguos villancicos de versificación acentual son cortos, pero tanto éstos, que eran siempre para cantar, como los bailes con letra —tales la *españoleta* o la *chacona*—, con el tiempo estimularon la producción de cantares extensos con coplas cuyos versos ya no eran silábicos. Este desarrollo sobreviene después de 1600; hasta entonces, la canción de verso irregular suele limitarse, como se advierte en las recopilaciones musicales, al estribillo y una copla o a lo sumo dos. Se exceptúan de esta brevedad la mayor parte de las paralelísticas y encadenadas; otras pocas, compuestas en seguidillas fluctuantes hacia la endecha, y unas cuantas burlescas del *Cancionero musical* [3].

Las canciones populares y vulgares, silábicas o irregulares, solían intercalarse, no sólo en obras dramáticas, según se ha visto, sino acumuladas en composiciones líricas, como el villancico de Santillana. Luego se llamó ensaladas a estas combinaciones: la más antigua, la que lleva música de Peñalosa en el *Cancionero musical* (número 438), representa la forma ruda, primitiva, en que las canciones se suman sin fundirse. De 1600 en adelante se escriben ensaladas o ensaladillas con relativa frecuencia, y ge-

---

[1] Véase la edición de 1644, del *Arte poética*, cap. XXXIII.
[2] *Arte grande*, págs. 271 y 282.
[3] Véase *Cancionero musical*, núms. 412 y 435; en el § 18 de este capítulo se analizarán los núms. 434 y 449.

neralmente figuran una escena campestre, donde sucesivamente se entonan diversos cantares[1]. Del villancico lírico sale también el dramático escrito para festividades religiosas desde fines del siglo XVI[2].

§ 17. LA SEGUIDILLA: COMIENZOS DE SU EVOLUCIÓN. — La seguidilla[3] tiene curiosa historia, que Hanssen esbozó en su magistral estudio sobre la estructura métrica y rítmica del tipo; todavía puede recibir adiciones. Sus más antiguos ejemplos no van más allá de mediados del siglo XV; uno en portugués literario, el del infante Don Pedro; otro en castellano, popular, transcrito e imitado por Álvarez Gato. El ejemplo portugués se distingue por el empleo de rimas agudas; el castellano se acerca mucho al paradigma que ha predominado a través del tiempo.

A éstas siguen las del *Cancionero Herberay*, contemporáneas o poco posteriores en fecha, con la curiosa tendencia hacia la copla de pie quebrado: una de ellas es seguidilla indudable, la otra es muy dudosa. Cabría agregar, como aproximación a la seguidilla, pero cercana a la copla de pie quebrado, el cantar de «Aquel

---

[1] Véase, en el cap. II, el § 22 y la nota sobre la ensalada. Rengifo la describe así: «Es una composición de coplas redondillas, entre las cuales se mezclan todas las diferencias de metros, no sólo españoles, pero de otras lenguas, sin orden de unos a otros, al albedrío del poeta; y según la variedad de las letras, se va mudando la música. Y por eso se llama ensalada, por la mezcla de metros y sonadas que lleva» (edición de 1644, cap. LXIV; da ejemplo en las últimas páginas del Apéndice). Hay que advertir que Rengifo emplea con suma amplitud, en este pasaje, el término *redondilla* (consúltese su amplia definición en el cap. XXII).

Como ejemplos de ensaladas, además de las de Mateo Flecha (1581) y de las que indica Carl Appel (artículo *Von Descort*, en la *Zeitschrift für romanische Philologie*, 1887, vol. XI, página 226), mencionaré las curiosas que he visto manuscritas en la Biblioteca Nacional de Madrid. En el manuscrito 3.913 (letra del siglo XVII) hay dos: una que principia, «Entre dos claros arroyos...», y una *letra* que lleva al principio el estribillo, «Quien madruga Dios le ayuda, /si va con buena intención.», y cuya parte narrativa comienza: «Bartholá la la de Loys...». La segunda está impresa, con muchas variantes, en el *Romancero general;* la parte narrativa comienza: «Dominga de Andrés Luys...» El *Romancero* contiene otra ensaladilla, que comienza: «Un lencero portugués»; está reproducida en el de Agustín Durán, núm. 1.772, vol. XVI de la Biblioteca de Rivadeneyra.

Al tipo de ensaladilla creo que pertenece otra composición, que en el mencionado manucristo 3.913 lleva el título de *romance*, y que comienza:

> La jabonada ribera
> de Manzanares corriente...

La reproduce Antonio Guzmán e Higueros entre las *Poesías de antaño* (núm. 11) que dió a luz en la *Revue Hispanique*, 1914, vol. XXXI.

[2] Véase § 12 y notas. Sobre el villancico en música, véase RAFAEL MITJANA, *Comentarios y apostillas al Cancionero... del siglo XVII*; en la *Revista de Filología Española*, 1919, págs. 21-23, 25, 29, 33 y 49-52.

[3] Sus formas se explican antes, cap. II, § 25.

pastorcico, madre...» [1]. Y hay otros ejemplos de aproximaciones.

En fecha, sigue probablemente el cantar de *Los Comendadores*, si aceptamos la tesis de que la glosa, y no sólo la endecha primitiva, pertenece a la época de los Reyes Católicos; inmediatamente después, las pocas que trae, dudosas o seguras, el *Cancionero musical de los siglos XV y XVI*.

§ 18. Las seguidillas del «Cancionero musical». — Según Hanssen, el único ejemplo seguro en el *Cancionero musical* es la composición núm. 132, con música de Diego Fernández:

> De ser mal casada
> no lo niego yo;
> cativo se vea
> quien me cativó.

La composición sigue como villancico hexasilábico:

> Cativo se vea
> y sin redención...

y el estribillo podría tomarse por endecha, a no ser porque está clasificado como seguidilla entre las que recogió Foulché-Delbosc en manuscritos del siglo XVII; el ritmo de la música nos confirma en la certeza [2].

Hanssen señala otros ocho cantares del *Cancionero* que tienen relaciones con la seguidilla. En tres (núms. 115, 378 y 412) la música permitiría pensarlo:

> Dos ánades, madre,
> que van por aquí,
> mal penan a mí.

Es canción anónima (núm. 115) y lleva música de Juan Anchieta; era todavía popular en el siglo XVII, pues Quevedo la menciona en la dedicatoria de su *Cuento de cuentos* [3]. La composición está incompleta, pero se ve que las coplas eran hexasilábicas; lo eran también las de Juan del Encina («Más sano me fuera...») en la composición (núm. 378) que encabeza con este estribillo popular:

> ¡Ay triste que vengo
> vencido d'amor,
> maguera pastor!

---

[1] Véase cap. III, § 4.

[2] Véase Hanssen, *La seguidilla*, § 14; Foulché-Delbosc, *Séguedilles anciennes*, en la *Revue Hispanique*, 1901 (seguidillas núms. 7 y 23.)

[3] Calderón también la recuerda en *Con quien vengo, vengo*, y Antonio de Solís *(Varias poesías*, Madrid, 1692, fol. 169). Véase Julio Monreal, *Cuadros viejos*, Madrid, 1878, pág. 63.

Si esas dos parecen más que trozos de seguidillas, endechas imperfectas, hay otra que parece una seguidilla invertida (núm. 412):

> Dale si le das,
> mozuela de Carasa,
> dale que le das,
> que me llaman en casa... [1]

Composiciones donde la música no concuerda con el ritmo de la seguidilla, pero la versificación sí, aunque parcialmente, son las que llevan los números 153, 162, 389, 404 y 449. La primera, incompleta:

> La vida y la gloria
> se apartan de mí
> en partirme de ti.
>
> ¡Oh triste ventura,
> qué desdicha es la mía!...

La segunda (162) se aproxima mucho más, en la copla; es también incompleta:

> No querades, fija,
> marido tomar
> para sospirar.
>
> Fuese mi marido
> a la frontera,
> sola me dejaba
> en tierra ajena.

Es menos interesante la núm. 389 («Placer y gasajo...»); algo más la 404:

> Iba a ver, la mi madre,
> a quien mucho amé;
> íbame cantando
> lo que os diré...

En fin, la burlesca núm. 449:

> Pero González,
> tornóse vuestra huerta
> cuernos albares...

cuyo estribillo es indiscutiblemente de seguidilla, y cuyas coplas están en metro desordenado, que oscila entre seguidilla y endecha, pero que va definiéndose más y más a medida que avanza:

---

[1] Se cita en *La Lozana Andaluza*, mamotreto XIV.

Compraste una huerta
en Alcaudete...

Veniste de la guerra
muy destrozado...

Veniste vos, marido,
desde Sevilla;
cuernos os han nacido
de maravilla;
no hay ciervo en esta villa
de cuernos tales,
que no caben en casa
ni en los corrales[1].

Es curioso que Hanssen no cite otra seguidilla, y ésta sí indiscutible, del *Cancionero*, el estribillo de la composición núm. 397, variante del cantar recogido por Álvarez Gato:

Tir'allá, que non quiero,
mozuelo Rodrigo... [2]

Atendiendo sólo al metro, y no a la música, todavía debe indicarse que tienen relaciones con la seguidilla los números 48, 400, 420 y 434. Vagamente la primera, que lleva música de Escobar:

Las mis penas, madre,
de amores son.
Salid, mi señora,
del sol naranjale,
que sois tan hermosa,
quemarvos ha el aire
de amores, sí.

La tercera, «Sola me dejastes...», es la que adoptan Sâ de Miranda y Rodrigo de Reinosa. La segunda y la cuarta son interesantes ejemplos de cantar paralelístico; aquélla se refiere a otro «mozuelo Rodrigo» como el de la seguidilla transcrita por Álvarez Gato:

Rodrigo Martínez
a las ánsares ¡ahé!
pensando qu'eran vacas
silbábalas: ¡He!

Rodrigo Martínez,
atán garrido,

---

[1] Como seguidillas clasifica éstas de *Pero González* RODRÍGUEZ MARÍN en *La copla* (pág. 20) y en *El Loaysa de «El celoso extremeño»* (págs. 276-277).
[2] Véase § 23 del cap. II.

los tus ansarinos
liévalos el río ¡ahé!
Pensando qu'eran vacas
silbábalas: ¡He!

Rodrigo Martínez,
atán lozano,
los tus ansarinos
liévalos el vado ¡ahé!
Pensando qu'eran vacas
silbábalas: ¡He!

La otra (434):

Perdí la mi rueca
y el huso non fallo,
si vistes ál,
al tortero andar.

Perdí la mi rueca
llena de lino;
hallé una bota
llena de vino;
si vistes ál,
al tortero andar.

Perdí la mi rueca
llena d'estopa;
de vino fallara
llena una bota;
si vistes ál,
al tortero andar.

Hinqué mis rodillas
dile un besillo;
bebí un azumbre
más un cuartillo;
si vistes ál,
al tortero andar,

Hallé yo una bota
llena de vino;
dile un tal golpe
y tiróme el tino;
si vistes ál,
al tortero andar.

Vino mi marido
y dióme en la toca;
¡ay de mí mezquina
y cómo estoy loca!
Si vistes ál,
al tortero andar.

127

> Caíme muerta,
> ardióse ell estopa,
> vino mi marido...

En el índice de composiciones que acompaña al *Cancionero musical*, pero que no llegaron a incluirse en él, se halla la indicación de otra especie de seguidilla, que se completa mediante el *Cortesano*, de Luis Milán (página 71):

> Quitad, el caballero,
> los ojos de mí,
> no me miréis ansí.

§ 19. LA SEGUIDILLA POPULAR A TRAVÉS DEL SIGLO XVI. — Si bajo los Reyes Católicos no alcanzó todavía la seguidilla gran popularidad, durante el siglo XVI va creciendo lentamente, hasta ponerse de moda hacia el final. Pero cabe pensar que el metro de seguidilla precedió en mucho tiempo a la música y al baile que recibieron luego igual nombre —pues éste no aparece hasta Mateo Alemán, cerca de 1600—, y, por tanto, los versos se cantarían con sones varios, antes de que tuvieran música propia y típica. Así lo indica el maestro Gonzalo Correas: «Parece que antes se comprendían en el nombre de *folías* con las otras coplillas sueltas que no pasaban de cuatro versillos; y las que se quedaban en menos, como cabezas de cantares»[1].

Entre el *Cancionero musical* y Cervantes, Hanssen indicaba sólo unas cuantas seguidillas: una de las de Alcázar; la del trébol, en el primer auto de *La Resurrección* (serie de Rouanet), y una, que parece endecha, en otro de aquellos autos, el del *Sacrificio de Abraham:*

> Estos convidados
> vienen a comer
> al que los convida:
> ¿cómo puede ser?

De ahí pasa Hanssen a Cervantes, a Lope de Vega, al *Romancero general* y a la colección de Foulché-Delbosc[2].

A las que he agregado —tomándolas de Montesino, Sâ de Miranda, Sebastián de Horozco, Andrade Caminha, Santa Teresa, San Juan de la Cruz, Alcázar, Montidea, Diego Cortés, Lope de Rueda, Miguel Sánchez y Tárrega—, hay que añadir otras, de colecciones anónimas.

---

[1] *Arte grande*, págs. 272 y 273. Ya se ha visto, sin embargo, que había seguidillas largas desde hacia 1500 (como la de los *Comendadores* y la de *Pero González*) y no solamente reducidas a cuatro o a tres renglones.

[2] Véase HANSSEN, *La seguidilla*, §§ 12 a 18, y las *Séguedilles anciennes*, de Foulché-Delbosc.

Seguidillas fluctuantes se encuentran aún a través del siglo; abundan, sobre todo, las que comienzan con hexasílabo, práctica que registra el maestro Gonzalo Correas, en 1626, como usual todavía, y las hay con versos más largos, hecho anotado también por aquel gramático.

Así, las que incluyen Juan Vásquez en sus *Villancicos* de 1551, y Miguel de Fuenllana en su *Orfénica Lira* de 1554:

> No sé qué me bulle
> en el calcañar,
> no sé qué me bulle
> que no puedo andar.
> Yéndome y viniendo
> a las mis vacas,
> no sé qué me bulle
> entre las faldas,
> que no puedo andar,
> no sé qué me bulle
> en el calcañar.

> Puse mis amores
> en Fernandino.
> ¡Ay, que era casado!
> Mal me ha mentido.
> Digas, marinero,
> del cuerpo garrido,
> en cuál de aquellas naves
> pasa Fernandino.
> ¡Ay, que era casado!
> Mal me ha mentido;
> puse mis amores
> en Fernandino [1].

[1] En el cantar «Puse mis amores...», Vásquez y Fuenllana traen igual el estribillo pero no la copla. En Fuenllana dice:

> Trájome engañada
> con su amor mentido;
> pues era casado
> mal me ha mentido.

Este cantar aparece imitado a lo divino en el manuscrito 14.070 de la Biblioteca Nacional de Madrid, fechado en 1566:

> Puse mis amores
> en el recién nacido:
> ¡ay, que es amor del cielo
> el que he sentido!

Allí aparece este otro cantar religioso en versificación irregular:

> — ¿Por qué lloras, Niño?
> — Lloro y muero por ti,

¿Cómo queréis, madre,
que yo a Dios sirva,
siguiéndom'el Amor
a la contina?
   Mientras más a Dios sirvo
Amor más me sigue;
mientras d'Amor más huyo,
más me persigue.
   Tal vida como ésta
no sé quién la viva
siguiéndom'el Amor
a la contina.

No me habléis, Conde,
d'amor en la calle;
catá que os dirá mal,
Conde, la mi madre.
   Mañana iré, Conde,
a lavar al río:
allá me tenéis, Conde,
a vuestro servicio.
Catá que os dirá mal,
Conde, la mi madre:
no me habléis, Conde,
d'amor en la calle [1].

Ejemplo de orden invertido de los versos, largo y corto:

¡Ay, que no oso
mirar ni hacer del ojo!
¡Ay que no puedo
deciros lo que quiero!

Y si os miro
con temor de enojaros
doy un suspiro,
y paso sin hablaros:

que te quiero y amo
y no te dueles de mí.
— ¿Qué hacéis llorando
sin remedio al yelo?
— Estoy remediando
la ofensa del suelo.
— ¿Qué os trajo del cielo
a padecer aquí?
— Desearte cerca,
que estás muy lejos de mí.

[1] *Ensayo*, de GALLARDO, vol. IV, cols. 922, 923 y 924, y *Catálogo de la Biblioteca de Salvá*, núm. 2.515.

todo es amaros
y nada lo que espero.

¡Ay, que no oso
mirar ni hacer del ojo! [1]

Diego Pisador, en su *Libro de música de vihuela*, 1552, trae:

Gentil caballero, dadme agora un beso,
siquiera por el daño que me habéis hecho.
Venía el caballero de Córdoba a Sevilla [2].

La canción de los *Ojos morenos*, que es meramente irregular
en el *Cancionero* antiguo, aparece aproximándose vagamente a
la seguidilla en la versión posterior de Juan Vásquez *(Recopilación* de 1559). Así lo trae Asenjo Barbieri (núm. 171), con música de Escobar:

Ojos morenicos,
irme yo a querellar
que me queredes matar.

Quejarme de mí,
que ansí me vencí,
que desque os vi
me aquejó el pesar,
que me queredes matar.

---

[1] GALLARDO, *Ensayo*, vol. IV, col. 922, y Salvá, núm. 2.515. Fué imitado
este cantar en coplas de pie quebrado: una versión aparece en el Cancionero
del siglo XVI, manuscrito 5.593 (antes P. supl. 279) de la Biblioteca Nacional
de Madrid, folio 97, y otra, no muy diferente, en la copia a mano (ms. 4.128,
antes M. 360) del cancionero *Flor de enamorados*, reunido por Juan de Lina-
res, dado a luz en Barcelona en 1573, y reimpreso varias veces hasta 1681 (no
conozco la obra impresa). En este cancionero no hay más versos irregulares
que esos y otros que principian «Zagaleja la de lo verde» y continúan en octosílabos.

[2] *Ensayo*, de Gallardo, vol. III, col. 123. Aparece también en Alonso Mudarra (1546) con variantes:

Gentil caballero,
désdeme hora un beso,
siquiera por el daño
que me habéis hecho.
Venía el caballero,
venía de Sevilla;
en huerta de monjas
limones cogía,
y la prioresa
prendas le pedía:
siquiera por el daño
que me habés hecho.

131

Así, en Vásquez:

> Ojos morenos
> ¿cuándo nos veremos?
>
> Ojos morenos
> de bonica color,
> sois tan graciosos
> que matáis de amor.
>
> ¿Cuándo nos veremos,
> ojos morenos? [1]

Del *Cancionero de Upsala* (núm. 49):

> Dezilde al caballero que non se quexe,
> que yo le doy mi fe, que non la dexe.
>
> Dezilde al caballero, cuerpo garrido,
> que non se quexe en ascondido,
> que yo le doy mi fe, que non la dexe.

En su *Comentario de la conquista de Baeza*, Ambrosio Montesino —no el fraile poeta, sino otro posterior, prosista, que escribía bajo Felipe II—, recoge un dicho con giro de seguidilla:

> Caballeros de Úbeda,
> salid al mercado,
> que Alonso Navarrete
> matará al toro vayo.

Le sugiere igualmente este otro:

> El Conde Don Lope,
> el vizcaíno,
> rico de manzanas,
> pobre de pan y vino [2].

En el manuscrito de *Tonos castellanos* que analiza Gallardo, indicando que la letra es de fines del siglo XVI, abundan ya las seguidillas. Cabe pensar que son muy del final, y son de origen culto:

> Sobre la esmeralda de verdes hojas
> cristalinas perlas el alba llora.
>
> Tengo unos amores
> a descontento;
> no le dé Dios a nadie
> tan gran tormento.

---

[1] *Ensayo*, vol. IV, col. 929.
[2] *Ensayo*, vol. III, cols. 863 y 865.

A la sierra viene
la blanca niña,
y en arroyos la nieve
huye de envidia.

Para todos alegres
para mí tristes,
bien conozco, mis ojos,
que dais en libres.

¿Quién ha sido la causa
de mis suspiros?
Y los ecos del valle
responden: iros.

Al espejo se toca
el sol de mi vida,
dando luz a la luna
donde se mira.

Mis amores, zagalas,
y mis contentos,
unos fueron aire
y otros son fuego.

Como no me dan celos,
no tengo temor,
aunque toquen el arma
ausencia y amor.

Al cantar de las aves
mi amor se durmió:
¡ay Dios, quién llegara
y le preguntara
qué es lo que soñó! [1]

Los últimos versos acaso no sean seguidilla, sino hexasílabos precedidos por un verso más largo. Los anteriores se presentan como cabezas de coplas hexasilábicas u octosilábicas.

En uno de los cartapacios literarios salmantinos del siglo XVI, extractados por Menéndez Pidal, se hallan estas seguidillas, alternando con otras coplas que parecen endechas:

Uno tengo al remo
y otro pienso echar;
quiérome ir a la popa
por verlo bogar.

---

[1] *Ensayo*, vol. I, cols. 1.194 a 1.202. Véase RODRÍGUEZ MARÍN, *El Loaysa*, pág. 277. «Al espejo se toca» está citada por CORREAS como seguidilla moderna *(Arte grande*, pág. 276).

Salen de Sevilla
barquetes nuevos:
de una verde haya
llevan los remos.

Mal haya la barca
que acá me pasó,
que en casa de mi padre
bien me estaba yo.

Pues que en esta tierra
no tengo nadie,
aires de la mía,
vení a llevarme.

Pues que en esta tierra
no tengo amor,
aires de la mía,
lleváme al albor.

Partíme de Murcia,
erré el camino,
fuí a dar a Lorca
y a ser lorquino.

Pues que en Sevilla
no puedo entrar,
válgame San Lucas
que es puerto de mar.

Hay unas pocas más todavía, de tipo burlesco [1].

En uno de los *Romancerillos de la Biblioteca Ambrosiana* aparecen éstas:

Aquel paxarillo
que vuela, madre,
ayer le vi preso
y hoy trepa el aire;
por penas que tenga,
no muera nadie;
yo le vi entre rejas
de estrecha cárcel,
cantando pasiones
mañana y tarde [2].

El *Romancero general*, en la primera edición de sus dos partes, no contiene seguidillas indiscutibles como estribillos de romances, sino más comúnmente cantares que se les aproximan, tales:

---

[1] *Boletín de la Academia Española*, Madrid, 1914 (vol. I, páginas 311 a 313).
[2] Se encuentran también entre las poesías atribuídas, con poca probabilidad, a Góngora.

Púsoseme el sol,
salióme la luna;
más le valiera, madre,
vèr la noche oscura [1].
Blanda la mano,
pensamiento vano,
blanda la mano.
No lloréis, casada,
de mi coraçón,
que pues yo soy vuestro
yo lloraré por vos [2].
Madrugasteis, vecina mía,
a sacar pollos;
plega a Dios no os encuentre
y os coma el coco.
No duermen mis ojos,
madre, ¿qué harán?
Amor los desvela:
¿si se morirán? [3].

[1] Se halla también como estribillo en Lope y en Juan de Salinas, muerto en 1643 *(Poesías,* dos vols., Sevilla, Sociedad de Bibliófilos Andaluces, 1869, vol. II, pág. 112); termina así en Salinas:

> Más me valiera, madre,
> la noche oscura.

Véase, además, Luis Vélez de Guevara, *La luna de la sierra:*

> En los olivares de junto a Osuna,
> púsoseme el sol, salióme la luna...

y Quiñones de Benavente lo parodia, en el entremés de *Las alforjas.*

[2] Aparecía ya en uno de los *Romancerillos de la Biblioteca Ambrosiana.*

[3] Según parece, las ediciones posteriores del *Romancero general* agregaron nuevos romances con estribos. Hanssen *(La seguidilla,* § 8) cita este estribillo como publicado en el *Romancero,* 1604, pág. 404:

> Galeritas de España,
> parad los remos
> para que descanse
> mi amado preso.

Este estribillo se halla también en las *Séguedilles* de Foulché-Delbosc (núms. 34 y 56) y en el *Laberinto amoroso,* cancionero de 1618, reimpreso por Karl Vollmöller en las *Romanische Forschungen,* de Erlangen, vol. VI, 1891.

Para otros romances con estribillo en seguidillas, publicados en diversas ediciones del *Romancero general,* véanse los números 1.683, 1.804, 1.805, 1.807, 1.811, 1.827, 1.833, 1.836 del *Romancero* de Durán, vol. XVI de la Biblioteca de Rivadeneyra.

Merecen atención las seguidillas que el maestro Correas llama viejas, en su *Arte grande de la lengua castellana* (págs. 274 a 276 de la edición de 1903): son, probablemente, del siglo xvi, como se ve en la del *Caballero de Olmedo*.

De la colección de *Seguidillas antiguas* que recogió y publicó Foulché-Delbosc hay unas treinta y cuatro (núms. 251 a 284 de la serie) que proceden de un manuscrito anterior a 1600. La mayoría son burlescas o, peor aún, obscenas; pero las cuatro primeras son de otro carácter, y muy interesantes:

> Río de Sivilla
> quién te passase,
> sin que la mi servilla
> se me mojase.
>
> Río de Sivilla,
> arenas de oro,
> dessa banda tienes
> el bien que adoro.
>
> Río de Sivilla,
> de barcos lleno,
> al passarlo el alma
> no passa el cuerpo.
>
> Río de Sivilla,
> rico de olivas,
> dile cómo lloro
> lágrimas vivas [1].

Aun puede citarse otra:

> Negra la cara, negro
> el coraçón,
> que como amor es fuego
> volvióm'en carbón.

(Núm. 269)

§ 20. LOS VERSOS DE GAITA GALLEGA. — Sabemos que los versos a estilo de gaita gallega, en que predomina la cadencia anapéstica, debieron en buena parte su difusión al influjo galaicoportugués [2] y subsisten hoy en los tres idiomas de la Península, relacionados a menudo con los cantos y bailes venidos de Occidente.

El ritmo de danza es perceptible en ellos, según la observación de Carolina Michaëlis, y, en efecto, durante los siglos xvi

---

[1] Véase también en el *Romancero de Barcelona*, manuscrito de principios del siglo xvii, de que dió noticia Milá y Fontanals en el *Jahrbuch für romanische und englische Literatur*, de Berlín (1861, vol. III, pág. 172).

[2] Véase cap. II, §§ 19, 20 y 28.

y XVII se aplicaron a no pocos bailes: la *zarabanda*, en ocasiones; la *españoleta*, la *Catalineta*, el de *Tárrega*, el de *Marizápalos*, el *sarao*, el *minué* [1]. Antes los hemos visto, tanto en la poesía cortesana —ejemplo el cossante de Hurtado de Mendoza el Viejo— como en la poesía anónima —«Soy garridilla...» y «Si desta scapo...» del *Cancionero Herberay*, los trozos que recogen Sebastián de Horozco, Lope de Rueda, Miguel Sánchez, Tárrega, Cervantes, Góngora («Clavelina se llama la perra...»).

Los tratadistas no hablan de estos cantares, excepto de modo general al referirse a los villancicos y coplas de versos desiguales. Correas llega, sin embargo, a anotar el verso de diez sílabas y da ejemplos de los más típicos, como el precioso cantar de ronda de la noche de San Juan:

> Si queréis que os enrame la puerta,
> vida mía de mi corazón,
> si queréis que os enrame la puerta,
> vuestros amores míos son [2].

Como el *arte mayor*, metro noble durante más de cien años, debió de bajar excepcionalmente hasta las clases populares —a juzgar por los cancioneros—, tal vez haya que clasificar entre los versos de gaita gallega, o cerca de ellos, cantarcillos como el que la expulsión de los judíos inspiró en 1492:

> Ea, judíos, a enfardelar,
> que mandan los reyes que paséis la mar,

conservado, música y letra, por el maestro Salinas [3].

Otro, de paralelismo simple, citado por Montesino, el historiador de Baeza, oscila entre el alejandrino y el arte mayor:

---

[1] El libro de *Discursos del arte del danzado*, de Juan de Esquivel Navarro, publicado en Sevilla en 1642, se dice que clasifica los bailes en populares (como el basto, la tárrega y la jácara), usuales (como el baile canario) y elegantes (como la españoleta). Es el tratado principal de baile (o tal vez el único) en los siglos de oro.

Véase MENÉNDEZ Y PELAYO, *Historia de las ideas estéticas*, vol. IV, pág. 687; JULIO MONREAL, *Cuadros viejos*, Madrid, 1878 (cap. II: Los bailes de antaño); FRANCISCO ASENJO BARBIERI, artículos sobre *Danzas y bailes de España en los siglos XVI y XVII*, en *La Ilustración Española y Americana*, de Madrid, noviembre de 1877; FRANCISCO RODRÍGUEZ MARÍN, *El Loaysa*, págs. 256 a 288 (habla especialmente de la zarabanda); COTARELO, Introducción a los *Entremeses, loas, bailes, jácaras y mojigangas*, especialmente la lista de danzas y bailes, págs. CCXXXIII a CCLXXIII. Sobre su difusión en el Nuevo Mundo traté en *Música popular de América*, en el tomo I de *Conferencias* del Colegio de la Universidad de La Plata, Argentina, 1930, págs. 198-202.

[2] Lope lo imita en su auto *De los cantares*. Véanse también el *Romancero espiritual* de Valdivielso (pág. 25) y las *Rimas del incógnito*, del siglo XVII, en la *Revue Hispanique*, 1916 (volumen XXXVII, pág. 333).

[3] *Cancionero musical de los siglos XV y XVI*, pág. 21.

137

Cantan de Oliveros, cantan de Roldán,
no de Zurraquín, que fué buen barragán.
Cantan de Roldán, cantan de Oliveros,
no de Zurraquín, que fué buen escudero [1].

Versos de cadencia anapéstica indudable los trae el *Cancionero musical*, aunque pocos:

Aquella mora garrida,
sus amores dan pena a mi vida...

Figuran como estribillos de una composición (núm. 164) en versos octosílabos, con los que alternan eneasílabos agudos (¿por fluctuación, o por regularidad según la ley de Mussafia?):

Mi madre por me dar plazer
a coger rosas me envía...

El autor de la música es Gabriel; probablemente se llamaba Gabriel Mena y era poeta además. El estribillo reaparece citado por Salinas *(De musica,* pág. 327):

Aquella morica garrida,
sus amores dan pena a mi vida.

Luego (núm. 401):

Gritos daban en aquella sierra;
¡ay, madre! quiero m'ir a ella.
En aquella sierra erguida
gritos daban a Catalina.
¡Ay, madre, quiero m'ir a ella! [2].

---

[1] Véase GALLARDO, *Ensayo,* vol. III, col. 863, y cita de TOMÁS ANTONIO SÁNCHEZ, en su opúsculo sobre *Orígenes de la poesía castellana,* publicado por MENÉNDEZ Y PELAYO en la *Revue Hispanique,* 1908 (vol. XVIII, pág. 429).

[2] En el *Tesoro de la lengua castellana,* de Covarrubias, s. v. leño:

Voces dan en aquella sierra:
leñadores son que hacen leña.

Aparece también en Pisador y en Mudarra:

Sí me llaman, a mí llaman,
que cuido que me llaman a mí.
Y en aquella sierra erguida
cuido que me llaman a mí.
Llaman a la más garrida,
que cuido que me llaman a mí.

Probablemente esta versión es el resto de una forma paralelística y encadenada.

Y otra con música de Escobar (núms. 427 y 428), con la copla en forma de zéjel:

> Paséisme ahora allá, serrana,
> que no muera yo en esta montaña.
> Paséisme ahora allende el río,
> paséisme ahora allende el río,
> que estoy triste, malherido,
> que no muera yo en esta montaña [1].

Abundan más estos versos en las colecciones musicales de mediados del siglo. Así, en Pisador y en Vásquez, este cantar de romería (o de vigilia):

> Por una vez que mis ojos alcé,
> dicen que yo le maté;
> como al caballero no le di herida,
> ansí vaya, madre, virgo a la vigilia [2].

En la *Recopilación*, de Juan Vásquez, de 1559, este cantar, imitado por Lope de Rueda y Alonso de la Vega:

> Caballero, queráisme dejar,
> que me dirán mal.
> ¡Oh, qué mañanica, mañana,
> cuando la niña y el caballero
> ambos se iban a bañar!
> Que me dirán mal,
> caballero, queráisme dejar [3].

En el *Cancionero de Upsala* (núm. 36), y en la *Silva de sirenas*, de Anríquez de Valderrábano, 1547, dos versiones distintas de este cantar:

> ¡Teresica hermana, de la fararira!
> Hermana Teresa, si a ti te pluguiese... [4]

En los *Tonos castellanos*, del siglo XVI, extractados del manuscrito por Gallardo:

---

[1] Sobre las serranas porteadoras, véase MENÉNDEZ PIDAL, *La primitiva poesía lírica española*, págs. 289-292; sobre «Paséisme ahora...» y su semejanza con el zéjel «Salteóme la serrana», véase la edición de *La serrana de la Vera*, de Vélez de Guevara, anotada por R. Menéndez Pidal y María Goyri de Menéndez Pidal, Madrid, 1916; además, MENÉNDEZ Y PELAYO, *Antología*, vol. IX, pág. 210.

[2] GALLARDO, *Ensayo*, vol. III, col. 1.236, y vol. IV. col. 931.

[3] GALLARDO, *Ensayo*, vol. IV, col. 928. Véase § 9 de este capítulo.

[4] Véase nota al núm. 36 en el *Cancionero de Upsala*, y véase nota del § 9 sobre la colección de autos de Rouanet.

Norabuena vengáis, Abril,
vengáis norabuena, qué galán venís.
Abril, qué galán venís [1].

Morenica ¿por qué no me vales,
que me matan a tus umbrales?

Daba el sol en los álamos, madre,
y a su sombra me recosté;
dormí, y cuando desperté,
no daba el sol sino el aire [2].

Arrullaba a la palomita
su regalado amador,
y deshecha en sabrosos gemidos
le da con el pico su corazón [3].

En el tratado *De musica*, de Francisco Salinas, el amigo de
Fray Luis de León (Salamanca, 1577):

— Meteros quiero monja,
hija mía de mi corazón.
— Que no quiero yo ser monja, non.

Más me querría un zatico de pan
que no tu saludar [4].

En el *Romancero general*:

La mujer que tal sueño sueña,
cozes y palos y golpes en ella.

Fuego de Dios en el bien querer,
fuego de Dios en el querer bien.

(Parte primera) [5]

---

[1] Véase Tirso, primera parte de *La Santa Juana*, y nota del § 11 sobre los
cantares de enhorabuena.

[2] Incluye esta canción, con música, E. M. TORNER, en su pequeño *Cancionero musical* (Biblioteca Literaria del Estudiante, Madrid, 1927).

[3] GALLARDO, *Ensayo*, vol. I, cols. 1.196 a 1.203.

[4] Págs. 302 y 320.

[5] El segundo verso sirve de título a una comedia de Calderón, que además lo recuerda en *Eco y Narciso*. Véase, también, Correas, *Vocabulario de refranes*, pág. 297.

Paxarito que vas a la fuente,
   bebe y vénte [1].

Lo que me quise me quise me tengo,
lo que me quise me tengo yo [2].

No sois vos para en cámara, Pedro,
no sois vos para en cámara, no [3].

Zagaleja del ojo rasgado,
vénte a mí que no soy toro bravo.
Vénte a mí, zagaleja, vénte,
que adoro las damas y mato la gente.
Zagaleja del ojo negro,
vénte a mí que te adoro y quiero.
Dejaré que me tomes el cuerno
y me lleves si quieres al prado;
vénte a mí que no soy toro bravo.

(Parte segunda) [4]

[1] Véase CORREAS, *Arte grande*, pág. 271, y *Vocabulario de refranes*, pág. 385;
Tirso, *La venganza de Tamar; Romancero de Barcelona*, descubierto por Milá,
reproducido en su integridad por Foulché-Delbosc en la *Revue Hispanique*.
1913 (vol. XXIX, pág. 181); MILÁ, *Del decasílabo y endecasílabo anapésticos*.
Compárese Esquilache:

> Zagaleja que vas a la fuente,
> déjala y vuelve;
> que si quieres agua que corra,
> de mis ojos corre siempre.

[2] Véase Valdivielso, auto *La amistad en el peligro*.

[3] CORREAS, *Vocabulario de refranes*, pág. 229. Compárese Valdivielso, *La amistad en el peligro* y *Ensaladilla al Santísimo Sacramento*, en el *Romancero espiritual* (pág. 139):

> No venís vos para en cámara, Pedro...

y también aparece con otro dístico (Covarrubias, *Tesoro*, s. v. *Consejo de cámaras*):

> No sois vos para en camara, Pedro,
> sino para en camaranchón.

[4] Esta canción, que según el texto se canta con guitarras, se halla en la
ensaladilla que comienza «Un lencero portugués...», publicada antes que en
el *General* en uno de los *Romancerillos de la Biblioteca Ambrosiana*.
En los *Juegos de Nochesbuenas* (1605), de Alonso de Ledesma:

> Vénte a mí, torillo hosquillo,
> toro bravo, vénte a mí.

Y en el *Tesoro*, de Covarrubias, artículo *hosco*.

Correas cita estos ejemplos típicos, muy semejantes a las modernas muiñeiras:

> — ¿San Juan el verde pasó por aquí?
> — Más ha de un año que nunca le vi.

> Póntela tú, la gorra del fraile,
> póntela tú, que a mí no me cabe.

> Arremanguéme y hice colada;
> no hay tal andar como andar remangada [1].

§ 21. LOS VERSOS ENEASILÁBICOS. — La tercera categoría, los grupos de versos donde el eneasílabo, predominando, da carácter al movimiento rítmico, no es menos interesante. Un solo verso de nueve sílabas basta para imprimir aire a un grupo (como en el cantar burlesco de «Allególe y enamoróle», donde disloca la regularidad de los octosílabos, o en el de «Madrugábalo el aldeana»), a menos que otro ritmo más vigoroso le arrolle, como el de la seguidilla, cuando se define, o, con bastante mayor frecuencia, el de gaita gallega.

El eneasílabo se relaciona estrechamente con los versos de gaita gallega, porque funciona como variante cataléctica del decasílabo: versos de uno y otro tipos andan mezclados, como se observa en ejemplos citados antes («Daba el sol en los álamos, madre...» y «Arrullaba a la palomita...»; compárense luego con «Ventecico murmurador...», «Cuando taño y repico al alba...», y otros más, donde el eneasílabo se impone numéricamente sobre el verso mayor). Se empleó a veces en danzas como la chacona, que gozó grandísima boga:

> Vida bona, vida bona,
> vida, vámonos a Chacona...;

en el cachupino, y, según parece, en la zarabanda y en la españoleta, en la cual dominaban los de gaita gallega [2].

---

[1] *Arte grande*, págs. 288 y 291, y *Vocabulario de refranes*, págs. 70, 88 y 244. Véase Tirso, segunda parte de *La Santa Juana*:

> Que la caperucita de padre
> póntela tú, que a mí no me cabe.

Muy semejante en Quiñones de Benavente, entremés *El mago*.

Para otros ejemplos de versos de gaita gallega, véase CEJADOR, *La verdadera poesía*, vol. I, págs. 105-108, 129-135, 148-160.

[2] Véase COTARELO, Introducción a los *Entremeses, loas*, etc., págs. CCXXXVI, CCXL a CCXLII (donde cita diversas variantes del estribillo de la *chacona*), CCXLIV y CCLXXI. Los versos característicos de la *españoleta* no eran los de ocho sí-

Los eneasílabos abundan mucho. El maestro Alonso López Pinciano los cita en su *Filosofía antigua poética* (1596), llamándolos nonisílabos, y da una muestra:

> Señores de toda la tierra...;

pero indica que se usan en combinación, «en composición», con otros, como ocurre con los decasílabos (de los cuales da ejemplo: «Súbito corre el tímido corzo»). Rengifo no los cita en su *Arte poética* (1592), pero sí el Bachiller José Vicens en las adiciones que hizo al célebre manual en 1703 (capítulos VIII y XLI del nuevo arreglo de la obra). Correas —a pesar del precedente del Pinciano— dice ser el primero que los describe, y quiere someterlos a reglas: «cuatro pies y cuatro acentos; los tres pies de dos sílabas, alta y baja, el uno de tres sílabas, alta la primera más de ordinario, la segunda menos veces» [1]. Las reglas se prestan a duda, porque Correas no dice el orden de los pies. La distribución más común parece ser así: dos cláusulas disilábicas con el acento en la primera sílaba, una cláusula trisilábica con acento en la segunda, y una cláusula disilábica final semejante a las dos primeras. Por ejemplo:

> Cuando | taño y | repico al | alba...
> Nora | buena | vengáis, a- | bril...

Correas cita como ejemplo otra acentuación menos frecuente, en que el pie trisílabo es dactílico o esdrújulo, según su regla (son suyos los acentos artificiales en *Débajó*):

> Déba | jó del | vérde ala | míllo...

Dentro de este patrón podrían clasificarse otros renglones en que faltan uno o dos de los cuatro acentos, o uno de ellos varía de posición; pero el verso se divide siempre en dos partes, la primera de cuatro sílabas y la segunda de cinco:

> Aquel árbol del bel mirar...
> Que non es valedero, non...

labas, como se podría pensar leyendo a Cotarelo, sino los anapésticos que Lope introduce en el auto de *Los cantares:*

> Madre de Dios, y Virgen entera,
> Madre de Dios, divina doncella.

Zamora, en *El juicio de París*, introduce en la españoleta el cantar de las *Naranjicas*, en versos de nueve y diez sílabas (véase luego en este párrafo).

[1] Véanse el cap. VII, *Del metro*, en la *Filosofía antigua poética*, de López Pinciano (reimpresa en Valladolid, 1894), y las págs. 287-288 del *Arte grande*, de Correas.

Dos a dos me los lleva el aire...
En la huerta nace la rosa...
Carillejo, y besarte he...
Allególe y enamoróle...
Madrugábalo el aldeana...
Mi gallejo está so la rama...
Vida, vámonos a la gloria...
Velador que el castillo velas...
Gritos daban a Catalina...
Y a su sombra me recosté...
Arrullaba a la palomita...
La mujer que tal sueño sueña...
Zagaleja del ojo negro...
A la gala del pastorcico...
A quién contaré yo mis quejas...

Pero existen —menos frecuentes— versos que se ajustan a otros tipos. Uno yámbico, que se divide en dos partes (la primera de cinco sílabas, con acento en la cuarta, y la segunda de cuatro) o en cuatro pies: las tres primeras cláusulas disilábicas con acento en la segunda sílaba y el cuarto una cláusula trisilábica, con acento también en la sílaba segunda:

Carillo, ¿quieres bien a Juana?
Como a mi vida y a mi alma...
¡Qué mal vecino es el amor!...

O modificaciones en que los acentos interiores se hacen menos evidentes:

Solíades venir, amor;
agora non venides, non...

Vuestros amores he, señora...
La rosa que no quema el aire...

El otro tipo es anfibráquico, tres cláusulas trisilábicas con acento en el centro:

Al alba venid, buen amigo...
Est'es el camino del cielo...
Aquella morica garrida...
Señores de toda la tierra...

La relación del eneasílabo con el decasílabo —del cual podría considerarse como variante cataléctica— puede observarse en el caso del tipo predominante:

Mi gallejo está so la rama;
su carilleja Menga le llama...

> Velador que el castillo velas,
> vélale bien y mira por ti...

Aquí se ha agregado una sílaba al primer pie del verso para producir el decasílabo compuesto de dos pentasílabos; pero la sílaba puede agregarse también al último pie, para producir el decasílabo anapéstico:

> Zagaleja del ojo negro...
> Zagaleja del ojo rasgado...
>
> Cuando taño y repico al alba,
> no repico ni taño al albor...

El decasílabo anapéstico también se obtiene añadiendo una sílaba al eneasílabo tripartito:

> Aquella morica garrida,
> sus amores dan pena a mi vida...

La difusión de este tipo de verso en la poesía popular, se debió en parte, quizá, a influencia galaicoportuguesa [1]. La poesía culta lo olvida desde el siglo XIV, pero el pueblo, con agudo sentido rítmico, lo conserva en sus cantares y danzas, de donde suelen pasar a las canciones vulgares y a las zarzuelas («Aunque me tachen de grosero...», «En un vagón de *sleeping car*...», «El abanico es gran recurso...», «Trabajando en un cafetal...», «No te puedo querer a ti...», «No te canses, déjame ya...»). A las muestras, populares todas, recogidas en Álvarez Gato, en Gil Vicente, en Castillejo, en Boscán, en Horozco, en Hurtado de Mendoza el Humanista, en Timoneda y en otros, hay que agregar no pocas, anónimas, del *Cancionero musical de los siglos XV y XVI:*

> Mano a mano los dos amores,
> el galán y la galana.
> El galán y la galana,
> ambos vuelven ell agua clara
> mano a mano.

(Núm. 53; probablemente incompleta)

---

[1] En la poesía galaicoportuguesa, los eneasílabos de diversas acentuaciones alternaban libremente (véanse núms. 1, 5, 6 y 9 del *Cancionero* del rey Don Dionís, por ejemplo). En la poesía culta, el eneasílabo se ha tomado a veces de Francia: así, los poetas de versificación irregular en el siglo XIII querían en ocasiones imitar el eneasílabo francés (véase cap. I, §§ 7 y 12). En el siglo XX también ha existido la influencia francesa sobre el eneasílabo castellano.

145

Ell amor que me bien quiere
agora viene.
Ell amor que me bien quería
una empresa me pedía.
Agora viene.

> (Núm. 98; probablemente incompleta;
> música arreglada por Ponce)

De Monzón venía el mozo,
mozo venía de Monzón.
La moza guardaba la viña,
el mozo por ahí venía,
mozo venía de Monzón.

> (Núm. 403; probablemente incompleta)

Aquí viene la flor, señoras,
aquí viene la flor.

> (Núm. 405)

Tristeza, quien a mí vos dió,
no ge lo merecía yo.

> (Estribillo del núm 12, con música
> de Alonso [1])

En uno de los cartapacios salmantinos del siglo XVI encuentra Menéndez Pidal este estribillo, que durante el siglo XVII reaparece en el maestro Correas *(Arte grande)*, en Lope de Vega (auto *La Adúltera perdonada)*, en *La pícara Justina* y en otras obras:

Recordad, mis ojuelos verdes,
que a la mañana dormiredes.

El segundo verso aparece con más frecuencia bajo otra forma:

Que a la mañanica lo dormiredes [2].

---

[1] Gil Vicente da otra variante en la tragicomedia *Fragoa d'amor:*

Tristeza, quien a vos me dió,
pues no fué la culpa mía,
no ge la merecí, no.

[2] Véanse los cartapacios literarios salmantinos en el *Boletín de la Academia Española*, 1914 (vol. I, pág. 304), y Puyol, edición de *La pícara Justina*, (vol. III, pág. 301).

De los *Villancicos y canciones*, coleccionados por Juan Vásquez en 1551:

> Lindos ojos habéis, señora,
> de los que se usaban agora.
> Abaja los ojos, casada.
> no mates a quien te miraba.
> Casada, pechos hermosos,
> abaja tus ojos graciosos.
> No mates a quien te miraba,
> abaja los ojos, casada.

> De los álamos vengo, madre,
> de ver cómo los menea el aire.
> De los álamos de Sevilla
> de ver a mi linda amiga.
> De ver cómo los menea el aire,
> de los álamos vengo, madre [1].

En el *Libro de vihuela*, de Pisador, 1552:

> Si te vas a bañar, Juanica,
> dime a qué baños vas,
> Juanica, cuerpo garrido [2].

> No me llames sega la erva.
> sino morena.

En el tratado *De musica*, de Francisco Salinas, 1577:

> Si le mato, madre, a Juan,
> si le mato matarme han.

---

[1] GALLARDO, *Ensayo*, vol. IV, cols. 923 a 931. «De los álamos vengo, madre» figura como estribillo en un villancico del *Romancero de Barcelona* (véase *Revue Hispanique*, 1913, vol. XXIX, pág. 183) y en una letrilla del *Laberinto amoroso* (en *Romanische Forschungen*, VI), núm. 59.

[2] GALLARDO, *Ensayo*, vol. III, cols. 1.235 y 1.237. Véase *Cancionero de Upsala*, núm. 31 (así aparece también en uno de los *Cancionerillos de Praga*, cuyas piezas raras reimprimió Foulché-Delbosc en su *Revue Hispanique*, 1924):

> Si te vas a bañar, Juanica,
> dime a qué baños vas.

Falta el tercer verso, que en cambio se encuentra en la vieja canción paralelística asturiana (véase el cap. II, § 20):

> ¡Ay Xuana, cuerpo garrido!

Véase CAROLINA MICHAËLIS DE VASCONCELLOS, *Cancioneiro da Ajuda*, vol. II, págs. 922, 923, 931 y 932, y *Notulas sobre cantares e vilhancicos*, en la *Revista de Filología Española*, 1918.

Aunque soy morenica y prieta,
a mí qué se me da;
que amor tengo que me servirá.

(Variantes en Correas, *Arte grande*, pág. 280,
y en las *Séguedilles anciennes*)

¡Ay, amor, cómo sois puntoso!
La darga dandeta.

Segador, tírate afuera,
deja entrar la espigaderuela.

Mal haya quien a vos casó,
la de Pedro Borreguero [o Vaquero].

¿Si jugastes anoche, amore?
Non, señora, none.

Amigo, si me bien queredes...

De las honduras llamo a ti;
óyeme, señor mío.

Si mis amores no me valen,
triste que yo moriré.

Cata el lobo do va, Juanica,
cata el lobo do va [1].

En el manuscrito de *Tonos castellanos*, del siglo XVI, que Gallardo extractó, aparecen estas canciones:

Arrojóme las naranjicas
con las ramas del blanco azahar,
arrojómelas y arrojéselas
y volviómelas a arrojar [2].

---

[1] *De musica*, págs. 306, 319, 321, 325, 326, 327, 343, 344, 350, 386, 416, 422 y 435. Hay que agregar «¿Qué me queréis, el caballero?» (véase la nota final a este párrafo); «¿A quién contaré yo mis quexas?» (véase cap. III, §3); «Aquella morica garrida...» (véase cap. III, § 20); «Solíades venir, amor» (véase cap. II, § 29); «¡Qué mal vecino es el amor!...» (véase cap. III, § 3). Sobre «Cata el lobo do va», véase la parodia que según el P. Diego de Rosales (*Historia de Chile*, cap. XVIII) se aplicó a Valdivia al escaparse al Perú; además, coplas en el ms. 3.168 de la Biblioteca Nacional de Madrid.

[2] Cantar popularísimo, transcrito o imitado varias veces por Lope (véase el romance «A las bodas venturosas...», escrito en Valencia en 1599, *Boletín de la Academia Española*, 1916, página 553; el auto sacramental *Las bodas entre el alma y el amor divino*, escrito en 1599 y publicado en *El peregrino en su patria;* la comedia *El bobo del colegio);* por Valdivielso en la *Ensaladilla de Navidad* («Porque está parida la reina») y en la del *Retablo (Romancero espiritual)*, luego por todo el teatro (véase Tirso, acto primero de *Antona García)* hasta llegar al siglo XVIII, con Antonio de Zamora, *El juicio de Paris* (1716), y Diego de Torres Villarroel, villancico *La gaita zamorana.*

Ventecico murmurador
que lo gozas y andas todo,
haz el són con las hojas del olmo,
que se duerme mi lindo amor [1].

Cuando taño y repico al alba
no repico ni taño al albor,
sino taño y repico
a que salga mi lindo amor.

Bailad en la fiesta, zagalas,
pues la gaita os hace el són,
que yo os mando unas castañuelas
guarnecidas con su cordón [2].

Al ladrón, al ladrón, señores,
tengan aquese ladrón,
que me lleva la vida y el alma
y me deja sin corazón [3].

Aún hay muchos más ejemplos en el siglo XVI, pues los versos eneasílabos fueron muy populares entonces:

Morenica me llaman, madre,
desde el día que yo nací.
Al galán que me ronda la puerta
blanca y rubia le parecí [4].

[1] «Ventecico murmurador» se halla también en el *Romancero de Barcelona* (véase *Revue Hispanique*, vol. XXIX, pág. 189); en el *Romancero espiritual* (pág. 93 de la edición de 1880) y el auto *El peregrino*, de Valdivielso, y en el *Romancero general*, tomo II.

[2] Véase LEDESMA, *Juegos de Nochesbuenas* («Bailad en esta ocasión...»), y poesías atribuídas a Góngora («Bailad en el corro, mozuelas...»).

[3] GALLARDO, *Ensayo*, vol. I, cols. 1.194 a 1.203. Véase la parodia de la última copla en Quiñones de Benavente, entremés de *Don Gaiferos:*

Aprisa, aprisa, muchachas,
tened, no se vaya, vaya el ladrón,
que me lleva la vida y el alma
y me deja sin corazón.

[4] *Romancero de Barcelona.* Mientras la poesía culta del siglo XVI, secuaz de la moda de Italia, hacía rubias a las demás y les atribuía ojos azules, la poesía popular hacía el elogio o la defensa de las morenas, ofreciendo la excusa del sol, como en el *Cantar de los Cantares*. Véanse, en las páginas anteriores: «No me llames sega la erva», y «Aunque soy morenica y prieta»; en el § 22: «Morenica m'era yo»; en el § 23: «Morenica, no deprecies la color»; en Ledesma: «Duelos me hicieron negra, | que yo blanca me era»; en el *Laberinto amoroso* (1618): «Con el aire de la sierra | híceme morena».

Los ojos verdes pueden ser don de belleza, como en «Recordad, mis ojuelos verdes», o poca fortuna, como en el cantar portugués (véase Camoëns):

Sois formosa, e tudo tendes,
senão que tendes os olhos verdes.

Casada serrana,
¿dónde bueno tan de mañana?

Salteóme la serrana
juntico al pie de la cabaña [1].

Garridica soy en el yermo
¿y para qué? [2].

Cerraré con este *chiste* que encontré en el cancionero manuscrito del siglo XVI, que lleva el núm. 5.593, en la Biblioteca Nacional de Madrid:

Adurmióseme mi lindo amor
siendo del sueño vencido,
y quedóseme adormecido
debajo de un cardo corredor [3].

---

[1] En Sebastián de Horozco, Vélez de Guevara, Lope y Valdivielso. Véase la nota sobre «Paséisme ahora...», § 20 del cap. III. Además, MENÉNDEZ PIDAL, *La primitiva poesía lírica española*, págs. 283-288.

[2] Véase MENÉNDEZ PIDAL, *La primitiva poesía lírica española*, pág. 294.

[3] Para darse cuenta de la abundancia del verso eneasílabo, basta recorrer las composiciones anónimas en cualquiera de los cancioneros. En el *Cancionero Musical* podrían anotarse aún, en el índice de las obras que faltan: «Que los amores e pastores», «Si de mí no os queréis servir» y «Una vejezuela del barrio»; y luego el núm. 114:

Queredme bien, caballero,
casada soy, aunque no quiero...

núm. 131 (reaparece en SALINAS, *De musica*, pág. 235, y en poesías de Juan Fernández de Heredia, Valencia, 1562):

¿Qué me queréis, caballero?
Casada soy, marido tengo...

núm. 159:

No he ventura, ¡mezquino yo!
no he ventura en amores, no...

núm. 191:

No desmayes, corazón,
que tus amores aquí son...

núm. 433:

Calabaza,
no sé, buen amor, que te faza.

núms. 410 y 411: «A la sombra de mis cabellos», que en otras versiones dice: «A la sombra» (GALLARDO, *Ensayo*, vol. I, col. 298).

O véanse los índices de primeros versos, como el de la *Recopilación* de Juan Vásquez en 1560 (GALLARDO, *Ensayo*, vol. IV, columnas 930 y 931), o el del

§ 22. VERSOS LIBRES: LOS BREVES. — Bajo este nombre, que en otro tiempo se usó para designar los endecasílabos sin rima, llamados también blancos o sueltos *(sciolti)*, y que ahora se aplica a la versificación irregular procedente de los simbolistas franceses comprendo la masa de versificación informe que no obedece a principios rítmicos claramente discernibles, o que mezcla ritmos diversos. Así ocurre con muestras, dadas antes, que proceden de Gil Vicente, Castillejo, Horozco, y de otras fuentes, como el cantar anónimo de «Quien amores tiene...», el cual, en la forma recogida por Vásquez, mezcla ritmos cortos y ritmos largos.

Puede esta masa informe, sin embargo, dividirse en dos grandes grupos: los versos breves y los versos largos; la mezcla de ambos no es muy frecuente. Entre los breves, he aquí algunos del *Cancionero musical:*

> En Ávila, mis ojos,
> dentro en Ávila.
> En Ávila del río
> mataron a mi amigo,
> dentro en Ávila.

> (Núm. 143; Barbieri cree que se relaciona con él el que sigue, 144, con sólo un verso: «Ojos, mis ojos, tan garridos ojos»)

pliego que menciona SALVÁ, *Catálogo de la biblioteca,* núm. 13), impreso hacia 1520, donde se hallan estos eneasílabos iniciales:

> Olvidar quiero mis amores...
> Dícenme que el amor no fiere...
> La dama que no mata o prende...
> Pues que no me queréis amar...
> A mi puerta mana una fonte...
> Si los pastores han amores...
> Descendid al valle la niña...

El último se halla, como octosílabo («Desciende al valle, la niña»), en el *Cancionero Musical* (núm. 416) y en Francisco de Ocaña («Acudí al valle, la niña»). O véanse el cancionero del siglo XVI, ms. 3.913 de la Biblioteca Nacional de Madrid:

> Peinadita traigo mi greña,
> peinadita la traigo y buena...

> No le den tormento a la niña,
> que ella dirá la verdad...

El último aparece también en la *Primavera y flor de los mejores romances,* Madrid, 1621.

O el *Cancionero de Évora* (Lisboa, 1875), núm. 25:

> Dí, zagala: ¿qué harás
> cuando vieres que soy partido?

Véanse otros ejemplos en CEJADOR, *La verdadera poesía,* vol. I, págs. 101-105, 123-129, 148-157, 181-189, 247-269; vol. IV, páginas 13, 18, 59, 76-83, 166, 199 y 307.

Allá se me ponga el sol
donde tengo el amor.
Allá se me pusiese
do mis amores viese,
antes que me muriese
con este dolor.
Allá se me aballase
do mi amor topase,
antes que me finase
con este rencor.

(Núm. 259; zéjel paralelístico)

Pámpano verde,
racimo albar;
¿quién vido dueñas
a tal hora andar?
Encinueco entre ellas,
entre las doncellas...

(Núm. 399; música de Torre; incompleta)

No me le digáis mal,
madre, a Fray Antón,
no me le digáis mal,
que le tengo en devoción.

(Núm. 451; música de Alonso de Alba) [1]

La muestra más singular de letra para baile cantado es la que
lleva el núm. 386; se ve que son indicaciones de movimientos de
danza, las cuales llegaron a cantarse, y en medio de ellas cruza
un trozo de verdadera canción:

Ora baila tú.
— Mas baila tú.
— Mas tú.
— Ya casaba el colmenero,
casaba su fija.
— Mas baila tú.
— Ora baila tú.

En los *Villancicos y canciones*, de Vásquez:

Amor falso, Amor falso,
pusístem'en cuidado,
y agora fallecístemé.

---

[1] En Salinas, *De musica*, pág. 309:

No me digáis, madre, mal del padre Fray Antón,
porque es mi enamorado y yo téngole en devoción.

Amor falso,
falso y portugués,
cuanto me dijiste
todo fué al revés.
Pusístem'en cuidado
y agora fallecístemé [1].

— Cobarde caballero,
¿de quién habedes miedo?
¿De quién habedes miedo
durmiendo conmigo?
— De vos, mi señora,
que tenéis otro amigo.
— Cobarde caballero,
¿de quién habedes miedo? [2]

En su *Recopilación*, de 1559, uno que otro verso largo se introduce entre los cortos:

Morenica m'era yo;
dicen que sí, dicen que no.
Otros que por mí mueren
dicen que no.
Morenica m'era yo;
dicen que sí, dicen que no.
Que yo, mi madre, yo,
que la flor de la villa m'era yo.
Íbame yo, mi madre,
y todos me decían: ¡garrida!
M'era yo.
Que la flor de la villa m'era yo [3].

En los *Tres libros de música*, de Alonso Mudarra, 1546:

Isabel, Isabel,
perdiste la tu faja:

---

[1] Gallardo, *Ensayo*, vol. IV, col. 922. Véase § 5 de este capítulo, nota sobre la alteración del acento de las palabras en el verso.

[2] Aparece también en Fuenllana.

[3] Gallardo, *Ensayo*, vol. IV, cols. 927-928.

«...Hacia 1495... Pinar manda a una dama de la Reina Católica que cante:

yo, madre, yo;
que la flor de la villa me so»,

dice Menéndez Pidal en *La primitiva poesía lírica española*, pág. 334.

> véla por do va,
> nadando por el agua.
> ¡Isabel atán garrida!

En el *Cancionero de Upsala*, 1557, se halla este cantar, cuyas variantes reaparecen en Lope de Vega, en Ledesma, en Valdivielso y en Vélez de Guevara:

> Ay luna, que reluzes,
> toda la noche me alumbres.
> Ay luna, tan bella,
> alúmbresme a la sierra,
> por do vaya y venga.
> Ay luna, que reluzes,
> toda la noche me alumbres [1].

Canción curiosa «la que cantaban los soldados del campo real [en el Perú] en la campaña contra el rebelde Francisco Hernández Girón por los años 1553-1554, aludiendo al Dr. Fr. Hierónimo de Loaysa, arzobispo de Lima, y al Licenciado Hernando de Santillán, oidor de aquella Audiencia...»:

> El uno jugar y el otro dormir,
> ¡oh, qué gentil!
> No comer y apercibir,
> ¡oh, qué gentil!
> El uno duerme y el otro juega:
> así va la guerra [2].

§ 23. VERSOS LIBRES: LOS LARGOS. — Sería posible multiplicar los ejemplos de esquemas libres, que en el siglo XVI abundan más, por ejemplo, que la seguidilla. Pero son menos, aun siendo muchos, los ejemplos de versos largos que los de versos cortos; los largos eran fácilmente atraídos hacia los ritmos de gaita gallega, mientras que los cortos apenas si encontraban la atracción, todavía débil, de la seguidilla.

En versificación extremadamente irregular está la composición núm. 435 del *Cancionero musical de los siglos XV y XVI* (coplas en zéjel):

> De aquel fraire flaco y cetrino,
> guardáos, dueñas, dél, que es un malino.
> No deja moza ni casada,
> beata, monja encerrada,

---

[1] Alonso de Ledesma, *Juegos de Nochesbuenas a lo divino*, 1605 (núm. 419 del *Romancero y cancionero sagrados*, vol. XXXV de la Biblioteca de Rivadeneyra); Valdivielso, ensaladilla al Santísimo Sacramento (versión interesante); Luis Vélez de Guevara, acto segundo de *La luna de la sierra;* ensaladilla «Quien madruga Dios le ayuda», en el *Romancero general*, segunda parte, 1605 (versión muy semejante a la de Valdivielso).

[2] MENÉNDEZ Y PELAYO, *Historia de la poesía hispanoamericana*, Madrid, 1911-1913, tomo II, pág. 138.

que dél no ha sido tentada,
y éste es su oficio de contino.
De vidas ajenas inquisidor,
de muchos famosos disfamador,
pues dí, de cizañas predicador,
¿siguió San Francisco este camino?...

Entre todas estas canciones de versificación libre, ninguna gozó de la extraordinaria popularidad que una en versos próximos al alejandrino, recogida por Anríquez de Valderrábano, Pisador, Fuenllana, Vásquez y el *Cancionero de Upsala:*

¿Y con qué la lavaré, la flor de mi cara,
y con qué la lavaré, que vivo mal penada?
Lávanse las mozas con agua de limones,
lavarm'e yo cuitada con ansias y dolores [1].

Al alejandrino se acerca también este delicado suspiro, que recoge Pisador:

Aquellas sierras, madre, altas son de subir;
corrían los caños, daban en el toronjil.
Madre, aquellas sierras llenas son de flores:
encima de ellas tengo mis amores [2].

---

[1] GALLARDO, *Ensayo*, vol. III, col. 1.236, y vol. IV, col. 931; Mitjana, nota a la composición núm. 29 del *Cancionero de Upsala;* CAROLINA MICHAËLIS DE VASCONCELLOS, *Notulas sobre cantares e vilhancicos.* Compárese «Ardé, corazón, ardé...», en el *Cancionero Musical* (núm. 77), en la *Silva de Sirenas,* de Valderrábano (fol. 26), en *El Delfín,* de Narváez, y en GALLARDO, *Ensayo*, vol. I, col. 151, glosa del Conde de Salinas:

Quebrántanse las peñas
con picos y azadones;
quebrántase mi corazón
con penas y dolores.

[2] GALLARDO, *Ensayo*, vol. III, col. 1.236. Da otra versión Fray Pedro de Padilla (*Tesoro de varias poesías*, Madrid, 1580):

La sierra es alta
y áspera de subir;
los caños corren agua
y dan en el toronjil.
Madre, la mi madre,
del cuerpo atán garrido,
por aquella sierra
en su lomo erguido
iba una mañana
el mi lindo amigo;
lláméle con mi toca
y con mis dedos cinco:
los caños corren agua
y dan en el toronjil.

155

Y este otro, que recoge Vásquez (1559):

> ¿Agora que sé de amor me metéis monja?
> ¡Ay Dios, qué grave cosa!
> Agora que sé de amor de caballero,
> agora me metéis monja en el monasterio.
> ¡Ay Dios, qué grave cosa! [1].

Si de esos tres podría suponerse que hay derecho a dividirlos en hemistiquios y reducirlos a versos cortos, quedan otros donde los versos no parecen fácilmente divisibles, como las *endechas de Canarias* que trae Pisador («Para ques, dama, tanto quereros») [2] y el cantar alusivo a la gaita, aunque no lleva su metro favorito, recogido por el manuscrito de *Tonos castellanos*, y luego imitado por Lope en *Los pastores de Belén* (libro III) y probablemente por Góngora (composición que se le atribuye):

> Tenga yo salud,
> qué comer, quietud,
> y dineros que gastar,
> y ándase la gaita
> por el lugar [3].

O en Vásquez, 1551:

> Perdida traigo la color;
> todos me dicen que lo he de amor.
> Viniendo de la romería
> encontré a mi buen amor.
> Pidiérame tres besicos,
> luego perdí mi color.
>
> Dicen a mí que lo he de amor.
> Perdida traigo la color,
> todos dicen que lo he de amor [4].

O en *El Cortesano*, de Luis Milán, el trozo que da como improvisación de una dama:

---

[1] GALLARDO, *Ensayo*, vol. IV, col. 928.

[2] Véase la nota final del § 9, cap. III.

[3] GALLARDO, *Ensayo*, vol. I, col. 1.197. Música de Francisco Gutiérrez. La composición sigue, haciéndonos pensar que aquellos irregulares versos se cantaban al són de la gaita:

[4] GALLARDO, *Ensayo*, vol. IV, col. 924.

> Para cuando haga el són
> la gaita murmuradora...

Quiñones de Benavente, en el entremés *La visita de la cárcel*, introduce el último verso del cantar.

No le tomara,
sino como a marido le presentara,
y en presentalle como servidor
e tomo con más amor [1].

O éste del *Cancionero de Upsala* (núm. 50) y de la *Recopilación* de Vásquez en 1560:

Dizen a mí que los amores he:
con ellos me vea si tal pensé.
Dizen a mí por la villa
que traygo los amores en la cinta;
dizen a mí que los amores he:
con ellos me vea si tal pensé [2].

O éste del cancionero manuscrito (núm. 19.661) de la Biblioteca Nacional:

Morenica, no desprecies la color,
que la tuya es la mejor [3].

Casos curiosos de versificación irregular son los tercetos monorrimos del *Cancionero de Évora* (Lisboa, 1875), que fluctúan alrededor del endecasílabo:

Aunque me veáis en tierra ajena,
allá en el cielo tengo una prenda;
no la olvidaré hasta que muera.

---

[1] Véase, además, en *El Cortesano*, de Milán, edición de 1872, las págs. 8, 12, 16, 37 , 52, 72, 74, 85, 148, 154, 178, 180, 207, 249, 253, 279, 307, 342, 361, 366.

[2] GALLARDO, *Ensayo*, vol. IV, col. 930.

[3] Otra versión en Montidea *(Billete de amor):*

No desprecies, morenica,
tu color tan morena,
que ésa es la color buena.

Sobre el color moreno, véanse las págs. 100, 112, 116, 131, 136, 140, 141, 148, 149, 153, 157, 164, 172, 183, 225 y 227.

Agréguese este cantar que recoge Daza, en estribillo y zéjel:

Gritos daba la morenica
so el olivar,
que las ramas hace temblar.
La niña, cuerpo garrido,
morenica, cuerpo garrido,
lloraba su muerto amigo
so el olivar,
que las ramas hace temblar.

Y en CORREAS, *Arte grande*, pág. 280, esta endecha (¿o seguidilla?):

Aunque soy morena,
blanca yo nací;
a guardar ganado
mi color perdí.

Extranjero soy, no lo quiero negar;
mas de mis amores haré un mar:
por ellos a mi tierra iré aportar...

(Núm. 58)

Muéstrame quien mi alma tanto quería
allá donde reposa al mediodía
en su eterna gloria e alegría...

(Núm. 59)

§ 24. LAS ESTROFAS. — Las composiciones en versificación irregular no son, por lo común, largas. Cuando, además del estribillo, son irregulares las coplas, toman la forma usual de zéjeles y villancicos: así, en el cantar del *Polvico*, de Cervantes, cuyas estrofas tienen siete versos; compárense con el villancico «Más vale trocar...», de Encina. O bien asumen otra forma más breve, con la peculiaridad de que en la *repetición* se cambia a menudo el orden de los versos del estribillo: así en «No me habléis, conde...», «Ojos morenos...», «Caballero, queráisme dejar...», «Abaja los ojos, casada...», y «De los álamos vengo, madre...»

Predomina la isometría de las estrofas: así, en Fray Ambrosio Montesino, Gil Vicente y demás; igualmente en las composiciones en seguidillas (véanse las de *Los Comendadores de Córdoba*, *Pero González* y *Rodrigo Martínez*). La isometría existe, sobre todo, en cuanto a la distribución de las rimas; pero los versos de igual medida no se repiten con exactitud en el lugar correspondiente de cada estrofa, y los poetas se contentan con la medida aproximada: así, en Gil Vicente se corresponden versos como «Estánse dos hermanas» y «Namorado se había dellas»; en Castillejo, «Hacíame del ojo» y «Asíame de la manga». La asimetría de las estrofas sí se halla después, en el siglo XVII.

Finalmente, del cantar paralelístico hay dos formas principales: una, la tradicional galaicoportuguesa, del cossante del árbol de amor y la canción «Al alba venid, buen amigo...», en que cada estrofa se duplica mediante el cambio de las palabras finales de los versos (tales, *amigo, amado; amaba, quería; mirar, veer*), y luego viene el encadenamiento, comenzando la tercera estrofa con el segundo verso de la primera, al cual se añade otro enteramente nuevo; otra forma, más elemental, en que hay duplicación y no hay encadenamiento.

De la primera se hallan probablemente en el *Cancionero musical* los últimos ejemplos escritos por poetas castellanos (puesto que Gil Vicente es portugués). Están en versos regulares, silábicos, y son el núm. 245:

Por vos mal me viene,
niña, y atendedme...

y el núm. 17, según la reconstrucción de Carolina Michaëlis de Vasconcellos:

Tres morillas me enamoran
en Jaén... [1].

De la segunda hay ejemplos en el *Cancionero musical* (núms. 259 y 400) y en Gil Vicente: así, la canción en alabanza de la Virgen María, donde la estrofa se repite tres veces. El cantar del *Polvico* en Cervantes, y el de bodas en Castillejo, hay que clasificarlos dentro del tipo simple.

Pero también se encuentra el tipo encadenado, sin duplicación paralelística, en el *Cancionero musical;* por ejemplo, núm. 423:

Por beber, comadre,
por beber...,

y en Gil Vicente: «En la huerta nace la rosa...» y otras canciones [2].

§ 25. Resumen. — Durante el período que se extiende desde el reinado de los Reyes Católicos hasta la ascensión de Felipe III al trono, en 1598, la poesía de versificación acentual o meramente libre alcanzó gran desarrollo permaneciendo anónima. Es sorprendente la fecundidad que ostentó, cultivada por las manos del pueblo y del vulgo, sin ayuda importante del mundo cortesano. Los tipos de esta versificación, en el siglo xvi, son en esencia los mismos de que se habían encontrado escasas muestras antes de los Reyes Católicos.

Entre tanto, los poetas cultos se aproximan a ella, poco a poco, con prudencia, tal vez con desdén aristocrático, excepto en casos como el del padre del teatro portugués. Al terminar el siglo xvi, los elementos populares, cuya ascensión hacia las letras cortesanas, desde la época de los Reyes Católicos, había sido gradual, pero constante, acaban por penetrar de lleno en el drama, en la poesía lírica, en la novela. Lope es el gran maestro de este movimiento en lo que atañe a la versificación, entre otras cosas. Coetáneos suyos, Cervantes, Góngora, los dramaturgos de Valencia, son quienes mejor contribuyen a la innovación. El carácter renacentista del siglo de Carlos V va cediendo cada vez más ante el reflujo de tendencias nativas que dan su peculiar sabor al siglo xvii en España.

---

[1] *Cancionero da Ajuda*, vol. II, pág. 935. Sobre la música de este cantar, véase Julián Ribera, *La música de las Cantigas*.

[2] Véase *Cancioneiro da Ajuda*, vol. II, págs. 920, 923, 926, 928, 930 y 931.

EL APOGEO DE LOS VERSOS IRREGULARES EN LA POESÍA CULTA

(1600-1675)

§ 1. Las fuentes: importancia de las literarias. — Al recorrer el siglo xvi, la revisión de los fragmentarios materiales de versificación irregular que recogen o escriben los poetas cultos es la mejor introducción hacia el caudal copioso que brinda la poesía anónima; al estudiar el siglo xvii, el proceso debe invertirse. La poesía anónima no presenta entonces la espontánea riqueza de la centuria anterior, o bien queda medio ahogada bajo la inundación de la poesía culta, que adopta los procedimientos populares, y los estribillos de sabor folk-lórico proceden, las más veces, de épocas anteriores. De 1600 en adelante, las recopilaciones de carácter popular, o más bien las vulgares, que son las que abundan, acogen muchas obras de poetas cortesanos y pierden su tipo antiguo; así se advierte en los florilegios impresos: las nuevas ediciones del *Romancero general;* el *Laberinto amoroso,* 1618; la *Primavera y flor de romances,* primera y segunda partes, 1621 y 1629; las *Maravillas del Parnaso,* Lisboa, 1637, reimpresas en Barcelona, 1640; posteriormente otros, como la *Lira poética,* citada en las ediciones de Vicens al *Arte* de Rengifo. Así se advierte, en fin, en las grandes colecciones manuscritas de poesía y de música que se custodian en la Biblioteca Nacional de Madrid. De esas y de otras semejantes proceden el *Romancero de Barcelona,* descubierto por Milá; el *Cancionero musical y poético del siglo XVII,* recogido por Claudio de la Sablonara y publicado por Jesús Aroca; las *Seguidillas antiguas,* publicadas por Foulché-Delbosc; las *Poesías de antaño,* publicadas por Antonio Guzmán e Higueros, y extractos diversos de Gallardo. Junto a esas fuentes anónimas, no muy prolíficas, la poesía culta asombra por la abundancia de versificación irregular de tendencia acentual:

Lope, Tirso, Valdivielso, Góngora, Quiñones de Benavente, Calderón ofrecen tesoros de poesía vaciada en moldes musicales, fuera de la regularidad silábica [1].

A) LOS TIPOS DE VERSIFICACIÓN EN LA POESÍA
CULTA Y EN LA POPULAR Y VULGAR

§ 2. EL ESPLENDOR DE LA SEGUIDILLA. — Desde 1600, la seguidilla crece prodigiosamente en popularidad, que conserva hasta hoy, especialmente entre el pueblo. Hasta el apogeo de Lope, y aun puede decirse que hasta el de Calderón, continúa presentándose con todas sus viejas peculiaridades. Unas veces, la fluctuación dentro de límites muy vagos:

> No cantéis, el ruiseñor,
> tan de mañana,
> que despertaréis a quien duerme
> y amores ama [2].

---

[1] Sobre el *Romancero general*, véase la nota final del § 3 del cap. II. Hay muchas reproducciones de él (especialmente de las reimpresiones) en el *Romancero* de Durán, vols. X y XVI de la Biblioteca de Rivadeneyra. También aprovechó esta y otras colecciones Quintana en su colección de *Poesías selectas castellanas...*, Madrid, 1807, reimpresa después bajo el nombre de *Tesoro del Parnaso español*.

El *Laberinto amoroso* fué reimpreso por Vollmöller en las *Romanische Forschungen*, vol. VI, 1891.

Durán reproduce en su *Romancero* muchas composiciones de la *Primavera y flor de romances* y de las *Maravillas del Parnaso*, edición de 1640; la edición de 1637 ha sido reimpresa por la Sociedad Hispánica, Nueva York, 1902.

La *Lira poética* no se menciona en el *Arte* de Rengifo, en la edición primitiva de 1592, ni en las adiciones de 1644, sino en las adiciones de José Vicens, 1703; he consultado la reimpresión de Barcelona, 1759. Pudiera ser la obra que menciona Gallardo, *Ensayo*, vol. IV, col. 441.

Del *Romancero de Barcelona* dió noticia MILÁ en el *Jahrbuch für romanische und englische Literatur*, de Berlín, 1861, vol. III, pág. 172. Foulché-Delbosc lo reprodujo íntegro en su *Revue Hispanique*, 1913, vol. XXIX.

El *Cancionero musical y poético del siglo XVII*, de Sablonara, apareció en el *Boletín de la Academia Española*, 1916 a 1918. Véanse, sobre él, los *Comentarios y apostillas*, de MITJANA, en la *Revista de Filología Española*, 1919.

Las *Séguedilles anciennes* de Foulché-Delbosc están en la *Revue Hispanique*, 1901, vol. VIII; las *Poesías de antaño*, en 1914, vol. XXXI.

Para extractos en el *Ensayo*, de Gallardo, véase vol. I, columnas 991 a 995 y 1.027 a 1.059.

Entre los cancioneros manuscritos que consulté en la Biblioteca Nacional de Madrid, mencionaré los núms. 3.168, 3.912, 3.913, 3.915, 4.051, 4.123 (antes M. 360), 5.168, 5.593 y 19.661. De las «Tonadillas y letrillas puestas en música», la caja 12.967, núms. 1 a 64.

[2] CORREAS, *Arte grande de la lengua castellana*, pág. 281. Recordaré nuevamente la importancia del estudio de HANSSEN, *La seguidilla*.

Toda va de verde
la mi galera,
toda va de verde
de dentro a fuera [1].

¡Cómo retumban las palas
de los remeros
en las claras aguas
del sacro Tejo! [2].

¿Qué quiere amor
coronado de flores?
No, no, no las abrase,
ya que las coge [3].

A pescar salió la niña
tendiendo redes
y en lugar de peces
las almas prende.

(El burlador de Sevilla).

Subiera Morales
en el su caballo,
la espuela de melcocha
y el freno de esparto.

(Calderón, El alcalde de sí mismo, acto I).

Lloraba la casada por su marido
y agora le pesa porque es venido.
Lloraba la casada por su velado
y agora le pesa de que es llegado [4].

Otras veces, el empleo de versos agudos, tratados como equivalentes de los llanos que tienen una sílaba métrica menos (ley de Mussafia), resultando de ahí la unificación de los versos y la confusión con la endecha o la aproximación a ella:

[1] CORREAS, *Arte grande.*
[2] *Laberinto amoroso*, núm. 23. —Véanse Lope de Vega, *Las flores de Don Juan*, y Alonso de Ledesma, *Al Nacimiento*, en los *Juegos de Nochesbuenas a lo divino:*

> ¡Cómo retumban los remos,
> madre, en el agua,
> con el fresco viento
> de la mañana!

Véase, además, la parodia en el *Entremés del Avantal*, de Quiñones de Benavente.

[3] Biblioteca Nacional de Madrid, caja 12.967, núm. 6, canción con música de Juan Hidalgo.
[4] CORREAS, *Vocabulario de refranes*, pág. 486. Duplicación paralelística.

A la mal casada
le dé Dios placer,
que la bien casada
no lo ha menester [1].

Aunque soy morena,
blanca yo nací:
a guardar ganado
mi color perdí [2].

Aunque el Carro se vuelva
y quiera amanecer,
yo del otro lado
me pienso volver [3].

Otras, el empleo de los agudos como propiamente tales, según las reglas de la métrica silábica moderna:

Mal haya la torre,
fuera de la cruz,
que me quita la vista
de mi andaluz [4].

Otras, en fin, la forma fluctuante se mezcla con la acentuación aguda:

¡Ay, que me muero de zelos
de aquel andaluz!
Háganme si muriere
la mortaja azul [5].

---

[1] *Séguedilles anciennes*, núm. 24.

[2] CORREAS, *Arte grande*, pág. 280. Y véase § 21 del cap. III, nota sobre «Morenica me llaman, madre...»

[3] Estribillo de Letrilla, manuscrito 3.913 de la Biblioteca Nacional de Madrid. Véanse *Poesías de antaño*, ed. Guzmán e Higueros, y GALLARDO, *Ensayo*, vol. I, col. 1.038. Además, manuscrito 3.700.

[4] *Séguedilles anciennes*, núm. 1. Véase la núm. 2. Y *La copla*, de RODRÍGUEZ MARÍN.

[5] *Cancionero musical y poético del siglo XVII*, de Sablonara, núm. 47. Parodiada por Lope (o, según él, por una de sus hijas), en carta al Duque de Sessa;

¡Ay, que al Duque le pido
aceite andaluz!
¡Ay, pues no me le envía,
cenaré sin luz!

Y Góngora la adopta y la continúa en una admirable composición (1620), «para D.ª María Hurtado, en ausencia de D. Gabriel Zapata, su marido»; la primera mitad es en seguidillas:

Mátanme los celos de aquel andaluz;
háganme, si muriere, la mortaja azul.

Las flores del romero,
niña Isabel,
hoy son flores azules,
mañana serán miel [1].

Generalmente, la seguidilla tiene sólo cuatro versos; abunda ya el paradigma moderno (7-5-7-5) junto con la otra forma usual entonces (6-5-7-5):

Manojitos de hinojo
coge la niña
y sus ojos manojos
de flechas tiran.

Vienen de Sanlúcar,
rompiendo el agua
a la Torre del Oro
barcos de plata.

Frescos airecitos
del prado ameno,
si abrasáis el alma,
no heléis el cuerpo [2].

Vengo de la guerra,
niña, por verte;
hállote casadita,
quiero volverme [3].

Perdí la esperanza de ver mi ausente:
háganme, si muriere, la mortaja verde.

Madre, sin ser monja, soy ya descalza,
pues me tiene la ausencia sin mi Zapata.

La mitad del alma me lleva la mar:
volved, galeritas, por la otra mitad...

[1] Este cantar podría parecer original de Góngora y va al frente de su romancillo que continúa «Celosa estás, la niña» (1608). De Góngora lo debieron de tomar —como tantos otros cantares— Calderón en *El alcalde de Zalamea* (acto III) y Lope para imitarlo en *Los pastores de Belén*, libro III:

Las pajas del pesebre,
niño de Belén,
hoy son flores y rosas,
mañana serán hiel.

Sin embargo, Gonzalo Correas lo da como popular *(Vocabulario*, pág. 153, y *Arte grande*, pág. 443) y dice haberlo oído en Salamanca:

La flor del romero,
niña Isabel,
hoy es flor azul
y mañana será miel.

[2] Manuscrito 3.913.
[3] *Los amantes de Teruel*, atribuída a Tirso. Variante, como endecha, en Sebastián de Horozco, *Cancionero*, pág. 27; otra, como seguidilla, en Correas, *Vocabulario de refranes*, pág. 437.

Ya se van haciendo raras las de solos tres versos, como una que Lope adapta en *Los pastores de Belén:*

> Callad un poco,
> que me matan llorando
> tan dulces ojos.

Tampoco abundan especialmente las de siete versos, frecuentísimas en nuestros días; pero se hallan, por ejemplo, en Tirso *(Tanto es lo de más como lo de menos)*, en Quiñones de Benavente (entremeses de *El guardainfante*, primera y segunda partes, y *El juego del hombre)* y en D. Juan Ruiz de Alarcón, único trozo de versificación irregular que se descubre en toda su obra:

> Venta de Viveros,
> dichoso sitio,
> si es cristiano el ventero
> y es moro el vino.
> Sitio dichoso,
> si el ventero es cristiano
> y el vino es moro.

(Acto II de Las paredes oyen) [1].

Existen otras de cinco versos:

> Óyeme tu retrato,
> niña Isabela,
> salvo ser justo,
> salvo ser propio,
> salvo que hiela [2].

Otras con *eco*, ya sea intercalado, ya sea al final de la copla, en Quiñones de Benavente:

> Como somos muchachas
> somos traviesas,
> y por eso nos guardan, *ardan*,
> todas las viejas.

> No pretendo por lindo
> ni por discreto,

---

[1] El tercer verso de la seguidilla de Alarcón se imprime generalmente «si el ventero es cristiano»; pero el paralelismo entre el verso tercero y el cuarto, semejante al de los versos sexto y séptimo, y reforzado por la inversión del verso segundo en el quinto, exige que se invierta el orden de las palabras como lo he hecho en el texto.

[2] Anónima, pág. 575 del vol. XLII de la Biblioteca de Rivadeneyra.

que me huele a pobrete, *vete,*
si no hay dinero.

(Entremés de *La capeadora,* 1.ª parte) [1].

Si recibes ofensas
de tu enemigo,
cásale y no le busques
mayor castigo.
—Castigo.

Díganle a mi velado
que no trabaje,
bástele por oficio
que sufra y calle.
—Calle.

(Dúo en el entremés *El tío Bartolomé).*

Todas reciben el nombre técnico de seguidillas, determinado por el canto y la danza [2]. En el arte coreográfico, el género comienza a subdividirse en especies durante la centuria: tales son los *bailes del río,* de *Juan Redondo,* del *Caballero* (a menudo con la vieja letra del *Caballero de Olmedo);* otros nacen después: la *chamberga,* que fué muy popular, debe de ser posterior a aquéllos. Todos se introducen en las obras teatrales que tenían la forma y el nombre de *bailes,* en las jácaras, las mojigangas y los entremeses. Todavía durante el siglo XVIII, nuevos bailes tomarán como metro para su letra el de la seguidilla [3].

---

[1] Véase CORREAS, *Arte grande,* págs. 277 a 279. — Además, el *Baile del aceitunero,* de Quiñones de Benavente, para otras maneras de repetición de palabras.

[2] En el *Cancionero* de Sablonara lleva el nombre de «seguidillas» la canción núm. 67, con música de Capitán:

Bullicioso y claro arroyuelo
que salpicas las guijas blancas,
de tu envidia los ruiseñores
van saltando de rama en rama.

Lucinda más bella
y cual bella ingrata,
a quien fuego abrasa
si la nieve abrasa.

Es posible que el nombre de seguidillas no pretenda abrazar a toda la composición, sino sólo a la parte en hexasílabos; aun así es extraño, puesto que esos versos son todos regulares.

[3] Véase la Introducción de COTARELO a los *Entremeses, loas, bailes, jácaras y mojigangas,* págs. CCXXXV, CCXLII y CCLII. En la pág. CCLXI puede verse cómo Moreto, en su baile *Las fiestas de Palacio* (1658), pone letra de seguidilla, en italiano corrompido, a la *tarantela.*

Se la halla, en fin, en arreglos más o menos libres, combinando sus propios versos en grupos desusados, o uniéndolos a otros tipos métricos:

Aves, fieras, fuentes y ríos,
pues de amor conocéis el dominio,
seguidlo volando,
corriendo seguidlo,
y las aguas saltando
rompan los vidrios,
que aun de amor no se escapa
lo cristalino [1].

Y las avecillas y fuentes,
si de envidia tristes,
de amor alegres,
unas ríen y otras lloran
y en mirando a Jacinta
se alegran todas [2].

A la esposa divina
cantan la gala
pajarillos al alborada,
que de ramas en flores
y de flores en ramas
vuelan y saltan.

(Lope, auto *La siega*) [3].

§ 3. LA SEGUIDILLA REGULAR. — Mientras entre el pueblo la seguidilla conserva sus libertades, en manos de los poetas cultos se va regularizando durante el período que abarca desde 1600 hasta 1675. Todavía, al principio, abundan los versos hexasílabos aun en las más regulares: Lope así las emplea constantemetne en

[1] *Labradoras*, con música de Juan Hidalgo, Biblioteca Nacional de Madrid, manuscritos, caja 12.967, núm. 8. Véase Luis Vélez de Guevara, *Los celos hacen estrellas*, con música de Hidalgo, en el *Teatro lírico español anterior al siglo XIX*, publicado por FELIPE PEDRELL (en 5 vols., Coruña, 1888...), vols. IV-V:

Estrellas, luceros, plantas y signos,
pues de amor conocéis el dominio,
domando, influyendo
pesares y alivios,
los celos disculpen
amantes delitos,
que de un amor no se escapa
lo cristalino.

[2] *Cancionero* de Sablonara, núm. 17.

[3] Para otras seguidillas, véase CEJADOR, *La verdadera poesía castellana* tomo I, págs. 226-245; II, págs. 23-24, 34, 37-42, 52-56, 74-75, 77, 101-104, 120, 124-125, 161-167, 276; IV, 20, 141, 195 y 311.

su novela pastoril a lo divino *Los pastores de Belén* (1612), en su *Romancero espiritual* (1624), en sus autos y en muchas de sus comedias [1].

[1] Seguidillas en Lope de Vega (sin pretender agotar la lista). En los autos y representaciones morales: *Las bodas entre el alma y el amor divino* («Zarpa la capitana, | Tocan a leva...»): reaparece en la comedia *El amete de Toledo* y en la novela *El peregrino en su patria;* véase *Rimas del incógnito:* «Con un tiro de leva | La capitana...»); *La Maya* («Echad mano a la bolsa, | Cara de rosa»; véase Miguel Sánchez); *El pastor ingrato* («La locura del mundo...» y «De Sión ausente»); *El nombre de Jesús* («Alegría, zagales...» y «Pastorcico nuevo, | Dulce Niño Dios, | No sois vos, vida mía, | Para labrador»); *Del pan y del palo* (cantarcillo popular que da base al auto: «Del pan y del palo | Me da mi esposo»); *La siega* («A la esposa divina | Cantan la gala»: seguidilla mezclada con otros versos irregulares); *El nacimiento de Cristo* («Gloria en las alturas, | Paz a los hombres»); *La vuelta de Egipto* («Oh, qué bien pareces, | Barco divino...» y «Venga con el día | Venga María, | Y con el albore | Jesús y el sole»); en los dos *Coloquios de la Concepción,* 1615 («Canten os la gala, | Divina Fénix, | Concebida sin mancha | Dichosamente»); en los autos: *La Circuncisión* («Hoy salen del templo»); *El misacantano* («Mañanitas de Pascua | De Resurrección»); *El Avemaría y el Rosario* («Al nacer el aurora»); *El pastor lobo* («Corderita nueva | De color de aurora, | No sois vos, vida mía, | Para labradora»; véase *El nombre de Jesús); La locura por la honra* («Con la luz de su Esposo»); *Los dos ingenios y esclavos* («A la gran Babilonia | Todos se mudan»); *Los cantares* («Que de noche le mataron | Al caballero» —de Olmedo—: véase § 13 del cap. III; «Qué bien os quedastes | Galán del cielo...» y «Porque Dios que le mira | Le echó la capa»), *La margarita preciosa* («A la rica tienda»), y *La isla del sol* («¡Oh, qué bien mira! | ¡Oh, qué bien baila!...» y «Sol hermoso y divino, | Sal muchas veces»).

En la comedia en prosa *La Dorotea* («Que no quiero favores...»; véase el § 13 del cap. III); en las comedias en verso, *El robo de Dina* («En las mañanicas | Del mes de mayo»: composición larga y hermosa; sobre cantares de mayo, véase la nota final al § 11 del cap. III); *El cardenal de Belén* («Mañanicas floridas | Del frío invierno»); *El acero de Madrid* («Mañanicas floridas | Del mes de mayo»; véase *Romancero de Barcelona,* en la *Revue Hispanique,* vol. XXIX, pág. 179); *Las bizarrías de Belisa,* escrita en 1634 («Mañanicas de mayo | Salen las damas...» y «Antes que amanezca»); *La madre de la mejor* («A la niña María | Cantan las aves»); *Los trabajos de Jacob* («En amor tan largo»); *El Santo Negro Rosambuco* («Por San Juan las damas...» —sobre cantares de fiestas de San Juan, véase § 20 del cap. III— e imitación del *Caballero de Olmedo* en lenguaje absurdo); *La juventud de San Isidro* («Regocijo, zagales»); *San Diego de Alcalá* («Dulce Virgen bella»); *La corona derribada,* atribución dudosa a Lope («Frescas aguas alegres | Del fértil Nilo»); *El rústico del cielo* («Aires de los cielos»); *La niñez del Padre Rojas,* escrita en 1625 («Zagalejas del prado»); *La limpieza no manchada* («Y repiten las aves | Del verde bosque», escrita en renglones dobles); *El truhán del cielo* («Al arma, guerra, guerra, | Muera el infierno...» y estribillo imitado del cantar de *El Caballero de Olmedo:* «A la gala de la gracia, | La flor del suelo»); *Adonis y Venus,* anterior a 1604 («Triunfa la hermosura»); *Las mujeres sin hombres* («No es posible que el fruto»); *El amor enamorado* («A la gala de Febo»); sobre cantares de gala, véase § 9 del cap. II, nota al cantar («A la gala de la panadera»); *Las almenas de Toro* («Por aquí daréis la vuelta»; véase § 13 del cap. III); *El galán de la Membrilla* (cantar base del drama: «Que de Manzanares era la niña, | Y el galán que la lleva, de la Membrilla», escrito en renglones dobles); *La niña de plata* («Caminad, suspiros | A donde soléis»); *El Caballero de Olmedo* (cantar base del

Igual cosa puede decirse de Tirso, de Valdivielso, de Quiñones de Benavente, y de todos los poetas que escriben entre 1600 y

drama; véase § 13 del cap. III); *El Caballero de Illescas* («Blancas coge Lucinda»); *Fuente Ovejuna* («Vivan muchos años | Los desposados...» y «Para qué te escondes, | Niña gallarda»); *Pedro Carbonero*, anterior a 1604 («Riberitas hermosas»; véase § 13 del cap. III); *Los Comendadores de Córdoba* (fundada en el cantar glosado en seguidillas); *Los Porceles de Murcia* (canción de romería: «A la Virgen bella | De aquesta ermita»); *El aldehuela* («Madre, la mi madre»; véase § 11 del cap. III; y «Salteáronme los ojos | De la mozuela»); *Los melindres de Belisa* («Madre, la mi madre»); *El mayor imposible* («Madre, la mi madre»); *El rey Don Sebastián* («A la Virgen bella | Rosas y flores»); *En un pastoral albergue* (estribillo: «Que de muerte tan bella | Nadie se escapa»); *El mármol de Felisardo*, anterior a 1604 («No corráis, ventecillos»); *Servir a señor discreto* («Mariquita me llaman...» y «Cuando ríen las fuentes»); *Si no vieran las mujeres* («Pero escucha el retrato | Del bien que adoro»: composición larga en seguidillas); *Lo que pasa en una tarde* («No me aprovecharon, | Madre, las yerbas»; véanse Pedro de Andrade Caminha, Góngora y Francisco de Trillo y Figueroa); *Lo cierto por lo dudoso* («Río de Sevilla»: véase § 19 del cap. III); *El amante agradecido* («Vienen de Sanlúcar...»: véase § 2 de este capítulo; y «En estas galeras»); *Amar, servir y esperar* (serie de seguidillas que comienzan como la de la comedia anterior, «Vienen de Sanlúcar...», pero continúan de modo diferente); *Al pasar del arroyo* (cantar base del drama: «Al pasar del arroyo | Del alamillo, | Las memorias del alma | Se me han perdido»; véanse *Séguedilles anciennes*, núm. 68, Calderón, comedia burlesca de *Céfalo y Procris*, acto I, y Quiñones de Benavente, entremés de *Don Gaiferos*; además, el moderno *Cancionero popular de Burgos); Las flores de Don Juan* («Salen de Valencia | Noche de San Juan...» y «Despertad, señor mío, | Despertad, | Porque viene el alba | Del señor San Juan»: véanse *El Santo Negro Rosambuco* y el tomo I de *Poesías líricas*, de Lope, edición Montesinos, págs. 165-169; «Cómo retumban los remos | Madre, en el agua»: véase seguidilla del *Laberinto amoroso*, § 2 de este capítulo); *Santiago el Verde* (probable base del drama «En Santiago el Verde | Me dieron celos»); *La mal casada* («De las desdichadas. | Yo soy la una»: véanse *Séguedilles anciennes*, núm. 22, y *Rimas del incógnito*, núm. 5); *Lo que ha de ser* («Ofendida me tienen»); *La boba para los otros y discreta para sí* («Ay mi querida aldea»); *El bobo del Colegio* | «Llevad mis suspiros | Aires suaves»); *Con su pan se lo coman* («A los verdes prados»); *El vellocino de oro* («Apacibles prados»); *La buena guarda* («Lavaréme en el Tajo»); *El desconfiado* («A los carreteros»); *La octava maravilla* («Cuantas veces me brindan»); *La dama boba*, edición según el manuscrito autógrafo en *The dramatic art of Lope de Vega*, de RUDOLPH SCHEVILL, Berkeley, 1918 (cantar «Amor cansado de ver», estrofas de cuatro versos octosílabos y cuatro de seguidilla: «Pasóse a las Indias, | Vendió el aljaba»).

La *Serranilla de la Zarzuela*. que tiene parentesco con la seguidilla, la imita Lope en las comedias *El sol parado*, anterior a 1604, y *Las paces de los reyes*, así como en los autos *La venta de la Zarzuela* y *Los cantares* (véanse § 10 del cap. I y § 24 del cap. II).

En la novela pastoril a lo divino *Los pastores de Belén* (1612): Libro I, el romance «Afligido está José» termina en seguidillas: «Bien podéis persuadiros, | Divino Esposo»; seguidillas largas: «Nace el alba María | Y el sol tras ella»; otras: «¿Dónde vais, zagala, | Sola en el monte?». —Libro II, endechas «Zagala divina» con estribillo: «Vuestras gracias me cuentan, | Zagala hermosa»; coplas con estribillo: «¿Qué mucho que dance | Juan tan alegre?». —Libro III, romance «Campanitas de plata» con estribillo: «Que los ángeles tocan, | Tocan y tañen»; romance de Niseida, con estribillo: «Nora-

1650. En la obra de Calderón, que se extiende de la tercera a la octava década del siglo XVII, compite la seguidilla de hexasílabos con la seguidilla de tipo moderno, toda en heptasílabos y pentasílabos; acaso el empleo sistemático del segundo tipo sea posterior al del tipo antiguo [1].

buena vengáis al mundo, | Niño de perlas, ¡ Que sin vuestra vista | No hay hora buena»; sobre cantares de enhorabuena, véanse nota del § 11 y § 20 del cap. III; romance de Nectalvo, con estribillo: «Pide al cielo la tierra ¦ La paz que adora»; canción de Rosarda, «Dejando Dios la grandeza», cuatro versos de romance y siete de seguidilla; canción de Alfesibeo, toda en seguidillas: «Manso corderito»; canción de Riselo, en endecha y seguidilla: «A mi niño combaten | Fuegos y hielos»; canción de Jorán, en endecha y seguidilla: «De una Virgen hermosa | Celos tiene el sol»; seguidillas largas: «Zagalejo de perlas, | Hijo del alba»; otras: «Una niña y un niño | Vengo de ver»; otras, las muy conocidas: «Pues andáis en las palmas, | Ángeles santos». — Libro IV, seguidillas largas: «La aldeana preciosa | Recién parida». —Libro V, endechas, con estribillo: «Venga con el día | El alegría, | Venga con el alba | El sol que nos salva»; seguidillas largas: «Buscaban mis ojos ¡ La Virgen pura»; otras: «Sea bienvenida | La blanca niña; | Venga norabuena | El niño de perlas».

En el *Romancero espiritual* (1624), de Lope, hay varios romances con estribillos en seguidillas: «Oh, qué firmes somos, ¡ Dios mío, yo y vos...»; «Hoy tendrás en mis brazos | Cuanto me pides...»; «Jesús, de María | Cordero santo...»; y toda una composición en seguidillas: «Cantad, ruiseñores, | Al alborada, | Porque viene el Esposo | De ver el alma». — Hay reimpresión facsimilar del *Romancero*, hecha por la Sociedad Hispánica.— Según parece, las *Rimas sacras* (1625) reproducen parte del material del *Romancero*.

[1] En Tirso no son muchas las seguidillas. Pero véase el auto *El colmenero divino* («Pastorcico nuevo ¦ De color de azor, | Bueno sois, vida mía, | Para labrador»: véase Lope, autos *El nombre de Jesús* y *El pastor lobo;* además, el romance «Del cristal de Manzanares...», de Alonso de Salas —¿Barbadillo?—, en GALLARDO, *Ensayo*, vol. I, col. 1.030); *La venganza de Tamar* («Cuando el bien que adoro | Los campos pisa»); *Antona García;* quizá sea seguidilla el cantar en que probablemente se inspiró esta comedia («Más valéis, vos, Antona, | Que la corte toda»: aparece también en la comedia *El cuerdo en su casa*, de Lope, quien tal vez escribió otra tomando el cantar como título; en *La pícara Justina*, de López de Úbeda, ed. Puyol, tomo I, pág. 89, y en CORREAS, *Vocabulario*, pág. 456); *La Santa Juana*, primera parte: se aproximan a la seguidilla los versos largos, de ritmo extraño, que comienzan: «Que la Sagra de Toledo mil fiestas hace»; luego, «Norabuena venga | Juana a mi casa»; *Tanto es lo de más como lo de menos* («¿Qué parecen valonas que adornan calvas?»: seguidillas de siete versos, escritas en cuatro renglones, dos largos, uno corto y uno largo; *El pretendiente al revés:* «Ah, mi señor Guargüeros, salga y baile» —caso semejante al de la *Santa Juana*—; *La villana de la Sagra* («Cómo alegra los campos | La dulce noche»); *Desde Toledo a Madrid* («El sombrero de tema | Y el rostro zaino»), y *Don Gil de las Calzas Verdes* («Alamicos del Prado, | Fuente del Duque»). Obras de atribución discutida: *El burlador de Sevilla* («A pescar salió la niña»); *Los amantes de Teruel* («Vengo de la guerra»); *La Condesa bandolera y ninfa del cielo* (aproximación: «Que si viene la noche, | Presto saldrá el sole»);*La madrina del cielo* («No te apartes del mundo, | Goza sus gustos...» y «De la gloria ha bajado | La flor divina»).

Valdivielso, en su *Romancero espiritual*, trae varios estribillos en seguidillas: «Que es el mayor santo» (pág. 2 de la edición de 1880); «Dadnos, Virgen bella» (pág. 16); «Aunque más te disfraces» (pág. 19); «Para qué son

Después de Calderón el metro adquiere fijeza en manos de los poetas cultos, bajo la norma de heptasílabos y pentasílabos (7-5-7-5). Las excepciones serán pocas y ya en el siglo XVIII raras hasta en la poesía popular.

§ 4. LOS VERSOS DE GAITA GALLEGA EN LAS DANZAS. — Los versos de gaita gallega (diez, once y doce sílabas, con quebrados de seis) adquieren popularidad grande después que la seguidilla. Continuaban usándose en bailes diversos, y, por lo tanto, en el teatro. Uno de esos bailes, la *españoleta*, que según Juan de Esqui-

disfraces» (pág. 49); «Ventecicos suaves | Templad la risa»; seguidillas mezcladas con otros versos (pág. 68); «Venga con el día, | El alegría»; «Venido ha al albore | El Redentore»: véase Lope, auto *La vuelta de Egipto* y *Los pastores de Belén*, libro V; «Los ángeles bellos» (pág. 109; escritas en renglones dobles); «Libre ser solía» (pág. 163); «Muy enhorabuena» (pág. 165); «Porque sin la vuestra | No hay buena vista» (pág. 221); «En la santa Iglesia» (pág. 279); «Venid, romerico», «Esperad, prisioneros», y «Yo me era morenica», en la *Ensaladilla del Retablo;* véase § 21 del capítulo III, nota sobre «Morenica me llaman, madre». —Composiciones en estrofas de cuatro hexasílabos y cuatro versos de seguidilla: «Unos ojos bellos» (pág. 115) y «Lágrimas del alma» (pág. 127). —Composiciones largas en seguidillas: «La puerta me ronda | Mi amado Esposo»; predominan los hexasílabos (pág. 201); «Qué mucho un soldado | Que tiene deudas» (pág. 305); «Aunque os viene nacido | El rico sayal» (pág. 315); «Vísteme tembrando», en lenguaje sayagués (pág. 332). Su imitación de la *Serranilla de la Zarzuela* (pág. 269) está en hexasílabos regulares.

Sería inútil pretender formar lista de las seguidillas que hay en los entremeses y demás obrillas de Quiñones de Benavente: las hay en casi todos. A menudo están escritas en renglones dobles.

De Calderón queda dicho que tiene seguidillas con hexasílabos y seguidillas de tipo regular moderno. De las primeras hay en los autos: *¿Quién hallará mujer fuerte?* («Déme el sacro texto | tan feliz letra»); *El valle de la Zarzuela* («A mí brindis, mortales, | A mí, que la sed»); *El sacro Parnaso* («Por que no de balde | Goce el corazón, | Llévele atravesado | Con flechas de amor», en las comedias y fiestas con música *Afectos de odio y amor* («Prisionero me tienen | Por un buen querer»); *El alcaide de sí mismo* («Subiera Morales»: una de las pocas canciones populares en Calderón); *La fiera, el rayo y la piedra* («Oye de mi coro | Las que yo traigo»); *El golfo de las sirenas* («Entre visto y oído | La ventaja es»: véase el auto *El valle de la Zarzuela:* «De su agrado a mi agrado | La ventaja es»); *El encanto sin encanto* («En la tarde alegre | Del Señor San Juan | Todo es bailes la tierra, | Músicas el mar»); *El laurel de Apolo* («Préstame esta noche | Tu arco y tus flechas»); *Celos aun del aire matan* («Dos zagales venían»: son largos). —A veces hay ejemplos de seguidillas aún más irregulares, pero no son muchas: en el auto *La primer flor del Carmelo*, grupo de seguidillas que comienza por tres versos, 7-7-5, y continúa en combinaciones desusadas; en *La fiera, el rayo y la piedra* (Teman, teman los mortales»). Hay seguidillas de tres versos en la comedia *El mayor encanto, amor* («Ya la obedezco...»).

El tipo regular (7-5-7-5) aparece en obras donde también figura el tipo fluctuante: *¿Quién hallará mujer fuerte?* («Clama, llora, suspira»), *El laurel de Apolo* («No desdeñes, Cupido, | Tu arco y tus flechas»); *La fiera, el rayo y la piedra* («Pues que todo en los cielos»), o bien en obras donde domina de modo absoluto: el auto *Lo que va del hombre a Dios* («Vuelva en hora dichosa»); *El jardín de Falerina* («Cesen, cesen rigores»); *La púrpura de la rosa* («A pesar de los celos»); *Darlo todo y no dar nada* («Condición y retrato»).

172

vel Navarro había envejecido hacia 1642 (fecha de sus *Discursos sobre el arte del danzado*), continúa apareciendo, sin embargo: se le halla en entremeses y en Sor Juana Inés de la Cruz; a principios del siglo xviii, en Zamora y Cañizares [1]. Lope la introdujo, durante la primera mitad del siglo xvii, en su auto de *Los cantares*, con versos acentuales que sirven de estribillo a coplas octosilábicas:

> Madre de Dios y Virgen entera,
> Madre de Dios, divina doncella.

Valdivielso introduce el curioso metro del *baile de Tárraga*, que pertenece a la misma familia, en el auto *El peregrino:*

> ¡Tárraga, por aquí van a Málaga!
> ¡Tárraga, por aquí van allá! [2]

y sigue con versos que pueden tomarse como decasílabos anapésticos y continuación de aquel metro (mediante hiato), o como eneasílabos (según la versión del auto anterior, anónimo, de *Los yerros de Adán:* «Est'es el camino del cielo»):

> Este es el camino del cielo,
> este es el camino de allá [3].

Hay otras curiosas letras de bailes como el *sarao*, que se conoce al menos desde la segunda década del siglo xvii [4]; la *Catalineta*, que se conocía desde antes, pues ya figura en la representación bailada de *Pásate acá, compadre*, publicada con comedias de Lope en 1617:

> Dí qué tienes, la Catalineta,
> dí qué tienes, la Catalineta,
> que te vas de aquí para allí,
> que te vas de aquí para allí.

---

[1] Véase cap. III, §§ 20 y 21, y especialmente nota sobre bailes y nota sobre la españoleta. Consúltese COTARELO, Introducción a los *Entremeses...*, pág. CCXLIV.

[2] Véanse COTARELO, Introducción a los *Entremeses...*, pág. CCLXII, y PUYOL, edición de *La pícara Justina*, vol. II, pág. 47, y vol. III, pág. 299; el baile se citaba ya en la *Comedia Florinea* (1554). —De la familia es el cantarcillo de dátiles que trae Góngora en su Letrilla de Carillo y Gil (1615):

> ¡Támaras, que son miel y oro!
> ¡Támaras, que son oro y miel!

Véase cap. III, § 9.

Véase COTARELO, Introducción a los *Entremeses...*, pág. CCLX.

173

> Abril y pitín, Abril y pitín,
> de aquí para allí,
> de aquí para allí,
> Abril y pitín, Abril y pitín [1].

Es posterior el baile de *Marizápalos*, del cual hay varias letras. Una, de la piececilla teatral, anónima, *Baile de Marizápalos*, de mediados del siglo:

> Marizápalos, vénte conmigo
> al verde sotillo de Vaciamadrid,
> que con sólo pisarle tu planta
> no ha de haber más Flandes que el ver su país.

Otra, de Jerónimo Camargo:

> Marizápalo bajó una tarde
> al fresco sotillo de Vaciamadrid...
> Marizápalos era muchacha
> muy adorada de Pedro Martín...

La popularidad de *Marizápalos* duró hasta el siglo XVIII, con Antonio de Zamora y Diego de Torres Villarroel [2].

El *minué*, en fin, adopta también estos metros:

> Si de Amarilis los ojos disparan
> flechas que hieren con dulce rigor,
> ¿de qué le sirve a Cupido la aljaba?,
> ¿para qué quiere Amor el arpón? [3]

§ 5 LOS CANTOS DEL MOLINO. — Los versos de cadencia anapéstica se emplean a veces en indudables *muiñeiras* castellanas, *molineras*, cantos de molino. A veces los cantares tienen versos

---

[1] Véase COTARELO, Introducción a los *Entremeses...*, págs. CLXXXIV y CCXXXVIII. Véase para la fórmula «de aquí para allí», frecuente en bailes, Lope, *Servir a señor discreto*, o el auto *La adúltera perdonada*, o Quiñones de Benavente, *La puente segoviana*, primera parte.

[2] Véase COTARELO, Introducción a los *Entremeses...*, páginas XCV, CXIII, CCXIII y CCLIII. En GALLARDO, *Ensayo*, vol. II, col. 204, hay una variante de la versión de Camargo, impresa en Madrid, 1657, como de Miguel López de Honrubia. Otra publicó Francisco Asenjo Barbieri en la revista *La Ilustración Española y Americana*, de Madrid, noviembre de 1877. Otra, recogida en América, da Carlos Vega, en *La música de un códice colonial del siglo XVII* (del virreinato del Perú), publicación del Instituto de Literatura Argentina, Universidad de Buenos Aires, 1931: véanse págs. 29-30, 54 y 74-75. Quevedo, en *La visita de los chistes*, menciona a Marizápalos.

[3] «Quiere amor» forma sinalefa, según la música. Minué con música de José Bassa, que vivía en 1701: aparece en el *Teatro lírico español*, de Pedrell. Hay allí otros minués con metros semejantes.

más cortos que los usuales en las muiñeiras de Galicia, como ocurre con éste del *Romancero general:*

> Parecéis molinero, amor,
> y sois moledor... [1]

o éste, de Trillo y Figueroa (Letrilla «En mi edad primera...»):

> Solía que andaba
> el mi molinó,
> solía que andaba
> y ahora no...

estribillo de coplas hexasilábicas [2].

El metro pleno de gaita gallega se encuentra en el dístico que recogen Tirso en *Don Gil de las Calzas Verdes* y Cosme Gómez Tejada de los Reyes:

> Molinico, ¿por qué no mueles?
> Porque me beben el agua los bueyes... [3]

y en el precioso cantar —original, a no dudarlo— que intercala Lope en *San Isidro labrador de Madrid* (acto primero):

> Molinito que mueles amores,
> pues que mis ojos agua te dan,
> no coja desdenes quien siembra favores
> que dándome vida matarme podrán.

---

[1] Véanse Trillo y Figueroa, Letrilla, y variante en Correas, *Arte grande,* pág. 283, y *Vocabulario de refranes,* pág. 468:

> Molinero sois, amor,
> y sois moledor.

Así también Tirso, en *Don Gil de las Calzas Verdes,* cuya preciosa escena de baile (octava del acto primero) es como un resumen de cantos de molino. En Tirso el cantar se continúa:

> Si lo soy, apártesé,
> que le enharinaré.

Véase § 5 del cap. III, nota sobre la alteración del acento de las palabras en el verso.

[2] Para la acentuación alterada de «molinó», véase nota en el § 5 del cap. III. El estribillo aparece en otra Letrilla, atribuída a Góngora, y, con otro sentido, imitado por Lope en *La mayor corona,* acto tercero:

> Solía que andaba
> el que ingrato es hoy.

[3] *Romancero y cancionero sagrados,* vol. XXXV de la Biblioteca de Rivadeneyra, núm. 554 de los *Autos al Nacimiento,* 1661, de Cosme de los Reyes. Véanse Correas, *Arte grande,* págs. 283 y 284; Gallardo, *Ensayo,* vol. I, col. 1.060, y Quevedo, romance «A la jineta sentado...».

> Molinico que mueles mis celos,
> pues agua te dieron mis ojos cansados,
> muele favores, no muelas cuidados,
> pues que te hicieron tan bello los cielos.

> Si mis esperanzas te han dado las flores
> y ahora mis ojos el agua te dan,
> no coja desdenes quien siembra favores
> que dándome vida matarme podrán.

§ 6 EVOLUCIÓN DEL METRO DE GAITA GALLEGA. — Entre 1600 y 1650, la versificación anapéstica se maneja con soltura, mezclando libremente sus distintas medidas de verso, y aun otras más, que lo hacían muy variado.

Así en Lope *(El cardenal de Belén*, acto I):

> Que quien vive sin gustos de Venus
> soledades al hielo y al sol,
> como bestia pasa la vida,
> que no es hombre de razón.
> Amor es un Dios
> de tanto valor,
> que no hay cosa más dulce que pida
> la humana imaginación.

> Que quien vive sin esta gloria
> soledades del yermo de Egipto,
> la naturaleza ofende
> y su ser pone en olvido.
> Amor es un niño
> tan tierno y tan lindo,
> que las almas heladas enciende
> y es de sus penas descanso y alivio.

Así en Tirso:

> Florecillas que Rut bella pisa
> mientras sus ojos regados os ven,
> no os riáis, no os riáis, que no viene bien
> con sus lágrimas vuestra risa,

> *(La mejor espigadera).*

> Norabuena vengáis, abril,
> si os fuéredes luego, volveos por aquí...
> pues que sois tan bello, risueño y gentil.

> *(La Santa Juana*, primera parte, acto I).[1]

[1] Véanse § 20 del cap. III, § 3 del cap. IV, nota sobre las seguidillas de Lope, y § 11 del cap. III, nota sobre los cantares de enhorabuena.

Así en Quiñones de Benavente, donde se alcanza la mayor libertad de combinaciones:

> — Mancebito, remedia mis males,
> que hay sobra de amores y falta de reales.
> — Muchachita ¿por qué no me dejas,
> que más quiero a un cuarto que a todas las hembras?

(Entremés Los cuatro galanes).

> — Si los dineritos no se sienten buenos
> — Y las mujercitas somos sus galenos
> — ¡Ay de los talegos!
> — Que con los deseos de salud mejor
> — Mientras más doctores llaman
> — Más aprisa corren y vuelan
>   a su perdición.
> — A su perdición. A su perdición.

(Entremés El talego, 2ª parte).

Cantares de origen popular, donde se emplean metros de esta familia:

> —Casadica, de vos dicen mal.
> —Digan, digan, que ellos cansarán.

> —Mariquita ¿y en sábado ciernes?
> —¡Ay, señor! Pensé que era viernes [1].

> ¡Válame Dios, que los ánsares vuelan!
> ¡Válame Dios, que saben volar! [2]

> Vayan cautivos el rey y la reina [3].

> Bío, bío,
> que mi tambo le tengo en el río [4].

> ¡Trébole, ay, Jesús, cómo huele!
> ¡Trébole, ay, Jesús, qué olor! [5]

---

[1] Correas, *Vocabulario de refranes*, págs. 326 y 441.

[2] Trillo y Figueroa, letrilla, y Correas, *Vocabulario de refranes*, pág. 431. Véase Valdivielso: «¡Válame Dios, que los ángeles se andan!» (pág. 46 del *Romancero espiritual*).

[3] Lope, comedia *El nacimiento de Cristo*.

[4] Lope, *Arauco domado*, acto III.

[5] Entre las muchas imitaciones de este cantar del trébol, véanse Lope, *Peribáñez, El capellán de la Virgen;* Tirso, segunda parte de *La Santa Juana, La fingida Arcadia, La villana de la Sagra;* Valdivielso, *Ensaladilla al Santísimo Sacramento;* ensaladilla anónima «Quien madruga Dios le ayuda», en el *Romancero general*, 1600 (primera aparición que conozco del cantar, fuera del manuscrito 3.913 de la Biblioteca Nacional de Madrid, que es anterior).

Que por vos, la mi señora,
la cara de plata,
correría yo mi caballo
a la trápala, trápala, trápala [1].

Caracoles me pide la niña,
y pídelos cada día [2].

Al cabo de los años mil
vuelven las aguas por do solían ir [3].

Dióle el novio a la desposada
corales y zarcillos y patenas de plata [4].

Que besóme en el Colmenemelo... [5].

Porque soplan quedito los aires
que mueven las hojas de los arrayanes [6].

Esta noche me cupo la vela,
¡Plega a Dios que no me duerma! [7].

Cervatica, que no me la vuelvas,
que yo me la volveré [8].

---

[1] Valdivielso, auto *El hospital de los locos* y *Ensaladilla de Navidad* (núm. 651 del *Romancero y cancionero sagrados*); véanse CORREAS, *Arte grande*, pág. 283, y Lope, *Gallarda* bailada en el auto de *Los cantares*:

> Corren caballos aprisa;
> tápala, tapa, tápala, tapa.

Véase, además, Quiñones de Benavente, entremés *El Mago, Baile de los gallos* y *Baile de los toros;* y aun Calderón, *Mujer, llora y vencerás* («Que tapatán, que esta varia alegría»), y «Tapa, tapa, tan | A la guerra van», en uno de los *Romancerillos de la Biblioteca Ambrosiana*.

[2] Estribillo de una canción atribuída a Góngora y a Trillo.

[3] Véanse Lope, *Barlán y Josafá, El hijo de los leones, Los Ponces de Barcelona,* auto *El heredero del cielo,* y Matías Duque de Estrada, *Cancionero,* en la *Revista de Archivos, Bibliotecas y Museos,* de Madrid, 1902. Quiñones de Benavente escribió el baile de *Al cabo de los bailes mil.* Hay una glosa de Antonio Henríquez Gómez (en *Poetas líricos de los siglos XVI y XVII,* Biblioteca de Rivadeneyra).

[4] Véase Lope, auto *La Maya,* y Valdivielso, *Romancero espiritual,* pág. 215.

[5] Tirso, *La villana de la Sagra* y auto *El colmenero divino.* Véanse, además, CORREAS, *Vocabulario de refranes,* pág. 307: «Besóme el colmenero...», y el ms. 2.621 de la Biblioteca Nacional de Madrid. Compárense el cantar de la espigaderuela en *La mujer espigadera,* de Tirso; el de la segaderuela, en *Los Benavides,* de Lope, y el de la colmeneruela, de Góngora. Sobre las canciones de segar, véanse MENÉNDEZ PIDAL, *La primitiva poesía lírica española,* págs. 309-310.

[6] Véanse las poesías atribuídas a Góngora, en la *Revue Hispanique,* 1906, vol. XIV, composición núm. 41.

[7] *Romancero de Barcelona,* núm. 37, y CORREAS, *Vocabulario de refranes,* pág. 136. Sobre cánticas de velador, véase § 17 del cap. II.

[8] Manuscrito 3.913 de la Biblioteca Nacional. Coplas en zéjel.

Al llegar a Calderón, la situación comienza a cambiar. Calderón muy raras veces recoge cantares del pueblo, prefiere tomarlos de poetas cultos o, más exactamente, de Góngora [1]; pero sí gusta de la versificación popular: tiene afición desmedida al metro de gaita gallega, y en él compone cantares que con frecuencia se prolongan, por repetición de uno o dos versos, interrumpiendo el diálogo de las comedias, a través de una o varias escenas, a veces de todo un acto. Pero, como ocurre en la seguidilla, en él se encuentran ya dos tendencias en conflicto: una, hacia el manejo libre del metro; otra, hacia la regularidad absoluta, en que sólo pueden alternar versos de diez y de doce sílabas, mezclándose a lo sumo con los de seis, pero desterrando los de once, los de nueve y cualesquiera otros. En cambio, hay una tendencia curiosa en sus versos de doce —la de tratar con gran libertad la cesura del medio, al punto de que es fácil leerlos como de trece sílabas, si se introduce el hiato o se da todo su valor silábico a una palabra esdrújula o todo su valor métrico posible a una palabra aguda—:

> Antorcha será que os alumbre sutil...
> Que allí todo un reino aquí el nombre de un rey...
> Humilde, postrado y rendido padece...
> Parad, suspended, remitid la violencia...

Ejemplos de manejo libre:

> Despertad, despertad, israelitas,
> del pálido sueño que ocioso dormís;
> no perezosos os tenga el descanso
> al ver que os espera una patria feliz...
>
> (Auto *La serpiente de metal*).

> Ruiseñor que volando vas,
> cantando finezas, cantando favores,
> ¡oh, cuánta pena y envidia me das!
> Pero no, que si cantas amores,
> tú tendrás celos y tú llorarás.
>
> (*Los dos amantes del cielo*, acto I, y *Fieras
> afemina amor*, acto II).

Ejemplos del tipo regular:

> A los años felices de Eco,
> divina y hermosa deidad de las selvas,

---

[1] Con exactitud ha dicho Gerardo Diego, que Calderón es «la academia de Góngora...; simetriza lo que en Góngora era equilibrado pero libre» (prólogo a la *Antología poética en honor de Góngora*, Madrid, 1927).

feliz los señale el mayo con flores,
ufano los cuente el sol con estrellas.

(Eco y Narciso, acto I) [1].

A la sombra de un monte eminente,
que es pira inmortal,
se desangra un arroyo por venas
de plata torcida y hilado cristal.

Sierpecilla escamada de flores,
intenta correr,
cuando luego detienen sus pasos
prisiones suaves de rosa y clavel.

Detenido en los troncos, suspende
el curso veloz
y adquiriendo caudales de nieve
malogra la rosa y tronca la flor.

A las ondas del Nilo furioso
se arroja a·morir
y parece su espuma una línea
que labra dibujos de plata y marfil.

(Danza de coros en el acto III de El castillo
de Lindabridis) [2].

Así en D. Francisco Manuel de Melo *(Letras para cantar):*

¿Qué me pides, zagal, que te cuente
del verde consorcio que ayer tarde vi,
si no han vuelto hasta ahora mis ojos,
que todos llevaron los novios tras sí?

Una tarde, que el bien viene tarde,
de un mes que se llama el mes del abril,
cata aquí que se rompen los cielos
y mandan al sol de tarde salir...

---

[1] Véase otra obra de Calderón, *El José de las mujeres,* acto tercero.

En este dichoso día
los triunfos de Eugenia bella
alegre los cuente el mayo con flores,
feliz los señale el sol con estrellas.

[2] Ejemplos de manejo libre del metro de gaita gallega en Calderón se ven en *El laurel de Apolo,* en *Celos aun del aire matan,* en *La púrpura de la rosa,* en *Fortunas de Andrómeda y Perseo,* en *Ni amor se libra de amor,* aunque a veces no hay otra irregularidad que la admisión del endecasílabo anapéstico.
Ejemplos de la versificación ya regularizada, además de los dos citados arriba, los hay en la *Loa* para *El golfo de las sirenas,* en el auto *La viña del Señor* («En la cena que hoy hace la Esposa...»), en *Teágenes y Cariclea,* en *La estatua de Prometeo* («Al festejo, al festejo, zagales...»). Pero es de notar que en Calderón el proceso de regularizar los versos de gaita gallega no ha ido tan lejos como el que atañe a la seguidilla, y que a menudo se detiene en la fórmula 10-11-12-6.

El tipo regular comienza a encontrarse desde temprano en los cancioneros del siglo XVII:

> Jilguerillo que al alba saludas
> con dulces primores, no debes amar,
> que no tiene quien ama de veras
> más glorias que penas, más dichas que el mal. [1]

Creo apenas necesario indicar que estos metros, a pesar de su parentesco con el de arte mayor del siglo XV, no pueden confundirse con él, porque, aun en las normas más regulares, emplean el decasílabo anapéstico; aún más, este resulta característico de la nueva forma regular. El metro de arte mayor, las pocas veces que se emplea, se emplea como metro arcaico, con sus características antiguas: así en *Los jueces de Castilla*, probablemente de Lope, retocada por Moreto.

§ 7. VERSOS ENEASILÁBICOS. — El metro acentual donde predomina la cadencia del eneasílabo continúa en boga durante el siglo XVII. Se emplea en danzas, según antes se vió; a veces en la *zarabanda*:

> Ándalo la zarabanda,
> que el amor te lo manda, manda... [2]

En la *chacona*, baile de América, cuyo estribillo usual era el de:

> Vida bona, vida bona,
> vida, vámonos a Chacona...,

o bien:

> Vida, vámonos a Tampico...

En la versión que se cantaba en el centro de España, tenía eneasilábicos los dos versos:

> Vida, vida, vidita, vida,
> vida, vámonos a Castilla. [3]

---

[1] Letra anónima de una *tonada humana*, con música de Juan Hidalgo: Biblioteca Nacional, manuscritos, caja 12.967, núm. 38.

[2] Véase COTARELO, Introducción a los *Entremeses...*, páginas CCLXV y siguientes, y consúltese Luis Briceño, *Método de tañer guitarra*, París, 1626.

[3] Véase COTARELO, Introducción a los *Entremeses...*, páginas CCXLI y siguientes, y el cancionero *Norte de la poesía española*, Valencia, 1616: «Así, vida, vida bona...»

181

Hay otros muchos bailes y cantares con versos eneasilábicos. Aunque a veces el estribillo parezca regular, por ser iguales los dos versos, recuérdese que siempre debe considerársele puramente acentual y aliado a la versificación irregular, como se ve estudiando la mayor parte de las coplas que los acompañan y recordando que el eneasílabo no existe entonces como tipo métrico aceptado en la versificación regular:

> Dábale con el azadoncito,
> dábale con el azadón [1].

> Corren toros y juegan cañas [2].

> Que si buena era la verbena,
> más buena era la yerbabuena [3].

> ¡Hola! Que me lleva la ola.
> ¡Hola! Que me lleva la mar [4].

> Por aquí, que el amor me mata [5].

> Matachín, que yo soy el tiempo [6].

> Toquen y tangan esas campanas,
> repícamelas a buen son [7].

[1] Véase Moreto, *La misma conciencia acusa*, y el entremés anónimo de *La Garduña*, de la segunda mitad del siglo XVII. Consúltese COTARELO, Introducción a los *Entremeses...*, págs. CXXXIII y CCXV.

[2] Véanse Lope, *La moza de cántaro*, acto III, y Valdivielso, ensaladilla «Porque está parida la Reina...».

[3] Véanse Lope, *Las mocedades de Bernardo del Carpio;* Tirso, *El pretendiente al revés* («Buenas eran las azucenas, | Mas las clavellinas eran más buenas»); Andrés de Claramonte, *Desta agua no beberé* («Que si lindo es el poleo; | Más lindo era el rey Don Pedro»); Rojas Zorrilla, *García del Castañar* («Que si buena es la albahaca, | Mejor es la cruz de Calibaca»); *Vocabulario de refranes*, de CORREAS, pág. 334 («Que si verde era la verbena | Séalo enhorabuena»); *Tesoro de la lengua castellana*, de COVARRUBIAS, *s. v. epithalamio* («Que si linda era la madrina, | Por mi fe, que la novia es linda»; lo cita también CORREAS, *Vocabulario*, pág. 334). —Cantares de flor, emparentados con los de trébol (véanse § 9 del cap. III y § 6 del cap. IV).

[4] Lope, representación moral *El viaje del alma* y comedia *El serafín humano;* Quiñones de Benavente, parodia en el entremés de *Las dueñas;* Góngora, «A la fuente va del olmo...» (1630): «¡Hola, que no llega la ola! ¡Hola, que no quiere llegar». —MENÉNDEZ Y PELAYO, introducción al tomo II de la edición académica de las *Obras* de Lope, supone origen galaico a este estribillo.

[5] Ledesma, *Juegos de Nochesbuenas a lo divino.*

[6] Antonio de Solís, Loa de Carnestolendas (1656) para *Un bobo hace ciento*, en el volumen de *Varias poesías sagradas y profanas*, Madrid, 1732. Véase COTARELO, Introducción a los *Entremeses...*, págs. CCXCV, CCCX y siguientes (baile de los *Matachines*, que ha sobrevivido en América: consúltese mi conferencia sobre *Música popular de América*, pág. 226, nota); además, *Villancicos* eclesiásticos, Madrid, 1692.

[7] Lope, auto *El misacantano.*

Abejicas me pican, madre:
¿qué haré, que el dolor es grande? [1]

Blanca me era yo
cuando entré en la siega;
dióme el sol y ya soy morena [2].

¡Ay, que tañen en San Martín!
¡Ay, que tañen en San Antón! [3]

Pascual, si el ganado ves,
baila, salta, y hagámonos rajas,
que aquí traigo las sonajas
y el pandero para después [4].

Alabásteisos, caballero,
gentil hombre aragonés;
no os alabaréis otra vez.
Alabásteisos en Sevilla
que teníades linda amiga;
gentil hombre aragonés,
no os alabaréis otra vez [5].

En poesía más culta:

Aunque el campo se ve florido
con la blanca y la roja flor,
más florido se ve quien ama
con las flores del amor [6].

Albricias pido,
que el esposo es ya venido,
que en lo hermoso le conocí.
— ¿Cómo ansí?
— Yo le vi cercado de amores,
yo le vi entre las blancas flores,
yo galán y en cuerpo le vi [7].

[1] Lope, *El galán de la Membrilla.*
[2] Lope, *El gran Duque de Moscovia.* —Véanse § 21 del cap. III, nota sobre «Morenica me llaman, madre...», y § 6 del cap. IV, nota sobre el *Colmeneruelo.*
[3] Lope, *No son todos ruiseñores.*
[4] Lope lo imita en el auto de *Los cantares* y en *Los pastores de Belén*, libro III: «Antón, si el muchacho ves...».
[5] Cantar que tiene el corte y el sabor de otros del siglo XVI que recogen Vásquez y Pisador (véase cap. III, segunda parte). Se halla en el *Baile curioso y grave*, impreso en 1616 con *La rueda de la fortuna*, de Mira de Mescua.
[6] Baile de *El ¡ay, ay, ay!* y el *Sotillo.*
[7] Valdivielso, *Romancero espiritual*, pág. 213. Véase Lope, *Los pastores de Belén*, libro III.

> Buscaba el amor en la llama,
> en la perla, el ave y la flor,
> y teníale dentro
> de mi corazón... [1].

Emplean el verso eneasílabo Lope, Valdivielso y muchos otros poetas:

> Desnudito parece mi niño
> dios de amor, que con flechas está;
> pues a fe que si me las tira,
> que le tengo de hacer llorar.

> (Lope, *Los pastores de Belén*)·

El que muestra predilección especial por él es Tirso de Molina, que lo prefiere a los demás tipos de versificación irregular:

> Borbollicos hacen las aguas
> cuando ven a mi bien pasar;
> cantan, brincan, bullen y corren
> entre conchas de coral.

> Y los pájaros dejan sus nidos,
> y en las ramas del arrayán
> vuelan, cruzan, saltan y pican
> toronjil, murta y azahar.

> (*Don Gil de las Calzas Verdes*, acto I).

> Que llamaba la tórtola, madre,
> al cautivo pájaro suyo,
> con el pico, las alas, las plumas
> y con arrullos, y con arrullos.
> Preso estaba el pájaro solo
> en las redes del cazador;
> pero más le prenden y matan
> memorias de su lindo amor.

> (*La elección por la virtud*, acto III).

> Pajaricos que hacéis al alba
> con lisonjas alegre salva...
> A las puertas de nuesos amos...

> (*La venganza de Tamar*).

> ¡Ay, que el novio y la novia es bella!
> El es lindo y linda es ella.

> (Auto *No le arriendo la ganancia*).

---

[1] *Solo humano*, de Juan de Navas, fines del siglo XVII, págs. 50-51 del tomo III del *Teatro lírico español anterior al siglo XIX*, publicado por PEDRELL. Las coplas son hexasilábicas en forma estrófica de zéjel.

> Y por el viento sutil
> abejitas de mil en mil...
>
> > (Auto *El colmenero divino;* véase parodia
> > de Quiñones de Benavente, en el *Entremés
> > del Avantal)* [1]

A veces —raras veces— se ensaya escribir el verso eneasílabo en estrofas isosilábicas [2].

A partir de 1650, el eneasílabo, en combinaciones rítmicas, se refugia en la poesía popular y en las obras breves del teatro —entremeses, sainetes, bailes, jácaras, mojigangas—, donde persiste hasta entrado el siglo XVIII. Pero, en la poesía culta, Calderón y su escuela le tienen muy poca afición, y acaba por desaparecer.

§ 8. ABUNDANCIA DE ESQUEMAS LIBRES. — Inútil es decir que las formas irregulares, sin ritmos definidos, o con gran mezcla de ritmos, adquieren boga también; pero, como rebeldes a reglas, a la tendencia unificadora que se inicia durante la segunda mitad de la centuria, acaban por desaparecer de la poesía culta y en el siglo XVIII desaparecen hasta de las obras breves del teatro.

Entre estos grupos de versificación libre, durante algún tiempo tiende a definirse uno, cuya característica es el empleo de los decasílabos bipartitos (5-5), existentes en el metro de gaita gallega como variantes del decasílabo anapéstico. Muestras de este verso se hallan desde el siglo XVI en las *endechas de Canaria* que trae Pisador en su *Libro de vihuela* [3]; después de 1600 hay muchas más, que a menudo se unen al eneasílabo. Así, en la danza del *Cachupino*, de origen americano:

> Vení, criollitas de Portobello...
> Cachupino, no te detengas...
>
> > *(Mojiganga del Folión*, hacia 1660) [4].

O en la *Danza de gitanos:*

> Canten y bailen las gitanillas...
>
> > *(Mojiganga de la gitanada*, hacia 1670) [5]

---

[1] Además de los trozos citados, véanse los cantares de la espigaderuela y de «Esta sí», en *La mejor espigadera*, los de *El pretendiente al revés* (véase nota a «Que si buena era la verbena...» en este mismo § 7), *Antona García* («Rastrillábalo el aldeana»; véase § 7 del cap. III) y *Todo es dar en una cosa* («Tan hermosa como la reina»).

[2] Véanse en el siglo XVI «Bailad en la fiesta, zagales...» (§ 21 del cap. III), y «Bullicioso y claro arroyuelo...» (§ 2 del cap. IV).

[3] Véase § 9 del cap. III, nota final.

[4] Véase COTARELO, Introducción a los *Entremeses...*, págs. CCXXXVI.

[5] Véase COTARELO, Introducción a los *Entremeses...*, pág. CCL.

O motes como éste:

> Pelota, pelotica del rey,
> que no me engañaréis otra vez... [1]

> —Este mundo es una escala
> que unos la suben y otros la bajan. [2]

> —Huéspeda, máteme una gallina,
> que el carnero me hace mal.
>> (Calderón, *El alcalde de Zalamea*, y Quiñones
>> de Benavente, *La visita de la cárcel).*

Pero su duración no es larga.

El apogeo de los esquemas libres se alcanza, más que en Lope —que prefirió los ritmos mejor definidos—, en Luis Quiñones de Benavente, gran maestro de los entremeses:

> ...Quien quisiere gozar del invierno,
> en lo templado y lo tierno,
> con más seguros compases,
> busque a Madrid con sus hipocrases,
> y si lo duda,
> San Martín y la Puebla son tragos de ayuda.
>> *(El invierno y el verano).*

> Hoy tenemos, como dicen en el cielo,
> el padre alcalde,
> que nos da pan y vino de balde:
> porque en este mundo cojo
> no le hallamos por un ojo,
> y pues hace a los hombres cosquillas,
> toquen y tañan las campanillas:
>> dilín, dilín,
> media capa es de San Martín;
>> dilón, dilón,
> y el cochino de San Antón. [3]
>> Dan, dan, dan,
> Y es testigo San Sebastián.
>> Loro, loro,
> trompeticas suenan de oro.
>> Tata, tata,
> campanicas repican de plata;
> coman los hombres del coeli coelorum
> per omnia saecula saeculorum.
>> *(Los gorrones).*

---

[1] Manuscrito 3.700, Biblioteca Nacional.
[2] Poesías atribuídas a Góngora.
[3] Véase en el § 7 «¡Ay, que tañen en San Martín!»

Otro ejemplo:

> Flores cogen las zagalejas, mas ¿para qué?
> Que ni lucen, ni huelen, ni tienen color,
> con mejillas y boca de grana y clavel.

(Lope, *El aldehuela*) [1].

> Corre, vuela, calla y verás
> cómo en las manos de un viejo
> pone hoy franca
> la palomica blanca;
> que pone, que pare:
> que pare como virgen,
> que pone como madre.

(Góngora, 1615).

§ 9. LAS ESTROFAS. — Poco hay que decir sobre las estrofas en el siglo XVII. La isometría —solamente relativa [2]— predomina; pero la asimetría se halla en diversas ocasiones: en Calderón, accidentalmente («Hola, aho, ah del valle, pastores», en *El laurel de Apolo*); en Moreto («Éste sí que es pan», en el auto *La gran Casa de Austria*); con frecuencia en Quiñones de Benavente y los autores de entremeses y bailes [3].

§ 10. RELACIONES CON LA POESÍA GALAICO-PORTUGUESA. — Sabemos que si la seguidilla y los esquemas libres, en su mayor parte, pueden considerarse de origen castellano, cabe atribuir parentesco galaico-portugués a los versos de gaita gallega, a los eneasílabos y a las estrofas paralelísticas y encadenadas [4]. Los poetas portugueses que escribían en castellano —en particular Gil Vicente, Sâ de Miranda, Andrade Caminha —fueron camino para mantener activa la influencia de la poesía popular de occidente en Castilla, a la vez que contribuían a difundir la poesía popular castellana en su país [5].

El juego de influencias entre Portugal y Castilla —influencias que principian a ser mutuas en el siglo XV, siendo probablemente uno de los primeros ejemplos de influjo castellano en oc-

---

[1] Véase en Lope, además, *Los pastores de Belén;* por ejemplo, en el libro III, «Toca, toca las campanillas...».

[2] Véase § 24 del cap. III.

[3] La cita de *Los gorrones* en el § 8 es buen ejemplo.

[4] Casos individuales de relaciones, ya directas, ya probables, entre los cantares castellanos y la poesía galaico-portuguesa, se han ido señalando a lo largo de los capítulos anteriores. Véanse cap. I, §§ 5, 7 y 8; todo el cap. II, y en especial los §§ 1, 3 a 5, 9, 11, 17 a 22, 28, 29 y 31; cap. III, §§ 5, 6, 7, 8, 9, 12, 14, 16, 20 y 24.

[5] Véase cap. II, §§ 5, 23 y 29; cap. III, §§ 3 a 6, 8, 9, 11, 14, 15 y 24, y nota 2, pág. 80. Además, el *Catálogo... de los autores portugueses que escribieron en castellano,* de García Peres.

cidente la seguidilla de Don Pedro de Portugal [1] — llega a su punto máximo en el siglo XVI y no cesa en la certuria siguiente.

Hay cantares portugueses o gallegos de versificación ya silábica, ya irregular, en las obras de varios poetas del siglo XVII, generalmente con el lenguaje estragado o mezclado, o cuando menos, mala ortografía: en Lope, *La mayor virtud de un rey* («Barqueriña fermosa, passaime») [2]; *El príncipe perfecto*, segunda parte («Em a fonte está Leonor» y «Sale a estela de alba»); *No son todos ruiseñores* (la misma *alba* anterior); en Valdivielso, *Romancero espiritual*, pág. 45 («Miño Sinor»); en Tirso, *La gallega Mari Hernández* («Cando o crego...») [3]; en Quiñones de Benavente, entremeses *El borracho* («Menina fermosa»), *El barbero* («Minino fermoso»), *Las nueces* («Quem te vera, corazón»), *Las dueñas* («Ca-tillaons que vais a ostanco»); en Rojas Zorrilla, entremés *El alcalde Ardite* («Ollay, mineña fermosa e graciosa»); en Jerónimo de Cáncer, entremés *El portugués* («Zarambeque»); en Luis Vélez de Guevara, *Reinar después de morir* (acto I: «Saudade minha» [4]); en la mejicana Sor Juana Inés de la Cruz —prueba de la gala literaria que representaban estas intercalaciones—, *Villancicos a San Pedro Apóstol* (Méjico, 1677); en Agustín de Salazar y Torres, Loa para *Dar tiempo al tiempo*, de Calderón («Con as carnestolendas | e con a gayta»); en Antonio de Zamora, *Baile de la Maya*, ya a principios del siglo XVIII:

> Por la pontiña de Zaragoza
> veinte y cinco ceguiños van;
> cada cego leva sua moza,
> cada moza leva seu can... [5]

y en autores desconocidos o dudosos: en *La lindona de Galicia*, atribuída a Juan Pérez de Montalván (acto II: «Esposo de Leonor»), en el *Entremés de la Hechicera*, impreso en 1644 con autos de Lope (versos irregulares); en la *Mojiganga del Folión*, hacia 1660 («Si vos, niña nay»); en el *Baile del Sotillo de Manzanares*, que precede a la comedia *El bastardo de Ceuta*, de Juan de Gra-

---

[1] Véase cap. II, § 23.
[2] Véase cap. II. § 11.
[3] Véase cap. II, § 11.
[4] Véase cap. III, § 6. —Para Rojas, véase COTARELO, Introducción a los *Entremeses*..., pág. LXXXVIII; para Cáncer, págs. CLIII y CCLXXII.
[5] Véase COTARELO, Introducción a los *Entremeses*..., pág. CCIV. — Hay también versos portugueses, octosílabos regulares, en las *Rimas del incógnito* (núm. 15); Góngora escribió un diálogo en portugués y castellano, la Letrilla de Carillo y Gil (1615): «¿A qué tangem en Castela?» Los personajes portugueses o gallegos que hablan su lengua no eran raros en el teatro. Durante el siglo XVI se hallan versos en lengua occidental en Castillejo (véase § 6 del capítulo III) y en el *Cancionero de Upsala* (núms. 9 y 54), entre otros ejemplos. Véanse, además, págs. CCXX y CCCI de la Introducción a los *Entremeses*... de Cotarelo.

jales, en edición de 1616 —una canción con eneasílabos—, «Non votéis a mi nina fora», y una muiñeira indudable:

> Asenteime en un formigueiro,
> docho a demo lo asentadeiro [1].
> Asenteime en un verde prado,
> docho a demo lo mal sentado.
> Yo pasé por la ciuz de ferro,
> voto fize volverme luego;
> non volví, porque allá en Castilla
> de follona soy polidilla.
> Soy de mi Pedro moza lozana,
> cuando me mira limpia y galana.
> Si pasáis por los míos umbrales,
> ¡ay de vos si no me mirades!
> Daime la mano si me queredes,
> miños ollos, ahora day, day, day,
> dadme la mano, day, day, day.

No sólo los cantares gallegos y portugueses demuestran la influencia occidental en Castilla: también la revelan los cantares castellanos relativos a la gaita, como el de «Ándese la gaita por el lugar» [2], o los que tienen las peculiaridades de las muiñeiras —no sólo el metro y la división de los versos en hemistiquios, y la frecuente disposición en dísticos, sino también las repeticiones de palabras del primer verso en el segundo y a veces el paralelismo elemental. Recuérdense los ejemplos de versos decasílabos que trae el maestro Correas: «Arremanguéme y hice colada» y «Póntela tú, la gorra del fraile»: el último trozo, muy popular en el teatro [3]. Véanse otros:

> ¡Ay, que a las velas de Casilda santa,
> Quintana de Burela se lleva la gala!
> ¡Ay, que a la vela de los lagos nuesos,
> a todos se la gana la gaita de Bueso!
> Que el pandero y la gaita de Ontoria
> táñela tú, que a mí no me toca.
>
> (Tirso, *Los lagos de San Vicente*, jornada III).

> Hilandera era la aldena:
> más come que gana, más come que gana.
> ¡Ay, que hilando estaba Gila!
> Más bebe que hila, más bebe que hila.
>
> (Tirso, *Antona García*).

---

[1] Véase Tirso, «Cando o crego...», § 11 del cap. II.
[2] Véase cap. III, § 23.
[3] Véase cap. III, § 20; además, §§ 7 y 11.

Seis reales dan por el tordo de Juana,
seis por el pico y seis por la lana [1].
Que no hay tal andar como estar en casa,
que no hay tal andar como en casa estar.

(Atribuído a Góngora.)

¿Yo qué la hice, yo qué la hago,
que me ha dado tan mal pago?
¿Yo qué la hago, yo qué la hice,
que palabra de amor no me dice? [2]

No tenéis vos calzas coloradas,
no tenéis vos calzas como yo [3].

Todavía a principios del siglo XVIII se registra en Diego de Torres Villarroel la primera aparición que conozco del cantar más célebre de la gaita gallega:

Tanto bailé con la gaita gallega,
tanto bailé que me enamoré de ella.
Tanto bailé, tanto bailara,
tanto bailé que me enamoricara [4].

§ 11. LA POESÍA CATALANA Y VALENCIANA. — No he tenido elementos para estudiar íntegramente las relaciones entre la poesía popular de Castilla y la de Cataluña y Valencia. La influencia de la versificación irregular castellana y galaico-portuguesa llegó hasta Cataluña, no hay duda, y allí se conocen e imitan como en toda España los cantares de gaita gallega [5].

Los poetas cultos de Cataluña que escribían en castellano recogen uno que otro fragmento de versificación irregular. Así, desde el siglo XV, Pedro Moner:

¿Dónde vas posar,
aguilílla caudal? [6]

---

[1] *Poesías de antaño*, pág. 275 del vol. XXXI de la *Revue Hispanique*.

[2] Valdivielso, *Ensaladilla del Retablo*.

[3] *Baile de Los locos de Toledo*, anónimo, 1616. Véase «No tenéis vos licor de lo caro», en el entremés de *Los órganos*, de Quiñones de Benavente; además el entremés del *Doctor Rapado*.

[4] Villancico de *La gaita zamorana*.

[5] Véase MILÁ, *Del decasílabo y endecasílabo anapésticos*, en *Obras*, vol. V, págs. 324, 325, 338, 339 y 340. — Además, *Obras*, vol. VI, págs. 74 a 81, 185 a 191 y 198 a 200.

[6] Véase *Antología de poetas líricos castellanos*, de M. MENÉNDEZ Y PELAYO, vol. VII, pág. CCXLVI.

Así, en el XVI, Boscán: «Allególe y enamoróle»; en el XVII, el canónigo Blanch, a quien cita Milá. Y, naturalmente, los valencianos como Timoneda y el Canónigo Tárrega [1].

Posteriormente no he encontrado signos de relaciones castellano-catalanas en la versificación acentual, sino en el *Cancionero de Upsala* (núms. 23, versos irregulares copiados como prosa, 35 y 45, ambos con elementos ligeramente irregulares) [2], y en el cantar paralelístico que introduce Calderón en *El pintor de su deshonra:*

> Veníu las miñonas
> a bailar al Clos.
> ¡Tararera!
> Que en las Carnestolendas
> se disfraz amor.
> ¡Tararera!'
> Veníu los fadrines
> al Clos a bailar.
> ¡Tararera!
> Que en las Carnestolendas
> amor se disfraz.
> ¡Tararera!

De Valencia vinieron la danza de las *Paradetas* y la llamada *Valenciana,* para la cual da esta letra Gaspar de Olmedo, a principios del siglo XVIII, en su piececilla *La Valenciana:*

> Chiquetes, cuidat,
> cuidat con el baile,
> chiquetes, cuidat,
> que ve el alcalde [3].

---

[1] Véase cap. III, §§ 9 y 10.

[2] El núm. 24, catalán, tiene versificación regular. — Acaso sería posible establecer relaciones entre los gritos onomatopéyicos del núm. 35 y los núms. 33 y 36, castellanos, del mismo *Cancionero* (véase cap. III, § 3, nota sobre Encina, § 9: «Teresilla, hermana...», y § 20). Véanse, además, la canción núm. 436, en italiano corrupto, del *Cancionero musical de los siglos XV y XVI,* el baile canario en *San Diego de Alcalá,* de Lope, el final del *Entremés del Platillo,* de Simón Aguado (1602), y podría hacerse cotejo también entre el son de campanas en el núm. 45 y en el romance «Campanitas de Belén» en el libro III de *Los pastores de Belén,* de Lope, y en su comedia *No son todos ruiseñores,* o en el *Baile del pastoral,* anónimo (colección de *Entremeses, loas, bailes, jácaras y mojigangas):* los ejemplos podrían multiplicarse.

[3] Véase COTARELO, Introducción a los *Entremeses...,* págs. CCLV y CCLXIII. Además, en Solís (COTARELO, *Introducción,* pág. XCV):

> A bailar con Juan Rana
> al uso catalán ¡faralela!,
> al uso catalán ¡faralela!

Y en EDUARDO LÓPEZ CHAVARRI, *Música popular española,* Barcelona, 1927, versificación irregular valenciana del siglo XVII.

§ 12. Los poetas anónimos de Castilla. — La mejor contribución del siglo XVII al tesoro de la versificación irregular castellana procede de los poetas cultos. Los versos de sabor popular que alcanzan boga vienen en su mayor parte del siglo XVI o de antes, según se comprueba en muchos casos y podría comprobarse en otros, si se buscara minuciosamente [1]. Letras estrictamente populares que sean del todo nuevas, me parece que no las hay en muy gran número; es probable que la mayor parte sean las de nuevos bailes, como el de *Marizápalos*. Desde la segunda mitad del siglo XVI se generaliza la tendencia a convertir en bailes muchas canciones que en su origen fueron puramente líricas, como la de las *Vacas* y la del *Caballero de Olmedo* [2]; la seguidilla hubo de ser canción solamente antes de ser baile: la transformación ocurrió poco antes de 1600 [3]. En el siglo XVII la multiplicación de los bailes, especialmente a partir del reinado de Felipe IV, es enorme, y se emplean en ellos letras antiguas o nuevas. Los *bailes* del teatro contienen multitud de ejemplos [4].

Fuera de las danzas, la poesía de autores anónimos que recogen los cancioneros no tiene a menudo sabor popular, aparte de los estribillos y de coplas muy breves [5]. A los ejemplos de sabor culto, aunque anónimos, citados ya («Cómo retumban las palas», «¿Qué quiere amor» o «Aves, fieras, fuentes y ríos»), pueden agregarse otros:

> ¡Ay, cómo siente!
> Mas ¡ay, cómo llora
> pasadas, perdidas glorias!
> ¡Ay, qué rigor,
> que llore Jacinta
> desprecios de amor!
> Mas llore y pene,
> porque sepa la niña
> sentir desdenes.

> (*Maravillas del Parnaso*) [6].

> Cantaréis, pajarillo nuevo,
> de rama en rama y de flor en flor,
> mas si vos salís al prado
> y os acecha el cazador,
> probaréis la liga,

---

[1] Véanse notas a los §§ 4 a 7, 9 a 11, 13, y 19 a 23 del cap. III.

[2] Véase cap. III, §§ 6 y 13.

[3] Véanse §§ 17 y 19 del cap. III.

[4] Véase COTARELO, Introducción a los *Entremeses*..., páginas CLXXII y siguientes.

[5] Véanse §§ 2, 5, 6 y 7 de este capítulo.

[6] Véase Góngora, § 17 de este capítulo.

lloraréis la prisión
de rama en rama y de flor en flor.

(Cancionero de Sablonara, núm. 67.)

Al son de los arroyuelos
cantan las aves de flor en flor
que no hay más gloria que amor
ni mayor pena que celos.

(Maravillas del Parnaso.)

Pastorcillo, gala del prado,
si por nieve a la sierra vas,
míralo bien, y advierte, zagal,
que Belisa la tiene en su frente.
Mas huye sus ojos, ¡ay de ti!, ¡ay de ti!,
advierte, zagal,
que sin nieve y con fuego vendrás.

(Obras musicales de Mosén Juan Bautista Comes, valenciano, 1568-1643, publicadas en Madrid, dos vols., 1888.)

B) El papel de los poetas cultos

§ 13. Lope de Vega (1562-1635). — La incorporación de elementos populares en el teatro artístico, iniciada desde los orígenes del drama moderno con Juan del Encina y Fernando de Rojas, vino a completarse con la triunfal irrupción de Lope de Vega. Lope fué en todo mucho más adelante que ninguno de sus precursores. De hecho, incorporó en el teatro toda la poesía del pueblo.

Muchos poetas y escritores han sentido en España la atracción del arte popular; ninguno tan hondamente como Lope. Apenas hay nota del espíritu del pueblo que Lope no sepa tocar: la sencilla solemnidad de sus asambleas, como en *Los jueces de Castilla;* la resuelta actividad de sus multitudes indignadas, como en *Fuente-ovejuna;* el amor al terruño y a las prácticas tradicionales, como en *Peribáñez y el Comendador de Ocaña;* la vivacidad y el ímpetu de sus costumbres y fiestas de ciudad o de campo; las romerías, las vigilias, las bodas, los banquetes, los bailes, los juegos y deportes. Le divertían los toscos chistes de los villanos, sirvientes y rústicos; quizá, de no ser así, no habría tendido en sus comedias a la prodigalidad, no siempre grata, de sus *figuras del donaire.*

El papel de la poesía popular, ya silábica, ya irregular, es muy variado en los dramas de Lope. Puede fundar sobre ella sus dramas; así, *Peribáñez* se basa en una cuarteta de romance:

Más quiero yo a Peribáñez
con su capa la pardilla,

193

que al Comendador de Ocaña
con la suya guarnecida.

El Caballero de Olmedo se basa en una seguidilla y *Los Comendadores de Córdoba* en una endecha glosada en seguidillas, cantares
ambos de asunto histórico; en seguidillas se basan *El galán de la
Membrilla* y *Al pasar del arroyo;* en un breve refrán asonantado,
El aldehuela:

> Más mal hay en el aldehuela
> del que se suena [1].

Puede emplear la canción, o el romance, como *leit motiv*, sin
hacerlos núcleo de la obra. Así, la serranilla de «Yo me iba, madre», en el auto *La venta de la Zarzuela*.

Puede emplearlos como reminiscencia, cita o imitación: tal
el romance de *Peribáñez* en *San Isidro labrador de Madrid* (acto
II) o el de Vellido Dolfos en el auto *La siega*. Puede entretejerlos
en la urdimbre de los dramas históricos sobre Fernán González,
Bernardo del Carpio, los Infantes de Lara y Doña Elvira en Toro.
Puede tomar de ellos el pie de glosas o letrillas, aunque en tales
casos usa también versos de poetas cultos, como Garcilaso, Alcázar o Góngora. Puede, en fin, adoptarlos o imitarlos para los
episodios de canto y de baile que existen en los autos — con pocas excepciones — y en muy cerca de la mitad de sus comedias.
A veces, siembra su obra original de trozos anónimos: así en el
auto de *Los cantares*.

Los cantares pueden estar en metros silábicos — tales el romance, el romancillo, la endecha, la redondilla — o en versos
irregulares: en general, prefiere Lope los que se ajustan a esquemas
claros, evidentes, como la seguidilla, los versos de gaita gallega,
los eneasílabos; de cuando en cuando se va hacia los esquemas
libres y aun a los informes de las rimas infantiles y de los refranes [2].

---

[1] Véase la nota sobre las seguidillas en Lope, § 3 de este capítulo. Otros
poetas, como Trillo y Figueroa, emplean como estribillo el refrán del *Aldehuela*. Después de Lope, se hace común escribir comedias con asuntos, o siquiera títulos, tomados de canciones, refranes o frases proverbiales; así:
Yo por vos y vos por otro, de Moreto; *La niña de Gómez Arias, Fuego de Dios
en el querer bien* y *Casa de dos puertas mala es de guardar*, de Calderón. En
nuestro tiempo, reaparece la costumbre con *La Dolores*, de Felíu y Codino;
La malquerida, de Benavente; *Mundo, mundillo*, de los Quintero. En la
Argentina ha existido, hacía 1920, la moda de buscar los títulos de los sainetes en los versos del *Martín Fierro*, de José Hernández (1872), y especialmente en los proverbios del viejo Vizcacha, de *La vuelta de Martín Fierro* (1878).

[2] Véanse cap. I, § 10; cap. II, §§ 11, 17, 22 y 27; cap. III, §§ 8, 9, 10, 11,
13, 19, 20 y 21; cap. IV, §§ 2 a 8 y 10. —Sobre las relaciones de Lope con
la poesía popular, véanse MENÉNDEZ Y PELAYO, *Antología*, vol. IX, págs.
259 y siguientes; MENÉNDEZ P:DAL, *La primitiva poesía lírica española*,
págs. 340-342, y JOSÉ F. MONTESINOS, en el excelente prólogo al tomo I
de *Poesías líricas* de Lope, Madrid, 1925 (*Clásicos de «La Lectura»*), págs.
34-45.

§ 14. Tirso de Molina (c. 1571-1648). — Lope fué precedido o acompañado en su empresa de popularización por Cervantes (en el teatro y la novela), Góngora y los dramaturgos de Valencia, para el cantar de versificación irregular, como por los dramaturgos de Sevilla (más exactamente, Juan de la Cueva, precursor indudable) para el romance. Cuánto le corresponde como impulsor de la tendencia, es difícil decidir: a menos que fuera posible (y no lo es) establecer las fechas de toda la literatura de aquel tiempo, no se podrían determinar con exactitud las precedencias. Lope fué tan creador como receptivo; la línea de demarcación entre lo que inicia y lo que acoge es siempre vaga en cualquiera de sus obras.

Su influencia es innegable, por lo menos, en los dramaturgos que le siguen: la mayoría de la escuela de Valencia en su pleno desarrollo, por ejemplo, o Tirso de Molina, que toma de él el tipo de la *comedia* y lo desarrolla con el sabor de su propia personalidad, llegando al fin a refluir sobre su modelo. Hombre muy diverso de Lope, más cuidadoso artista y agudo estudiante de la naturaleza humana, Tirso sólo cede ante él en amor y entendimiento de las cosas del pueblo. Sus cantares de verso irregular son de los más deliciosos, por su sabor nativo y su encanto musical. Entre los distintos metros irregulares, escogió, para darle música especial, aquel en que predomina el eneasílabo. Con Lope, y con él, se hizo costumbre, no sólo transcribir o imitar las letras populares, sino introducir cantares de versificación irregular en las comedias [1].

§ 15. Los otros dramaturgos. — Don Juan Ruiz de Alarcón (c. 1580-1639), con sus tendencias aristocráticas y didácticas, huye de las formas populares; excepción: la seguidilla de *Las paredes oyen*. El espíritu del criollo mejicano no se compenetró totalmente con el español peninsular, lleno del rústico vigor del terruño castizo.

Los demás dramaturgos sí proceden como Lope y Tirso; Valdivielso en sus autos; los autores de Villancicos para Navidad y otras fiestas eclesiásticas, los cuales comienzan entonces a multiplicarse como rudimentarios dramas líricos en las grandes iglesias de toda España [2]; los dramaturgos menores, como el valenciano Gas-

---

[1] Véanse cap. II, § 11; cap. III §§ 7, 10, 11, 20 y 21; cap. IV, §§ 2, 3, 5, 6, 7 y 10.

[2] Véase cap. III, §§ 12, nota final, y 16, nota final. Los ejemplos quizá más accesibles de estos Villancicos eclesiásticos son los de Sor Juana Inés de la Cruz, escritos y publicados en Méjico, entre 1677 y 1690, y reimpresos en los tomos I y II de sus *Obras*, ediciones de los siglos XVII y XVIII, hechas en España. Después de la primera edición de este libro, Cejador entresacó muchos ejemplos de poesía a la manera popular, en su mayor parte de versificación acentual, de los Villancicos eclesiásticos: véase *La verdadera poe-*

par de Aguilar, Andrés de Claramonte, Monteser, Antonio Hurtado de Mendoza, Salas Barbadillo, Castillo Solórzano; los de mayor distinción, como Mora de Mescua y Vélez de Guevara [1]. En años posteriores, Calderón, Rojas Zorrilla, Moreto y toda la legión de la segunda época del gran teatro, continúan la costumbre; pero en sus manos comienzan a regularizarse los metros irregulares [2].

Si los cantares de versificación irregular abundan en las comedias, son mucho más frecuentes —punto menos que indispensables— en las obras dramáticas breves: los autos, antes y después de su maestro supremo, Calderón; las zarzuelas y otras fiestas con música, donde Calderón también impera; los entremeses, los sainetes, las jácaras, las mojigangas, y en particular las obrillas que reciben el nombre de bailes. En éstos domina Luis Quiñones de Benavente: nadie le alcanzó en sus excesos de desconyuntamiento rítmico; el efecto cómico en tales esquemas extravagantes es visible [3]. Durante muchos años, hasta el siglo XVIII, cuando la versificación irregular había dejado de serlo en las comedias, los géneros menores del teatro la conservaron.

---

sía castellana, vol. I, págs. 278-302; vol. II, págs. 42, 56, 114, 128-137, 140-167, 236, 298-300, 311, 359 y 376; vol. IV, págs. 15, 22, 47-59, 63-69, 84, 90-97, 108, 124, 141, 164, 183, 187, 207, 219, 225, 227, 243, 291 y 311.

[1] De los dramaturgos mencionados, contemporáneos de la madurez o de la vejez de Lope, véanse *El mercader amante*, de Aguilar (coplas finales: «¿Que su oficio ha Juan dejado?»); *El valiente negro en Flandes*, *Desta agua no beberé* y *El infanzón de Illescas*, de Claramonte; *El Caballero de Olmedo* y entremeses y bailes, de Monteser; entremeses de Mendoza, Salas y Castillo Solórzano (de quienes hay también versificación irregular en poesía lírica o novela); *La rueda de la fortuna*, de Mira de Mescua; *La serrana de la Vera*, actos I y II (edición Menéndez Pidal, notas, pág. 151), *Reinar después de morir* y *La luna de la sierra*, de Vélez de Guevara (véanse también sus versos líricos en el *Ensayo*, de GALLARDO, vol. I, cols. 1.029 y 1.054, y el tranco VI de *El diablo cojuelo*).

[2] De Rojas, véase *Entre bobos anda el juego* («Mozuelas de la corte, | todo es caminar»); *Lo que son mujeres* (seguidillas «Hoy cumple quince años», 6-5-7-5); *García del Castañar* («Si vengo de Toledo | Teresa mía...»; véanse, además, cap. III, § 10 y cap. IV, § 7); *Lo que quería ver el Marqués de Villena* (seguidillas 7-5 y versos de gaita gallega); *Don Pedro Miago* (cantar del juego de cañas, en esquema libre); auto *La viña de Nabot* («Viñaderas, hola», esquema libre).

De Moreto, véanse *La misma conciencia acusa* («Dábale con el azadoncito»; véase cap. IV, § 7); *Antíoco y Seleuco* («Al empeño de amor más lucido», versos de gaita gallega en esquema regular); auto *La gran Casa de Austria* («Este sí que es pan», versos irregulares de gaita gallega); baile *Las fiestas de Palacio*, véase cap. IV, § 2, y *La zamalandrana* (véase COTARELO, Introducción, pág. CXCII); Loa a los años del Emperador de Alemania, 1655 (seguidillas).

[3] Ensayé obtener el promedio de versos irregulares en relación con el número total de versos en las obras de Quiñones de Benavente, pero desistí del propósito después de haber obtenido la proporción en unas diez: los resultados son demasiado desiguales para que el promedio represente cosa semejante a los obtenidos por Morley respecto de Alarcón o Moreto. En una

§ 16. LA POESÍA RELIGIOSA. — Fenómeno curioso, revelador del carácter popular, folk-lórico, que adquirieron en España las creencias cristianas: la poesía religiosa hizo constantemente uso del pueblo como elemento y fuente de arte, tanto introduciendo al pastor y al villano en persona como adaptando los productos de su musa ingenua. Así se hizo, en la poesía religiosa que asume forma dramática —las comedias de santos y de asuntos bíblicos, los autos del Sacramento y del Nacimiento, los Villancicos de Navidad y de otras solemnidades—; así se hizo en la poesía lírica. A principios del siglo XVII, son varios los poetas cuyos versos líricos de asunto religioso remedan el tono de la poesía humilde sobre todo si cantan el misterio de la humildad divina en el portal de Belén: Alonso de Ledesma, cuyos *Juegos de Nochesbuenas a lo divino* (1605) transportan en sentido religioso las reliquias de fórmula infantil o de canción irregular con que se ejecutaban, y se ejecutan aún, las evoluciones de muchos entretenimientos y representaciones en miniatura, como el *Abejón* y *Cuántos panes hay en el arca* y *Lirón, lirón* (moderno *A la limón*), y cuyos *Conceptos espirituales* (1602 a 1612) contienen estribillos de canto y danza [1]. De modo semejante proceden otros poetas contemporáneos suyos: Francisco de Ocaña, en su *Cancionero para cantar la noche de Navidad y las fiestas de Pascua* (1603); Francisco de Ávila, en sus *Villancicos y coplas curiosas al nacimiento del Hijo de Dios* (1606); Andrés de Claramonte, y tantos más [2].

---

obra, la relación entre los versos irregulares y el total era 11 por 100; en otra, 17; en otra, 27; en otra, 33; en otra, 37. Hay, en fin, entremeses sin versos irregulares; en cambio, bailes donde la proporción de los irregulares respecto del total es hasta de 85 por 100. Para citas de Quiñones de Benavente, véanse cap. III, §§ 4, 10, 11, 19, 21 y 23; cap. IV, §§ 2 a 4 y 6 a 10.

[1] Véase cap. II, § 17. En el vol. XXXV de la Biblioteca de Rivadeneyra están reproducidos los *Juegos de Nochesbuenas* (núms. 375 a 429) y parte de los *Conceptos espirituales*. *Juegos* dignos de mención: 375, «Corran, caballeros», relacionado con el de *Lirón, lirón*, núm. 409, que también está en el *Baile de la Maya*, atribuído a Miguel Sánchez (véase cap. III, § 10); 385, «Sopla, vivo te lo do. —¿Para do?» (véase Sebastián de Horozco, cap. III, § 7); 394, *Pájara pinta* (la versión moderna usual está en versos irregulares; Ledesma sólo da el título); 400, «Norabuena venga» (véase cap. III, §§ 11 y 20); 403, *Al Nacimiento*, como ensaladilla, donde se intercalan los cantares de «Cómo retumban las palas» (véase cap. IV, § 2), «Bailad en esta ocasión» (véase cap. IV, § 21), «Dejadme llorar» (véase Góngora y *El valor de las mujeres*, de Lope), y «Que miraba la mar | la mal casada; | que miraba la mar | cómo es ancha y larga» (cantarcillo popular del siglo XVI, que aparece en uno de los *Romancerillos de la Biblioteca Ambrosiana* y en el Príncipe de Esquilache); 419, «Luna que reluces» (véase cap. III, § 22); 420, «Caracol, col, col, | saca tus cuernos al rayo del sol» (véase *Poesías de antaño*, pág. 278, y *Cantares españoles*, de Rodríguez Marín, núm. 119); 426, «Vente a mí, torillo hosquillo, | toro bravo, vente a mí» (véase cap. III, § 20)

[2] Véanse el vol. XXXV de la Biblioteca de Rivadeneyra, y GALLARDO, *Ensayo*, vol. I, col. 343, seguidillas: «Portalico divino...», «Pues el rey de los cielos...», «Este niño chiquito...», del maestro Ávila, y vol. III, col. 1.007; además, para otros poetas de este tipo, véase vol. IV, col. 635 (Lope de Sosa *Villancicos*, 1.603), y col. 983 (Francisco de Velasco, *Cancionero*, 1.603).

Sobre todos ellos se levanta Lope, cuya presencia es inevitable en toda manifestación literaria de su tiempo, con la delicada inspiración de su *Romancero espiritual* (1624), de sus *Rimas sacras*, en parte reimpresión del anterior (1625), y, más aún, con las exquisitas flores de devoción que contiene su novela sacra *Los pastores de Belén* (1612).

Hay otro poeta digno de mención especial, porque en muchas ocasiones llega a competir con Lope en devoción ingenua: Fray José de Valdivielso, singular por la ternura y la unción. Se distingue por su exquisito sentido musical; su empleo |de los metros irregulares, combinado con la dulzura de su lenguaje, da a sus canciones sabor delicado [1].

§ 17. GÓNGORA. — En la poesía lírica *humana*, como entonces se decía, en las *prosas profanas*, Góngora es en aquellos tiempos la figura de más alto prestigio; es el favorito de los músicos, es el poeta de los poetas, cuyos cantares intercalan o imitan en sus obras nada menos que Lope y Calderón [2]. Si Góngora hubiera producido sólo la mágica arquitectura plateresca de sus versos de corte italiano —los sonetos, el *Panegírico*, el *Polifemo*, las *Soledades*, las obras que le dieron su fama última y crearon su inmensa y extraña influencia—, podría admirársele como artífice, pero no se le sentiría tanto como lírico ni se le aprendería de memoria. Góngora acudió también, como Lope y Tirso, a la fuente popular para descifrar el secreto de los sentires vivos y frescos; no sólo a la fuente castellana y andaluza, sino la gallega y portuguesa, donde el sentimiento ha sido tradicionalmente delicado y melancólico.

Góngora no adopta canciones occidentales, como Lope o Tirso [3], aunque sí escribe en portugués; pero él es quien se acerca' más a menudo que otros, al tono femenino, al tono de suspiro y de misterio que dominó en la arcaica poesía galaico-portuguesa y perduraba en buena parte de los cantares castellanos del siglo

---

[1] Véanse cap. II, § 30; cap. III, §§ 9, 10, 11, 20, 21 y 22; cap. IV, §§ 3, 4, 6, 7 y 10.

[2] Lope toma pie de poesías de Góngora, o de estribillos usados por él, para dos comedias suyas: *En un pastoral albergue* y *No son todos ruiseñores*. Entre las glosas e imitaciones están la de «Las flores del romero» en *Los pastores de Belén*, la de «La más bella niña...» en *La adúltera perdonada*, y las diversas de «Aprended, flores, de mí», después innumerables en todo el teatro y la poesía lírica. Las deudas de Calderón a Góngora, además de «Las flores del romero» en *El alcalde de Zalamea*, se verán en seguida. Aun los autores anónimos de entremeses y *bailes* teatrales se inspiran en Góngora como se ve en el *Baile del Pastoral*, en el de la *Colmeneruela* y en el *Entremés de los Romances*, 1613. Moreto lo imita «a lo divino» en la *Loa del Corpus*.

[3] Los versos con que comienza la letrilla de Gil y Carillo, 1615, dialogada en castellano y portugués, no creo que provengan de un cantar:

—¿A qué tangen en Castela?
—A maitines.

XVI, como «Dezilde al caballero», o «Y con qué la lavaré», o «Aquellas sierras, madre». [1]

Góngora, al contrario de los poetas a quienes se ha mencionado antes, no compone él mismo cantares largos de versificación acentual [2]: en general compone apenas estribillos, pero los que toma del pueblo, combinándolos con sus coplas originales, se clavan en la memoria, muchas veces, como música penetrante, *haunting;* otros son burlescos, y se combinan con sus ingeniosas letrillas satíricas [3]. Otros cantares, en fin, obra original suya, tienen curioso sabor culto.

> Dejadme llorar,
> orillas de la mar [4].

> Déjame en paz, amor tirano... [5]

> ¿Qué lleva el señor Esgueva?
> Yo os diré lo que lleva... (1605)

> Trepan los gitanos
> y bailan ellas;
> otro nudo a la bolsa
> mientras que trepan... (1605)

> Las flores del romero... (1608) [6]

> Zambambú, morenica de Congo... (1609) [7]

> No son todos ruiseñores
> los que cantan entre flores
> sino campanitas de plata
> que tocan al alba,

---

[1] Véase cap. III, §§ 19 y 23.

[2] Véase, como excepción, el cantar en seguidillas «Mátanme los celos...» (1620), § 2 del cap. IV. Torner, sin embargo, en el estudio que se indicará en nota posterior, cree que toda la serie de seguidillas es popular, salvo retoques como «Zapata».

[3] Véase E. M. TORNER, *Elementos populares en las poesías de Góngora* en la *Revista de Filología Española*, 1927, vol. XIV, págs. 417-424.

[4] El *Romancero general*, en 1600, imprime estos dos versos así, irregulares, y no, como en ediciones modernas, reduciendo el segundo verso a «orillas del mar». Hay versiones del siglo XVII que traen «orillas de la mar, de la mar». Con todo, el autorizado manuscrito Chacón, que se custodia en la Biblioteca Nacional de Madrid, trae los versos regulares, y así aparece en la edición de Góngora, publicada por Foulché-Delbosc, con ayuda de Alfonso Reyes (tres vols., Nueva York y París, 1921). Véase § 16 de este capítulo, nota sobre Ledesma. Además, Lope, *El valor de las mujeres.*

[5] Para las demás poesías de Góngora, escritas entre 1580 y 1600, véase cap. III, § 13.

[6] Véase cap. IV, §§ 2 y 16.

[7] Composición que comienza «Mañana de Corpus Christi...». Otras cuatro poesías de 1609, dedicadas también al Sacramento, contienen versificación irregular; la hay, además, en una *A Nuestra Señora de Villaviciosa.*

sino campanitas de oro
que hacen la salva
a los soles que adoro... (1609) [1]

Al campo te desafía
la colmeneruela;
vén, Amor, si eres dios, y vuela...

Dímelo tú, sépalo él,
dímelo tú, si no eres cruel...

Que una abeja le lleva la flor... [2]

¡Ay, cómo gime!
Mas ¡ay, cómo suena
el remo a que nos condena
el niño Amor!
Clarín que rompe el albor
no suena mejor... (1614) [3]

Cuando toquen a los maitines
toquen en Jerusalem... (1615)

Písalo, mas como yo,
queditico.
Pisaré yo el polvico... [4]

Támaraz, que son miel y oro,
támaraz, que son oro y miel.

A voz el cachopinito,
cara de rosa,
la palma os guarde hermosa
del Egipto.
Támaraz... [5]

Algualete, hejo... (1615) [6]

---

[1] En la comedia de Lope, inspirada por este cantar, hay estas variantes:

...los que cantan entre las flores...
...que tañen al alba...

[2] En la especie de ensalada «Apeóse el caballero...» (1610). Véase nota sobre «Besóme en el Colmeneruelo...», § 6 de este capítulo. Además, *Dicha y desdicha del hombre*, de Calderón, y el *Baile de la Colmeneruela*, en la colección de Cotarelo.

[3] Véase cap. IV, § 12. Calderón reproduce íntegro este cantar en su comedia *En esta vida todo es verdad y todo mentira* y solamente los dos últimos versos en *La vida es sueño*. Además, Sor Juana Inés de la Cruz en sus Villancicos a Santa Catalina.

[4] Véase el cantar del Polvico en Cervantes y otros, § 11 del cap. III.

[5] En el diálogo «No sólo el campo nevado...» (1615). Véanse §§ 4 y 17 de este capítulo.

[6] En habla de moriscos.

Corre, vuela, calla y verás... (1615) [1]

Mátanme los celos... (1620) [2]

¡Hola! Que no llega la ola... [3]

Mala noche me diste, casada... (1625) [4]

—¿Doña Menga, de qué te ríes?
—Don Pascual, de que porfíes... (1626)

De poesías atribuídas a Góngora, y probablemente suyas:

> Pasa el melcochero,
> salen las mozas
> a los cascabeles,
> a las melcochas:
> mozas golosas,
> bailan unas y comen otras,
> y al tabaque se llegan todas.
> Tenga yo salud... [5]

En poesías atribuídas a Góngora, cuya autenticidad no acepta el editor, se hallan estos cantares:

> Sierras venturosas de Guadalupe,
> ¿qué es de mi esperanza, que en vos la puse?
> (Romance «Compitiendo con los cielos...»)

> Con el son de las hojas
> cantan las aves...
> Fugitivos cristales
> corred y volad.
> (Romance «La más lucida belleza...»)

> Cielo son tus ojos
> en ser azules...
> (Romance «Lluvias de mayo y de octubre...»)

—Que no hay tal andar como estar en casa... [6]

—Caracoles pide la niña... [7]

---

[1] Véase § 8 de este capítulo.
[2] Véase § 2 de este capítulo.
[3] Compárese con la página 182.
[4] En la especie de ensalada «A la fuente va del olmo...». Véase § 7 de este capítulo. Compárese Lope de Rueda: «Mala noche me diste, | María del Rión...»
[5] Véase § 23 del cap. III.
[6] Véase § 10 de este capítulo.
[7] Véase § 6 de este capítulo.

—Bailad en el corro, mozuelas... [1]

—Este mundo es una escala... [2]

—Aquel pajarillo que vuela, madre... [3]

—No me llame fea, calle,
que la llamaré vieja, madre.

—Soy toquera y vendo tocas...

—Porque soplan quedito los aires... [4]

§ 18. Poetas y novelistas. — La poesía lírica que trataba de asuntos humanos fué, con todo, influída por el verso popular mucho menos que la religiosa. El carácter del Renacimiento perduró en la lírica cortesana cuando ya se había borrado de la mayor parte de la literatura española. Con el carácter renacentista perduró la afición a los metros silábicos, y se dan muchos casos de poetas líricos que se sustraen a todo contacto con la musa del pueblo: los Argensola, Rioja, Valbuena, Jáuregui, Villegas, y grupos de artistas esencialmente literarios como la «escuela de Antequera» y la «escuela de Granada».

En el grupo contrario hay muchos poetas menores, en quienes la versificación irregular suele aparecer con las reminiscencias populares: Juan de Salinas, Pedro de Quirós, Antonio Hurtado de Mendoza —a quien no le falta gracia ni don musical—, Cosme Gómez Tejada de los Reyes, el Príncipe de Esquilache, el Conde de Rebolledo, el portugués D. Francisco Manuel de Melo, el gallego Francisco de Trillo y Figueroa, con varios puntos de contacto e influencia con Góngora [5]. En unos, los metros irregulares

[1] Véase § 21 del cap. III.
[2] Véase § 8 de este capítulo.
[3] Aparece también en los *Romancerillos de la Biblioteca Ambrosiana*.
[4] Véase § 6 de este capítulo.
[5] Véanse §§ 3, 5, 6, 7 y 10 de este capítulo. Añádanse a estos poetas, cuyas obras pueden verse en sus volúmenes propios o en la Biblioteca de Rivadeneyra, otros que pueden verse especialmente en el *Ensayo* de Gallardo (por ejemplo, Francisco López de Zárate, vol. III, col. 531, y Baltasar Elisio de Medinilla, col. 699) y las *Rimas del incógnito*, escritas hacia 1640 y publicadas por Foulché-Delbosc en *Revue Hispanique*, 1916, vol. XXXVII. Tomo dos ejemplos de la *Antología poética en honor de Góngora*, publicada por Gerardo Diego. De Melo (8-9-10-10):

> Garcecillas, son, Juanico,
> garcecillas son cuantas ves,
> que si airosas remojan los pies
> más airosas sacuden el pico.

De Medrano, estribillo:

> Caraquí, caraquí, caracoles,
> que la vida mata de amores,

aparecen en estribillos, y sólo la seguidilla obtiene algún desarrollo; otros —pocos—, como Melo, los emplean en composiciones largas: así, «¿Qué me pides, zagal, que te cuente...?» [1].

El mayor nombre en la poesía profana, entre los no mencionados aún, D. Francisco de Quevedo (1580-1645), también aprovechó los ritmos populares; generalmente para efecto cómico:

> Dijo a la rana el mosquito
> desde una tinaja:
> mejor es morir en el vino
> que vivir en el agua [2].

> El que sólo promete
> mete cizaña...

> ...Y si Dios me socorre
> no seré culto.

> Yo que lo sé, que lo vi, que lo digo,
> yo que lo vi, que lo digo, lo sé.

Como composición larga en versificación irregular tiene unas seguidillas de asunto religioso:

> La palabra del Padre te da la hostia:
> pase la palabra de boca en boca...

y la sátira contra Alarcón [3].

El conde de Villamediana (c. 1582-1622), aunque se atenía a la métrica silábica en lo que conozco de sus obras, empleaba la versificación de gaita gallega al componer motes burlescos:

> El duque de Uceda
> esconde la mano y tira la piedra.
> Mas, viendo su engaño,
> el mal de los otros ha sido su daño.

---

[1] Véase § 6 de este capítulo. Es suya, además, la letrilla con este estribillo:

> Garcecillas son, Juanico,
> garcecillas son cuantas ves,
> que si airosas remojan los pies
> más airosas sacuden el pico.

[2] Antecedente popular en CORREAS, *Vocabulario de refranes*, pág. 288.

[3] En el vol. LXIX de la Biblioteca de Rivadeneyra que contiene las poesías de Quevedo, deben verse sus *Bailes* (núms. 350 a 359), sus *Entremeses*, tres de los cuales (el de *Peralvillo de Madrid*, el de *La ropavejera* y el de *El marido fantasma*) terminan en versificación irregular, y diversos romances y letrillas. Véanse § 10 del cap. III y § 5 de este capítulo.

203

El duque de Osuna,
Nápoles llora su buena fortuna.
Mas, ya que está preso,
Nápoles se alegra de su mal suceso [1].

Último desarrollo curioso de la versificación irregular es su aparición en las novelas a partir de Cervantes, en trozos escritos por los novelistas. Figura en no pocas: en las de Doña María de Zayas, por ejemplo, las seguidillas [2]; en las de Salas Barbadillo, las seguidillas, o esquemas libres que tienden al ritmo de gaita gallega:

Encontrándose dos arroyuelos
al pasar de un verde valle,
uno a otro se tiran perlas,
riñen, y rifan, y saltan y bullen;
y por que se amansen
meten paz cantando las aves [3].

Esquemas de tipo semejante, y de seguidillas, se encuentran en Castillo Solórzano, en sus *Noches de placer* (1631) y en *La garduña de Sevilla* (capítulos V, VI, IX, X y XVI).

§ 19. CALDERÓN Y SU ESCUELA. — Calderón (1600-1681) y los dramaturgos de su escuela o de su tiempo, como Rojas Zorrilla o Moreto, se alejan de la poesía del pueblo, que rara vez adoptan, pero no pierden la afición a los versos irregulares. Al contrario, Calderón —ya se ha dicho— emplea no pocas seguidillas y se aficiona en especial a los versos de gaita gallega: sus autos y sus obras para música están llenos de unas y otros, y, lo que es más, hasta hay brevísimos pasajes de diálogo en verso irregular, cosa que no ocurría en los dramaturgos anteriores (véanse la escena II del acto III de la comedia *Celos aun del aire matan* y los autos *El valle de la Zarzuela, ¿Quién hallará mujer fuerte?* y *La nave del mercader*). Pero acaso en la afición misma estaba el peligro: en sus manos, la versificación que fué irregular comienza a volverse regular [4]. La seguidilla, de sus formas fluctuantes, que todavía se encuentran en obras como *El alcaide de sí mismo*, pasa a la forma en que todavía penetran los hexasílabos (6-5-7-5, o, en raras ocasiones, 7-5-6-5) y, finalmente, a la forma estrictamente regular (7-5-7-5). La versificación de gaita gallega, que podía mezclar libremente sus propios versos (10-11-12 con 6 y 5) y combinarlos

---

[1] Véase GALLARDO, *Ensayo*, vol. IV, cols. 677 y 702.

[2] Véanse *El castigo de la miseria, El prevenido engañado, La inocencia castigada*. En Doña María de Zayas se observa una nueva confusión de la seguidilla con otro metro, que no es ya la copla de pie quebrado ni la endecha, sino el verso endecasílabo: véase *La esclava de su amante*, al final.

[3] Véanse *El caballero puntual* y *La sabia Flora marisabidilla*, de donde son los versos citados arriba. Además, poesías líricas en GALLARDO, *Ensayo*, vol. I, col. 1.030.

[4] Véase la opinión de Gerardo Diego, citada en nota del § 6 de este capítulo.

con otros (de nueve sílabas o menos), comienza a presentarse reducida a los decasílabos y dodecasílabos o a su combinación con hexasílabos.

En Moreto (1618-1669) y Rojas Zorrilla (1607-1648) no es posible hacer observaciones extensas, porque sus contribuciones a la versificación irregular no son muchas [1]. Pero, en los dramaturgos que les siguen, el proceso de regularización va en aumento, y puede considerarse terminado, fuera de las obras breves del teatro, entre 1675 y 1700. En la poesía lírica, el caso es idéntico y la evolución paralela o acaso más rápida.

§ 20. RESUMEN. — El apogeo de la versificación irregular en las manifestaciones cultas de las letras castellanas coincide con la época de mayor esplendor del teatro, a la vez del profano y del religioso. Se adaptaba a maravilla esa versificación a los episodios de canto y danza que formaron parte principal del espectáculo cuyo núcleo era la comedia y cuyos incidentes y accesorios, a veces excesivos en número, requerían a menudo el empleo de la música.

La versificación irregular mantiene el contacto con la poesía del pueblo, sobre todo antes de 1650; pero los poetas la escriben libremente en ocasiones, ya sea tratando de imitar el estilo popular, como ocurre con Lope y Tirso, ya sea sin reminiscencia alguna de los orígenes, como ocurre con Calderón o con Castillo Solórzano. La versificación sigue girando dentro de sus círculos originarios: la seguidilla, el metro de gaita gallega, el metro donde predomina el eneasílabo. Durante poco tiempo, trata de definirse otro en que habría predominado el decasílabo bipartito. Fuera de ésos, continúan los esquemas libres: los más de ellos, durante el siglo XVII, con predominio de las medidas largas.

Las combinaciones estróficas son de tres clases: o se limitan al estribillo, que no se repite; o se repiten isométricamente, pero sólo en cuanto al número de versos y la distribución de las rimas, pero no en cuanto a la repetición de las diferentes medidas de verso en cada lugar de la estrofa; o, en fin, sin atención ninguna a la isometría: ejemplos de ello se encuentran en los poetas mayores, de cuando en cuando, pero, sobre todo, en los poetas cómicos como Quiñones de Benavente.

A partir de 1650, toda esta brillante variedad se irá regularizando y reduciendo. Las seguidillas y los versos de gaita gallega se volverán regulares, sometidos a las leyes del isosilabismo, como la silva de origen italiano; los otros esquemas desaparecerán al fin. La versificación irregular, después de prolongar su existencia en relativa oscuridad en el teatro cómico, desaparecerá de toda poesía culta y volverá al seno de las masas anónimas de donde había subido hacia las cortes.

[1] Véase § 15 de este capítulo.

205

ECLIPSE Y RESURGIMIENTO DE LA VERSIFICACIÓN IRREGULAR

(1675-1920)

§ 1. La transformación de los metros irregulares en la poesía culta (1650 a 1725). — Al esplendoroso apogeo que alcanzaron los metros irregulares entre 1600 y 1650, sucede el gradual proceso de transformación que les quita sus cualidades mejores: soltura, variedad, flexible adaptación a la música. Desaparecidos los poetas en quienes alentaba con segunda vida el alma popular, los que tenían puesto el atento oído a los rumores del terruño, les suceden hombres de letras que, cualesquiera que fuesen sus méritos —geniales a veces, como en Calderón—, poseían gustos más artificiales, más retóricos. Ya en raras ocasiones imitan directamente a los cantos del pueblo; poco a poco, los metros que del pueblo tomaron sufren el influjo de los hábitos literarios.

Durante breve tiempo la versificación irregular, alejada así de su fuente nativa, no sólo aparece en estribillos o finales de poesías líricas y cantares intercalados en dramas o novelas, sino en composiciones enteras, más que antes (véase Quevedo, o Melo, o el *Romancero de Barcelona*), y aun en breves pasajes del diálogo dramático (autos de Calderón). Su éxito iba a ser la señal de su desaparición o transformación: bien pronto se abandonarían unos metros —como el de base eneasilábica— y se regularizarían los otros, los de gaita gallega y la seguidilla. De éstos, ya se sabe que el primero se redujo a la combinación deca-dodecasilábica, con la posibilidad de añadir el hexasílabo como quebrado, y a veces tolerando todavía el endecasílabo anapéstico como variante del dodecasílabo; el segundo se redujo a los versos alternos de siete y de cinco sílabas, tolerando también, de tarde en tarde, uno que otro hexasílabo, hasta fines del siglo xvii [1].

---

[1] Véase cap. IV, §§ 3, 6 a 8, 19 y 20.

En los poetas líricos y dramáticos de la segunda mitad del siglo XVII, que históricamente se agrupan en torno de Calderón, se observan iguales vacilaciones que en el maestro: así, en el portugués Matos Fragoso (1608-1688), es irregular la canción de *El sabio en su retiro* (acto II), pero son regulares (7-5-7-5) las seguidillas de *El yerro del entendido* (acto II); en Antonio de Solís (1610-1686) hay esquemas libres (en la Letrilla al Sacramento, estribillo «¡Oh, qué bien cantan!»), pero son regulares muchas de sus seguidillas y los eneasílabos de la Loa para *Un bobo hace ciento* [1]; en Agustín de Salazar y Torres (1642-1675) hay combinaciones irregulares en el segundo y el tercer acto de *Elegir al enemigo*, pero hay seguidillas regulares en el primero y estrofas deca-dodecasilábicas regulares en varias de sus Letras y Letrillas líricas y en sus Loas [2]; en Bancés Candamo (1661-1704) hay versos irregulares en el auto *Las mesas de la fortuna* y en *El duelo contra su dama*, pero escribe seguidillas regulares [3]. La vacilación continúa todavía en Zamora († 1728) y Cañizares (1676-1750), que prolongan el espíritu del siglo XVII en los comienzos del XVIII.

En Sor Juana Inés de la Cruz (1651-1695) predominan los metros irregulares sobre los regularizados, pero es en sus Villancicos eclesiásticos, escritos entre 1677 y 1690, género que gozó de mayor libertad, como las formas breves, cómicas, del teatro público. Pero aun en las obras breves la seguidilla comienza a volverse regular

[1] Solís, *Varias poesías sagradas y profanas*, Madrid, 1732 (véanse especialmente págs. 137 a 147 y 160; obras para teatro, de la pág. 199 a la 284, especialmente las representaciones graciosas tituladas *El retrato de Juan Rana* y *El baile perdido;* y el *mote* en la pág. 319).

[2] Salazar, *Cythara de Apolo*, dos vols., Madrid, 1694. Entre las combinaciones de origen acentual, pero regularizadas ya y repetidas isométricamente, se encuentra la estrofa de *A la Purísima Concepción de Nuestra Señora* (única libertad: el endecasílabo anapéstico puede ser sustituído por el dodecasílabo):

> Si es Aurora nítida
> y precursora luziente del Sol
> que ignoró crepúsculos
> y aun el primer matutino esplendor,
> su puro candor
> luego el Cielo copia
> y la Tierra no.
>
> Si es Cedro, que al Líbano
> ornó de hermosura en perpetuo verdor,
> quando a essotros árboles
> la pompa desnuda infeliz Aquilón,
> tanta perfección
> luego copia el Suelo,
> pero el Cielo no...

[3] En *El sastre del Campillo*, Bancés introduce, en medio de una canción octosilábica, este verso que luego será popularísimo y que en el romance de *Malbrú* reemplazará al verso francés de «Mironton, mironton, mirontaine»:

> ¡Ay, qué dolor, qué rigor, qué pena!

desde temprano, y lo es en la mayoría de los casos en los entremeses, bailes y demás piececillas de Lanini, Francisco de Avellaneda, Sebastián de Villaviciosa, Alonso de Olmedo o Gil López de Armesto [1].

En tendencia general, los poetas cultos que escriben entre 1650 y 1700 regresan a la preferencia, común antes de Lope, por los metros silábicos usuales (la silva, las redondillas octosilábicas, los villancicos hexasilábicos) para los cantares que introducen en las comedias y las letras para música; crece la tendencia —cuyo principio puede verse en el *Romancero general* de 1600— a usar, como estribillos de letrillas o romances, versos de corte italiano en vez de motes populares o de canciones como la seguidilla. Ejemplos: en Lope, el primero de sus romances (octosilábicos) a Filis, «El lastimado Belardo...», que es del siglo XVI:

> ¡Ay, triste mal de ausencia,
> y quién podrá decir lo que me cuestas!

En Esquilache, romance «Llamaban los pajarillos...»:

> Yo, sola, triste, al son
> de todos lloro libertad y amor.

Después de 1700 se define más el proceso; entre 1725 y 1750, con la aparición del clasicismo académico, toda irregularidad en la versificación queda desterrada de la poesía culta.

§ 2. DEL SIGLO XVIII AL XIX EN LA POESÍA CULTA (1725 a 1895). — Al romperse la tradición de Lope, de Góngora, de Tirso, de Calderón y de Quevedo en la poesía lírica y en el teatro, la literatura española conserva solamente metros isosilábicos y estrofas isométricas, salvo los endecasílabos blancos y las silvas a la manera italiana. El fenómeno es general y se observa hasta en las obras que señalan el límite entre la producción culta y la producción del pueblo anónimo o del vulgo: los sainetes de Ramón de la Cruz (1731-1794) y de Juan Ignacio González del Castillo (1763-1800). En ellos la seguidilla es regular y la combinación deca-dodecasilábica ha desaparecido. Apenas si se halla en Cruz

---

[1] COTARELO, Introducción a los *Entremeses, loas, bailes...*, págs. CII, CX, CXIII, CXIV, CXVI, CXCIII, CXCIV, CXCIX, CCI, y los entremeses de Lanini y otros en *Migajas del ingenio*, tomo del siglo XVII, reimpreso en Madrid, 1908.

Desde principios del siglo XVII se hallan seguidillas regulares en las mojigangas de Simón Aguado, dos de las cuales tienen fecha de 1602. Véanse los números 58, 59 y 60 de la colección de Cotarelo.

Para otras seguidillas regulares, entre muchas, véase *Las glorias del mejor siglo*, del P. Valentín de Céspedes (coplas de siete versos); *El montañés Juan Pascual*, de Hoz Mota.

este *Aire de vendimiadora*, todo en versos decasílabos, en el sainete de *La mesonerilla;*

> Al pasar por un campo de flores
> encontré una zagala de perlas...

La seguidilla de los poetas cultos, aunque no admite la ligera irregularidad del hexasílabo llano, frecuente aún en Calderón y su escuela, admite de cuando en cuando la acentuación aguda, que subsiste hasta principios del siglo XIX, en Iglesias y Lista[1]. Es muy natural en poetas como el modesto y maniático seguidillero Antonio Valladares de Sotomayor:

> Antes de que ejecutes
> debes bien pensar;
> mira que los errores
> se corrigen mal.
> Si son de un sabio,
> se vuelve vituperio
> lo que fué aplauso.

O en Ramón de la Cruz *(Los panderos):*

> Por mudar de chismosas
> en el Lavapiés,
> me he mudado a la calle
> de Santa Isabel;
> que es calle ancha,
> y allí nadie murmura
> que entre ni salga[2].

Hacia el final del siglo XVIII, la antigua versificación irregular ha desaparecido a tal punto de la literatura, que ni siquiera sus reliquias parecen peligrosas a los clasicistas académicos, y se co-

---

[1] En Iglesias (c. 1753-c. 1791) hay todavía ligeras alteraciones de la regularidad (7-5-7-5):

> Si yo cuando a otros muerdo
> mordido me hallo,
> es que no hay hombre cuerdo
> si monta a caballo.

[2] Véase HANSSEN, *La seguidilla*, § 11, sobre *La desaparición del hexasílabo*, y § 21, sobre *Las seguidillas del siglo XVIII*, donde indica que el metro disminuye como letra y estribillo, pero tiene auge como tipo aparte (canto coreográfico, poesía o epigrama) y que prevalece el tipo de siete versos sobre el de cuatro o tres. Pero se contradice a sí mismo Hanssen cuando afirma que el hexasílabo llano desaparece desde mediados del siglo XVII (lo único que puede asegurarse es que comienza a desaparecer), y luego cita poetas que aún lo emplean, como José Pérez de Montoro, muerto en 1694, Calderón, Salazar y Torres, Melo, Solís.

mienzan a exhumar versos desusados, como el endecasílabo de
gaita gallega o el eneasílabo o el dodecasílabo o el decasílabo bipartito, para emplearlos en combinaciones isosilábicas e isométricas. Así, Tomás de Iriarte (1750-1791), que llega a permitirse
combinar los versos largos con sus quebrados:

> Cierto lobo, hablando con cierto pastor...
> Al diablo los doy,
> tantos libros lobos como corren hoy.

> De frase extranjera el mal pegadizo...

> Cierta criada la casa barría...
> Por donde pasa
> aun más ensucia que limpia la casa...

> Cierto ricacho, labrando una casa...

> Si querer entender de todo
> es ridícula presunción...

> Escondido en el tronco de un árbol
> estaba un mochuelo...

Y Leandro Fernández de Moratín (1760-1828), pontífice de
toda simetría:

> Id, en las alas del raudo céfiro...

> Suban al cerco de Olimpo luciente.

Hasta cuando se imita el arcaico arte mayor, se le reduce a
dodecasílabos, y a veces se le escribe en lenguaje antiguo:

> A vos, renovando lejana escriptura,
> cual vos el recuerdo de grandes cabdillos,
> mi pénnola acata, y en metros sencillos
> se postra a la vuestra perínclita altura.
>
> (Ramón Roca) [1].

Ya en el siglo xix, el decasílabo anapéstico renace —solo—
en los himnos patrióticos y en otras especies de poesía; el eneasí-

[1] Ramón Roca fué un buen poeta granadino, que vivía en Méjico hacia
1820. Véanse el Estudio preliminar de Luis G. Urbina, en la *Antología del Centenario*, compilada por Urbina, Pedro Henríquez Ureña y Nicolás Rangel,
México, 1910 (págs. ccxxiv y 1.002), y Pedro Henríquez Ureña, artículo
sobre *La métrica de los poetas mexicanos en la época de la independencia*, publicado en el Boletín de la Sociedad Mexicana de Geografía y Estadística,
1914, y reproducido en el presente volumen, págs. 361-368: allí pueden verse
unos cuantos curiosos ejemplos de confusión entre el verso decasílabo y el
eneasílabo.

labo goza de boga relativa durante breve tiempo [1]; el dodecasílabo y el decasílabo bipartito renacen tímidamente, con menos boga, pero con más resistencia. En las óperas, cantatas y otras creaciones cortesanas, hay una que otra vez combinaciones medianamente libres, y Juan María Maury se desliza hasta este desorden al final de su *Oda en ritmo ditirámbico*, imitada de Dryden, *El festín de Alejandro*:

> ˙ Aplauden los grandes, el rey los apoya,
> que empuña una tea con torva alegría;
> destocada va Tais de guía,
> al estrago alumbrando la vía,
> y a fuer de nueva Elena, incendia nueva Troya.

Y Manuel María de Arjona (1771-1820) se atreve a regresar a las viejas fluctuaciones de la seguidilla; eso sí, preparándolas debidamente por varias coplas pentasilábicas *(Himno epitalámico)*:

> Gloria a Himeneo,
> dios de delicias,
> pues de sus claras teas
> gozó ya Elisa.

En la época romántica, los versificadores más audaces ensayan gran variedad de metros: Espronceda; la Avellaneda; Bello, en *Los duendes*, siguiendo a Víctor Hugo. La nueva escuela favorecía el empleo de metros diversos, y no sólo en composiciones distintas, sino dentro de cada composición; pero sus tendencias en cuestiones de métrica no llegaron a producir más perdurable efecto que las de los últimos clásicos académicos. El isosilabismo no lo violaron nunca los románticos (apenas hubo uno que otro desliz de Espronceda, momentáneamente, cuando se enredaba en algún intento métrico extravagante), y sus ataques contra la isometría de las estrofas, audaces al principio, fueron reduciéndose gradualmente, hasta desvanecerse.

De la irregularidad silábica sólo se salen, en rigor, unos pocos intentos de resucitar la cantidad grecolatina: los más interesantes son los de Juan Gualberto González.

---

[1] Sobre el eneasílabo, véanse cap. I, §§ 6 y 7; cap. II, §§ 8, 10, 17, 29 (especialmente) y 31; cap. III, § 21; cap. IV, § 7.

Agréguense unos cuantos ejemplos más: Francisco Sánchez Barbero (1764-1819) «¡Melilla, tu Venus adora!» en la cantata *La Venus de Melilla*, 1816; Juan María Maury (1772-1845), «Suene otra vez la lira de oro», en *El festín de Alejandro;* Dionisio Solís (1774-1834), «Al pie del leño de que pende | El moribundo Redentor», en *Cánticos sagrados*, I; y «A las orillas de este río», en *Filis llorosa;* José María Heredia, el cubano (1803-1839), «Cuando el Creador, en hora infausta...», en *La desesperación*, y «El hijo imbécil de la nada...», con acentuación libre, en *Dios al hombre*.

Este imperio de la uniformidad isosilábica durará hasta 1895, más o menos.

§ 3. EL TEATRO MUSICAL (1725 a 1920). — El teatro culto, literario, hasta los linderos que representa el sainete de Cruz y de Castillo, adoptó el canon isosilábico. Pero el teatro musical y coreográfico de origen popular no podía someterse con igual facilidad: hasta dónde lo hizo, sólo cabría determinarlo mediante el examen minucioso de gran número de producciones cuyo acceso no es fácil. La tendencia regularizadora invadió también estos campos: la extraordinaria licencia que existía en tiempos de Quiñones de Benavente disminuyó mucho; pero, de todos modos, la música y la tradición del pueblo permitían libertades que habían desaparecido del teatro literario.

En el villancico eclesiástico persistía la ficción rústica. Hasta fines del siglo XVII se observa en la monja de Méjico; y aunque desde entonces penetra en esos modestos dramas líricos el tono de los solemnes autos sacramentales de Calderón, es probable que persistiera la libertad rítmica [1]. El tono calderoniano penetra, por ejemplo, en el *Oratorio*, escrito por Gerardo Lobo (1679-1750) para la Virgen del Pilar, en Barcelona, pero la versificación no es rígida aún:

> Desdoble la idea de mudas señales
> oscuros conceptos, enigmas divinos,
> y en los arcanos de lumbre sagrada
> enciendan las sombras la luz del prodigio.

En su Villancico de Navidad *Las aldeanas*, Diego de Torres Villarroel (c. 1693-1770) introduce este cantar:

> ¡Ah, zagala!
> Alto a buscar el pandero y sonaja
> y al niño cantemos alguna tonada.

En el Villancico de *La gaita zamorana* introduce el cantar de las *Naranjicas* [2], el de la gaita de Galicia [3] y otros versos de tipo acentual, en uno de los cuales aparece la alteración musical del acento de la palabra:

> Todos me preguntan
> por la mi Mariana;

---

[1] La comprobación tendría que hacerse principalmente mediante el estudio de la colección de Barbieri, custodiada en la Biblioteca Nacional de Madrid (véase § 12 del cap. III, nota final).

[2] Véanse § 21 del cap. III y § 10 del cap. IV.

[3] Véase cap. III, § 21.

213

esa fanfarrona
conmigo no habla,
Tumbailá, mi Marianita,
tumbailá, mi Marianá [1].
Triste de Jorge,
si el alcalde le prende o le coge.
Triste de él
si el alcalde le llega a prender [2].

En Méjico, a fines del siglo, muestra curiosa libertad el P. Sartorio en sus diálogos en alabanza de la Virgen (fluctuando alrededor del endecasílabo y el heptasílabo):

—¿Oyes, Partenia fiel? Vén, vamos juntas
al monte de la mirra.
—Enhorabuena,
vamos unidas.
—¿Y sabes a qué vamos?
—A llorar con María.
—¿Sabes que pena?
—Muy afligida.
—¿Harás por consolarla?
—Es madre mía.
—¿Y lágrimas bastantes
darás? —Corridas.
—¿La aliviarás?
—Confia...
—Hermana, vamos,
y en el viaje que hacemos
mátenos el dolor...

En el teatro musical profano hay más pruebas de que perdura la versificación irregular, aunque sólo la documentación completa podría establecer la proporción a que se hallaba reducida frente a la silábica. Cuando entre 1675 y 1725 aumenta la tendencia hacia la regularización, las obras breves del teatro se exceptúan de ella en buena parte, y sólo adoptan con rapidez la simplificación de la seguidilla [3]. Después de 1725, es probable que la libertad se limite a las obras teatrales estrictamente musicales y coreográficas, puesto que los sainetes y otras obras en que predomina el diálogo no la conservan.

---

[1] Véase § 5 del cap. III, nota sobre la alteración del acento de las palabras en el verso.

[2] Obras de Torres Villarroel, tomo VIII, Salamanca, 1752: véanse los Villancicos religiosos, págs. 110 a 139, y las obrillas profanas, págs. 181, 204, 270, 273, 277, 293, 298, 298 y 318

[3] Véase COTARELO, Introducción a los *Entremeses*..., páginas CXXI, CXXIII, CXXIV, CXXXVIII, CCIII a CCXXI, CCXLIV, CCLIII, CCLIV, CCLXXXVII a CCXC, CCC a CCCVII.

Ejemplos: en el entremés anónimo *La burla del figonero*, refundición de otro anterior, hecha hacia 1740:

> El *jíquiri-guaico*, galán jamaiquín,
> se baila y se bulle y se canta así:
> ¡ay, qué chusco, ay, qué lindo,
> ay, qué alegre le vi venir,
> al *jíquiri-guaico*, galán jamaiquín! [1]

En la tonadilla de *Entra moro*, de 1746:

> Entra moro, sale moro,
> titiraina,
> el salerito, la cincha y la albarda
> y el borriquito para traer agua.

En el Fin de fiesta para la *Galería mágica*, 1748, tonadilla:

> Que a tu gusto me pongo yo el gavio;
> ¡qué chusco, qué bello, qué cuco, qué majo,
> qué mono! —¿Me quieres? —Es chasco.
> —Si yo a ti te adoro. —¡Ay, que eso es engaño!
> —Pues llega, mi cielo, y dáme un abrazo.

En la *Tonadilla del pintor*, con música de Luis Misón, entre 1760 y 1765, esquema libre a base de seguidillas:

> Esta frente espaciosa,
> campo de guerra,
> campo de perlas,
> ¡ay, qué hermosa!
> ¡ay, qué bella!
> donde Cupido quiso
> plantar bandera.
> ¡Ay, que me abraso!
> ¡Ay, que me quemo!
> ¡Ay, que es mucha la pena
> que yo padezco!

En la tonadilla *Garrido de luto*, con música de Pablo Esteve, 1781:

> Mire usted cómo galopean
> los caballos de la maestranza,
> y si les aprietan las riendas,
> del galope a la carrera pasan.

---

[1] Compárese «Entra mayo y sale abril...» en el § 10 del cap. III.

En la tonadilla *La decantada vida y muerte del general Malbrú*, con música de Jacinto Valledor, 1785:

> Malbrú se fué a la guerra a pelear;
> su ausencia me mata con tanto tardar.
> —Allí Madama aguarda ya.
> Con la noticia se arañará.
> —¡El paje aquí! ¿Qué hay de novedad?
> —Ninguna, señora. Malbrú muerto está [1].

En la tonadilla *Los duendecillos*, con música de Esteve, en 1782, esquema caprichoso con elementos de seguidilla:

> ...Y se apareció entonces
> un duendecillo.
> Se acercó a mí.
> Yo me aturdí;
> pero, en fin, me esforcé.
> Dije: ¿quién eres?
> Y él respondió:
> —El duende protector
> de las mujeres... [2].

En el siglo XIX, la zarzuela hace uso también de gran libertad en la versificación. Rubén Darío, en el prefacio de *Cantos de vida y esperanza* (Madrid, 1905), describía así la situación de la métrica en España entre 1800 y 1900: «En cuanto al verso libre moderno ¿no es verdaderamente singular que, en esta tierra de Quevedos y de Góngoras, los únicos innovadores del instrumento lírico, los únicos libertadores del ritmo, hayan sido los poetas del *Madrid cómico* y los libretistas del género chico?».

La zarzuela explota a menudo versos desusados en otros géneros, como el eneasílabo cuando no estaba de moda (en *La tempestad*, de Miguel Ramos Carrión: «Cuando en las noches del estío...»; «El alma mía enamorada...»; en *El rey que rabió*, de Ramos Carrión y Vital Aza, hacia 1890: «Ella, infeliz enamorada...»; «Dios ilumine al soberano...»; en *Certamen nacional* de Guillermo Perrín y Miguel Palacios, 1888: «Trabajaba una mulatita...»; en *La verbena de la Paloma*, de Ricardo de la Vega, 1894: «Una

---

[1] «Mironton, mironton, mirontaine», del original francés, se traduce en la tonadilla de Valledor «Mirontón, tontón, mirondela». En versiones posteriores, que se cantan hoy, es donde aparece el verso empleado por Bancés Candamo (véase nota en el § 1 de este capítulo).

[2] Véanse PEDRELL, *Teatro lírico español anterior al siglo XIX*, vol. I, pág. XXI; vol. II, págs. V, VII y XIV; COTARELO, Introducción a los *Entremeses...*, pág. CCLXXXIX. —Es posterior a la primera edición de este libro el de José SUBIRÁ, *La tonadilla escénica*, tres vols., Madrid, 1929-1930; el tomo III contiene textos y música.

morena y una rubia...»; en *Venus Salón*, de Félix Limendoux
y Enrique López Marín, 1903: «En un vagón *eslipincar*...»)[1];
el endecasílabo anapéstico *(Marina*, arreglo de Ramos Carrión,
«Entre la parda y espesa neblina...»; *Certamen nacional*, versos en castellano pronunciado al modo gallego: «Tengu, garrida, que darte un recadu...») [2], y el verso de trece sílabas *El
lucero del alba:* «Lucerillo me llaman en Andalucía, | Lucerillo del
alba que brinda alegría...»).

Versos irregulares: se aproximan mucho *La gallina ciega*, de
Ramos Carrión, 1873 («De la patria del cacao, | del chocolate,
y del café...»), y *La canción de la Lola*, de Ricardo de la Vega,
1880 («Con el capotín, tin, tin, tin, | Esta noche va a llover») [3].
Marcos Zapata, en *El anillo de hierro*, 1878:

> Venid, venid,
> bogad, bogad,
> que ya está en las playas
> el fruto del mar.
>
> Eso es una bola de mi país...

Felipe Pérez y González, *La gran vía*, 1886:

> —Somos las calles, somos las plazas
> y callejones de Madrid
> que por un recurso mágico
> nos podemos congregar aquí.
> Es el motivo que nos reúne
> perturbador de un modo tal
> que solamente él causaría
> un trastorno tan fenomenal.
> —Caballero de Gracia me llaman,
> y efectivamente soy así...[4]

Eugenio Sellés, *La balada de la luz*, 1900:

> ¡Qué importa ser ciega! Por tierras y mundos
> con mi mano cogida te llevo

---

[1] Véanse notas sobre el eneasílabo en el § 2 de este capítulo y el § 29 del
cap. II.

[2] Recuérdese también la canción, popularísima en el norte de la América española, «Abén Ame, al partir de Granada...», traducida de la *romance
mauresque* del *Aben Humeya*, de Martínez de la Rosa (París, 1930): consúltense mi artículo *El endecasílabo castellano*, en la *Revista de Filología Española*, 1919, VI, nota final, y mi conferencia *Música popular de América*, pág. 202.

[3] Las combinaciones caprichosas, aunque no enteramente irregulares,
abundan en todas las zarzuelas: véase por ejemplo, *El olivar*, de García Aris-
ta y Melantuch, 1902 («Es mi tierra la tierra primera | Que hay en España»).

[4] En *La gran vía* hay, además, endecasílabos anapésticos: «Ya nuestro
barco cual ruda gaviota...»; «Yo soy un baile de criadas y de horteras...».

y al sentir los calores que abrasan mi ⸱ulso
y al sentir cómo tiemblo,
si no ves lo que dicen mis ojos
pasa a ti lo que siente mi pecho.

Carlos Arniches y Enrique García Álvaɪez, en *El terrible Pérez*, 1903 (eneasílabos y decasílabos):

¡Ay, mamita del alma mía,
ay, no sé lo que va a pasar;
ay, mamita, que está la España
sin que la sepan ni gobernar! [1]

Jacinto Benavente, *Todos somos unos*, 1907:

¡Ay, cuánto tiempo
que ya no bailamos así!
—No dirás nunca
que ha sido la cosa por mí...
¡Cualquiera te quita a ti
lo que tienes bailao! [2]

Serafín y Joaquín Álvarez Quintero no sé si imitan o si adaptan (probablemente lo primero) cantares del pueblo. En *Las flores*, 1901:

Tiene mi serrana
la cara como una rosa
cuando dispierta por la mañana [3].

Igual cosa se observa en la canción vulgar y especialmente en la canción del teatro: tal, la que recibe ahora el nombre de *cuplé*. Mencionaré como ejemplo, los que se cantaban y se vendían en Madrid en 1917: los de *¡Vaya, vaya!* («Diciendo anda la gente»), *La mocita verbenera* («Nena, nenita»), *La mimosa*, *Serranillo* y la popularísima *Agua que no has de beber*, de Martínez Abades:

No te ocupes de mí,
no he de ser para ti,
no te canses, déjame ya.

---

[1] En Arniches y García Álvarez hay muchos *números* en versificación irregular: así, en *El pobre Valbuena*, de 1904 («Japonesa, sí, sí»); en *El pollo Tejada*, de 1906 («Mira, mira, mira»).

[2] De Benavente, véanse además *Teatro feminista*, 1898, y *Viaje de instrucción*.

[3] En el teatro de los Quintero, tanto en el lírico como en el puramente literario, abundan los cantares; pero, por su origen andaluz, son regulares en su mayoría.

Agua que no has de beber
déjalá, correr,
déjalá, déjalá.

§ 4. LA POESÍA POPULAR (1725 a 1920). — Como el teatro lírico y la canción vulgar, la canción del pueblo, generalmente nacida en los campos y las aldeas, conservó la libertad rítmica. Pero no como antes: el principio del isosilabismo había bajado también hasta las masas anónimas desde el siglo XVI. Todavía en el siglo XV, la poesía popular castellana, en los romances o en las canciones conserva mucho de la fluctuación primitiva: en las composiciones de tipo popular, si se excluyen los romances, en el *Cancionero musical de los siglos XV y XVI*, la versificación irregular está en igual número que la isosilábica. En el siglo XVI, si se toman como ejemplo las recopilaciones de Juan Vásquez, se verá que la proporción ha crecido ligeramente a favor de los metros regulares [1]. Desde entonces, el isosilabismo hace progresos en la poesía popular; en la de hoy predomina indudablemente: la versificación irregular está en minoría.

Dos tipos son los preferidos por el pueblo: la copla octosílaba y la seguidilla. La copla tiene cuatro versos (rara veces tres, como en las *soledades*, o cinco), con rima en los pares; la seguidilla tiene siete, como ésta de Andalucía:

Desde que te ausentaste,
sol de los soles,
ni los pájaros cantan
ni el río corre.
¡Ay, amor mío!
Ni los pájaros cantan
ni corre el río [2].

O cuatro, como estas delicadas de Asturias:

Dicen que está llorando
la molinera,
porque los sus amores
van a la guerra.
Yo también, madre mía,
suspiro y lloro,
porque a la guerra llevan
al bien que adoro.

[1] Véanse las recopilaciones de Vásquez en 1551 y en 1559; en la primera predomina la versificación irregular; en la segunda, la regular; sumando las dos, la proporción de versos regulares es ligeramente mayor que la de los irregulares. —Consúltese cap. III, segunda sección.

[2] Inversión, como ya se hacía desde el siglo XVI: véase la de «Venta de Viveros...», que trae Alarcón en *Las paredes oyen*.

De vez en cuando se tropieza con seguidillas que conservan irregularidades, además de la vieja libertad de introducir el hexasílabo agudo en lugar del pentasílabo llano (ley de Mussafia) o de la libertad moderna de emplear el pentasílabo agudo:

> Y eres la que le quita
> los rayos al sol,
> a la nieve lo blanco
> y al oro el valor.
> Tú eres la del amor.
>
> (Salamanca).

> Aunque me ves que canto,
> no canto yo:
> canta la lengua, llora
> el corazón.
>
> (Burgos) [1].

De otros tipos sobreviven principalmente los de gaita gallega, difundidos por toda España desde hace siglos. Cantares del tipo de las modernas muiñeiras de Galicia los encontramos desde el siglo XVI: las había en gallego, como en *La mayor virtud de un rey*, de Lope; en *La Gallega Mari Hernández*, de Tirso; en *El alcalde Ardite*, de Rojas; en el anónimo *Baile de Sotillo de Manzanares*. Las había en castellano: dísticos como «Póntela tú, la gorra del fraile» y cuartetas como «Hilandera era la aldeana» [2]. Desde la primera mitad del siglo XVIII, Torres Villarroel recoge el cantar clásico de la gaita gallega, el cantar de gaita gallega por excelencia, mil veces repetido y parodiado en los tres idiomas románicos de la Península:

> Tanto bailé con la gaita gallega,
> tanto bailé que me enamoré de ella...

Después, es probable que no haya región de España donde no se conozca el metro; pero asume formas menos libres que en Galicia [3].

---

[1] La seguidilla andaluza «Desde que te ausentaste» es la núm. 3.455 en la colección de Rodríguez Marín; la salmantina procede del *Cancionero salmantino* de Ledesma; la de Burgos, de la colección de Olmeda (véanse indicaciones posteriores sobre estas recopilaciones). La seguidilla asturiana «Dicen que está llorando» se cantaba en toda España en los años 1916 y 1917. La seguidilla ha pasado a todos los idiomas de la Península ibérica: al gallego-portugués, al catalán-valenciano y hasta al vasco.

[2] Véanse § 11 del cap. II y § 10 del cap. IV.

[3] Resulta extraño que Menéndez y Pelayo diga *(Antología de poetas líricos castellanos*, vol. X, pág. 141) que los endecasílabos anapésticos no existen en castellano popular fuera del cantar de *Xuana* en Asturias. Ya Milá, su maestro, había señalado endecasílabos anapésticos en la poesía del pueblo

Hay colecciones generales de cantos modernos del pueblo español, como la de Emilio Lafuente y Alcántara, *Cancionero popular* (dos volúmenes, Madrid, 1865), la de Rodríguez Marín, *Cantos populares españoles* (cinco volúmenes, Sevilla, 1882-1883), y las series de Inzenga, *Cantos y bailes populares de España;* pero la primera no contiene sino seguidillas regulares y coplas octosilábicas, la segunda es principalmente andaluza, y la tercera se subdivide por regiones. Es preferible, pues, estudiar las regiones separadamente [1].

§ 5. ASTURIAS. — Los versos de gaita gallega es probable que se hayan conocido siempre en León y Asturias, ligados a Galicia por el parentesco dialectal y por la vecindad geográfica. Antiguo es allí el cantar de «Ay probe Xuana de cuerpo garrido» [2].

En tiempos modernos [3] se han recogido cantares en dodecasílabos o endecasílabos anapésticos en que generalmente no hay —como no la hay en el de *Xuana*— alternancia de medidas diversas, según el modo de Galicia, sino repetición isosilábica como si la tendencia regularizadora se hubiera extendido a ellas:

> No le daba el sol, que le daba la luna,
> no le daba el sol de la media fortuna.

> Vénte conmigo a la orilla del mar
> por ver las olas subir y bajar,
> Vénte conmigo a la orilla del mar
> a ver las olas qué buenas están.

Igual regularidad se observa en las series que forman otros versos de tipo acentual:

de diversas regiones, y las muestras que se darán más adelante en este capítulo lo comprueban todavía mejor. Recuérdense, además, las zarzuelas, como *La gran vía* y *Marina*.

[1] No conozco el *Cancionero musical popular español* de FELIPE PEDRELL, cuatro vols., Valls, 1918-1921. Después de la primera edición de este libro han salido a luz *Treinta mil cantares populares*, recogidos por E. VASCO, dos vols., Valdepeñas, 1930, y la *Antología musical de cantos populares españoles*, selección de A. MARTÍNEZ HERNÁNDEZ, con prólogo de Subirá, Barcelona, 1931.

[2] Véase la cita en el § 20 del cap. II. Además, JULIÁN RIBERA, *De música y métrica gallegas*, en el *Homenaje a Menéndez Pidal*, Madrid, 1925, tomo III, págs. 10-21, sobre la música de la muiñeira (cuyo origen arcaico trata de probar) en las canciones de *La molinera* («Gasta la molinera ricos zapatos...») y de «Tantarantán que los higos son verdes», circulantes en Asturias, León y Castilla.

[3] Véase JOSÉ HURTADO, *Cien cantos populares asturianos*, Bilbao, 1890, (con música); MAYO Y RODRÍGUEZ LAVANDERA, *Alma asturiana*, Gijón, sin fecha (con música). Son posteriores a la primera edición de este libro el *Cancionero musical de la lírica popular asturiana*, de EDUARDO M. TORNER, Madrid, 1930, y *Esfoyaza de cantares asturianos*, de AURELIO DE LLANO ROZA DE AMPUDIA, Oviedo, 1924.

A coger el trébole, el trébole, el trébole,
a coger el trébole la noche de San Juan.
A coger el trébole, el trébole, el trébole,
a coger el trébole los mis amores van.

Yo no soy marinero, no,
yo no soy cadena de amor.

No se va la paloma, no,
no se va, que la traigo yo.

Manolillo, si vas al molino,
    si vienes y vas.
¡Ay, señora!, que vengo a deshora
    y no puedo más.
Aunque venga el arroyo, morena,
    voy a la fuente,
a la de cuatro caños, morena,
    sólo por verte.

Puede atribuírsele origen en versificación irregular, aunque
aparece ya regularizada, a la combinación de octosílabos con decasílabos bipartitos, que se presenta a menudo:

En casa del tío Vicente
hay mucha gente, mi Dios, ¿que habrá?
Los hijos van de soldados
y la Tomasa llorando está.

Si vas al río de Lena,
no bebas agua, que allí la habrá
para las niñas bonitas
que van cantando la soledad.

La seguidilla, que está muy difundida, forma a veces parte
de canciones que tienen otra clase de versos, como la de «No le
daba el sol», o «No se va la paloma», o «Yo no soy marinero».
Pero también se presenta en combinaciones irregulares:

Aquí que hay parras,
aquí que hay uvas,
toda la noche anduve
a las maduras.
    Mirando estaba:
si venía el amo me reñiría,
después de haber cogido
las que quería.

Si la nieve resbala,
¿qué hará la rosa,
que se va deshojando

la más hermosa?
¡Ay, amor!
Si la nieve resbala,
¿qué haré yo?

A veces conserva caracteres de las seguidillas primitivas (hexasílabos, ley de Mussafia, confusión con la endecha, y hasta alteración del acento, como en las del *Polvico*):

Arbolito verde,
seco la rama,
debajo del puente
retumba el agua.

Tres hojitas tiene,
madre, el arbolé,
la una en la caña
y dos en el pie [1].

Otros casos de versificación curiosa:

En el mar planté un clavelal
y ahora le vengo de recortar.
¡Ay, marinero, sácame del mar
que soy niña y no puedo navegar!

Todas las flores, madre,
traigo aquí,
menos el trébole,
que no le vi.

§ 6. La montaña de Santander. — El maestro Rafael Calleja, en 1901, recoge en las antiguas Asturias de Santander

[1] Véase Hurtado, *Cien cantos*, pág. 83. Véase, en el *Cancionero popular venezolano*, recogido por José E. Machado, Caracas, 1919,

Arbolito, te secaste
teniendo el agua en el pie...

En otra canción que se canta en Asturias y Salamanca se halla el verso que he mencionado antes:

Verdes, azules y coloradós.

He oído la canción varias veces, pero olvidé los otros versos.
Sobre el cambio de acentuación, véase nota en el § 5 del cap. III.
Federico García Lorca ha recordado este rasgo peculiar del cantar asturiano en su poesía que lleva como estribillo.

Arbolé, arbolé,
seco y verdé.

cantares que existen también en las antiguas Asturias de Oviedo: «No se va la paloma» y «Si la nieve resbala» [1].

Hay versos de gaita gallega en combinaciones simétricas:

> El pañuelo de mi niña,
> que ella lavándole estaba,
> ¡ay, ay, ay, que me lo lleva el río!
> ¡ay, ay, ay, que me lo lleva el agua!

> Dorotea, como eres tan fea,
> de verte la cara me da carraspera
> y al mirarte la cara que pones
> se asusta la vaca, la burra y los chones.

> Una tarde fresquita de mayo
> cogí mi caballo, me fuí a pasear...

> Poderoso Jesús Nazareno,
> de cielos y tierra rey universal,
> hay un alma que os tiene ofendida,
> pide que sus culpas queráis perdonar.
> Sígueme y verás.

> No hay tal andar como andar a las dos... [2]

§ 7. SALAMANCA. — El P. Dámaso Ledesma, en su *Cancionero Salmantino* (Madrid, 1907), recoge cantares muy semejantes a los de Asturias y Santander, como éste, que es reminiscencia del de *Xuana*:

> Muerta la dejan aquellos villanos,
> muerta la dejan entre aquellos llanos.

Hay otros, cuyo origen no sé, pero que también se encuentran en Asturias, bajo distintas versiones:

> Yo no soy molinera, no,
> yo no soy cadena de amor.

> El pobre del tío Vicente
> con tanta gente ¿cómo le irá?
> Que los hijos le salen soldados
> Y la Tomasa en su casa está.

---

[1] *Cantos de la Montaña, colección de canciones populares de la provincia de Santander*, harmonizadas por el maestro Rafael Calleja, Madrid, 1901.

[2] Véase EDUARDO M. TORNER, *Elementos populares en las poesías de Góngora*, págs. 420-421: citas de Asturias, Salamanca y Santander. Recuerda «Que no hay tal andar como estar en casa...» (véase § 10 del cap. IV de este libro).

El esquema de octosílabos y decasílabos de Asturias se altera en esta versión del *Tío Vicente*, pero reaparece en toda su regularidad en otro cantar de *Tomasa:*

> Tomasa, que no está en casa,
> que no está en casa, ¿dónde estará?
> Se ha ido con los llaneros
> y pimienteros a Portugal.

La *pasión* «Poderoso Jesús Nazareno...», de Santander, se halla también en Salamanca.

Otros ejemplos de versificación irregular:

> Por entrar, por entrar en tu cuarto
> y un ratito de conversación,
> vino la justicia nueva,
> prisionero me llevó.
> ¡Qué dolor, qué dolor y qué pena!
> ¡Qué dolor para la mi morena! [1]

> Serrano, la Virgen de Francia te llama.
> Dile que no voy, que se vaya,
> que estoy muy malito en la cama;
> que estoy muy malito y no puedo,
> que soy del amor prisionero.

> Serrana, la Virgen del Carmen te llama.
> Descoloridita,
> ¿qué tienes?
> La Virgen del Carmen,
> ¿qué has hecho?
> Descoloridita
> te has puesto.

> Reyes Magos dichosos,
> desde la Arabia finos traéis
> oro, mirra, incienso,
> y al Rey de reyes les ofrecéis.
> ¡Oh quién, oh quién le pudiera ver!

> No son todas palomitas
> las que pican en el montón;
> no son todas palomitas
> que algunos palomitos son [2].

---

[1] Véanse §§ 1 y 3 de este capítulo, notas sobre Bancés Candamo y sobre Valledor.

[2] Recuérdese «No son todos ruiseñores...», en Góngora. Véase Torner, *Elementos populares en... Góngora*, págs. 417-418. Para la región leonesa, véanse las *Canciones leonesas*, recogidas por Rogelio Villar. En Palencia,

§ 8. Castilla. — En su *Folk-lore de Castilla* o *Cancionero popular de Burgos* (Sevilla, 1903), el P. Federico Olmeda recoge versiones modernas de cantares antiguos, como

> Al pasar del arroyo
> de Santa Clara,
> se me cayo el anillo
> dentro del agua [1].

> A la gala de la bella rosa,
> a la gala del galán que la goza.
> A la gala de la rosa bella,
> a la gala del galán que la lleva [2].

> Sale marzo y entra abril:
> florido le vi venir.
> Sale abril y entraba mayo
> con las flores relumbrando [3].

Si la primera y la tercera han adquirido ya formas enteramente isosilábicas, hay en Burgos otras canciones, como la segunda, que aún recuerdan sus orígenes rítmicos, especialmente los estribillos. Así ésta que pertenece al tipo existente en Asturias, Santander y Salamanca —dístico combinado con seguidillas—:

> Yo no soy la del cántaro, madre,
> yo no soy, que se rompió ayer tarde [4].

región leonesa en su origen, recoge G. Castrillo, *El canto popular castellano* Palencia, 1925:

> Duérmete, mi alma,
> duérmete, mi vida,
> que tu padre el malo
> se fué con la blanca niña
> y nuevo amor.

[1] Véase «Al pasar del arroyo del alamillo», en Lope. Consúltese cap. IV, §§ 3 y 13.

[2] Véase § 9 del cap. III, nota sobre los cantares de gala.

[3] Véase § 10 del cap. III: «Entra mayo y sale abril...», en Miguel Sánchez. Además, cita de *La burla del figonero*, en el § 3 de este capítulo.

[4] Hanssen, en *La seguidilla*, se equivoca al medir los versos de este cantar así:

> Yo no soy la del cántaro,
> madre, yo no soy
> que se rompió ayer tarde,

produciendo así una seguidilla anómala. Los versos forman un dístico de la familia de las muiñeiras gallegas y de otros cantares de Asturias, Santander y Salamanca, como «Yo no soy marinero», «Yo no soy molinera» y «No se va la paloma». La seguidilla sigue:

> Si se rompió ayer tarde,
> que se rompiera,
> y otro le está aguardando
> en la cantarera.

Luego se repite el dístico, como en las otras canciones.

No se va el pajarito al mar,
no se va, que lo he de embarcar.

Otros:

Me casó mi madre
con un pícaro pastor;
no me deja ir a misa
ni tampoco al sermón.
Quiere que me esté en casa
remendando el zurrón.
Él regruñir,
yo regañar:
no se le tengo yo de remendar,
el zurrón para que lleve el pan [1].

Que dáme las llaves del cuarto,
que dónde las tienes metidas.
Que me voy al triste campo
a llorar mi triste vida.
Que dáme las llaves.

¡Ay molinera!
Dále a la rueda con aire, que muela.

—¿Dónde le tienes el amor, salada?
—Soldadito, le tengo en la Habana.
—¿Dónde le tienes el amor, morena?
—Soldadito, le tengo en la guerra [2].

Vámonos, niña, vamos los dos,
vámonos, niña, para Aragón.
Vámonos, niña, si quieres venir,
vámonos, niña, pa Valladolid.

Que no le quiero soldado, no,
porque no forma de mi batallón,
ni le ha formado ni le formará.
Vaya un salero, vaya una sal,
vaya una niña para enamorar.

Tente, que me caigo, marinero de la mar,
tente, que me caigo, no me puedo levantar,
tente, que me caigo, a las orillas de la mar.

La seguidilla presenta todavía formas muy libres:

Mañana voy a Burgos,
vénte si quieres;

---

[1] *Cancionero*, de Olmeda, pág. 106; otra versión, pág. 117.
[2] Nótese el esquema paralelístico.

verás y veremos
los chapiteles.

Brincan y bailan los peces en el río,
brincan y bailan de ver a Dios nacido.
Brincan y bailan los peces en el agua,
brincan y bailan de ver nacida el alba.

(Como seguidilla invertida).

Eres hermosa, niña,
de boca y labios;
pareces a la Virgen
de los Milagros.

Cómo llueve,
cómo ha llovido:
hasta los chapiteles
han florecido.
¡Cómo llueve!
¡Qué serenita cae la nieve!
¡Ni el aire cierzo la detiene!

En Segovia y cercanías recoge Gabriel M. Vergara muy poca cosa en versificación irregular; hay seguidillas todavía con hexasílabos llanos:

Veladiez hermosa,
ramo de flores,
consuela al triste
con sus dolores...

y con hexasílabos agudos:

Si supiera que estabas
en el melonar,
melonera del alma,
te fuera a buscar...

y versos de gaita gallega, en cantar que declara conocer como muy antiguo:

Aunque me ves con estos alamares,
soy señorita de siete lugares... [1]

---

[1] *Cantares populares recogidos en diferentes regiones de Castilla la Vieja, y particularmente de Segovia y su tierra*, por GABRIEL MARÍA VERGARA, Madrid, 1912. — NARCISO ALONSO CORTÉS publicó una colección de *Cantares de Castilla* en la *Revue Hispanique*, octubre y diciembre 1914. Como versificación irregular, véanse principalmente los núms. 3.617, 3.631, 3.650, 4.360 y 4.867.

§ 9. MURCIA. — Poco es lo que recoge Inzenga de versificación irregular en Murcia [1]; la combinación decadodecasilábica aparece en el estribillo del aguinaldo «Metió Marco en el caldero»:

> Y se le atrancó,
> y por señas pedía la bota
> porque le faltaba la respiración,

y en el conocido *Rosario de la aurora*, el cual, sin embargo, no debe de ser cantar de Murcia, sino de Castilla o Andalucía, pues Modesto y Vicente Romero lo recogen en Alcalá la Real, y Olmeda en Burgos; se encuentra también en Aragón y Cataluña [2].

§ 10. ANDALUCÍA. — En Andalucía [3], donde el sentido de las formas simétricas es mayor que en León y Castilla, el proceso de regularización parece haber ido más lejos que en el resto de España, si atendemos a recopilaciones como la de Manuel Díaz Martín, hecha en 1884, y la vastísima de Rodríguez Marín, que es principalmente andaluza: los cinco volúmenes del investigador sevillano contienen una inmensa mayoría de coplas octosilábicas y

---

[1] Posterior a la publicación de este libro es el *Cancionero popular murciano* de ALBERTO SEVILLA, Murcia, 1921. Existen también, pero no los he visto, el libro de *Cantares populares murcianos*, recogidos por JOSÉ MARTÍNEZ TORNEL, Murcia, 1892, y *El cancionero panocho*, de PEDRO DÍAZ CASSOU, Madrid, 1900.

[2] INZENGA, *Cantos y bailes populares de España*, sección de Murcia (Madrid, 1888), pág. 37. Hay reimpresión de 1910. — *Cancionero* de OLMEDA (Burgos), pág. 195. — MODESTO Y VICENTE ROMERO, *Colección de cantos y bailes populares españoles* (con música): véanse Alcalá la Real y Teruel. — MILÁ, *Del decasílabo y endecasílabo anapésticos*.

La versión de Alcalá la Real dice:

> Los hermanos del Santo Rosario
> al brillar el día van a despertar,
> con sus cantos que alegran la aurora,
> las almas devotas de nuestra hermandad.

La de Burgos es la más popular en su lenguaje. La de Murcia es humorística:

> Un devoto por ir al rosario
> por una ventana se quiso arrojar,
> y la Virgen María le dijo:
> Detente, devoto, por la puerta sal.
> Devotos, venid;
> hermanos, llegad;
> que la Virgen María os llama:
> su santo rosario venid a rezar.

[3] Además de los *Cantos populares españoles* de RODRÍGUEZ MARÍN y de su conferencia *La copla*, véanse FERNÁN CABALLERO, *Cuentos y poesías populares andaluces* (primera edición, Sevilla, 1859, reimpresas varias veces: es, probablemente, el primer intento de colección folk-lórica española, en verso, en el siglo XIX); *Colección de cantes flamencos*, de Demófilo (ANTONIO MACHADO Y ÁLVAREZ), Sevilla, 1881; *Colección de cantares andaluces recogidos y anotados por Manuel Díaz Martín*, Sevilla, 1884.

de seguidillas regulares de cuatro o de siete versos. En éstas se halla aún el hexasílabo agudo en lugar del pentasílabo llano:

> Estando en la ventana
> me dijo un galán:
> — Águila real hermosa,
> ¿cuándo volarás?
> Yo le respondí:
> — Cuando tú, vida mía,
> me saques de aquí.

La seguidilla sirve de letra en Andalucía para innumerables bailes: oles, polos, boleros, tiranas, sevillanas, rondeñas, malagueñas.

La seguidilla flamenca o gitana no es de la familia de las otras: está compuesta de cuatro versos hexasílabos, interrumpidos a la mitad de la copla por un pentasílabo o por otro hexasílabo; generalmente el pentasílabo se escribe unido al hexasílabo tercero, produciéndose así la apariencia de un tercer verso endecasílabo:

> Campanita 'e plata
> mira que no quiero
> er que se sepa, compañera mía,
> lo que nos queremos.

Forma más irregular:

> Calle 'e la Porvera,
> no serás tú caye,
> sino montonsitos de arenita y tierra
> que se los yeba el aire [1].

Sin embargo, Rodríguez Marín recoge algo de versificación irregular: la mayor parte, en las porciones dedicadas a rimas infantiles, adivinanzas y otras fórmulas semejantes, que sólo parcialmente pertenecen a la poesía, puesto que el paso del tiempo ha ido destrozándolas; su antigüedad se comprueba con los *Juegos de Nochesbuenas*, de Ledesma (1602), y los *Días geniales o lúdicros*, de Rodrigo Caro (1626). Fernán Caballero había recogido ya buena parte de ellas. Merecen atención las que contienen aún en buen estado versos de tipo acentual:

> Todas las monjas se van a acostar;
> la madre abadesa se queda a rezar.

---

[1] Véase HUGO SCHUCHARDT, *Die Cantes flamencos*, en la *Zeitschrift für romanische Philologie*, 1881, vol. V.
Véase la colección de DÍAZ MARTÍN, núms. 59, 72, 76, 101, 112, 226, 343 y 406.

Anda y no la quieras,
que tiene andares de mula gallega.

María Chucena su choza techaba...
— María Chucena,
¿techas tu choza o techas la ajena?... [1].

§ 11. AMÉRICA. — No hay grandes colecciones de cantares recogidos en América, ni la poesía popular del Nuevo Mundo puede compararse en variedad ni en belleza con la de España. Se han recogido romances en el Ecuador, el Perú, Chile, la Argentina y el Uruguay; en Cuba, Santo Domingo y Puerto Rico; en Méjico y en el Suroeste hispánico de los Estados Unidos. La cosecha es más o menos igual, cuantitativamente, en cada país, y el contenido no muy desemejante. Se sabe que se cantan romances en Colombia, en Nicaragua, y es indudable que sobreviven en todos los demás países de lengua española. En varios de ellos, especialmente Méjico, el romance ha continuado produciéndose sobre temas nuevos, locales: así el de *Macario Romero*, popular en ambos lados de la frontera entre Méjico y los Estados Unidos.

Incidentalmente, en la investigación de los romances, se han recogido canciones líricas [2]; hay también colecciones de cantares [3].

[1] Véase vol. V, págs. 110 y 193.

[2] Véanse el *Romancerillo del Plata*, de CIRO BAYO, Madrid, 1913, y las contribuciones de AURELIO M. ESPINOSA al *Journal of American Folk-Lore*, de Nueva York, y a la *Revue Hispanique*, en 1914 y 1915.

[3] RAMÓN DE PALMA, estudio sobre los *Cantares de Cuba*, en la *Revista de La Habana*, 1854, tomo III; *Cancionero bonaerense*, publicado por VENTURA R. LYNCH, Buenos Aires, 1865, reimpreso por el Instituto de Literatura Argentina de la Universidad de Buenos Aires, 1925; *Cantares del pueblo ecuatoriano*, publicados por JUAN LEÓN MERA (tomo II de la *Antología ecuatoriana*), Quito, 1892: no contiene versificación irregular; ADOLFO ERNST, *Cancionero venezolano*, Buenos Aires, 1904; C. GONZÁLEZ BONA, *Trescientas cantas llaneras*, ¿Caracas?, 1903; JOSÉ E. MACHADO, *Cancionero popular venezolano*, Caracas, 1919 (segunda edición aumentada, 1922); *Cancionero popular*, recogido por ESTANISLAO S. ZEBALLOS, en la *Revista de Derecho, Historia y Letras*, de Buenos Aires, 1905; publicaciones diversas en los *Anales de la Universidad de Chile;* por ejemplo, RODOLFO LENZ, *Sobre la poesía popular impresa en Santiago de Chile*, 1919; ELEANOR HAGUE, *Spanish-American Folk-songs*, Lancaster y Nueva York, 1917: los núms. 12, 34, 48, 50, 51, 56, 57 y 64, por lo menos, son de origen español, no americano; otros no son populares, sino vulgares y aun literarios. Después de la primera edición de este libro, ha publicado CHARLES F. LUMMIS su colección de *Spanish songs of old California*, Los Angeles, 1924. Son posteriores también el *Cancionero popular rioplatense*, cuidadoso trabajo de JORGE M. FURT, 2 vols., Buenos Aires, 1923-1925; C. VEGA LÓPEZ, *La poesía popular de la América española*, Madrid, 1924; JUAN ALFONSO CARRIZO, *Antiguos cantos populares argentinos (Canciones de Catamarca)*, Buenos Aires, 1926; *Cancionero popular de Salta*, Buenos Aires, 1933, *Cancionero popular de Jujuy*, Tucumán, 1935, y *Cancionero popular de Tucumán*, Buenos Aires, 1937; JULIO ARZENO, *Del folklore musical dominicano*, Santo Domingo, 1927; RUBÉN M. CAMPOS, *El folklore y la música mexicana*, México, 1928; N. GA-

En América, como en España, puede asegurarse que predomina el isosilabismo en la poesía popular de hoy. Pero, muchas veces, el cantar español de versificación irregular ha pasado al Nuevo Mundo: así se ve en los juegos infantiles, como el de *Abejón*, que sel conoce en Santo Domingo en forma probablemente parecida a la que pudo conocer Ledesma (bajo la forma moderna de *Periquillo el aguador* se conoce en Andalucía, en Méjico y en los Estados Unidos) [1], o la canción de la *Pájara pinta*, conocida ya por Ledesma, recogida en España por Rodríguez Marín, y conocida en las Antillas, en Méjico y en la Argentina. Otras veces el cantar moderno se ha difundido, como ocurre con el montañés de «Una tarde fresquita de mayo...» y el asturiano de «En un delicioso lago...»[2].

En América han nacido nuevas combinaciones, con los cantos y danzas locales, bajo la influencia indígena o la africana, o como nuevos desarrollos. Ya en 1600 se atribuía origen americano a diversos bailes: así se mencionan la *gayumba*, el *retambo*, el *zambapalo*, el *sarandillo*, el *cachupino* —que pudiera proceder de Méjico, dado el nombre de apariencia nahoa— y la *chacona*, de la cual se dijo que provenía de Guayaquil, aunque una de sus letras alude también a Méjico. «Vida, vámonos a Tampico». En tiempos modernos, la *habanera*, la *danza* tropical, el *danzón* de Cuba, el *tango* del Río de la Plata, prefieren, en general, la versificación isosilábica [3]. Pero hay canciones en verso irregular aquí y allí:

> En Matanzas me han dado un pescado
> y me han dicho que a ti te lo dé.
> Te lo doy, te lo doy, te lo doy.
> Si me pides el pescado, te lo doy [4].

> Caimán, caimán,
> ¡caimán en el guayabal!

RAY, *Tradiciones y cantares de Panamá*, s. l., 1930; ANTONIO JOSÉ RESTREPO, *Cancionero de Antioquia*, Barcelona, 1930; MARÍA CADILIA DE MARTÍNEZ, *La poesía popular de Puerto Rico* (para versificación irregular, véanse págs. 25, 26, 38, 121, 124, 131-133, 152, 236 ss., 259-269, 272, 275-277, 298, 301, 305, 306, 311 ss., 319, 321, 324, 325, 329-333, 336, 338, 342); JUAN DRAGHI LUCERO *Cancionero popular cuyano*, Mendoza, 1938; *Cantos populares*, recogidos por EUSEBIO R. CASTEX, Buenos Aires, 1923.

[1] Véase cap. II, § 17.

[2] Véase mi conferencia *Música popular de América*, páginas 198-202.

[3] LEOPOLDO LUGONES, en su artículo *La musique populaire en Argentine*, de la *Revue Sud-Américaine*, de París, mayo de 1914, dice que toda la métrica popular del Plata se resume en los versos de cinco, seis, siete y ocho sílabas, y que hay combinaciones: heptasílabo y pentasílabo, o seguidilla, en los bailes de la *zamba* y el *gato;* hexasílabo y tetrasílabo, en el *caramba;* a veces, octosílabo y hexasílabo, en la *vidalita*. El *caramba* y la *vidalita* son de formación americana probablemente; hasta se supone que la música de la *vidalita* tenga origen quechua.

[4] Letra de *danzón* cubano, popular en 1914.

Tumba la caña,
anda ligero,
mira que viene el mayoral
sonando el cuero [1].

¿Dónde está?
Míralo, vélo.
¿Dónde está?
Mira pa'l cielo
y lo verás.
Niña tan buena moza
y de tan lindo pelo,
¿cómo te vas a casar
con ese míralo-vélo? [2]

Zamba, qué mal que has quedado,
cabeza'e borrego, pescuezo'e venado [3].

Caracoles y más caracoles
vamos a buscar a San Juan;
chiquiticas y zambullidores,
vamos a buscar a San Juan.

Usté verá, usté verá
en lo que viene a parar;
usté verá, usté verá
la barriga de San Juan Abá [4].

Fui al monte, corté un palito,
vine a mi casa, ¡a bailar se ha dicho!

Por ese sol que está alumbrando,
por ese Dios que me está viendo,
que como tú me sigas amando
yo te seguiré siempre queriendo [5].

Yo me paseaba por las orillas del agua
y el mar inmenso con sus olas me tapaba.
Yo a esa prieta no le vuelvo a ver la cara,
prieta orgullosa que por otro me dejara.

—Juliana, te vinieron a pedir.
Mi parecer yo no lo quise dar.
—Pues oiga, mama, con ése me he de casar.

---

[1] *Canciones de caña*, de los negros del campo en Cuba. En Cuba se observan combinaciones de octosílabos que terminan en versos diferentes, de diez sílabas (como «El chimpancé con patilla...») o de doce (como el danzón del *Pagaré*, 1910).

[2] Canción de los campos de Santiago de los Caballeros, en Santo Domingo.

[3] Canción popular del Perú.

[4] Canción tradicional de la noche de San Juan, en Santo Domingo.

[5] De Santo Domingo. Véase *Al amor del bohío*, de RAMÓN EMILIO JIMÉNEZ, Santo Domingo, 1927.

—No, Juliana; te vas a enfelizar
¡Con un hombre que no sabe ni cumplir!;
¡con un hombre que no sabe trabajar!
—Pues oiga, mama, con ése me he de casar.
—No, Juliana; te vas a enfelizar [1].

Yo me llamo Francisco Moreno,
que me vengo de confesá
con el cura de la parroquia,
que me entiende la enfemelá.
Curumbé, curumbé, curumbé [2].

La seguidilla existe en su forma típica, regularizada. Pero a veces se encuentran variantes:

Aunque venga de la cumbre,
no soy serrana;
mi padre, de Bolivia:
soy boliviana.

Que son centellas, sí,
memorias tristes;
llorando me dejastes
cuando te fuistes.

Planta de ají,
perlas de ancoche:
¿dónde estará mi negra
paseando en coche? [3]

La célebre habanera *La paloma* —si su letra es realmente americana— tiene estribillo irregular, y en sus coplas dos tipos métricos que pudieran ser, ambos, seguidillas:

Cuando salí de la Habana,
¡válgame Dios!,
nadie supo mi salida,
si no fuí yo...

Si a tu ventana llega
una paloma,
trátala con cariño,
que es mi persona...

[1] Canciones de Méjico. La última con música de *danza*.
[2] Canción de negros del Uruguay en 1830. Recogida —con otras— por ILDEFONSO PEREDA VALDÉS en su libro *Raza negra*, Montevideo, 1929.
[3] CARRIZO, *Antiguos cantos...argentinos*, núms. 4, 700 y 988.

El pentasílabo llano puede ser sustituído por el agudo; así en las *cuecas* de Chile:

> Sólo por ella late
> mi corazón,
> y ser correspondido
> es mi ilusión... [1]

o por el hexasílabo agudo:

> Lejos del bien amado
> no puedo vivir;
> para vivir penando,
> más vale morir [2].

La seguidilla gitana no existe que yo sepa, pero la *vidalita* del Río de la Plata tiene igual base: cuatro hexasílabos, a los cuales se les agrega, no un pentasílabo, sino (dos veces) la palabra que da nombre al género:

> Palomita blanca *(vidalitá)*,
> pecho colorado,
> llévale un suspiro *(vidalitá)*
> a mi bien amado [3].

> Palomita blanca *(vidalitá)*,
> de color de nieve,
> al pasar me heriste *(vidalitá)*.
> ¡Ay, cómo me duele! [4].

La versificación irregular sube a menudo hasta las letras escritas para música de compositores conocidos. Así, la habanera *Tú*, letra y música de Eduardo Sánchez de Fuentes, que ha dado la vuelta al mundo:

> En Cuba,
> la isla hermosa del ardiente sol,
> bajo su cielo azul,
> adorable trigueña,
> de todas las flores
> la reina eres tú.
> Fuego sagrado
> guarda tu corazón,

---

[1] Véase Hanssen, *La seguidilla*.
[2] Carrizo, *Antiguos cantos... argentinos*, núm. 800.
[3] Popular en la Argentina.
[4] Introducida por Benavente en *Todos somos unos*, en boca de una brasileña, a quien habría sido más lógico atribuirle un cantar en portugués.

> y el claro cielo
> su alegría te dió,
> y en tus miradas
> ha confundido Dios
> de tus ojos la noche, y la luz
> de los rayos del sol...

§ 12. RESURGIMIENTO DE LA VERSIFICACIÓN IRREGULAR EN
LA POESÍA CULTA (1895 a 1920): RUBÉN DARÍO. — El libro que
señala el resurgimiento de la versificación irregular en la literatura es *Prosas profanas*, de Rubén Darío, publicado en Buenos
Aires en 1896. El movimiento, como se ve, principia en la literatura de América: es reflejo del movimiento en favor del moderno verso libre, que tiene su centro en Francia y de allí irradia a
muchos países [1].

Caracteriza al libro de Rubén Darío la gran variedad de metros, manejados todos con rara perfección, con exquisito sentido
de sus cualidades musicales, sin repetir nunca demasiado ritmos
iguales dentro de cada tipo de verso. El deseo de hacer de todos
los metros conocidos en castellano instrumentos igualmente fle-
xibles —deseo que nace en el siglo XIX— llega aquí a su realiza-
ción, no lograda ni por los últimos clásicos académicos ni por los
románticos. Como versificador, Darío equivale en castellano a
Shelley o a Swinburne en inglés [2].

---

[1] Se dice a veces que el *verslibrisme* francés tiene su punto de partida en
Walt Whitman; pero Whitman no es sino influencia colateral. El *vers libre*
de los simbolistas franceses es fluctuante alrededor de paradigmas conocidos;
el de Whitman es propiamente amétrico.

[2] En *Azul*... (Santiago de Chile, 1888), DARÍO no había ensayado muchas
novedades, ni había intentado la versificación irregular. —La nueva acentuación del alejandrino («Los suspíros se escápan de su bóca de frésa», en vez
de «Me díce más pujánte: Tu Diós se acerca a tí») probablemente fué emplea-
da por Francisco Gavidia (el Salvador, antes que por nadie, véase su artículo *Historia de la introducción del verso alejandrino francés en el castellano*,
1904, donde dice que él le mostró el camino a Darío con una traducción de
Stella, de *Les châtiments*, de Hugo; además, su *Idilio de la selva*, parte de *La
defensa de Pan*, 1883, en su tomo de *Versos*, 1904 y *La vida de Rubén Darío
escrita por él mismo*, Barcelona, 1916, pág. 89); con esa ligera innovación se
inicia, piensa DARÍO, el movimiento de renovación de la métrica. A Iriarte,
entre sus muchos ensayos, no le había faltado: «Yo leí, no sé donde, que en
la lengua herbolaria...», ni a Moratín, «La bella que prendió con gracioso
reír...». En realidad, antes de Zorrilla el alejandrino castellano era libre en
la acentuación interna de sus hemistiquios; así en José María Heredia, en Esteban Echeverría, en Juan Carlos Gómez, en Ignacio Rodríguez Galván, en
Juan Valera: «Dichosos, si durasen las horas de ese sueño | Como duran y vuel-
ven las del sueño común...» (Echeverría, *La guitarra*). En *Azul*... se encuentran, dice DARÍO en la *Historia de mis libros* que aparece en el volumen *Antología* (Madrid, 1916), «*Caupolicán*, que inició la entrada del soneto alejandrino en nuestra lengua —al menos según mi conocimiento» (como curiosidad, puede recordarse el soneto alejandrino de Pedro Espinosa en el siglo
XVII, «Como el triste piloto que por el mar incierto»)—. Luego dice: «(Apli-

Adquieren nuevo brillo en *Prosas profanas* el doble octonario (en *Año Nuevo)*, el alejandrino, el eneasílabo (combinado con el alejandrino en el *Responso a Verlaine*, como en *Las orientales* y *Las hojas de otoño*, de Hugo), dos tipos de versos de diez sílabas (el anapéstico y el bipartito) y dos tipos de versos de doce (el anfibráquico, como el de arte mayor, y el nacido de la seguidilla[1]). El último se emplea precisamente *En elogio de la seguidilla:*

> Metro mágico y rico que al alma expresas...

El endecasílabo italiano vuelve a admitir todas sus variantes de origen, sobre todo la de acento interior sobre la sílaba cuarta, que duró del siglo XVI al XVIII:

> Sones de bandolín. El rojo vino
> conduce un paje rojo. ¿Amas los sones
> del bandolín, y un amor florentino?
> Serás la reina en los Decamerones.
>
> *(Divagación)* [2].

---

cación a igual poema de forma fija, de versos de quince sílabas, se advierte en *Venus»* (a la distancia, Darío se equivocó: los versos de su *Venus* son de diez y siete sílabas: «En la tranquila noche, mis nostalgias amargas sufría»; pero efectivamente escribió sonetos en versos de quince sílabas —así el intitulado *A Francia*, en 1893: «¡Los bárbaros, Francia! ¡Los bárbaros, cara Lutecia!»)—. Otros sonetos alejandrinos en *Azul...* son *De invierno, Leconte de Lisle, Catulle Mendés, José Joaquín Palma*. Los sonetos *Salvador Díaz Mirón* y *Walt Whitman* están en dodecasílabos de seguidilla: «Tu cuarteta es cuadriga de águilas bravas...»

[1] Julián del Casal tiene dodecasílabos nacidos de la seguidilla:

> En la popa desierta de un viejo barco...
> *(Páginas de vida*, 1892).
> Tu sueñas con las flores de otras praderas...
> *(Virgen triste*, 1893).

Rueda cultiva los dos tipos de dodecasílabos:

> Por las altas montañas del verde Asturias...
> *(El canto de las carretas*, 1892).
> En el resonante tablado flamenco...
> *(El tablado flamenco*, 1892).

[2] Véase mi artículo sobre *El endecasílabo castellano*, 1919, reproducido en el presente volumen, págs. 271-347.—Darío mezcla los ritmos del endecasílabo, especialmente en la *Balada de las musas de carne y hueso* y en *La cartuja*. Después tratan el endecasílabo con mayor libertad aún que Darío, María Eugenia Vaz Ferreira, del Uruguay (véase *El cazador y la estrella)*, Manuel Magallanes Moure, de Chile (véase *Tardes de la ciudad)*, y, naturalmente, entre los españoles, el grande Juan Ramón Jiménez. Cf. mi trabajo *El endecasílabo castellano.*

El laborioso escritor JULIO VICUÑA CIFUENTES en sus *Estudios de métrica española*, Santiago de Chile, 1929, págs. 107-142 y 195-202, habla de los diferentes tipos de endecasílabo como preceptista y dice que «defiendo la validez» del acentuado en la sílaba cuarta, «verso proteico que de todas mane-

Y el tipo anapéstico reaparece, con el *Pórtico* en honor de Salvador Rueda:

> Libre la frente que el casco rehusa...
> Urna amorosa de voz femenina,
> caja de música de duelo y placer... [1].

Pero todos estos ensayos son dentro de combinaciones isosilábicas e isométricas. La versificación irregular está representada en *Prosas profanas* por pocas composiciones. En el *Canto de la sangre* hay una ligera aproximación; se combina el endecasílabo yámbico con los dodecasílabos de arte mayor:

> Sangre de Abeal. Clarín de las batallas,
> Luchas fraternales, estruendos, horrores...

y en la penúltima estrofa aparecen inesperadamente dos heptasílabos:

> Sangre que la Ley vierte.
> Tambor a la sordina.
> Brotan las adelfas que riega la muerte...

ras está mal». Pero en mi trabajo arriba citado no he «defendido» este tipo de endecasílabo: he demostrado que fué el tipo fundamental en los ensayos españoles antes de Boscán; he comprobado su vida normal desde Boscán y Garcilaso hasta Moratín y su reaparición con Darío (los casos del siglo XIX son esporádicos). El decidir si «está bien» o si «está mal» es cuestión de gustos o de hábitos: yo no hago preceptiva.

[1] Véase el artículo *Dilucidaciones*, pág. XIX, en *El canto errante* (Madrid, 1907). Cuando *Clarín*, cediendo a la costumbre de discutir si los tipos métricos son buenos o malos, censuró el *Pórtico*, el poeta e investigador chileno Eduardo de la Barra hizo la historia de esta forma de verso en *El endecasílabo dactílico*, Rosario, 1895. En años posteriores, Darío ensayó otro tratamiento más libre y más musical del verso de gaita gallega, en el soneto *Gaita galaica;*

> Gaita galaica, sabes cantar
> lo que profundo y dulce no es.
> Dices de amor, y dices después
> de un amargor como el de la mar.
> Canta. Es el tiempo. Haremos danzar
> al fino verso de rítmicos pies...
> Tiempo de esparcir y de recoger,
> tiempo de nacer, tiempo de morir.

Y ensayó también otro tipo de endecasílabo (6 + 5) en el soneto que comienza:

> Del país del sueño tinieblas, brillos...

Pudo encontrar modelo en la antigua poesía galaico-portuguesa:

> ¡Ay frores, ay frores do verde pino!

En *La página blanca* se combinan versos de diez y de doce sílabas con otros de tres, de cuatro y de seis, en estrofas asimétricas:

> ...Otro lleva
> una caja,
> en que va, dolorosa difunta,
> como un muerto lirio la pobre Esperanza...
> Y el hombre,
> a quien duras visiones asaltan,
> el que encuentra en los astros del cielo
> prodigios que abruman y signos que espantan,
> mira al dromedario
> de la caravana
> como al mensajero que la luz conduce
> en el vago desierto que forma
> la página blanca.

Otro esquema libre, a la francesa, se presenta en *Dice mía:*

> Mi pobre alma pálida
> era una crisálida.
> Luego mariposa
> de color de rosa.
> Un céfiro inquieto
> dijo mi secreto.
> —¿Has sabido tu secreto un día?
> ¡Oh Mía!
> Tu secreto es una
> melodía en un rayo de luna.
> —¿Una melodía? [1]

En *Dice mía* el verso tiende a fundarse en pies trisílabos y el efecto es musical; pero en *Heraldos* desaparece todo paradigma y hasta la rima se reduce a transitorias asonancias:

> ¡Helena!
> La anuncia el blancor de un cisne.
> ¡Makbeda!
> La anuncia un pavo real.
> ¡Ifigenia, Electra, Catalina!
> Anúncialas un caballero con un hacha.
> ¡Ruth, Lía, Enone!
> Anúncialas un paje con un lirio...

---

[1] En *Historia de mis libros* dice Darío: «*Mía* y *Dice mía* son juegos para música, propios para el canto, *lieds* que necesitan modulación».

¡Aurora, Isabel!
Anúncialas de pronto
un resplandor que ciega mis ojos.
¿*Ella*?
(No la anuncian. No llega aún.) [1]

Y en *El país del sol* (1893) se ensaya la prosa rítmica, con rimas al comienzo y al final del párrafo-estrofa, y con estribillo:

«Junto al negro palacio del rey de la isla de Hierro —¡oh cruel, horrible destierro!— ¿cómo es que tú, hermana armoniosa, haces cantar, al cielo gris, tu pajarera de ruiseñores, tu formidable caja musical? ¿No te entristece recordar la primavera en que oíste a un pájaro divino y tornasol

en el país del sol?» [2].

En *Cantos de vida y esperanza*, libro publicado en Madrid en 1905, Darío vuelve al problema del verso cuantitativo a la manera grecolatina, y escribe la *Salutación del optimista*, en versos libres, sin rima, cuya larga serie fluctuante sugiere de modo vago el rumor del hexámetro:

---

[1] DARÍO, *Historia de mis libros:* «En *Heraldos* demuestro la teoría de la melodía anterior. Puede decirse que en este poemita el verso no existe, bien que se imponga la notación ideal. El juego de las sílabas, el sonido y color de las vocales, el nombre clamado heráldicamente, evocan la figura oriental, bíblica, legendaria, y el tributo y la correspondencia...»

[2] DARÍO, *Historia de mis libros:* «*El país del sol*, formulado a la manera de los *lieds de France*, de Catulle Mendés, y como un eco de Gaspard de la Nuit...».

Las principales declaraciones técnicas de Darío se hallan en el prefacio de *Cantos de vida y esperanza;* en *Historia de mis libros* (volumen *Antología*, págs. 19, 25, 26, 30, 34 y 36), y en su autobiografía, *La vida de Rubén Darío escrita por él mismo*, págs. 89, 168 a 171 (donde aparece otro poema en prosa, *God save the Queen*, de 1894), 183, 185, 192 a 194 (relativas a Jaimes Freyre) y 196, donde dice que, hacia 1898, en la Argentina, «Carlos Alfredo Bécu publicó una *plaquette*, donde por primera vez apareció en castellano versos libres a la manera francesa; pues los versos de Jaimes Freyre eran combinaciones de versos normales castellanos». Afirmación inexacta, pues está visto que, en una forma o en otra, Darío mismo había usado antes que Bécu versificación que se aproximaba al tipo libre francés.

Véase también el estudio de Rodó sobre Darío, en las ediciones parisienses de *Prosas profanas*, págs. 19-20, 21-22, 26-27, 28, 29, 35, 41-42 y 42-43. Además, MAX HENRÍQUEZ UREÑA, *Rodó y Rubén Darío*, La Habana, 1919, y LAUXAR (Osvaldo Crispo Acosta), *Rubén Darío y José Enrique Rodó*, Montevideo, 1924, págs. 123-140. Lauxar tiene razón al rectificar antiguas opiniones mías sobre el alejandrino de Darío (en mi ensayo juvenil *Rubén Darío*, 1905, del libro *Horas de estudio*, París, 1910), indicando que el poeta nicaragüense lo escribió tripartito en diversas ocasiones («Ojos de víboras de luces fascinantes...»). Sobre la conversión de esdrújulos en agudos, véase mi nota sobre la alteración del acento de las palabras en el verso, § 5 del cap. III.

¡Ínclitas razas ubérrimas, sangre de Hispania fecunda!
Espíritus fraternos, luminosas almas, salve...

En versos semejantes escribe después la *Salutación al águila*
(1907), y en este camino le siguen Guillermo Valencia, de Colombia; Alfonso Reyes, de Méjico, y otros poetas, no muchos. Manuel
González Prada, del Perú, imitó metros latinos, principalmente
los de Horacio, pero, como Carducci, con frecuencia los traspuso
de moldes cuantitativos a moldes silábicos con acentos interiores
fijos; hizo además el expeimento de la prosa cortada en estrofas.

Otra novedad ensaya Darío —esbozada ya en *Dice mía*—:
fundar la versificación de una poesía en un pie determinado (en
estos casos, el pie trisílabo con acento en la sílaba central), que se
multiplica ad libitum, como en la *Marcha triunfal* y la *Salutación
a Leonardo:*

> ...Y así, soberano maestro
> del estro,
> las vagas figuras
> del sueño, se encarnan en líneas tan puras
> que el sueño
> recibe la sangre del mundo mortal
> y Psiquis consigue su empeño
> de ser advertida a través del terrestre cristal... [1]

Los ensayos de verso libre no repiten ya la forma amétrica
de *Heraldos*, sino que fluctúan alrededor de algún paradigma:
el paradigma de la silva a la manera italiana (versos de once y
de siete sílabas, éstos duplicados a menudo), en el final de «Divina Psiquis...»; el de la alternancia de alejandrinos y eneasílabos (regular en el *Responso a Verlaine*, combinación de origen
francés), en el comienzo «¡Oh, miseria de toda lucha!...»; el del
octosílabo en *Aleluya*. Los esquemas son más libres, sin paradigmas —pero con ritmos más marcados y musicales que en *Heraldos*—, en *Augurios* (versos que oscilan entre tres y catorce sílabas) y «En el país de las alegorías...». Los esquemas libres —aunque nunca muy libres— se repiten en los libros posteriores, donde
Darío fué gradualmente abandonando su antiguo amor de los ritmos delicados, su «locura armoniosa de antaño», para expresar
preocupaciones intensas en forma desnuda.

El *Canto a la Argentina* (Buenos Aires, 1910), después de co-
menzar (I, II, III) con versos que van desde siete hasta trece sí-

---

[1] No con mucha exactitud dice Darío en *Historia de mis libros* que la *Salutación a Leonardo* está «escrita en versos libres franceses»: la memoria,y
la atención, le flaqueaban en sus últimos años. Escribe después *La canción
de los osos*, de base tetrasílaba (en *Poema del otoño*, Madrid, 1910).

labas, se desarrolla, como *Elena y María* o la *Razón de amor* en el siglo XIII, en versos de nueve y de ocho sílabas libremente distribuídos:

> ...Los éxodos os han salvado:
> ¡hay en la tierra una Argentina!...
> Hallasteis otras estrellas,
> encontrasteis prados en donde
> se siembra, espiga y barbecha...
> Hijos de Castilla la noble,
> rica de hazañas ancestrales;
> firmes gallegos de roble;
> catalanes y levantinos...

Muy semejante es la versificación fluctuante en *Raza* (en el libro *Poema del otoño*, 1910): versos de seis, siete, nueve, once y catorce sílabas. Igualmente la versificación de *Pax*, 1914.

§ 13. LOS CONTEMPORÁNEOS Y SUCESORES DE DARÍO EN AMÉRICA: VARIEDAD DE ENSAYOS. — Antes de *Prosas profanas*, Darío encuentra compañeros en el trabajo de «poner en circulación» muchos metros, pero manteniéndose dentro de los moldes isosilábicos: tal es la actitud de Martí y de Casal en Cuba, de Gutiérrez Nájera en Méjico. Sólo en uno de sus empeños de otra especie tiene Darío un precursor: en el de crear metros en que se multiplique libremente un mismo pie silábico, como en la *Salutación a Leonardo*. José Asunción Silva, de Colombia, escribió en 1895 ó 96 —no mucho antes de su muerte— el célebre *Nocturno*, cuya base es tetrasílaba con ocasionales deslices hacia la disílaba:

> Una noche,
> una noche toda llena de perfumes, de murmullos y de música de alas,
> una noche
> en que ardían en la sombra nupcial y húmeda las luciérnagas fantásticas...
> y se oían los ladridos de los perros a la luna,
> a la luna pálida... [1].

---

[1] Es posible que Silva haya encontrado la sugestión de este metro en la traducción del *Cuervo*, de Poe, hecha por el venezolano Pérez Bonalde entre 1875 y 1890:

> Una fosca negra noche, trabajando en mi aposento...
> Dijo el cuervo: Nunca más.

Pero, según él declaraba, la idea le vino de la fábula de Iriarte sobre *El caballo y la ardilla*.

Domingo Estrada, de Guatemala, en su versión de *Las campanas*, de Poe, combina versos de cuatro, de ocho y de diez y seis sílabas.

Otro antecedente, que no se había señalado todavía, es la composición

Probablemente, Silva precedió a Darío también en la afición al eneasílabo:

> El emperador de la China...

Los versos puestos en circulación comienzan a combinarse en estrofas, ya isométricamente repetidas, ya asimétricas. El poeta que más se distingue en estos nuevos intentos es Ricardo Jaimes Freyre, de Bolivia: en *Castalia bárbara* (Buenos Aires, 1897) combina versos de doce y de diez y seis sílabas, y versos de diez y seis con versos de trece:

> Canta Lok en la oscura región desolada
> y hay vapores de sangre en el canto de Lok.
> El pastor apacienta su enorme rebaño de hielo
> que obedece, gigantes que tiemblan, la voz del pastor.
> Canta Lok a los vientos helados que pasan
> y hay vapores de sangre en el canto de Lok.

En *Los sueños son vida* (1917), la libertad es mayor:

> En un frágil trirreme surcaste
> el oceano profundo y sonoro
> que ocultaba con olas de sombra y espumas de nieve
> el jardín de los frutos de oro.
>
> *(Alma helénica)* [1].

de Ventura Ruiz Aguilera (1820-1881), *El otoño* (1853); tiene pies de cuatro sílabas:

> ¿Veis qué tristes van muriendo lentamente,
> cómo doblan la arrugada y mustia frente
> cuantas flores
> con aromas y colores
> eran gloria de la verde soledad?

El español José María Gabriel y Galán, en *Las canciones de la noche* y otras composiciones, revela la influencia de Silva; emplea la combinación del dodecasílabo (4 + 4 + 4: «Una noche rumorosa y palpitante...») con el octosílabo.

También el murciano Vicente Medina, en *La canción de los trigos*, sigue a Silva:

> Han granado... Sazonadas las espigas
> se inclinaron, y agitadas por el viento
> cosas trágicas cantaron
> tristemente, gravemente, con susurros de misterio.

Juan Valera (1824-1905) había empleado versos de quince sílabas constituídos por cinco pies trisílabos, en su *Fábula de Euforión:*

> Dejadme del alma romper las endebles cadenas...

---

[1] Jaimes Freyre ha publicado, no sólo libros de versos, sino un estudio sobre las *Leyes de la versificación castellana* (Tucumán, 1912). Formula la interesante teoría de los *períodos prosódicos* como unidades métricas.

Lugones, ya en 1896, empleaba el pie trisílabo multiplicado en *La marcha de las banderas* [1], y también un argentino, Leopoldo Díaz, en sus *Poemas* (Buenos Aires, 1896), combinaba versos de diferentes medidas sobre base de pies idénticos: de tres, de cuatro o de cinco sílabas. Otros antecedentes de la *Marcha triunfal* y de la *Salutación a Leonardo*.

Enrique González Martínez, de Méjico, obtiene resultados brillantes con otras combinaciones, como la de versos de nueve con versos de trece sílabas (en estrofas isométricas):

> Huye el enjambre que semeja
> nube que flota, viene y va.
> La vida dice: No hay un alma en cada abeja;
> mas tiene un alma el rumoroso colmenar... [2].

De las combinaciones de dos o más versos distintos, la que mayor boga tiene es la deca-dodecasilábica, resucitada, que se mantiene dentro de moldes isosilábicos por lo general, salvo excepciones como *La página blanca*, de Darío, y el *Idilio*, de Salvador Díaz Mirón, de Méjico:

> ...al que a un tiempo la gloria y el clima
> adornan de palmas la frente...

> Monótono y acre gangueo
> que un pájaro acalla soltando un gorjeo...

[1] En *Nosotros*, Buenos Aires, mayo-julio de 1938, pág. 125.

[2] *La canción de la vida*, en *La muerte del cisne*, Méjico, 1915. Después ha ido francamente a la versificación irregular, cuya libertad consiste en mezclar tipos de verso ya existentes en la métrica regular, rarísima vez tipos nuevos: en *El romero alucinado*, Buenos Aires, 1924, véanse *La pesadilla, Radiograma, La pareja, La niña de la escuela, Retorno, Invierno, Misa negra, El tragaluz, El reloj;* en *Las señales furtivas*, Madrid, 1925; véase *Ánfora rota, La amenaza, El néctar de Ápam, La ventana, La apacible locura:*

> Frescura en el alma... Frescura
> en la canción...
> y una apacible locura
> guardada en la cárcel oscura
> del embrujado corazón.

De este tipo es la poesía *Coplas* de Gabriela Mistral (aunque normalmente la poetisa chilena prefiere el verso regular):

> Todo adquiere en mi boca
> un sabor persistente de lágrimas:
> el manjar cotidiano, la trova
> y hasta la plegaria.
> Yo no tengo otro oficio,
> después del callado de amarte,
> que este oficio de lágrimas, duro,
> que tú me dejaste...

Una rústica grácil asoma
como una paloma... [1].

§ 14. LA VERSIFICACIÓN AMÉTRICA EN LA POESÍA HISPANO-
AMERICANA. — La versificación plenamente irregular, amétrica,
iniciada de modo tímido por Darío, continúa difundiéndose y
adquiere brillo en los poemas de José Santos Chocano, del Perú,
y en el *Lunario sentimental* (Buenos Aires, 1909), de Leopoldo
Lugones, de la Argentina, antiguo jefe de la *extrema izquierda* en
el movimiento que se llamó *modernista*. En Lugones ha servido
principalmente para propósitos de humorismo sutil:

Con la extática elevación de un alma,
la luna, en lo más alto de un cielo tibio y leve,
forma la cima de la calma
y eterniza el casto silencio de su nieve.
Sobre el páramo de los techos
se eriza una gata oscura;
el olor de los helechos
tiene una farmacéutica dulzura [2].

En Chocano sirve a los fines de la lírica pindárica, como en la
Oda salvaje (con asonancias en los versos pares):

...Selva de mis abuelos,
diosa tutelar de los Incas y los Aztecas,
yo te saludo desde el mar, y te pido
que en la noche —en la noche que está cerca—
me sepultes
en tus tinieblas
como si me creyeses un fantasma
de tus religiones muertas,

---

[1] Otros ejemplos de esta versificación más o menos libre, de base deca-
dodecasilábica, son: *Eran dos hermanos*, de Enrique González Martínez *(Los
senderos ocultos*, 1913); *Nocturno*, de José Gálvez, del Perú *(Palabras líricas);
La buena canción*, de Mariano Brull, de Cuba *(La casa del silencio*, Madrid, 1916).
De base alejandrina son *Bogotá*, del cubano Emilio Bobadilla (1898),
y *Alma pagana* y *Nirvana*, del dominicano Max Henríquez Ureña *(Án-
foras*, Valladolid, 1914). De base endecasílaba, las *Odas nuevas*, del mejicano Balbino Dávalos *(Las ofrendas*, Madrid, 1908). De base eneasílaba,
Simplicitas, y de base octosílaba, *Una y otra*, del mejicano Amado Nervo
(Elevación, Madrid, 1917).

[2] Antes del *Lunario sentimental*, Lugones había escrito en versificación
irregular, siempre rimada, cinco poesías de *Los crepúsculos del jardín* (Buenos Aires, 1905). El poemita humorístico *Los burritos* es contemporáneo
del *Lunario;* son posteriores los *Poemas solariegos* (Buenos Aires, 1929).
En artículos publicados en el diario *La Nación*, de Buenos Aires, de 1924
a 1930, Lugones se declara contrario a la versificación irregular si no lleva
rima.

y me brindes, para salvajizar mis ojos
con reverberaciones de fiesta,
en la punta de cada uno de tus árboles
ensartada una estrella... [1]

§ 15. La versificación fluctuante en España (1900-1920).
A partir de 1900, la presencia de Rubén Darío en España suscita los problemas de métrica que ya apasionaban a la América
española.

Eduardo Marquina adopta innovaciones de Darío, entre ellas
el hexámetro. Su versificación no alcanza gran libertad: véanse,
en *Elegías* (Madrid, 1905), *Se pinta el mar*, en versos fluctuantes
alrededor de medidas usuales (7-8-9-11-14), y *En un dolor de la
amiga* (7-8-11).

Van más lejos otros poetas, como Enrique Díez-Canedo, en
sus traducciones *(Del cercado ajeno*, Madrid, 1907; *Imágenes*, París, c. 1909; *La poesía francesa moderna*, en colaboración con Fernando Fortún, Madrid, 1913), y en sus *Versos de las horas* —originales— (Madrid, 1906): véanse *Las canciones del río, Fantasía
nocturna* y *Elegía de otoño*, donde la versificación fluctúa alrededor de paradigmas. Igual tendencia, procedente de Darío, se observa en Ramón Pérez de Ayala: *La paz del sendero*, Madrid, 1913;
Estaciones y *La sombra negra del sauce; Prometeo*, Madrid, 1916:
unos cuantos de los preciosos comentarios líricos de las novelas.
En el *Coloquio entre la parábola y la hipérbola* llega al verso totalmente libre:

—¿De dónde vienes? ¿Adónde vas?
—Soy la piedra, el canto errático.
Voy en parábola hacia el cielo
hasta que caigo
en la tierra prístina.
—¿Cúya es la mano
que te arrojó?
—Una mano divina.
Me arrojó de soslayo
hacia la espalda.
Piedra de pedernal; el rayo
jovial
de mis entrañas...

---

[1] En *Alma América* (Madrid, 1906), Chocano no adoptaba aún la
versificación enteramente irregular. Solamente había adoptado la de base
tetrasilábica multiplicada libremente *(La elegía del órgano, El salto del
Tequendama, El alma primitiva, Lo que dicen los clarines, Los caballos de
los conquistadores)* y versos desusados, como el de diez y siete sílabas en
Ante las ruinas («Parece que estoy viendo sobre las crestas de una montaña»), el de doce como seguidilla invertida en *Momia incaica* («Momia que
duermes tu inamovible sueño)», y el de diez y seis.

En tiempos recientes, Juan Ramón Jiménez se convierte en el principal cultivador de los metros libres. En sus últimos libros, *Diario de un poeta recién casado* (Madrid, 1917), *Eternidades* (1918), *Piedra y cielo* (1919): emplea constantemente la versificación irregular [1]

> Inteligencia, dádme
> el nombre exacto de las cosas.
> ...Que mi palabra sea
> la cosa misma
> creada por mi alma nuevamente...
>
> *(Eternidades, III.)*

> Eres tan bella
> tú, como el prado tierno tras el arco iris...
> Como tus ojos verdes con mi risa grana,
> como mi hondo corazón con tu amor vivo.
>
> *(Eternidades, XXIII.)*

> Inmenso almendro, en flor,
> blanca la copa en el silencio pleno de la luna,
> el tronco negro en la quietud total de la sombra;
> ¡cómo, subiendo por la roca agria a ti,
> me parece que hundes tu troncón
> en las entrañas de mi carne,
> que estrellas con mi alma todo el cielo!
>
> *(Piedra y cielo, I, 24.)*

§ 16. RETORNO A LA VERSIFICACIÓN ACENTUAL POPULAR. — En obras anteriores a *Eternidades*, Juan Ramón Jiménez se había inspirado en la versificación acentual del pueblo, elemento que faltó en la innovación de Rubén Darío (salvo el soneto *Gaita galaica*), porque la poesía popular de la América española, menos interesante que la de España, ha ejercido muy poca influencia sobre los poetas cultos [2].

---

[1] Ejemplos: en *Eternidades*, números 3, 11, 14, 23, 33, 34, 37, 50, 58, 62, 76, 114; en *Piedra y cielo*, I: 5, 13, 24, 30, 42, 54; II: 3, 7, 8, 11, 15; III: 5, 7, 14, 16, 25. Unas son francamente amétricas; otras tienden a paradigmas de eneasílabos, endecasílabos u otras medidas.

[2] Sin embargo, la versificación libre de tipo acentual aparece en poetas de América: véase, Alfonso Reyes, *Coro de sátiros en el bosque* (1908), *En las viñas de Galaad, El mal confitero* (1918), *Conflicto* (1919); tiene también versos fluctuantes alrededor del endecasílabo en *Fantasía del viaje* (1915), *Octubre* (1919) y *Ventanas*, V (1921) — véase el volumen *Pausa*, París, 1926 —, y en la tragedia *Ifigenia cruel*, Madrid, 1925. Versos amétricos, muy largos: *La pipa del Cantábrico* (1921). — Ocasionalmente, hizo también versificación irregular Ramón López Velarde (1888-1921): véase *Todo*, en *Zozobra* (Méjico, 1919).

Jiménez ha vuelto a componer, sobre bases populares, canciones que recuerdan las de Lope, Góngora y Valdivielso:

> Dios está azul. La flauta y el tambor
> anuncian ya la cruz de primavera.
> Vivan las rosas, las rosas del amor
> entre el verdor con sol de la pradera.
> Vámonos al campo por romero,
> vámonos, vámonos,
> por romero y por amor...

> El humo del romero quemado nubla, blanco y redondo, el sol.
> ¡Qué olor, qué olor, qué olor!

> ¡Cómo suena el violín por la viña,
> por la viña amarilla!...

> > *(Baladas de primavera*, 1910.)

José Moreno Villa, en su libro *Garba* (Madrid, 1913), vuelve también a la versificación acentual:

> Arpas y liras, violines, rabeles
> — ¡ah, y la guitarra de mi corazón! —,
> forman el coro que sabe de mieles,
> de mirra, de incienso, de consagración...

> > *(Irreverencia.)*

> Yo la he cogido del brazo, y le digo,
> pausadamente, palabras tan viejas,
> que de puro rancias,
> parecen ingenuas.
> ¡Los siglos que lleva este arroyo
> cantarino cruzando la sierra!

> > *(Reconocimiento.)*

> Con todo el brío
> que tiene la mar,
> no rebasa el borde
> de su heredad...

> > *(Las sugestiones del mar.)*

Don Ramón del Valle Inclán ha imitado el ritmo de las muiñeiras de Galicia:

> Cantan las mozas que espadan el lino,
> cantan los mozos que van al molino,
> y los pardales en el camino...

... El molinero cuenta un cuento,
en la espadela cuentan ciento,
y atrujan los mozos haciendo el comento[1].

Manuel Machado se acerca a la versificación acentual:

Pobre Juan de la tierra clara,
pobre Juan de la triste cara,
pobre poeta.
Canto sincero,
oloroso y humilde
como el romero.

Y Antonio Machado, en *Apuntes y canciones*, se acerca a la antigua versificación de los cantares de Castilla, en ritmos sordos, del siglo XVI:

— Y los bolcheviques
(sobran rejas y tabiques)
dí, madre, ¿cuándo vendrán?
— Si te oye Don Lino
¡válgame la Trinidad!
La honrada mocita,
coser y esperar.

§ 17. CONCLUSIÓN. — Como se ve, el movimiento iniciado en América entre 1890 y 1895, y extendido a España desde 1900, ha restaurado en la poesía culta los dos tipos de versificación irregular que habían existido en castellano: el amétrico, que domina desde el siglo XII hasta el XIV, y el acentual, que florece del XIV al XVII. El tipo amétrico moderno, aunque unas veces coincida con el medieval en la tendencia a aproximarse a paradigmas isosilábicos, otras veces desecha toda aproximación a la regularidad y busca efectos singulares. Cerca de ellos se encuentran los ocasionales ensayos de prosa rítmica, la cual, por definición, debería distinguirse del verso, faltándole la unidad que debe caracterizarlo.

Hay, además, ensayos nuevos, como el de la multiplicación del pie silábico, que produce resultados interesantes, y hay retornos a los intentos de versificación cuantitativa a la manera de la antigüedad.

Los dos extremos en que puede caer la versificación irregular

---

[1] En su poema dramático *Cuento de abril* (1910) hay trozos en versificación irregular, como «Trovador galán y gentil...», y también ligeras irregularidades en pasajes de versificación regular.

son la prosa y el sonsonete de baile [1]. El tipo amétrico, manejado por versificadores que no posean el sentido justo de la unidad rítmica que constituye el verso, puede llegar a no distinguirse de la prosa. El tipo acentual puede convertirse en sonsonete monótono, si el versificador no cuida de variar los efectos con la distribución de los golpes o altas, a la vez que el número de sílabas, como lo hacen los poetas de idiomas en que la poesía es meramente acentual, sin sujeción al número fijo de sílabas. De uno y otro extremos deberán huir los poetas de lengua castellana, si quieren mantener viva y eficaz la riqueza de versificación conquistada durante los últimos años.

---

[1] Entre 1920 y 1930, la versificación irregular ha adquirido el predominio en castellano entre los jóvenes, con las escuelas de vanguardia. De los dos peligros en que pensé, se evita el del sonsonete, pero no siempre el de la confusión con la prosa. En España, hacia 1925, hay reacción hacia el verso regular, con Jorge Guillén, Rafael Alberti, Pedro Salinas, y, en parte, Gerardo Diego (véase el núm. 1 de su revista *Carmen*, de Madrid, 1927), y Federico García Lorca, aficionado, además, a libres ritmos acentuales. Pero el verso libre ha persistido: ejemplos, en direcciones muy diferentes, Gerardo Diego, León Felipe, Vicente Aleixandre, Juan Larrea, Adriano del Valle.

De América, son ejemplos, en direcciones también muy diversas, Juana de Ibarbourou, Fernán Silva Valdés, Carlos Sabat Ercasty, en el Uruguay; Jorge Luis Borges, Leopoldo Marechal, Nora Lange, Francisco Luis Bernárdez, en la Argentina; Vicente Huidobro, Pablo Neruda y Salvador Reyes, en Chile: José María Eguren, en el Perú; Jorge Carrera Andrade, en el Ecuador; Ricardo Arenales, en Colombia; Rafael Arévalo Martínez, en Guatemala; Salomón de la Selva, en Nicaragua; Genaro Estrada, Carlos Pellicer, Jaime Torres Bodet, Xavier Villaurrutia, Salvador Novo, José Gorostiza, en Méjico; Agustín Acosta y Mariano Brull, en Cuba; Juan Bautista Lamarche, Domingo Moreno Jiménes, Andrés Avelino y Héctor Icháustegui Cabral, en Santo Domingo.

OTROS ESTUDIOS

I

EN BUSCA DEL VERSO PURO

¿Será cierto que hay dos únicos modos de expresión verbal: el verso y la prosa? ¿Y será cierto que el verso y la prosa deben mantenerse puros, antitéticos e inconfundibles entre sí? Vivimos bajo el terror de que nos descubran parentesco con el inmortal *bourgeois gentilhomme*. Y más si el parentesco existe. Pero padecemos escrúpulos innecesarios. Quizás M. Jourdain era menos tonto de lo que Molière creía, como Bouvard y Pécuchet eran menos tontos de lo que Flaubert creyó. Quizás no era M. Jourdain quien se equivocaba, sino el maestro de retórica, según hábitos de su tribu. Recordemos al árabe describiendo la prédica de Mahoma: «No es poesía, ni es prosa, ni es lenguaje mágico, pero impresiona, penetra...»

BARRIDO. — Las nociones usuales sobre el verso son incompletas, o limitadas, o equivocadas. Cada quien parte, para definirlo, de su idioma propio y de sus propios métodos de versificar. Con tal punto de partida equivocan la ruta y hasta descarrilan. Hace falta la noción genérica. La gente de lenguas germánicas no oye el verso de lenguas romances sino después de aprendizaje especial. Filólogos alemanes hay que se enredan al explicar el verso italiano: se empeñan en ajustarlo a nociones germánicas sobre el acento y hasta sobre el valor de las vocales en grupo. Pulula en escritores ingleses la confesión de sordera para el verso francés: cosa sencilla les estorba, el valor pleno que conservan para el metro las sílabas mudas. Pero creo que muchos ingleses no entienden todavía su propio verso, hijo confuso de dos familias contrarias, capaz de traicionar unas veces al padre acento y otras veces a la madre sílaba: así me lo confirman los formidables volúmenes de Saintsbury. Donde no por eso falta la perentoria declaración de que ningún extranjero comprende el verso inglés... ¿Y el secular problema semítico? ¿Y todos los problemas de Oriente, lejano y cercano, de India y de China, de Persia y de Arabia, con su multitud de formas intermedias entre el verso y la prosa?

253

En español, después de siglos beatos de realismo ingenuo, desde Luzán nos dedicamos laboriosamente a complicar y falsear nuestra noción del verso. Tiempo y paciencia lo alcanzaron al fin: los preceptistas latinizantes decidieron que procedíamos como en Grecia y Roma, combinando sílabas largas y breves. Por fortuna, los poetas no leían los tratados y componían «de oído», como el músico de pueblo «que no sabe nota»; confiándose al hábito, evitaban el error de los libros. Después que Bello y Maury nos devolvieron a la ley real de la sílaba de cantidad única, padecimos cerca de cien años nueva sordera: toda obra poética del idioma creímos explicarla con el verso de número fijo de sílabas. Hombres eminentes perdieron largas horas de su vida en el minucioso error de constreñir en medida exacta los poemas de versificación irregular: Cornu con el *Cantar de Mio Cid*, Marden con el *Fernán González*; Pietsch con los *Disticha Catonis*. La historia de las letras españolas nos avisa que nuestro verso puede ceñirse a tres normas —la medida, el acento, la rima— o vivir libre de cualquiera de ellas. Los vanguardistas, ahora, nos gritan que debe libertarse de las tres. La actual invasión de los ejércitos del verso sin medida ni rima es para muchos desazón y plaga, es la lluvia de fuego, la abominación de la desolación. Pero *es*.

RITMO. — Desatando al verso de la cadena de rigores con que se pretende sujetarlo, todavía se aferra al último eslabón: la ley del ritmo. ¿Es justa, entonces, la familiar definición del verso como *unidad rítmica*?

Sí: la definición es justa siempre que se encierre dentro del círculo exacto de definición mínima, siempre que se recoja estrechamente dentro de la noción limpia y elemental de *ritmo*, apartando de sí cualquier enredo con la idea de acento o de tono o de cantidad, cualquier exigencia de igualdades o siquiera de relaciones matemáticas.

El verso, en su esencia invariable a través de todos los idiomas y de todos los tiempos, como grupo de fonemas, como «agrupación de sonidos», obedece sólo a una ley rítmica primaria: la de la repetición. Ritmo, en su fórmula elemental, es repetición. El verso, en sencillez pura, es unidad rítmica porque se repite y forma series: para formar series, las unidades pueden ser semejantes o desemejantes [1].

---

[1] En todo ritmo de sonidos hay por lo menos dos elementos distintos: los sonidos y el intervalo de silencio que los separa: «El ritmo concreto —dice Paul Verrier, *Essai sur les principes de le métrique anglaise*, tres vols., París, 1909-1910— «...está constituído por una división perceptible del tiempo o del espacio en intervalos sensiblemente iguales» (intervalos rítmicos). O bien «el ritmo está constituído por el retorno, a intervalos sensiblemente iguales, de determinado fenómeno o siquiera del signo que hace perceptible la división del tiempo o del espacio». Los intervalos de verso a verso, las *pausas*, son «sen-

La unidad aislada carece de valor: la serie le da carácter rítmico y la frecuencia del uso le presta apariencia de entidad. Cuando decimos que frases como «Lo cierto por lo dudoso» o «Amar sin saber a quién» o «En un lugar de La Mancha» son versos octosílabos, es que la abundancia de aquel tipo métrico en la poesía española crea costumbre y obliga al oído a reconocerlo suelto o dentro de la prosa [1]. Cualquier tipo de versificación, cuando es nuevo, cuando falta la costumbre de él, desconcierta al oyente: los tradicionalistas sentencian que «no es verso», que «suena mal al oído». Así se dijo del endecasílabo español en el siglo XVI; así, a fines del XIX, de la rica versificación de Rubén Darío y los suyos; todavía se oyen ecos de aquella disputa cuando estalla otra nueva.

VERSO, MÚSICA Y DANZA. — La definición mínima, abstracta, como no pide igualdades, ni relaciones matemáticas, se contenta con cualquier serie de unidades fluctuantes. Pero la realidad histórica del verso impuso limitaciones. El verso nace junto con la música, unido a la danza: nace sujeto al ritmo de la vida, que si con el espíritu aspira a la libertad creadora, con el cuerpo se pliega bajo la necesidad inflexible: sobre el cuerpo pesan todas las leyes de la materia, desde la gravitación. El hombre que habla, como su esfuerzo físico es escaso, puede olvidarlo y gozar la ilusión de la libertad: en su ilusión ningún cauce lo contiene, ningún dique lo detiene. Río inextinguible de la palabra pura cuyo murmullo trasciende a la plática encendida de Santa Teresa y al cuento de nunca acabar que es el *Quijote* [2]. Pero el hombre que danza no se siente libre: corazón y pulmones le dictan su ritmo breve.

siblemente iguales», pero los versos, las unidades contenidas dentro de las pausas, pueden no ser iguales, ni siquiera semejantes. No debe olvidarse que el ritmo, en el arte, es mental, es impuesto por el espíritu, aunque se apoye en fenómenos concretos.

[1] «El hábito de los metros artísticos —observa LANDRY, *La théorie du rytme et le rytme du français déclamé*, París, 1911— ha creado en nosotros la tendencia a ver el metro en todas partes, hasta donde no está». Del «papel activo del espíritu en la percepción métrica» trató, con ejemplos abundantes de versos castellanos, el pensador uruguayo CARLOS VAZ FERREIRA en su libro *Sobre la percepción métrica*, Barcelona, 1920.

[2] «El ritmo de la voz es casi completamente libre. El peso de los órganos... insignificante... No hay más resistencia que la de la atmósfera», dice Landry. Pero «las series rítmicas... están limitadas por la necesidad de respirar...» «Ejemplo notable de desproporción entre la energía motriz y la sonora». Landry le llama metro a la especie de ritmo cuyos caracteres son el isocronismo de los tiempos y la acentuación o diferenciación de intensidad: «El ritmo, actividad del cuerpo, es esencialmente energía y desarrollo continuo de la energía; el metro, creación del espíritu, es ante todo duración e igualdad de duración en una serie discontinua». Así, en el verso, «el isosilabismo es creación del espíritu»: se da en idiomas donde la sílaba es siempre variable en su duración, sin cantidad aproximadamente fija como en las lenguas de la India antigua y de Persia, de Grecia y de Roma.

La danza está obligada a la conciencia del límite: cada paso de danza tiene su límite.

Históricamente, el verso nace con la danza: es danza de palabras: danza de sonidos de la voz. Los nombres arcaicos que designan el verso y la música y la danza son, en su origen, comunes a los tres: *areito* entre los indígenas de Santo Domingo, o *coro* entre los griegos, son nombres indivisos del baile con canto. Y hasta nuestros días las artes del hombre rústico, y aun las del vulgo en las ciudades populosas (tango en Buenos Aires o jazz en Nueva York), conservan los tres metales en confusión, como en veta nativa.

LIMITACIONES HISTÓRICAS. — Así, el verso, al nacer, no se modela sobre la onda inagotable de la charla libre, sino en los giros parcos de la danza [1]. La primera limitación que padece va contra la longitud: ha de ceñirse a formas breves: no admite prolongación indefinida: de ahí que la conciencia del límite perdure hasta en Whitman o en Claudel o en Apollinaire. El español antiguo no se arredraba ante dieciocho sílabas; ni el griego ante veinticuatro; ni el árabe ante treinta. Pero tales cifras se alcanzan raras veces con la sílaba como elemento puro: se requieren apoyos rítmicos. En la métrica regular del español, el verso llega sin dificultad hasta nueve sílabas; de ahí en adelante, para construir la entidad sonora, pide auxilios: cortes o cesuras, acentos interiores fijos.

Sobre la unidad fluctuante, elástica, con que se contenta la definición mínima, la realidad histórica impone nuevas limitaciones al verso: el grupo de sonidos, de fonemas, que lo constituye, a más de no prolongarse indefinidamente, requiere contornos exactos. Hay que saber dónde empieza y dónde acaba la entidad rítmica. Y siendo la palabra punto en que se cruzan sonido e idea, el término se fija, o por procedimiento fonético, o por procedimiento intelectual.

Entre los procedimientos fonéticos, el más fácil será exigir

---

[1] No existiendo disparidad de esencia, sino de organización, entre el habla y el canto, la música de la voz —origen de toda música— nace libre, sin vallas, como la plática. ¿Estará olvidada en América la jugosa tradición española de la mujer que canta todo el día sobre sus labores? ¡Y el pájaro! El baile es quien dictó a la música el compás. Y en él arraiga la profusa vegetación de leyes rítmicas que el Occidente hizo culminar, como en finales, supremas, abrumadoras flores de invernadero, en las rosas centifolias de la sonata, el cuarteto y la sinfonía. Después, la influencia de los ritmos danzantes ha ido declinando: la «melodía infinita» de Wagner es en su esencia el ideal contrario a la danza. Separada del baile, la música fluctúa con amplia soltura rítmica: el Occidente la conoce en el canto llano de la Iglesia Católica y en el cante hondo de los gitanos, herencias de civilizaciones orientales con largas tradiciones de música libre, música sin compás. Sobre los posibles orígenes del verso son muy interesantes las observaciones de KARL BUCHER en su famoso libro *Arbeit und Rhythmus*, donde habla del ritmo del trabajo como antecedente del ritmo métrico.

semejanza, aproximación aritmética entre los versos de cada serie: en su natural desarrollo, esta tendencia llevará a pedir igualdades estrictas. La fluctuación no nace como libertad absoluta. En sus comienzos históricos, el verso fluctúa dentro de márgenes que nunca rebasa: el número de sílabas no crece ni mengua demasiado. Se sabe cuándo el poeta canta en versos largos y cuándo en versos cortos: dominando la fluctuación hay siempre paradigmas inconscientes. Menéndez Pidal ha descubierto la ley matemática que, a hurto de los poetas, gobierna la fluctuación, según la frecuencia del uso, en seis o siete poemas de la Edad Media española. En el verso largo del *Cantar de Mio Cid* (siglo XII) y de *Roncesvalles* (siglo XIII) predominaba la medida de catorce sílabas; le seguía, en orden de frecuencia, la de quince; luego, la de trece; luego la de dieciséis... La fórmula aritmética es curiosa: doble corriente de medidas que crecen y de medidas que decrecen:

$$15 \quad 16 \quad 17 \quad 18$$
$$14$$
$$13 \quad 12 \quad 11$$

Y el verso corto de la cántica de los veladores, en el *Duelo de la Virgen*, del maestro Gonzalo de Berceo, fluctúa en sentido contrario:

$$8$$
$$9$$
$$10$$

La fluctuación inicial, con sus ondulaciones graduales, no permite que conscientemente se hagan alternar versos de longitudes disímiles. La historia nos da como tardía la combinación de versos francamente desiguales, especie de síncopa de la versificación. En Grecia, el metro épico, en hexámetros uniformes, precede al metro elegíaco en dísticos de hexámetro y pentámetro; todavía son posteriores las combinaciones complejas, como en las odas de Píndaro y los coros de la tragedia. En España, la copla de pie quebrado hace su aparición después de tres siglos de renglones parejos, regulares o irregulares.

El procedimiento intelectual para definir la entidad rítmica será exigir que cada verso termine en el final de una palabra (no a la mitad de ella, como en Sófocles o en Simónides) y lleve sentido completo: frase, por lo menos; si oración, mejor. En los orígenes del verso, y todavía después mientras vive como hijo del pueblo, cada unidad rítmica es unidad de sentido. La alteración de esta ley, cuando ocurre, es fruto de edades cultas. Existen idiomas que nunca se permiten violarlas: el árabe, el finlandés. En español, la ley rigió desde el *Mio Cid* hasta el *Rimado de Palacio,* y el cantar del pueblo la cumple todavía: en la poesía culta, la alteración es normal desde los tiempos de Juan de Mena. El siglo XII nos irá dando tantos conceptos como versos:

> Mio Çid fincó el cobdo, en pie se levantó,
> el manto trae al cuello, e acdeliñó pora'león;
> el león cuando lo vió assí envergonçó,
> ante Mio Çid la cabeça premió e el rostro fincó.

El cantar del pueblo, en el siglo XVI:

> Morenica me llaman, madre,
> desde el día que yo nací;
> al galán que me ronda ia puerta
> blanca y rubia le parecí...

El siglo XVIII, en cambio:

> El polvo y telarañas son los gajes
> de su vejez. ¿Qué más? Hasta los duros
> sillones moscovitas y el chinesco
> escritorio, con ámbar perfumado,
> en otro tiempo de marfil y nácar
> sobre ébano embutido, y hoy deshecho,
> la ancianidad de su solar pregonan...
>
> (Jovellanos)

El verso libre de idiomas europeos, en nuestros días, tiende espontáneamente a cumplir la vieja ley, porque no necesita romper las unidades de sentido para construir unidades rítmicas:

> Inmenso almendro en flor,
> blanca la copa en el silencio pleno de la luna,
> el tronco negro en la quietud total de la sombra,
> cómo, subiendo por la roca agria a ti,
> me parece que hundes tu troncón
> en las entrañas de mi carne...
>
> (Juan Ramón Jiménez)

> Con mi soledad
> tu ausencia se torna grande y sencilla
> como la noche que baja al arrabal cansado...
>
> (Nora Lange)

> ¿Qué correspondencia tendrá mi faz con la luna?
> ¿Qué correspondencia tendrá mi alma con el viento?
> Soy el que fuí hace siglos y no me conozco...
>
> (Domingo Moreno Jimenes)

Apoyos rítmicos. — En los largos amaneceres de la poesía, el verso escinde sus caminos: uno, para acompañar a la danza y a la música; otro, para recorrerlo con la música sola, hasta aprender a separarse de ella. Y este verso que sólo se canta —o se canturrea— admite suma sencillez: así se ve en la poesía narrativa de los tiempos heroicos, capaz de crecer y multiplicarse en bosques de epopeyas. Pero el verso de la danza, como la música danzante, tiende al compás preciso. Ante todo, el verso largo se parte en dos, como la célula: el poema épico, en general, no llega a abandonar la norma: las dos porciones del renglón serán aproximadamente iguales, como en el *Mio Cid*, o francamente desiguales, como en el *Roland*. Pero la división avanza, y hay entonces, en vez de hemistiquios, pies, o ambas cosas.

Y en vez de la medida fluctuante, la danza impuso medidas exactas: *acentos* de intensidad bien marcados, o *tonos*, o valores de sílabas *(cantidad)*, o, finalmente, *número fijo de sílabas*. Apoyos rítmicos que definen agudamente la estructura del verso.

O bien el apoyo rítmico se busca en la homofonía, en la repetición de sonidos: la *rima* —igualdad o semejanza en la terminación de las palabras (a veces como en el latín eclesiástico, basta la repetición del último fonema, vocal inacentuada, o, como en chino, la equivalencia de los tonos, sin equivalencia de los fonemas)—; o la *aliteración* —rima al revés, rima de los comienzos de las palabras, en que basta la igualdad de sus sonidos iniciales o en ocasiones (como en el inglés antiguo) el regulado contraste entre ellos. Rima y aliteración ocurren en el interior o en los extremos del verso: en el hecho histórico, la aliteración ha sido las más veces interior; la rima, exterior, de verso a verso. Pero la rima interior es más frecuente que la aliteración exterior.

Para ligar verso a verso se acude a la repetición, no ya de simples fonemas o tonos, sino de palabras enteras: el recurso halla su máximo desarrollo en el *encadenamiento*, muy conocido en la poesía trovadoresca de todos los idiomas románticos. La repetición ideológica toma principalmente la forma de *paralelismo*, rima de ideas, típico de la poesía hebraica.

Últimos son los recursos convencionales que nacen de la escritura y que el oído no atrapa, como el *acróstico*. Desdeñados como juegos pueriles en las literaturas occidentales, reciben mejor acogida en Oriente: así, el acróstico alfabético entre los hebreos [1].

Fórmulas de versificación. — Para desvanecer el prejui-

---

[1] Los versos, al ligarse entre sí, es natural que produzcan combinaciones diversas. En la literatura arcaica de muchos pueblos se les encuentra en series amorfas, de longitud indefinida —tipo que representan los poemas homéricos y hesiódicos, el *Roland*, el *Cid*, el *Beowulf* de los anglosajones, el *Cantar de los Nibelungos*, y también en agupaciones simples, la *sloka* de dos versos en el *Ramayana* y el *Mahabharatta*, el dístico desigual de la elegía helénica, los dísticos y tercetos paralelísticos de los hebreos, de los babilonios, de los egipcios, de los finlandeses, los dísticos rimados de *Aucassin et Nicolette* o del *Mis-*

259

cio de que sólo es verso el de nuestro idioma en nuestro tiempo, de que sólo merece el nombre aquella unidad rítmica cuyas leyes nos son familiares, nada mejor que una peregrinación a tierras lejanas [1]. Los pueblos que nos son exóticos hablan lenguas cuyos sistemas gramaticales resultan irónicamente contrarios al nuestro: su música se organiza sobre escalas distintas de las nuestras. ¿No será natural que el verso difiera? Lo es.

El verso varía de pueblo a pueblo, de siglo a siglo. Pero varía menos que las armazones lingüísticas o los sistemas tonales, porque trabaja con material uniforme: la sílaba, arcilla sonora sujeta a modulaciones pero intacta en su esencia.

Si representamos con abreviaturas los recursos principales del verso, podremos resumir en fórmulas la versificación de todos los idiomas. Sean: V, la unidad fluctuante, de medida elástica; Vv, la combinación de versos ostensiblemente desiguales; Ces, la cesura; Num, el número fijo de sílabas; Cant, la regulación de la cantidad, el número fijo de valores de sílabas (largas y breves); Int, los acentos de intensidad; T, la regulación de los tonos o diferencias de altura musical entre las sílabas; R, la rima; Alit, la aliteración; Enc, el encadenamiento; Par, el paralelismo; Acr, el acróstico.

China. La historia de su versificación, a juzgar por las descripciones, da estas fórmulas: V + R; Num + Int; Num + T + R; Vv + Num + R; Num + T + Par; Num + T + R + Par. La principal es, según parece, Num + T + R + Par: número fijo de sílabas y de tonos, con rima y paralelismo. La regulación del tono musical de las sílabas, cuyo cambio altera el sentido de las palabras, tiene formas sutiles: combinada con el paralelismo —que es antiguo de tres mil años— crea complicaciones microscópicas.

Japón. Num; Vv + Num (la versificación típica; ejemplo, el Hai Kai, métricamente parecido al final moderno de las seguidillas españolas: tres versos, uno de cinco sílabas, uno de siete, otro de cinco). A veces hay paralelismo: Num + Par. Versificación cuya sencillez contrasta con los artificiosos enredos de la China. No hay rima en ningún caso.

Los Hebreos. V + Par; Int + Par; Ces + Int + Par; Vv + Ces + Int + Par; Ces + Int + Enc + Par; Ces + Int + Par.

---

terio de los *Reyes Magos*, los tercetos monorrimos del *Dies irae*, los cuartetos monorrimos de la cuaderna vía de Berceo y el Arcipreste. De ahí nace la estrofa: una vez nacida, toma las veredas de la complicación, hasta llegar a la selva de formas rigurosa y minuciosamente legisladas de la poesía china, o de la árabe, o de la sánscrita, o de la provenzal.

[1] Hallé estímulo para esta investigación en la discusión (1926-1927) entre dos de los mejores poetas argentinos, Leopoldo Lugones y Leopoldo Marechal, el uno en contra y el otro en favor del moderno «verso libre»; pero los dos hablaban atribuyéndole al verso los caracteres del español, o, a lo sumo, del latino y el griego, como si no existiesen otros tipos.

Después de centurias de discutir y divagar, la investigación ha llegado a puerto, gracias al timón de Sievers: la versificación hebraica en los poemas y cantares de la Biblia está constituída por pies acentuales, con número variable de sílabas. El paralelismo es usual, bajo formas varias: simples igualdades, o progresiones, o contrastes. El verso más común es el de tres acentos (Libro de Job; muchos Salmos); frecuente el de cuatro (Salmos); el de cinco es usual en la Kiná, la Lamentación. El apoyo rítmico del acento, como todos los de carácter fonético, se usa con libertad; en su uso hay curiosas asimetrías, y ante ellas se ve perplejo el europeo acostumbrado a versificación regular. George Adam Smith [1] las explica como casos de la tendencia, general en Oriente, que él llama *simetrofobia:* «Como el paralelismo es el principio característico y dominante del verso hebreo, y el poeta busca constantemente el ritmo de las ideas, se ve obligado a modificar sus ritmos de sonidos. Como su propósito primordial es producir renglones paralelos en ideas, es natural que esos renglones no siempre resulten iguales en longitud... Como la ley de los versos hebreos exige que sean, cada uno, oración o frase completa, tenderán, dentro de ciertos límites, a variar de longitud, a variar en el número de acentos... En toda especie de arte oriental descubrimos la influencia de lo que podría llamarse simetrofobia: aversión instintiva a la simetría absoluta, que, en casos extremos, se expresa en alteraciones arbitrarias y aun violentas del estilo o el plan de la obra artística... A la luz de lo que sabemos sobre la poesía de los semitas y de otros pueblos, el empeño de reducir los versos en la poesía hebraica a métrica estricta, y el paralelismo a simetría absoluta, me parece anticientífico».

Pero el verso principal, en la Biblia, el de mayor número de obras, no es el de los poemas y cantares: es el de las profecías. Normalmente, el verso de los profetas no es acentual sino fluctuante, con el solo apoyo del paralelismo (V + Par) y a ratos sin él; así en el libro que corre bajo el nombre de Isaías, voz de dos vates poderosos, con adición de cosas menores y ajenas.

La rima cruza la Biblia muy de tarde en tarde (trozos del *Cantar de los Cantares;* Salmos VI y XVIII); pero la poesía hebrea de los últimos diez siglos la adopta, bajo el influjo árabe.

Asiria y Babilonia. Ces + Int; Vv + Ces + Int (fórmula principal); Vv + Ces + Int + Par. El acento es la norma esencial. El paralelismo, importante. Incidentalmente se usan la rima, la aliteración, el encadenamiento, el acróstico. La interpretación del sistema poético de los asirios y los caldeos ha sido fácil, gracias a la excepcional precisión de las inscripciones, que separan con líneas horizontales y verticales las estrofas (en su mayoría dísticos y trísticos), los versos y los pies acentuales. El verso de cuatro acentos es el de la epopeya.

[1] *The early poetry of Israel,* Londres, 1912.

Fundamento tradicional de la liturgia arcaica de Babilonia, los himnos sumerios, en la lengua de aquel pueblo extinto, con antigüedad hasta de cincuenta siglos, no parecen llevar sino el verso simple, fluctuante (V): a modo de complemento único añaden conatos de paralelismo, repeticiones verbales, íntegras o con variaciones, y respuestas de letanía.

Los árabes. V + Ces + R; Ces + Int + R; Vv + Ces + Int + R; Ces + Num + Int + R; Vv + Ces + Num + Int + R. La rima es esencial en la versificación de los árabes desde épocas remotas, desde el Saj', el «arrullo de paloma», que en su retórica clasifican ellos como prosa rimada (como verso tendría la fórmula V + R). Hay quienes erigen la hipótesis del Saj' primitivo, fluctuante y vago, sin rima, pero tal vez paralelístico a la manera hebraica (V + Par). Muy peculiar la cesura: cae, en muchos versos, a mitad de palabra. La versificación de la era clásica está llena de artificios laboriosos, de que se han contagiado las literaturas de Turquía, de Persia y de la India.

Egipto. En el verso de la antigua literatura egipcia entraban, en medidas diversas, al parecer, el principio del número fijo de sílabas, el de los acentos, el paralelismo, la aliteración y hasta la rima, en cantares mágicos.

Lenguas Indoeuropeas. Si las lenguas del Extremo Oriente, como el chino y el japonés, construyen su verso sobre el fundamento sonoro de la sílaba pura, y las lenguas semíticas, como el babilonio, el hebreo, el árabe, sobre el acento, las indoeuropeas en su origen lo asentaron sobre la cantidad, el juego de sílabas largas y sílabas breves. A pesar de la importancia que tuvo para la estructura de las palabras, el tono musical, explica Meillet, no ejerció influencia ninguna sobre el ritmo de la frase en la primitiva lengua indoeuropea de donde proceden las nuestras. El acento de intensidad, tampoco. «Pero como toda sílaba del indoeuropeo tenía una cantidad breve o larga fija (salvo, en cierta medida, la final), las oposiciones cuantitativas eran muy perceptibles para el oído y eran constantes. Por lo tanto, sólo en el retorno regular de sílabas largas y sílabas breves en lugares determinados, junto con ciertas reglas sobre los finales de palabra, se funda la métrica de los *Vedas* y del griego antiguo: en otros términos, el ritmo del indoeuropeo era un ritmo puramente cuantitativo, no un ritmo de intensidad». La cesura debió de existir también: «en el verso de más de ocho sílabas, el védico, el avéstico y el griego antiguo llevan generalmente un corte, que consiste en un final de palabra obligado, en lugar definido: igual cosa en el saturnio de los romanos»[1]. Después, los nuevos idiomas en que se partió el indo-

---

[1] Pero en el verso antiguo de los idiomas indoeuropeos hay problemas complejos que MEILLET trata en su estudio *Les origines indo-européennes des métres grecs*, París, 1923: los caracteres peculiares del hexámetro, por ejemplo, que le hacen pensar en origen egeo.

europeo trastornaron el equilibrio sonoro de la lengua madre. «El ritmo deja de ser puramente cuantitativo —dice luego Meillet—: la cantidad misma se altera, o desaparece totalmente, como en griego desde el siglo segundo antes de la era cristiana, en latín durante la época imperial, o en armenio».

El griego clásico conservó la cantidad en su versificación (fórmulas: Cant; Ces + Cant; Vv + Ces + Cant) hasta el siglo IV de la era actual: en su última época la conservaba artificialmente, porque el ritmo del habla había dejado de ser cuantitativo. Los pies subían desde dos hasta cinco sílabas, y se enlazaban en multitud de formas, con enorme variedad de efectos, desde la solemne monotonía del hexámetro homérico y la llaneza cotidiana del trímetro de los diálogos teatrales hasta el salto y el vuelo de las odas corales y los interludios de la tragedia y la comedia. El latín arcaico, en el carmen saturnium, había abandonado el principio indoeuropeo de la cantidad para escribir versificación fluctuante atribuyéndole tal vez importancia al acento, y sobre todo a la cesura; pero el influjo helénico restauró el principio cuantitativo, y el latín clásico trató de serle fiel hasta sus últimos días. Bajo el Imperio, el latín vulgar, aceptando descaradamente la realidad fonética, adopta el número fijo de sílabas uniformes, sin distinguir entre largas y breves. El cuento de sílabas persiste a lo largo de la Edad Media y domina por fin en la poesía de la iglesia cristiana, donde se le incorpora la rima, ignota para griegos y latinos clásicos. Los idiomas célticos, cuando los conocemos (siglo VI) no conservan la cantidad, pero sí la cesura del antiguo indoeuropeo, y poseen acentos fuertes, aliteración, rima, y hasta número fijo de sílabas. Y los idiomas germánicos, en los más antiguos restos sobrevivientes de su poesía, se presentan ya bajo el sistema acentual, abandonado el cuantitativo, y guardando solamente la arcaica cesura: añaden la aliteración, que dura en ellos más de mil años. La rima surge, tardía, y espontánea al parecer, en Alemania, en Islandia y aun en Inglaterra: desde el siglo XI la refuerza el influjo francés; convive con la aliteración, y acaba por desplazarla.

Porque entre tanto, a lo largo de la Edad Media, de entre los cien dialectos en que se partió el latín, como su progenitor el indoeuropeo, emergían hacia la luz los que iban a imponerse sobre sus rivales y a crear literaturas. La poesía de las lenguas románicas se organiza bajo el princpio común de la rima, y tiende a contar números iguales de sílabas, pero no con éxito igual en todas partes: Francia, en el Sur y en el Norte, lo alcanza desde temprano; Italia, muy pronto; Portugal, también; pero Castilla tarda mucho —hasta fines del siglo XIV— en llegar francamente al isosilabismo. La cesura ha persistido en los versos largos: el acento, esencial siempre al final del renglón, se vuelve obligatorio también en el interior del verso largo, con la cesura o sin ella, y en el verso corto sirve de apoyo rítmico variable [1].

La versficación regular de Francia, Provenza e Italia, durante toda su historia desde la Edad Media hasta la aparición del verso libre, se resume fácilmente en fórmulas: Num + R; Vv + Num + R; Num + Int + R; Ces + Num + Int + R; Vv + Ces + Num + Int + R. Hay que agregar el verso blanco de Italia (Num + Int). Pero la versificación española, junto a esas fórmulas, tiene otras suyas. El español ofrece, como pocas lenguas, el espectáculo del mundo que acaba de brotar del caos y ensaya laboriosamente, bajo nuestra mirada, figuras y formas. La versificación irregular de metros cortos, como en *Santa María Egipcíaca* o *Elena y María*, tiene como recurso único la rima (fórmula: V + R):

> Qui triste tiene su coraçón
> venga oir esta razón
> odrá razón acabada
> feita d'amor e bien rimada.

(Razón de amor)

Los poemas épicos y los poemas de clerecía en que no se acertó a aplicar el principio de las «sílabas cuntadas», como el *Libro de buen amor*, vuelven —atávicamente— a partir el verso en dos hemistiquios (fórmula: V + Ces + R): como la cesura cae siempre después de la palabra acentuada, los exigentes requerirán que se cuente también el acento (fórmula modificada: V + Ces + Int + R). El verso de arte mayor en el siglo xv posee número variable de sílabas, pero cesura y acentos fijos, con rima (Ces + Int + R):

> Tanto anduvimos el cerco mirando
> hasta que topamos con nuestro Macías.

(Juan de Mena)

La versificación irregular de los cantares líricos populares entre el siglo xv y el xvii ofrece unas cuantas especies: el cantarcillo (V + R):

---

[1] H. GAVEL, en su estudio *De coro, decorar* (del *Homenaje a Menéndez Pidal*, tomo I) supone que acaso el verso irregular haya precedido al regular en la epopeya francesa, como en la poesía española, y sugiere como antecedente posible la salmodia litúrgica de la Iglesia Católica; pero las pruebas faltan. En los poemas anglonormandos de lengua francesa se halla versificación irregular, pero como degeneración de la regular. Y cosa semejante ocurre con poemas franco-italianos. Problema curioso es el que suscita el verso libre de los vascos: véase GEORGES HÉRELLE: *La versification dramatique des basques et l'origine probable du vers libre*, en los *Annales du Midi*, Tolosa, 1921.

> Guárdame las vacas,
> carillejo, y besarte he;
> si no, bésame tú a mí,
> que yo te las guardaré...

la seguidilla arcaica (V + Vv + R):

> Ojos de la mi señora
> ¿y vos qué avedes?
> ¿por qué vos abaxades
> cuando me veedes?...

los cantares de verso largo, tipo muiñeira, cuyo recurso característico es el acento de intensidad, distribuído con escasa regularidad (V + Int + R):

> Molinico ¿por qué no mueles?
> Porque me beben el agua los bueyes...

Los cantares paralelísticos, populares todavía en Asturias; los cantares paralelísticos y encadenados:

> Amigo, el que yo más quería,
> venid a la luz del día,
>
> Amigo, el que yo más amaba,
> venid a la luz del alba.
>
> Venid a la luz del día,
> non traigáis compañía.
>
> Venid a la luz del alba,
> non traigáis gran compaña [1].

---

[1] En su estudio sobre *La cantidad silábica en unos versos de Rubén Darío* (en la *Revista de Filología Española*, Madrid, 1922), TOMÁS NAVARRO TOMÁS trata de la cantidad en las sílabas castellanas, medida científicamente por su duración en centésimas de segundo. Los versos de la *Sonatina* de Rubén Darío (dos estrofas), le sirven, ante todo, como material de investigación fonética, para continuar sus estudios sobre la cantidad en nuestro idioma *(Manual de pronunciación castellana*, Madrid, 1918; sexta edición, 1953; en la *Revista de Filología Española: Cantidad de las vocales acentuadas*, 1917; *Diferencias de duración entre las consonantes españolas*, 1918; *Historia de algunas opiniones sobre la cantidad silábica española*, 1921). Le sirven, después, para averiguar si hay ley cuantitativa que presida a la versificación castellana. Los resultados son: existen grandes diferencias de duración entre las sílabas castellanas, hasta la proporción de uno a cuatro; pero esas diferencias no dependen de la estructura de la sílaba (como en griego o en latín, donde el diptongo, por ejemplo, era «largo por naturaleza»): dependen de su colocación dentro del conjunto. Las causas de la superioridad cuantitativa de unas sílabas respecto de

Portugal comparte con Castilla, probablemente, todas sus especies de versificación: tal vez una que otra, como la épica, haya de discutírsele; en cambio, ejerce señorío sobre el cantar paralelístico y encadenado.

EL VERSO CONTEMPORÁNEO. — La excursión a través de unas cuantas literaturas de Asia, Africa y Europa revela cuántos fenómenos distintos reciben el nombre de verso. ¿Qué habrá de común entre el Hai Kai de los japoneses, cuyo único recurso

otras son «el acento rítmico, el énfasis y la posición final ante pausa». «El hecho de que las sílabas hayan sido o no gramaticalmente acentuadas no ha sido fundamento para hacerlas largas o breves. El hecho de que hayan sido abiertas o cerradas tampoco... Las sílabas no han manifestado tener por sí mismas una cantidad propia. Toda sílaba, cualquiera que haya sido su naturaleza o estructura, ha recibido una u otra duración, según las circunstancias rítmicas, psíquicas o sintácticas en que se ha pronunciado». Las diferencias de duración «ni van ligadas en nuestra lengua a la significación propia de las palabras, ni se dan en éstas en proporción regular y constante, ni tienen en nuestra ortografía signo alguno que las represente, como lo tienen por ejemplo, la entonación, el acento y las pausas, todo lo cual basta para explicar el hecho de que dichas diferencias pasen, en general, inadvertidas». «No es posible fundar sobre esas diferencias ninguna versificación castellana: de ahí el fracaso de nuestros ensayos de métrica cuantitativa al modo griego o latino. La idea de una métrica cuantitativa a la manera clásica resulta completamente insostenible». La distribución de la cantidad de las sílabas castellanas resulta asimétrica dentro de las normas de la versificación de las lenguas clásicas: en la *Sonatina*, las sílabas donde caen acentos rítmicos llevan, en general, aunque no siempre, mayor duración que las inacentuadas adyacentes: pero la sílaba final de los versos llanos, inacentuadas, es por lo común de igual o mayor duración que las sílabas donde caen acentos rítmicos interiores.

Pero los versos de la *Sonatina* tienden a equilibrarse en su duración total: a pesar de las desigualdades entre las sílabas, consideradas aisladamente, la suma de sus cantidades da resultados muy semejantes (fluctuación de menos del diez por ciento). Todavía más: el Sr. Navarro descubre que dentro de cada verso hay pies cuyo núcleo es el acento rítmico, el *tiempo marcado*, y esos pies, en el verso llano, tienden a ser iguales, isócronos. Cuando no lo son, a veces se compensan entre sí en la suma total del verso.

Problema interesante: los versos agudos, en el experimento de la *Sonatina*, quedan siempre, poco o mucho, por debajo de la duración media del alejandrino llano. ¿Nuestro hábito de equiparar versos agudos y versos llanos es asimetría deliberada? La resistencia contra el final agudo en el endecasílabo, por ejemplo (véase M. MENÉNDEZ Y PELAYO, *Antología de poetas líricos castellanos*, tomo XIII, *Boscán*, Madrid, 1908, págs. 219 a 226), pudiera fundarse en el hábito de la simetría rítmica. Recuerdo, de mi adolescencia, la lectura del *Tabaré* de Zorrilla de San Martín, donde abundan las sugestiones musicales (el leit motiv, entre otros): el poema se desenvuelve en endecasílabos y heptasílabos llanos, salvo unos cuantos pentasílabos arrulladores en las canciones de la española cautiva: después de muchas páginas, en el primer diálogo entre Blanca y Tabaré los versos pares se vuelven agudos:

> ¡Tú hablas al indio, tú, que de las lunas
> tienes la claridad!

El cambio de los finales llanos a los agudos me produjo la impresión brusca de pasar a la plena música, con extraño compás lleno de síncopas.

rítmico es la regularidad aritmética de la serie de sílabas, y el poema germánico, con sus incisivos acentos, pausas y aliteraciones, pero de medida silábica vaga? ¿Qué habrá de común entre la estrofa de Safo o de Anacreonte, tejida con delicados filamentos de matices en la duración del sonido, y la profecía hebraica, en versículos de extensión indeterminada, unidos por la duplicación o el contraste de los pensamientos o las imágenes? ¿Qué habrá de común entre las rigurosas runas finlandesas del *Kálévala*, todas de ocho sílabas, con cuatro acentos fijos, con aliteración y paralelismo, y los vagos contornos del cantarcillo español, ceñidos apenas por el lazo pueril del asonante? De común sólo existe la noción mínima, esencial, de unidad rítmica (la fórmula V) [1].

A la unidad rítmica, desnuda y clara, se atiene el verso libre a que se consagran hoy, en típica confluencia, poetas jóvenes de la más divergentes naciones occidentales. Si es verdad que nuestro tiempo cava hasta llegar a la semilla de las cosas para echarlas a que germinen de nuevo y crezcan libres; si el empeño de simplificación y de claridad toca a los fundamentos de los valores espirituales, y del valor económico, y de la actividad política, y de la vida familiar, ¿por qué no ha de tocar a las formas de expresión? Reducido a su esencia pura, sin apoyos rítmicos accesorios, el verso conserva intacto su poder de expresar, su razón de existir. Los apoyos rítmicos que a unos les parecen necesarios, a otros les sobran o les estorban. Y tales apoyos tienen vida limitada: recorren

---

[1] Se ve ahora por qué yerran definiciones como la del Diccionario de la Academia Española: «Palabra o conjunto de palabras sujetos a medida y cadencia, según reglas fijas y determinadas». Exige demasiado: número estricto de sílabas y distribución regular de acentos. Y yerran teorías como las de LIPPS en su *Estética* (1903): su base es el acento, legítima para el verso de lenguas germánicas, pero inaceptable para otras tan diversas entre sí como el japonés y el griego, donde la cantidad silábica iba muchas veces en franco desacuerdo con el ictus, el golpe de intensidad. Lipps estudia, después de partir del acento, la pausa, el tono musical, el número de sílabas, la rima (consonancia y asonancia solamente) y la aliteración; reconoce las posibles y hasta frecuentes oposiciones entre los apoyos rítmicos; pero permanece inconmovible en su base acentual. No es menos rígido —y falso— en su estética de la música, suponiéndola irremediablemente atada al compás y asumiendo como escala única la diatónica de Europa, con ligeras incursiones cromáticas. Admite, eso sí, la elasticidad del ritmo, y con ella vagas implicaciones del verso libre. MEUMANN, a pesar de sus preocupaciones retóricas, admite la elasticidad, en sus célebres *Investigaciones sobre la psicología y la estética del ritmo* (1894), define el ritmo como fenómeno intelectual, y reconoce en el verso dos tendencias: una hacia el orden, otra hacia la libertad. Todo verso necesita elementos de desorden: la regularidad absoluta resulta intolerable. Pero la base, para Meumann, está en el acento. La preocupación germánica de explicar todo verso por los acentos cunde fuera de Alemania, sin otra justificación que la procedencia. Explicar toda la versificación francesa, por ejemplo, como acentual conduce a la paradoja de convertir en versos libres, en virtud de la irregularidad de los acentos, muchos renglones que los poetas escribieron como regulares en virtud de la igualdad del número de sílabas.

ciclos y desaparecen. Desapareció la cantidad en los viejos idiomas indoeuropeos; desapareció la aliteración en los germánicos... El siglo XIX, en Europa, está lleno de quejas contra la rima. ¿Por qué la rima resiste todavía el ataque? Cuando se la expulsa, se va con ella el cuento de sílabas: de otro modo, habríamos creado especies nuevas de verso blanco en medidas exactas. Y el verso blanco está lejos de la «prosa monótona»: órgano de sonoridades rotundas o diáfanas bajo las manos de Shakespeare y de Milton, de Keats y de Shelley, de Goethe y de Leopardi, aún hoy en inglés busca apoderarse de «los tonos de la voz hablada» en los poemas de Robert Frost; pero su fuerza parece exhausta. No hay formas universales ni eternas.

Aceptemos la sobriedad máxima del ritmo; el verso puro, la unidad fluctuante, está ensayando vida autónoma. No acepta apoyos rítmicos exteriores; se contenta con el impulso íntimo de su vuelo espiritual [1].

POESÍA Y PROSA. — No atribuyo importancia a la romántica discusión — que es significativo encontrar ya en Rousseau— de si la poesía reclama el verso o existe sin él. Mero conflicto verbal. Unos dicen: doy el nombre de poesía a la obra cuyo contenido en emoción, imagen y concepto, a la vez que en manera expresiva, sea de la calidad que llamamos poética, aunque esté en declarada prosa. Otros dicen: doy el nombre de poesía sólo a las obras escritas en franco verso. Y el problema se reduce a la acepción del vocablo poesía. No hay modo de forzar a los unos ni a los otros para que cambien sus usos.

El problema de definir la poesía —significación espiritual— queda intacto después de definir el verso, fenómeno del orden de los sonidos. Si al verso alcanzamos a encerrarlo dentro del círculo de la noción mínima, es porque existe como entidad sonora en todas las lenguas, y despojado de sus variaciones persiste como unidad rítmica que se desarrolla en series. Pero queda el otro problema adyacente, el de los límites entre la prosa y el verso. Y este problema, que muchos pretenden resolver con el tajo brusco entre las dos formas, sólo admite una solución: la separación entre el verso y la prosa no es absoluta: del verso a la prosa hay grados, escalones, etapas descendentes.

Se dice con la solemnidad del maestro de M. Jourdain, que hablamos en prosa. Distingo. Hay dos acepciones de prosa, una negativa y otra positiva. Si —según el arbitrio popular— decidimos aplicar el nombre de prosa a cualquier uso del lenguaje que

---

[1] Como el castellano, a diferencia del francés, nunca olvidó las dos especies de rima que conoce, nuestros poetas del verso libre se aprovechan del asonante en ocasiones como puente intermedio entre la tiranía de la consonancia y la libertad entera (Juan Ramón Jiménez, Alfonso Reyes, Moreno Villa, Gerardo Diego, Nora Lange, Borges).

no sea verso, podrá tolerársele su explicación al retórico de la comedia. Pero si el nombre se aplica a una forma de expresión literaria, obra de esfuerzo consciente y claro propósito, no hablamos en prosa. Hablamos, y nada más.

La historia no deja dudas: la prosa no nace como mera proyección del lenguaje hablado: se crea como derivación y a ejemplo del verso. Nuestro *período*, en los discursos, es una imitación de la estrofa. El orador clásico se sentía cercano al poeta, al punto de hacer acompañar su declamación con música de flautas. Y las huellas de aquellos orígenes podemos rastrearlas: todavía existen oradores cuya entonación es como de himno exaltado, especie de canto solemne para el público, sin semejanza con la conversación familiar. La prosa del Antiguo Testamento está todavía cortada en trechos que calcan el versículo de los poetas. Y, como en la literatura babilónica, hay pasajes de corte dudoso. La Gadya, en sánscrito, es prosa que «guarda el aroma del metro». Y con las *Prosas profanas* de Rubén Darío se ha divulgado entre nosotros la curiosa —pero significativa— circunstancia: nuestra palabra románica para designar la forma de expresión opuesta al verso representó, en su origen, una especie de versificación suelta, sin medida pero con rima. Esas prosas litúrgicas ejercieron influjo que no conocemos bien. En los comienzos de la prosa castellana, en la *Crónica general* compilada bajo la inspiración de Alfonso el Sabio, tropezamos con barrocas confusiones y vaivenes: los autores prosifican, para convertirlos en historia, los poemas épicos, y en la prosificación dejan rastros de verso: pero en ocasiones trabajan al revés: versifican a medias la prosa que les sirve de fuente.

Con oriental precisión, los persas distinguen cuatro modos de componer: verso, con medida y rima; lenguaje rimado pero no medido; prosa poética, medida y no rimada; prosa pura, sin metro ni rima. Para los árabes hay formas intermedias entre verso y prosa; el saj', el arrullo de la paloma, su versificación irregular, rimada, es para ellos la fuente de los dos ríos, y el Corán está situado en el punto en que se inicia la divergencia de corrientes. Los chinos poseen el wun chang, prosa medida pero no separada en renglones, con frecuentes efectos paralelísticos.

En Occidente, la prosa se nos revela en su desenvolvimiento gradual a través de la historia, desde el dibujo incipiente en que apenas se separa del verso hasta las más complejas arquitecturas. Una de sus formas avanzadas es la exposición sistemática de ideas abstractas. Pero su última conquista es la copia exacta de la conversación real: justamente la más difícil hazaña ha sido parecerse a aquello con que torpemente se la confunde. En español, por ejemplo, salvo antecedentes excepcionales como el de Moratín, el lenguaje de la conversación sólo ha penetrado en el teatro con nuestro siglo, y no por cierto con Benavente, cuyo diálogo estuvo cargado de artificio durante largo tiempo. Hay tipos de prosa como hay tipos de versificación, y en general se alejan del verso en la medida

269

en que los asuntos se alejan de la calidad poética. Se les ha estudiado ampliamente desde el punto de vista del estilo, pero no en su aspecto simple de organización de sonidos en series y grupos. Los trabajos que existen son apenas esbozos, a veces muy discutibles, como los de Saintsbury. Ejemplo: la obra experimental de Patterson, *The rhythm of prose*, fascinadora por su modo de exponer ideas y datos, se queda clavada en el comienzo del camino, sin ir más allá de la diferenciación elemental entre el ritmo del verso, con su tendencia a las repeticiones uniformes, y el de la prosa, con sus ritmos entrelazados y sincopados. Eso no basta. Quedan intactos los puntos intermedios, los grados entre verso y prosa: con excesiva ligereza, Patterson los da por indemostrables, sólo porque no cabían en sus ingeniosos experimentos, enderezados hacia fines preconcebidos. Y quedan intactos los tipos de prosa. Hay que estudiar, por ejemplo, la medida. En otra obra experimental, *Pause*, Miss Snell da estos resultados, que sólo atañen al idioma inglés: la unidad de frase, en el verso endecasílabo, lleva solamente seis sílabas como término medio: la unidad, en la prosa imaginativa, de sabor literario, es de ocho sílabas: en la prosa simple, de tipo periodístico, es de catorce sílabas [1].

La escala, artística e histórica, baja desde el verso en sus formas estrechas, complicadas y difíciles, como se dan en chino, en árabe, en finlandés, en provenzal, en el castellano de los «siglos de oro»; pasa a través de formas sencillas, como las japonesas y las hebraicas hasta llegar al límite del *verso puro*, de unidades fluctuantes, impulsadas rítmicamente por la serie. Debajo de la terraza del verso simple principian los escalones de formas variadas que tienden hacia la prosa y conservan reliquias de verso: rima, en particular. Después se llega a la prosa de la oratoria clásica: el discurso —oda de Demóstenes y de Cicerón, de Bossuet y de Castelar—, y de grada en grada se alcanzan las contemporáneas imitaciones de la conversación. Un paso más, y hemos abandonado la escala de las formas artísticas para descender al llano de la conversación en la vida cotidiana. Existe, sí, todavía, para los inquietos, la galería subterránea donde la prosa de Edouard Dujardin, de James Joyce, de John Dos Passos, de Virginia Woolf, copia el íntimo fluir del pensamiento.

---

[1] Son importantes las investigaciones de Marbe y su escuela sobre la prosa alemana.

II

EL ENDECASÍLABO CASTELLANO

El verso endecasílabo castellano, en su forma ortodoxa, según las definiciones usuales, se compone de once sílabas, con acentos interiores necesarios en la sexta:

Flérida para *mí* dulce y sabrosa (tipo A),

o bien en la cuarta y en la octava:

Más que la *fru*ta del *cer*cado ajeno (tipo B)[1],

Así lo definen Juan María Maury, Andrés Bello, Manuel Milá y Fontanals, Eduardo Benot [2], y la multitud de tratadistas que en ellos se apoyan; así lo definían ya, en el siglo XVI, Rengifo y el maestro Alonso López Pinciano [3], Como la acentuación cae siempre en las sílabas pares, se le denomina *yámbica*, adaptando, no muy bien, el término cuantitativo de la Antigüedad clásica a

---

[1] Hay además, desde luego, acento final obligatorio en la sílaba penúltima, según se exige en todo verso castellano.

[2] MAURY, en la *Espagne poétique* (1826) y en la carta a Vicente Salvá, que éste incluye en nota de su *Gramática* sobre el endecasílabo (1831); a falta de las obras originales, pueden verse las citas que trae el CONDE DE LA VIÑAZA en su *Bibilioteca histórica de la filología castellana*. BELLO, en su tratado de *Ortología y métrica* (1835), capítulos VI y VII del *Arte métrica*. MILÁ, *Principios de literatura general*, en sus *Obras completas*, Barcelona, 1888-1896 (v. tomo I, págs. 337 y 393). BENOT, en su extravagante tratado de *Prosodia castellana y versificación* (v. especialmente el párrafo V del sumario e índice).

[3] RENGIFO, *Arte poética española*, (1592): v. el capítulo XI, en la edición de 1644, que he consultado; los ocho tipos de endecasílabo que menciona se reducen a los dos arriba indicados. LÓPEZ PINCIANO, *Filosofía antigua poética* (1596): v. la página 285 en la reimpresión de Madrid, 1894.

nuestro moderno ritmo acentual. El nombre de *yámbico* se aplica a veces exclusivamente, así como el de *heroico*, al tipo A; al tipo B se le da el nombre de *sáfico* [1].

I. EL ENDECASÍLABO ITALIANO. — Los escritores españoles modernos, al hablar del endecasílabo italiano, del cual procede el nuestro actual, tienden a considerarlo sujeto a idénticas leyes que las que fijan para el castellano. Pero basta consultar los buenos tratados y estudios de métrica italiana para convencerse de que no es así [2]; el endecasílabo de Italia puede acentuarse interiormente, ya en la sexta sílaba:

Nel mezzo del cammin di nostra vita (tipo A),

ya en la cuarta:

Vidi Cammilla e la Pentesilea (tipo B[1]).

---

[1] Creo que el endecasílabo castellano debe definirse desde el punto de vista de la medida y el acento; no me avengo a ninguna definición que lo presente como verso compuesto de cinco pies acentuales, según se hace todavía, a veces, para el endecasílabo italiano. Toda tentativa de explicar la versificación castellana por pies falla en sus fundamentos, salvo en casos especiales como los del *Nocturno* de Silva y la *Marcha triunfal* de Darío, en que deliberadamente se parte del pie en la construcción del verso.

En el caso del endecasílabo, el supuesto tipo ideal de cinco acentos, todos en sílabas pares, se realiza raras veces:

Y oyendo el *són* del *mar* que en ella *hier*...e

(Garcilaso)

Es normal que falten uno o dos de esos acentos; a veces faltan tres, cuando el único acento interior cae en la cuarta sílaba (tipo B[1], que estudiaré en este trabajo):

Y vence*dor* con la sabidu*ría*...

(Alonso de Acevedo)

o bien en la sexta:

Mas por el s*o*bres*al*to de los *ce*los...
Entre la mosta*cho*sa artille*ría*...
Sino permane*cer* en su por*fía*...
En manifesta*ción* de sus *eno*jos...

(Lope, *Gatomaquia*)

[2] Por ejemplo: R. FORNACIARI, *Grammatica italiana dell'uso moderno*..., séptima edición, Florencia, 1913 (v. parte I, págs. 151-152). Agrego, en confirmación: FRANCESCO D'OVIDIO, *Sull'origine dei versi italiani* en su libro *Versificazione italiana e poetica medievale*, Roma, 1910; CHARLES HALL GRANDGENT, edición de la *Divina Comedia*, Boston, 1909-1913 (v. pág. XXXV de la Introducción); EDMUND STENGEL, § 56 de su *Romanische Verslehre*, en el *Grundriss der romanischen Philologie*, de Gröber; KARL VOSSLER, *Historia de la literatura italiana*, traducción castellana de Manuel de Montolíu, Barcelona, 1925.

Ejemplos de este tipo:

> *Quivi, secondo che per ascoltarse.'..*
> *Non avea pianto, ma che di sospiri...*
> *Pregar, per pace e per misericordia...*
> *Movesse seco di necessitate...*
> *Per la puntura della rimembranza...*
> *E quel che segue in la circonferenza...*
>
> (Dante, *Divina Commedia*)

> *Cantar, danzare alla provenzalesca...*
>
> (Folgore di San Gimignano, *Aprile*)

> *S'i' fosse vento, lo tempesterei...*
>
> (Cecco Angiolieri, Soneto «S'i' fosse foco...»)

> *Non già per odio, ma per dimostrarsi...*
>
> (Petrarca, *Trionfo della morte*, I)

> *E di Morgante si maravigliòe...*
>
> (Pulci, *Morgante maggiore*, II)

> *Tanto soave, che nel rammentare...*
>
> (Boiardo, Soneto «Io vidi...»)

> *E se' più dolce che la malvagìa...*
>
> (Lorenzo de Médicis, *Nencia da Barberino*)

> *Fra tante tube che lo esalterano...*
>
> (Maquiavelo, *Pastorale*)

> *Per quest'io so che l'inesperienza...*
> *Le da l'anello, e se le racommanda...*
>
> (Ariosto, *Orlando furioso*, VII)

> *E poscia ogni anno la coroneremo...*
>
> (Trissino, *Sofonisba*)

> *Famosi assai ne la cristianitate...*
>
> (Berni, *Orlando innamorato*, I, 17)

> *Che verrà tempo che ti pentirai...*
>
> (Torquato Tasso, *Aminta*, I)

> *Eran nemici a la Tedescherìa...*
>
> (Tassoni, *La secchia rapita*)

> *E questa è una delle dilezioni...*
>
> (Benedetto Menzini, Soneto)

Per vituperio de la Poësìa...

(Parini, *Il lauro*)

Chi più mi parla di filosofìa...

(Casti, *La grotta di Trofonio*, I)

Di que' soldati settentrïonali...

(Giusti, *Sant' Ambrogio*)

Le gentilezze, le consolazioni...

(Giulio Perticari, *Cantilena di Menicone*)

Vorrai vedermi e mi conoscerai...

(Francesco dall'Ongaro, *La livornese*)

In un cantuccio la ritroverai...

(Stecchetti, «Quando cadran...»)

E a la grand' alma di Guatimozino...

(Carducci, *Miramare*)

E s'abbracciava per lo stregolato...
L'imperatore nell'eremitaggio...

(Pascoli, *Romagna*)

Papa Giovanni per Teodorico
Edificata con le fondamenta...

(D'Annunzio, *La nave*, III)

Anche il tuo corpo, anche la vagabonda...

(Ada Negri, *Voce del mare*)

En este tipo B¹ hay cinco sílabas inacentuadas entre la cuarta y la décima. Como en italiano, no menos que en español, es cosa poco común que en una serie de cinco sílabas no haya acento, este tipo no se presenta puro muy a menudo, y ha producido dos variantes: una con acento en la octava sílaba, en que se conserva el ritmo yámbico:

*Mi ritro*vai *per una selva oscura...*(tipo B²),

y otra con acento en la séptima sílaba, con la cual el ritmo anapéstico sustituye al yámbico:

Che ricordarsi del tempo felice...(tipo B³) ¹

¹ Milá designa este endecasílabo con el nombre de anapéstico (estudio *Del decasílabo y endecasílabo anapéstico*, 1875, en el tomo V de sus *Obras completas);* Bello le da el nombre de dactílico, atendiendo al acento —frecuente, pero no obligatorio— en la primera sílaba:

Puro e disposto a salire alle stelle...

En Italia se le ha llamado *siciliano.*

Ejemplos de este tipo:

> *L'ora del tempo e la dolce stagione...*
> *Cerbero, fiera crudele e diversa...*
> *La chiarità della fiamma pareggio...*
> *In forma dunque di candida rosa...*
> *E cominciò questa santa orazione...*
> *Termine fisso d'eterno consiglio...*
> *O vita intera d'amore e di pace...*
> *O senza brama sicura ricchezza...*
> *Donne ch'avete inteletto d'amore...*
> *Angelo chiama in divino inteletto...*
> *E par che sia una cosa venuta*
> *Di cielo in terra a miracol mostrare...*
>
> (Dante)

> *E rassemblargli la rosa e lo giglio...*
> (Guinizelli, Soneto «Voglio del ver...»)

> *Fatta di gioco, in figura d'Amore...*
> (Guido Cavalcanti, «Era in pensar...»)

> *Molto mi spiace allegrezza e sollazzo...*
> (Cino da Pistoia, Soneto «Tutto ció...»)

> *Che lo mio padre m'a messa in errore...*
> (Compiuta Donzella, Soneto «Alla stagion...»)

> *Che s'io vedessi la propria persona...*
> (Boccaccio, «Io mi son giovinetta...»)

> *Non ti sovvien di quell' ultima sera...*
> (Petrarca, Soneto «Solea lontana...»)

> *E mal vestite parete angiolelle...*
> *Torniam la sera del prato fiorito...*
> (Franco Sacchetti, «O vaghe montanine...»)

> *Benchè la terra abbia forma di ruota...*
> *Tal che potrebbe arrosirne le gote...*
> *E puossi andar giù nell'altro emisperio...*
> *Sospesa sta fra le stelle sublime...*
> (Pulci, *Morgante*, XXV)

> *La rosa aprir d'un color sì infiammato...*
> (Boiardo, Soneto «Giá vidi...»)

> *Giuso gravato dall'infimo pondo...*
> (Pandolfo Collenuccio, *Canzone alla morte*)

> *Amor gli strale onde cresce il suo regno...*
> (Lorenzo de Médicis, Soneto «O man mia...»)

275

Anzi contento nel foco morrei...
(Poliziano, Balada «Benedetto sia 'l giorno...»)

Più chiaro il sol che per l'altre contrade...
(Chariteo, Canción VI)

Che 'l vento guasti o la nebbia ricuopra...
(Maquiavelo, *Mandragola*, Canción inicial)

E l'arche gravi, per molto tesoro...
(Bembo, Octavas para el carnaval en Urbino)

Quivi fa assunto e trovò compagnia...
Torbido 'l mare, anzi nero apparire...
Là che l'abisso e l'inferno si scopra...
E non è luce se non di baleni...
Egli sta sopra ed ha nuda la testa...
(Ariosto, *Orlando*, XXXIV y XXV)

Di Dante dico, che mal conosciute...
(Miguel Angel, Soneto a Dante)

Che fioriran per qualunque sentiero...
(Molza, *La ninfa tiberina*)

Accompagnata dal proprio martire...
(Vittoria Colonna, Soneto «Dal vivo fonte...»)

Questo ser Cecco simiglia la corte
E questa corte simiglia ser Cecco...
(Berni, «Ser Cecco non puó star...»)

Di pelo biondo e di vivo colore...
(Gaspara Stampa, Soneto «Chi vuol conoscer...»)

Se'l ciel vi pasca di carne e di latte...
(Torquato Tasso, *Le gatte di Sant' Anna*)

Io amava Clori, che insin da quell'ora...
(Zappi, Soneto «In quell'etá...»)

Mole a traversi de l'arida costa...
(Parini, *La tempesta*)

Del cor traendo profondi sospiri...
(Alfieri, Soneto a Dante)

Pronto, iracondo, inquieto, tenace...
(Foscolo, Soneto «Solcato ho fronte...»)

Volò a ruggir con la rabbia inumana...
(Aleardo Aleardi, *Le città italiane*, V)

Spiriti forse che furon, che sono...

(Carducci, *La chiesa di Polenta*)

Voce velata, malata, sognata...

(Pascoli, *Ceppo*)

Fiore, l'anel de la bocca vermiglia...
Stanca sedeste, ove il raggio lunare...

(D'Annunzio, «*Sal y pimienta*»)

Los tipos A y B² son los que predominan. Los tipos B¹ y B³ no disfrutan igual suerte: desde el siglo XVI hay poetas que los evitan, especialmente los de principios del siglo XIX, como Leopardi y Manzoni; pero vuelven a plena boga desde Carducci, y todavía la tienen [1].

En los comienzos, y hasta Petrarca, hubo otra variedad de endecasílabo italiano, el tipo *creciente*, que admitía una sílaba de exceso:

Questa anima gentile, che si disparte...

Esta licencia tiene semejanza con la del endecasílabo francés medieval y del castellano de Fernán Pérez de Guzmán (v. *infra*): no ocurre solamente en la cesura, sino en cualquier punto del verso. Sí es de notar que las palabras donde va la sílaba de exceso son aquellas cuya vocal final puede ponerse o quitarse a voluntad y que acaso se sintiera, por eso, como una semimuda: *oro* u *or*, *sole* o *sol*, *pensieri* o *pensier*, *mano* o *man*; de hecho, Petrarca borra a veces en copias ajenas de sus versos la vocal sobrante:

E'l rimembrare e l'aspettare m'accora...
D'errore sì novo la mia mente è piena...

En cambio, otras veces escribe él mismo la vocal, o la repone si se omitió:

Destando i fiori per questo ombroso bosco...
E sì le vene e il core m'asciuga e sugge...

---

[1] Así, no es posible afirmar, como lo hace Menéndez y Pelayo (*Antología de poetas líricos castellanos*, tomo XIII, págs. 186 y 214), que el tipo B³ sólo aparece «por casualidad o descuido...en antiguos poetas italianos», o que lo usan «alguna vez para producir determinados efectos de armonía imitativa».

> *Ma io che debbo fare del dolce alloro...*
> *La crespe chiome d'oro puro lucente...* [1]

EL ENDECASÍLABO EN FRANCÉS Y EN PROVENZAL. — El endecasílabo del tipo B[1], acentuado en la sílaba cuarta, es el primitivo de la poesía francesa (en francés, es bien sabido, se le llama *décasyllabe*) [1]. Desde el siglo XI aparece en la *Canción de Rolando:*

> *Dient plusor: Çost* (doble) *aefinemenz...*

Aparece también en provenzal, de donde probablemente pasará al italiano:

> *Qu' elh no vol re mas reconoyssemen...*
> (Folquet de Marsella) [3]

Los tipos B[2] y B[3] existían entonces, bien se comprende, como formas indiferenciadas de B[1]. En francés:

> *Fendu en est olifanz el gros...*
> *Compaign Rodlanz, car sonez l'olifant...*
> (*Chanson de Roland*)

---

[1] Consúltese MARIANGELA SERRETTA, *Endecasillabi crescenti nella poesia italiana delle origini e nel Canzoniere del Petrarca*, Milán, 1933. La autora indica que este endecasílabo-dodecasílabo reaparece a fines del siglo XIX con Pascoli y D'Annunzio, que adoptan de nuevo las libertades métricas del Trecento:

> A me tendete, siccome io le tendo...
> (Pascoli, *Il giorno dei morti*)

En los siglos intermedios es muy raro; pero tropiezo con estos ejemplos (si no se deben a erratas de imprenta) en Fulvio Testi *(Serenata):*

> O strepito importuno mai non ti svegli...

y en Zappi (Soneto «In quella etá...»):

> Io amava Clori, che insino, da quell'ora...

[2] Se cree que los modelos del endecasílabo de las lenguas románicas son el sáfico y el senario latinos, a su vez derivados del griego: metros cuantitativos, que se convierten gradualmente en silábicos de ritmo acentual al avanzar la Edad Media.

[3] Consúltese PAUL VERRIER, *Les vers français*, París, 1931-1932, tomo II, libro VII, *Les décasyllabes*. El ejemplo más antiguo de endecasílabos indudables está en el poema provenzal *Boecio*, de fines del siglo X o principios del XI; pero en francés existe el ensayo (irregular) de endecasílabo de la *Cantilena de Santa Eulalia*, fines del siglo IX.

En provenzal:

> *E per camís non anará sautiers...*
> *Ans será* rics *qui tolrá volontiers...*

(Beitran de Born)

Entre el verso épico francés y el verso lírico provenzal hay diferencias. La cesura del francés lo divide en dos porciones: la primera puede tener una sílaba de más, sin acento, después de la acentuada:

> *Les roches bises, li destreit merveillos...*
> *Portet ses* armes, *molt li sont avenan ...*

(*Chanson de Roland*)

El tipo A, de acento en la sexta sílaba, existió también en francés y en provenzal:

> *Gaiete el Orior, serors germaines...*

(*Chanson d'histoire*, siglo XII)

> *En Provenza tramet joy e salutz...*

(Bernart de Ventadour)

Los dos tipos, originariamente, no debían mezclarse, pero de hecho se mezclaron: la tendencia de los idiomas románicos a prestar mayor atención al número de sílabas que al ritmo acentual, según se observa en los versos cortos [1], alcanza también a los largos, y provoca, no sólo la alternancia de los tipos A y B, sino ocasionales dislocaciones del ritmo:

> *Mais vole guerra filz del rei d'Etobia...* [2]

(Raimbaut de Vaqueiras)

La poesía italiana, al recibir de la provenzal el endecasílabo, emplea juntas, libremente, todas las formas [3]. La provenzal se

---

[1] Así se ve en la historia del endecasílabo castellano: los intentos de imponerle acentuación interior fija quedan siempre vencidos.

[2] Dislocaciones semejantes se hallan a menudo en la poesía galaico-portuguesa y en la catalana, influídas por la provenzal; en castellano son muy raras antes del siglo XX, y no pueden contarse sino como caídas momentáneas de la atención en el poeta. En la Edad Media sí se encuentran tales dislocaciones en los versos del príncipe Juan Manuel (v. *infra*).

[3] F. D'OVIDIO, en su citado libro *Versificazione italiana e arte poetica medievale*, pág. 198, dice que el verso italiano difiere del francés en «la mezcla de los endecasílabos con acento principal en la sexta y los de acento en cuarta y octava o séptima, no permitida en francés [medieval], donde todos los endecasílabos son *a minori* o *a maiori*» y en «la continuidad plena de todo el verso, porque nuestra cesura no es sino una cesura en el sentido grecolatino, mientras que en el francés antiguo la llamada cesura es una verdadera pausa o corte del verso».

extingue lentamente a partir del siglo XIII; la francesa se mantendrá sin interrupción hasta nuestros días: en ella acabará por ser normal la mezcla de los dos tipos de endecasílabo:

> Jeune, gente, plaisant et debonnaire,
> Par ung prier qui vault commandement,
> Chargié m'avez d'une balade faire,
> Si l'ay faicte de cueur joyeusement:
> Or la veuillez recevoir doulcement...
>
> (Charles d'Orléans, Balada)

El tipo B será siempre el que domine. Como en francés, aún más que en español y en italiano, es difícil que entre la cuarta y la décima sílabas no haya acento, el tipo B se da muy pocas veces en su pureza teórica (B¹):

> Del grant solaz de la compaignie...
>
> (El castellano de Coucy)

> Je pense bien que ta magnificence...
>
> (Marot, Al rey en el destierro)

Las formas usuales de B en francés son, por lo tanto, B² y B³.

> En cependant que le chemin est sur...
>
> (Ronsard, A su libro)

> Tenant la vie et la mort en sa main...
>
> (Joachim du Bellay, Du jour de Noël)

> Où fuyais-tu, ma timide colére?
>
> (Marcelline Desbordes-Valmore, «Je ne sais plus...»)

> Un air subtil, un dangereux parfum...
>
> (Baudelaire, Le chat)

Desde Verlaine, el endecasílabo francés se permite normalmente grandes libertades rítmicas:

> Votre âme est un paysage choisi
> Que vont charmant masques et bergamasques
> Jouant du luth et dansant et quasi
> Tristes sous leurs déguisements fantasques...

> De parfums lourds et chauds, dont le poison
> —Dahlia, lys, tulipe et renoncule—
> Noyant mes sens, mon âme et ma raison,
> Mêle dans une immense pâmoison
> Le Souvenir avec le Crépuscule...
>
> (Verlaine)

...*Et quand tu roules, démâtée, au large,*
A travers les brisants noirs des nuages!
Astre atteint de cécité, fatal phare
Des vols, migrateurs de plaintifs Icares!...
O Diane a la chlamyde très dorique,
L'Amour couve, prends ton carquois et pique...

(Jules Laforge, *Clair de lune*)

La scintillation sereine sème
Sur l'altitude un dédain souverain...
Après tant d'orgueil, après tant d'étrange
Oisivité, mais pleine de pouvoir,
Je m'abandonne à ce brillant espace...
Sais-tu, fausse captive des feuillages...
Quel corps me traîne à paresseuse?...
Maigre immortalité noire et dorée,
Consolatrice affreusement laurée...

(Paul Valéry, *Le cimetière marin*) [1]

[1] Los ingleses tomaron del francés el endecasílabo, desde el siglo XIV; para ellos, este verso, que comúnmente llaman *pentameter* o *iambic pentameter*, consta de cinco pies acentuales, con cinco acentos:

He was *as* fressh *as* is *the* mon*the* of May...
(Chaucer, Prólogo de los. *Cuentos cantuarienses*)

Farewell: buy food, *and* get *thyself in* flesh...
(Shakespeare, *Romeo*, V, 1)

And time *for* all *the* works *and* days *of* hands...
(T. S. Eliot, *The love song of Prufrock*)

Uno que otro de estos acentos puede faltar, con lo cual la versificación adquiere elasticidad. Teóricamente no deben caer acentos fuertes sobre sílaba impar en posición dominante, pero a veces ocurre:

How many bards gild the lapses *of time!*
(Keats, Soneto que comienza así)

El tipo B[1] es punto menos que imposible en idioma, como el inglés, de palabras cortas y fuertes acentos, pero hay uno que otro caso (aunque habrá prosodistas que cuenten como acentuado *if*):

It were done quickly, if th'assassination...
(Shakespeare, *Macbeth*, I, 7)

The mathematics and the metaphysics...
(Shakespeare, *The taming of the shrew*, 1)

El número de sílabas no es fijo: puede haber más o menos de diez (u once, según la manera española de contar):

O me!—you juggler! you canker-blossom!...
See me no more, whether he be dead or no...
(Shakespeare, *Sueño de una noche de verano*, III, 2)

The soldier's virtue, rather makes choice of loss...
(Shakespeare, *Antonio y Cleopatra*, III, 1)

281

EL ENDECASÍLABO EN CATALÁN Y EN PORTUGUÉS. — El endecasílabo trovadoresco penetró desde temprano —siglo XII, si no antes— en dos de los idiomas de España: en catalán:

> Plangen mon dan e sa desconaxença...

(Rocabertí)

y en galaico-portugués:

> E sei de fix que ensandecerei...

(Fernan Figueira)

El endecasílabo catalán, a pesar de ocasionales desviaciones, se mantiene fiel a la ley del acento en la cuarta sílaba hasta el siglo XV. Durante el largo eclipse de la literatura catalana (siglos XVI a XVIII), los pocos cultivadores de la lengua recibían influencias de Castilla, como ya en el siglo XV los que de cuando en cuando adoptaban el *arte mayor;* todavía en el siglo XVI mantenían el tipo medieval de endecasílabo Pere Serafí y Juan Pujol, y a principios del siglo XVII el rector de Vallfogona, Vicente García [1]; después debió de darse acogida al tipo ítalo-castellano de endecasílabo, que es el usual en el renacimiento catalán del siglo XIX.

El endecasílabo galaicoportugués de la Edad Media a veces se descoyunta de tal modo que puede decirse que no observa otra regla sino la de tener once sílabas; los acentos caen en cualquier parte: así se observa tanto en poetas del *Cancionero del Vaticano* como del *Cancionero de Ajuda.*

Ejemplos sacados del rey Dionís:

> E quer' ir algunha terra buscar...
> Non se pode per dizer acabar...
> Se nom que matades mi, pecador...
> De matardes mim, que merecedor...
> Que razom cuidades vos, mha senhor...

> To say extremity was the trier of spirits...

(Shakespeare, *Coriolano*, IV, 1)

> But that the sea, mounting to the welkin's cheek...
> Being once perfected how to grant suits...

(Shakespeare, *La tempestad*, I, 2)

Sobre uno de los poetas que mayores libertades se permiten con el endecasílabo inglés, consúltese el artículo de Arnold Stein, *Donne's prosody,* en *Publications of the Modern Language Association of America,* 1944, LIX, págs. 373-397. Donne se permite acentuaciones como éstas (señalo sólo los acentos que interesan para compararlos con los del verso castellano):

> Nor are they vicars, but hangmen to fate...
> Are they not loke singers at doors for meat...

---

[1] Consúltese M. MENÉNDEZ Y PELAYO, *Antología,* XIII, págs. 454-468.

Ejemplos sacados del *Cancionero de Ajuda:*

> *Al me tolhe de que me faz peor...*(XLIII)
> *Nen me leixan encobrir com meu mal...*(LXXXI)
> *Nen lh'o peço, nen querria melhor...*(CCIII)
> *Porque moiro, u mentira non á...*
> *E por esto baratará melhor...*(CCLIII)
> *O que vus agora guarda de mi...*(CCCXLV)

Es frecuente la tendencia al ritmo anapéstico (B³):

> *O que do mar meu amigo sacou...*
>
> (Payo Gomez Charinho)

Existe también la tendencia al ritmo anfibráquico, con acento en las sílabas segunda y quinta (tipo C):

> *Ai frores, ai frores do verde pino...*
>
> (Rey Dionís) [1]

En Galicia y Portugal, sin embargo, debió de existir en boca del pueblo otro verso parecido al endecasílabo, pero no de sílabas contadas, sino de medida fluctuante; del contacto de las dos formas de versificación pudieron derivarse el *arte mayor* de Castilla, fluctuante también, y las modernas *muiñeiras* que se acompañan con la gaita gallega. La influencia de la fluctuación popular explicaría versos como éstos de Alfonso el Sabio:

> *Rosa das rosas e Fror das frores,*
> *Dona das donas, Sennor das sennores...*

o éstos de Juan Zorro:

> *Pela ribeira do rio salido*
> *trebelhey, madre, con meu amigo...*

o éstos atribuídos a Ayras Nunes:

> *Baylemos nós já todas, todas, ay amigas,*
> *só aquestas avelaneyras frolidas...*

El endecasílabo trovadoresco desaparece de la poesía culta de Galicia y Portugal en el siglo xiv; después, en el xvi, Sá de Mi-

---

[1] Este tipo C lo imitó Rubén Darío en el siglo xx (v. *infra*).

randa introduce el endecasílabo ítalo-castellano. Entre la desaparición del uno y la aparición del otro, se adopta el *arte mayor* de Castilla [1].

Pero el endecasílabo popular sobrevive subterráneamente y de tarde en tarde aflora hasta la superficie, hasta desembocar en las *muiñeiras* [2].

EL ENDECASÍLABO CLÁSICO EN CASTELLANO. — El castellano es el último de los idiomas románicos de Occidente que adopta de modo definitivo el endecasílabo; su introducción, en el siglo XVI, escinde en dos porciones la historia de nuestra poesía. Después de repetidos y fracasados intentos a lo largo de la Edad Media (v. *infra*), Boscán y Garcilaso logran imponerlo.

Castilla recibe su endecasílabo de Italia, donde, a diferencia de los demás países de lenguas románicas, era normal desde temprano la mezcla libre y constante de la acentuación en la sílaba sexta (tipo A) con la acentuación en la sílaba cuarta (tipo B con todas sus variantes: B[1], B[2], B[3]). El tipo A predomina en nuestro idioma y se convierte en eje; el tipo B y sus variantes funcionan como formas subsidiarias.

En castellano, el predominio del tipo A influye en que se prefiera, entre las variantes de B, el tipo B[2], y desde el final del siglo

---

[1] Ejemplos de *arte mayor* en portugués: en el *Cancionero de Resende* (1516), folios XC vto. (Diego Brandam), XCVIII vto., CII y CIII vto. (Luis Anríquez), CXI vto. (Anríque de Saa); el auto de la *Historia de Deus*, de Gil Vicente.

[2] De la supervivencia popular del viejo endecasílabo galaicoportugués hay no pocas pruebas:

> *Barqueriña fermosa, passaime...*
> *Passaime, miñ'alma, que por vos morro...*
>> (Lope de Vega, *La mayor virtud de un rey*, II)

> *Um galan traye da cinta na gorra,*
> *diz que lla deu la sua señora...*
> *Quérole bem a lo fillo do crego...*
>> (Tirso, *La gallega Mari Hernández*, II)

> *Ollay, mineña fermosa e graciosa...*
>> (Rojas Zorrilla, *El alcalde Ardite*)

> Tanto bailé con la gaita gallega...
>> (Torres Villarroel, Villancico de *La gaita zamorana*)

Sobre los endecasílabos galaicoportugueses: M. MILÁ Y FONTANALS, *De la poesía popular gallega* y *Del decastlabo y endecastlabo anapésticos* (tomo V de sus *Obras completas*); HENRY ROSEMAN LANG, *Das Liederbuch des König Denis von Portugal*, Halle, 1894, págs. CXIV, CXVI y CXVII; THEOPHILO BRAGA y CAROLINA MICHAËLIS DE VASCONCELLOS, *Geschichte der portugiesischen Litteratur*, en el *Grundriss* de Gröber, parágrafos 20, 26 y 42; FRIEDRICH HANSSEN, *Zur spanischen und portugiesischen Metrik*, Valparaíso, 1900, y *Los versos de las Cantigas de Santa María del rey Alfonso X*, en los *Anales de la Universidad de Chile*, 1901; además, ver en este volumen *la poesía castellana de versos fluctuantes*, capítulo II, parágrafos 10-11, 20 y 28, y capítulo IV, parágrafo 10.

xvi los tratadistas declaran legítimos sólo esos dos tipos. ¿Por qué? Porque el verso con acentos en ias sílabas cuarta y octava es equivalente, para el oído, al de acento en la sexta, en el centro estricto. El oído ejercitado en el verso castellano que escucha una serie de endecasílabos limitada exclusivamente a los tipos A y B² no distingue el uno del otro, a menos que deje de prestar atención al sentido de las palabras y sólo la conceda al ritmo; no pocos poetas comienzan a componer endecasílabos mezclando A y B² sin percibir que son dos tipos de verso. «On peut se représenter —decía Juan María Maury en su *Espagne poétique*, explicando cómo en las series de endecasílabos castellanos se equivalen A y B²— une image matérielle de cette disposition rythmique par des barres horizontales que soutiendraient en équilibre, soit un appui au point du milieu, soit deux appuis à des distances égales des extrémités» [1].

La acentuación en sexta sílaba predominará siempre en castellano; predomina hoy, en medio de las libertades que se conceden al endecasílabo. A este tipo de acentuación corresponden más de las tres cuartas partes de los versos en los poemas de Ercilla, de Alonso de Acevedo, de Juan Rufo [2]; en el *Arauco domado* de Pedro de Oña es el único que se emplea [3]. Pero poetas de sensibilidad afinada para la forma, como Lope y Góngora, hacen alternar con mucho mayor frecuencia la acentuación en sexta sílaba con la de cuarta y octava: si bien el oído no las discierne de golpe cuando se suceden en serie, sí percibe la matización del ritmo sin necesidad de indagar el cómo. En Lope, por ejemplo, es común el soneto que comienza con el verso de acentos en cuarta y octava sílabas —ritmo despacioso, adecuado para iniciar la exposición del tema— y termina con el verso de acento en la sílaba sexta, tipo de acentuación enérgica que lo hace apropiado para la síntesis final. Ejemplos: «Suelta mi manso, mayoral extraño...», «Cuando pensé que mi tormento esquivo...», «Merezca yo de tus graciosos ojos...», «Cayó la torre que en el viento hacían...», «Cuelga sangriento de la cama al suelo...» *(Judit)*. Creo que la elección es inconsciente y no deliberada. Y no es éste, desde luego, el único esquema del soneto en Lope: hay también el esquema

---

[1] La equivalencia de los tipos A y B² hace pensar en el *paralelogramo de fuerzas* en mecánica: los acentos en las sílabas cuarta y octava serían dos líneas de fuerzas iguales y concurrentes, equidistantes del centro del objeto a que se aplicaran; el acento en la sexta sílaba, centro del verso, equivaldría a la diagonal del paralelogramo. Pero esta explicación vale sólo como ilustración comparativa: las fuerzas que concurren, en mecánica, deben actuar simultáneamente; los acentos del endecasílabo actúan sobre el oído en forma sucesiva.

[2] En el poema de *La creación del mundo*, de Acevedo, de los 824 versos del Canto I pertenecen 664 al tipo A, 145 al tipo B² y 15 al tipo B¹; en la *Austríada*, de Rufo, de los 928 del Canto I, 847 son del tipo A, 66 del tipo B², 15 del tipo B¹.

[3] Sobre la versificación de Pedro de Oña, v. *infra*, nota a versos de Ercilla.

que empieza y acaba con la acentuación en sexta sílaba, como el vigoroso de «Rota barquilla mía, que arrojada...», con el remate de «Ni temas a la mar ni esperes puerto», o el esquema que empieza y acaba con la acentuación en cuarta y octava sílabas, como el tierno «¿Qué tengo yo que mi amistad procuras?» (final: «Para lo mismo responder mañana»), o el ingenioso «Daba sustento a un pajarillo un día» (final: «Que tanto puede una mujer que llora»). Y no había de faltar el soneto de comienzo enérgico y final blando, como «Canta pájaro amante en la enramada...», donde el verso inicial pinta al amor libre de cuidados y el verso final lo pinta lleno de temores: «de pensamiento en pensamiento vuela» [1].

La tendencia a reducir el endecasílabo a los tipos A y B² existió en italiano también —sirvan de ejemplo Monti, Pindemonte, Manzoni, Leopardi— y hasta penetró en tratados de métrica, pero nunca se impuso del todo. ¿A qué se debe esta diferencia entre el italiano y el castellano? En Italia, los maestros del endecasílabo eran Dante y Petrarca: maestros de variedad rítmica. En España, Garcilaso lo es también; pero muchos poetas que tomaron ejemplo de él se esforzaron por reducir las variaciones del endecasílabo. Ante todo, suprimieron el tipo anapéstico (B³), que contradecía el ritmo yámbico de acentuación en las sílabas pares y provocaba confusiones con el *arte mayor:* esta complicación no existía para los italianos, y conservaron siempre el anapéstico.

Sin embargo, los poetas de España, salvo excepciones —Montemayor, Gil Polo, Arguijo, Rioja— no se decidieron a desterrar el verso acentuado sólo en la cuarta sílaba (B¹); más aún, a veces lo usan con insistencia: Góngora, Bartolomé de Argensola, Alonso de Acevedo, Valdivielso, entre otros. ¿Por qué? Porque esta acentuación no contraría el ritmo yámbico: la afloja, pero no la destruye, como el anapéstico, y puede servir para efectos delicados, como la sensación de suave desmayo que obtiene Darío cuando dice

> Que encerrada en silencio no salía
> sino cuando en la dulce primavera
> era la hora de la melodía[2]

---

[1] Sobre la versificación de Góngora, consúltese DÁMASO ALONSO, *La simetría en el endecasílabo de Góngora,* en la *Revista de Filología Española,* 1927, XIV, págs. 329-346; sobre procedimientos de Góngora y otros contemporáneos suyos, otro trabajo de ALONSO, *Versos plurimembres y poemas correlativos,* en *Revista de la Biblioteca, Archivo y Museo de Madrid,* 1944, XIII (y tirada aparte, 191 págs.).

[2] En trabajos míos ya muy antiguos *(Rubén Darío,* 1905; *El verso endecasílabo,* 1909) demostré la persistencia del tipo B¹ desde Boscán hasta Leandro Fernández de Moratín. Tanto Maury (desde 1831 por lo menos) como Juan Gualberto González (v. el tomo III de sus *Obras en prosa y verso,* 1844) habían advertido el uso frecuente del tipo B¹; su valiosa observación quedó olvidada, y no tuve noticia de ella hasta después de publicados mis trabajos. Menéndez y Pelayo la había echado en olvido: no la menciona en su estudio sobre Boscán *(Antología,* tomo XIII), y luego, en carta particular que me dirigió (1910),

De todos modos, este tipo B¹ dura cerca de tres centurias en castellano, a pesar de los tratadistas, hasta que se le destierra. Su desaparición en España, coincide aproximadamente con su parcial eclipse en Italia. En la reaparición, luego, el italiano (con Carducci) se anticipa al castellano (con Darío). Después, en el siglo xx, el endecasílabo recobra todas sus libertades antiguas y adquiere libertades nuevas.

EL ENDECASÍLABO CASTELLANO ANTES DE BOSCÁN. — Antes de Boscán, el tipo B¹ es el origen de la mayor parte de los intentos de endecasílabo en nuestro idioma.

1. En el *Cantar de Mio Cid* y en el fragmento de *Roncesvalles* hay versos que se deben a influencia del tipo francés de la *Chanson de Roland* (B¹): tienen pausa fuerte después de la cuarta sílaba:

> En Casteión / todos se leuantauan... (verso 458)

y, como en francés antiguo, cuando el primer hemistiquio tiene cinco sílabas no disminuye la medida del segundo:

> Abren las puertas, / de fuera salto dauan... (verso 458) [1]

Los poetas del *Cid* y del *Roncesvalles* escribían en versos fluctuantes: el eje a que tendían instintivamente era de catorce sílabas, pero se ve que a veces, cuando descendían hasta once sílabas, tendían a mantenerse algún rato alrededor de esta medida, que les era familiar en los poemas franceses.

2. El endecasílabo de Juan Manuel proviene, mediata o inmediatamente, del trovadoresco; ha perdido el ritmo acentual y conserva la medida, el número de sílabas:

> El danno, que non le pueda venir...
> A las cosas ciertas vos comendat...
> Non te quexes por lo que Dios fiziere...

El tipo B¹ —con tendencia al B³— abunda, pero no se sostiene:

> En el comienço deve omne partir...
> Ten que es derecho si te arrepentieres...
> Bive tal vida que mueras onrrado...

---

afirma que el tipo B¹ es «una especie de anapéstico vergonzante», opinión insostenible (B³ es variante de B¹, y no al revés). Suponía yo que en la persistencia del tipo B¹ en castellano había influencia unida de la versificación provenzal, catalana y galaicoportuguesa; ahora me parece innecesaria e infundada la suposición, pues el ejemplo italiano bastaba.

[1] Consúltese R. MENÉNDEZ PIDAL, *Cantar de Mio Cid*, texto, gramática y vocabulario, págs. 78, 79, 96, 97, 101, 102.

Una que otra vez obtiene el tipo A:

> Non castigues al moço maltrayendo...

En ocasiones combina versos de once y de doce sílabas, como después el *arte mayor* [1].

3. Se ha discutido si el Arcipreste de Hita escribió endecasílabos. Piensan que sí Menéndez Pelayo y Julio Puyol; no así Hanssen. Sus endecasílabos se presentan como combinaciones de versos de cinco y de siete sílabas, con rima interna:

> Quiero seguir / a ti, flor de las flores,
> siempre dezir / cantar de tus loores,
> non me partir
> de te servir, / mejor de las mejores...

Pertenecen al tipo B[1], con pausa fuerte después del acento en la cuarta sílaba; a veces llevan una sílaba de exceso después del acento interior, como en la epopeya francesa:

> Nunca fallece / la tu merced complida... [2]

4. El endecasílabo galaicoportugués, en su forma popular, fluctuante, penetró en Castilla en el siglo XIV, como se ve en el *cossante* del árbol de amor, del Almirante Mendoza, «Aquel árbol que mueve la foxa...»:

> Ya se de*mues*tra: sa*lid*las a ver...
> Vengan las *da*mas las *fru*tas cortar...

y en composiciones anónimas, populares, del *Cancionero Herberay* (siglo xv):

> Una mo*zu*ela de *vil* semejar... [3]

---

[1] Consúltese FRIEDRICH HANSSEN, *Notas a la versificación de Juan Manuel*, en los *Anales de la Universidad de Chile*, 1901.

[2] M. MENÉNDEZ Y PELAYO, *Antología*, tomo III, pág. c; JULIO PUYOL Y ALONSO, *El Arcipreste de Hita*, Madrid, 1906, pág. 214. En contra: F. HANSSEN, *Los metros de los cantares de Juan Ruiz*, en los *Anales de la Universidad de Chile*, 1902; sus razones son insuficientes, pues cree que los versos no son endecasílabos porque su ritmo es yámbico y no dactílico —o, como prefería decir Milá, anapéstico—; en realidad, la acentuación yámbica también podía encontrarla el Arcipreste en la poesía galaicoportuguesa, si es que allí buscaba sus modelos.

[3] Sobre el endecasílabo galaicoportugués, v. *supra* (y nota con indicaciones bibliográficas).

5. Nuestro *arte mayor* es probablemente de origen galaico-portugués: así lo afirmaba el Marqués de Santillana. El dodeca-sílabo, que es su eje, compuesto de dos hemistiquios exactamente iguales («Amores me dieron corona de amores...»), se combina con el endecasílabo anapéstico (B³):

> Tanto andovimos el cerco mirando
> que nos fallamos con nuestro Macías
> e vimos que estava llorando los días...

El tipo B¹, a pesar de su escasa fuerza rítmica, se encuentra a veces en el arte mayor:

> Cuando punava por descabollirme... ¹

Es importante recordar que en los endecasílabos de arte ma-yor hay pausa fuerte después del acento en la sílaba cuarta, y el verso no es simple, sino compuesto de dos secciones, como el do-decasílabo.

6. En el *Arte de trovar*, de Enrique de Villena, escrito en 1433, hay al final ejemplos de endecasílabo, con cesura después de la sílaba cuarta. No se sabe si son del autor del libro o ajenos:

> Quien de tro*bar* reglas pri*mero* dió... (B²)
> Quando que*rrás* rece*bir* la fortuna... (B³)
> Vuestra bon*dat*, por ser de *mí* lòada... (B²)
> Abrá sa*zón* que sea *más* conocida... (B³)
> Cuidado *tengo* yo de *ti*, ay alma... (B²)

7. En el verso de arte mayor, el dodecasílabo predomina. En Micer Francisco Imperial, por excepción, hay intento de adoptar el verso de Dante. Es probable que en el oído de Imperial se pro-

---

¹ Versos de Juan de Mena: cito según el *Cancionero castellano de siglo XV*, colegido por Raymond Foulché-Delbosc, Madrid, 1912.
Aunque en el arte mayor se encuentran de tarde en tarde versos semejan-tes a nuestros modernos A y B², debe recordarse que los poetas del siglo xv no los leían como tales; para ellos, el único acento que contaba en estos casos era el de la cuarta sílaba:

> Por el a*rena*   seca passeando...
> Non dedes   *causa* Gibraltar que faga... (Mena)

Sobre el arte mayor, consúltese: BELLO, *Ortología y métrica*, FOULCHÉ-DELBOSC, *Étude sur le «Laberinto» de Juan de Mena*, en la *Revue Hispanique*, 1902 (o traducción de Adolfo Bonilla y San Martín, *Juan de Mena y el arte mayor*, Madrid, 1903); HANSSEN, *El arte mayor de Juan de Mena*, en los *Ana-les de la Universidad de Chile*, 1906, especialmente pág. 186.

dujera una confusión entre los ritmos del arte mayor y los del endecasílabo dantesco; su metro aparece desorganizado:

> El tiempo poder pesa a quien más sabe,
> e donde aqueste principio yo tomo
> non es menester que por mí se alabe...
> Cerca la ora que el planeta enclara
> al oriente, que es llamada aurora,
> fuíme a una fuente por lavar la cara
> en un prado verde que un rosal enflora...
> Escripto todo con oro muy fino,
> e començaba: *En medio del camino*...
> Onde omilde enclinéme delante,
> faziéndole debida reverencia... [1]

8. Según Menéndez y Pelayo [2], el caso de Fernán Pérez de Guzmán es parecido. Pero examinando con atención los metros del señor de Batres, se descubre que si unas veces escribe versos de arte mayor, donde a ratos muestra predilección marcada por el endecasílabo auxiliar (B[3]), otras veces escribe endecasílabos a la francesa (B[1]), distintos de los anapésticos [3]. En arte mayor están, por ejemplo, las coplas de la *Confesión* y el *Dezir* en memoria del Almirante de Castilla, donde abunda el endecasílabo B[3]:

> Hombre que vienes aquí de presente,
> tú que me viste ayer almirante...
> Gloria e honras, estado e plazer
> me desamparan aquesta sazón...

Pero endecasílabos a la francesa (B[1]), que a menudo tienen una sílaba de exceso, átona, después de la cuarta acentuada, son los versos de las coplas *Que más virtud da la buena criança que la generación* («Yo digo assí que la buena criança...») y *Aceptando ser hombre a bien vivir y suplicando a Dios se vencen los pecados naturales* («Si la costumbre es tornada en natura...»), que forman parte de los *Vicios y virtudes*, los del himno *A Nuestra Señora* («¡Oh sacra esposa del Espíritu Santo!») y los de la *Oración a Nuestra Señora en fin de toda la obra* («Virgen preciosa de muy dulce aspecto...»):

---

[1] Cito por el *Cancionero de Baena*, Madrid, 1851 (núm. 250). Examínense también las composiciones que llevan los números 226, 231, 239, 521, 548, y consúltese M. MENÉNDEZ Y PELAYO, *Antología*, tomo III, págs. LXVII, LXIX y LXXII, y tomo XIII, págs. 209 y 210.

[2] *Antología*, XIII, pág. 211.

[3] Ya lo había observado HANSSEN, en *Los versos de las Cantigas de Santa María del rey Alfonso X*, en los *Anales de la Universidad de Chile*, 1901: v. pág. 538.

¡Oh sacra esposa / del Espíritu Santo,
de quien nasció / el sol de la justicia,
oh resplandor, / oh grandiosa leticia
del paraíso, / e del infierno espanto!

La mejor prueba de que no están en arte mayor es que nunca
se encuentra entre ellos el verso fundamental de aquel metro, el
dodecasílabo dividido en dos hemistiquios estrictamente iguales
(6 + 6), a pesar de que abundan los renglones de doce sílabas
(5 + 7) producidos por la adición de la sílaba átona después de
la cuarta acentuada:

Renderte gracias / nin fazer tal seruicio
Señora mía / lo podrá regraciar...
Nin tú, Señora, / cesas intercediendo...

9. Si el modelo de Fernán Pérez de Guzmán es el endecasílabo
francés —que precisamente durante el siglo xv estaba muy en
boga en Francia—, el modelo del Marqués de Santillana fué el
endecasílabo italiano. La pausa después de la cesura ha desaparecido; el verso es ya, como en italiano, una unidad. Como sus
maestros de Italia, el Marqués emplea dos acentuaciones: la de la
cuarta sílaba (B[1]), con sus variantes B[2] y B[3], y la de la sexta (A).
La primera es la que abunda más:

Quando yo veo la gentil criatura
quel cielo, acorde con naturaleça,
formaron, loo mi buena ventura,
el punto e ora que tanta belleça
me demostraron, e su fermosura...

(Soneto I)

Doradas ondas del famoso río
que baña en torno la noble cibdad
do es aquella cuyo más que mío
soy e posee la mi voluntad...

(Soneto XIX)

Ejemplos de A:

Traen los caçadores al marfil
a padescer la muerte enamorado,
con vulto e con aspecto femenil...

(Soneto XXI) [1]

---

[1] Quince de estos sonetos tuvieron en el siglo xv un glosador anónimo:
consúltese *Ensayo de una biblioteca española de libros raros y curiosos*, de Bartolomé José Gallardo, tomo I, columna 585.

Boscán y mendoza [1]. — Cuando Boscán trasplanta el endecasílabo italiano a nuestro idioma, y el ejemplo magnífico de Garcilaso lo impone, se conservan todas sus características. A lo largo
del siglo XVI sufrirán modificaciones.

Dos de los primeros poetas del movimiento italianista, Boscán
y Diego Hurtado de Mendoza, escribieron a veces endecasílabos
que lo son sólo según el número de sílabas, pero de acentuación
anárquica; así en la canción «Quiero hablar un poco...», de Boscán, y en la epístola de Mendoza «El no maravillarse...» [2]. Probablemente en tales desaciertos, y en otros ajenos de composiciones
hoy no leídas o no conocidas, se inspira la parodia de Cristóbal
de Castillejo; prueba que, a los oídos de muchos, los primeros endecasílabos de los italianistas sonaban como versos sin ritmo:

> Y ya que mis tormentos son forzados,
> bien que son sin fuerza consentidos,
> qué mayor alivio en mis cuidados... [3]

Cuando Boscán y Mendoza logran mayor dominio de la versificación, y sus renglones de acentuación anárquica son menos
frecuentes, conservan todavía los cuatro tipos italianos de endecasílabo (A, B^1, B^2 y B^3).

El poeta aragonés Johán de Villalpando, a mediados del mismo siglo XV,
escribió también sonetos —cuatro—, pero no en endecasílabos a la italiana,
sino en versos de arte mayor:

> Si las diversas passiones que siento,
> ya que mi caso las trae consigo,
> pudiesse por nombre dezir el tormento...

Consúltese el *Ensayo* de GALLARDO, tomo I, columnas 535-536.

El sevillano Hernando Díaz tradujo en 1520 el soneto de Petrarca «Se amor
non è...» y fragmentos de la *Divina Comedia*, todo en versos de arte mayor.
En arte mayor compuso Juan del Encina unas octavas reales (1509), y antes
que él el rosellonés Pedro Moner; Gutierre de Cetina, después, un soneto.

Poetas españoles que escribieron endecasílabos en italiano: Bartolomé
de Torres Naharro, Bertomeu Gentil, el Chariteo (el catalán Bernardo Ga-
reth) y el Tapia autor de cinco composiciones en tercetos que figuran en el
Cancionero general de Hernando del Castillo, edición de 1520. Consúltese M.
MENÉNDEZ Y PELAYO, *Antología*, XIII, págs. 229-232 y 436-454.

[1] Sobre Boscán y la definitiva adopción del endecasílabo italiano en España, consúltese M. MENÉNDEZ Y PELAYO, *Antología*, XIII, págs. 161-239;
además, ANDRÉS BELLO, observaciones citadas por Miguel Luis Amunáte-
gui en el prólogo al tomo V de las *Obras completas de su maestro*.

[2] Para los versos mal acentuados de Boscán, consúltese M. MENÉNDEZ
Y PELAYO, *Antología*, XIII, págs. 213-220. El ilustre crítico señala bien (pág.
214) los versos del tipo B^3, pero no hace cuenta aparte del tipo B^1.

[3] Se advierte que Castillejo creía que los italianistas hacían diéresis en
todos los diptongos.

Ejemplos de B[1] y B[3]:

> El alto cielo que en sus movimientos...
> La noche sigo, mas mi fantasía...
> Estando el alma con mil accidentes...
> Revuelve y dice la desconfianza...
> Mi mal es tanto que me ensañaría...
> El mal escojo, por determinarme...
> Si por amor, o por mi desconcierto...
> Amor me tiene por su desenfado...
> La mano al punto de la fantasía...
> Dichoso el día, dichosa la hora...
> Do el sobresalto, si alguno quería...
> Cosa es común en los enamorados.
> Y de medroso acometo al cuidado...
> Cobrado he miedo a cualquier aventura...
> Dulce gozar con lo que me engañaba...
>
> (Boscán, *Sonetos*)

> Cuando quisieres, cual pobre pastor...
> (Mendoza, Égloga «En la ribera...»)

> En tu descuido y mi desconfianza...
> (Mendoza, Canción «Cómo podré cantar...»)

> Nacida en medio del Andalucía...
> La culpa al mundo y a su desconcierto...
> Sirviendo al rey por mi satisfacción...
> (Mendoza, Carta a don Luis de Zúñiga)

GARCILASO. — Iguales muestras se hallan en Garcilaso:

> Tus claros ojos ¿a quién los volviste?... [1]
> Cuál es el cuello que como en cadena... (¿B[3]?) [2]

[1] Este verso, «verso divino», dice Enrique Díez Canedo, ha sido citado como ejemplo de acentuación defectuosa y rechazado por los preceptistas tradicionales.

[2] *Como*, relativo, es palabra inacentuada. Así otras disílabas, en versos que se citarán: *para, sino, entre, donde (*y *do)*, por ejemplo: consúltese el decisivo estudio, resultado de trabajos experimentales, de D. TOMÁS NAVARRO TOMÁS, *Palabras sin acento*, en la *Revista de Filología Española*, 1925, XXII págs. 335-375. En cambio son palabras acentuadas *no, ni, muy,* los artículos *un* y *una*, los adverbios *bien* y *mal* (los poetas los consideraban acentuados hasta dentro de palabras compuestas), las formas verbales *he, ha, es, son:*

> Bien es verdad que no está acompañada...
> (Garcilaso, Elegía I)

> La mía sé que no se mudará...
> Y entrególa a quien no la merecía...
> (Mendoza, Égloga «En la ribera...»)

Con la memoria de mi desventura...

(Égloga I)

Hinchen el aire de dulce armonía... (B³)
Al sueño ayudan con su movimiento...
Y al disponer de lo que nos quedaba...
Ora clavando del ciervo ligero... (B³)

.

Errando por las no vistas montañas...
(Cristóbal de Mesa, Égloga VI de Virgilio)

Porque algún tiempo no le respondía...
(Montemayor, Canción de *La Diana*)

No tuvieron o no guardaron leyes...
(Guillén de Castro, *El amor constante*)

De vientos no conjuración alguna...
(Góngora, *Soledades*)

Con sobresalto ni desconfianza...
(Fray Pedro de Padilla, Soneto «Felicidad ni gusto...»)

Y en todo aquesto, ni por pensamiento...
(Lope, *La discreta enamorada*, I)

Con que las vengue muy a su contento...
(Francisco de Castilla, *Fábula de Acteón*)

También mirad la bienaventuranza...
(Cervantes, Soneto sobre Isabel de Valois)

Tiene por sola bienaventuranza...
(Quevedo, Epístola a Olivares)

Cantan las almas bienaventuradas...
(Fray Pedro de Padilla, Canción «Oye la voz...»)

Moverme yo, de mal ejercitada...
(Garcilaso, Égloga III)

Y con su duque mal aconsejado...
(Cetina, Epístola I)

Y a ver los pasos por do me ha traído...
(Garcilaso, Soneto I)

Es probable que Garcilaso considerase acentuadas palabras como *quien,
cuanto, cuando, donde, do* (demostrativos-relativos o simplemente relativos),
los adjetivos *nuestro, vuestro, cada*, delante de sustantivo, la preposición *contra*:

Aquí está quien te ayudará a sentillo...
Entonces, como cuando el cisne siente...

(Égloga II)

Enredó sobre nuestros corazones...

(Epístola a Boscán)

Del mal ajeno de la compañera...
Se engarrafaba de la que venía...
El largo llanto, el desvanecimiento...
Verde tejida, aquel valle atajábamos... (B²) [1]
Luego mis ojos le reconocieron...
Cómo pudiste tan presto olvidarte... (B³)
Oh lobos, oh osos, que por los rincones...

Por testigo de cuanto os he encubierto...

(Canción II)

Y en esto no voy contra el juramento...

(Soneto VII)

Que no encubre de cuanto se avecina...

(Elegía I)

Según eso, no deben clasificarse en el tipo B¹ estos versos:

¿Tú no violaste nuestra compañía?
Mas no acabó con cuanto me dijese
Quedé yo entonces como quien camina...
De aquesta vida cada partecilla...
Y caminando por do mi ventura...

(Égloga II)

Los blancos cuerpos cuando sus oídos...

(Égloga III)

Y cuántas otras, cuando se acababa...

(Elegía I)

Digo que vine cuanto a lo primero...
Mas el amor de donde por ventura...

(Epístola a Boscán)

Quién me dijera, cuando en las pasadas...

(Soneto X)

Dada la posición en que se halla *como*, en «Me quejo a vos, como si en la verdad...», su supuesto acento no influye en el ritmo del verso; pero sí en «Guardarme como en los pasados años» (Canción IV) y en «Cuál es el cuello que como en cadena» (quizá haya que contarlo como anapéstico).

[1] Tanto *aquel* como *valle* tienen acento, pero el de *valle* es dominante. Tal vez, en razón de la estructura sintáctica, deberían contarse entre los anapésticos otros versos de la Égloga II: «Adiós, montañas; *adiós*, verdes prados...» y «Tentar el mal, y si es *malo* el suceso...», éstos de la Elegía I: «Con gran razón podrá *ser* la presente...» y «Bien es verdad que no es*tá* acompañada...», éste de la Canción IV: «En un temor que me ha *puesto* en olvido...», y éste del Soneto XVI: «Me quitó al mundo y me ha en *ti* sepultado...». En italiano no es raro el uso, deliberado al parecer, de estas acentuaciones dudosas:

Zefiro torna, e 'l bel tempo rimena,
E i fiori e l'erbe, sua dolce famiglia...

(Petrarca, Soneto que comienza así)

Allí se halla lo que se desea...
Que volvió el alma a su naturaleza...
Salir el humo de las caserías...

(Égloga II)

Oh cuántas veces, con el dolor fuerte... [1]
¿Algunos premios, o agradecimientos?...
Tú, gran Fernando, que entre tus pasadas...

(Elegía I)

Se contradicen en lo que profieren...

(Elegía II)

De daros cuenta de los pensamientos...

(Epístola a Boscán)

Y se convierta a do piense salvarme... (B³)
Y de mis males arrepentimiento...

(Canción I)

Un campo lleno de desconfianza...
Le dí, que es causa, cuya fortaleza...
Alguna parte de lo que yo siento...

(Canción IV)

Hallo, según por do anduve perdido... (B³)
Libre el lugar a la desconfianza...
Yo no nací sino para quereros... [2]
En tantos bienes porque deseastes...
Pienso remedios en mi fantasía...
A poder mío y mi consentimiento...
En salvo destos acontecimientos...
Cortaste el árbol con manos dañosas... (B³)
Después acá de lo que consentí...
A romper esto en que yo me metí... (B³)
Mas es a tiempo que de mi bajeza...
Un dulce amor, y de mi sentimiento... [3]

---

[1] Este verso tiene un acento entre la sílaba cuarta y la décima, el de *dolor*, pero, como está situado en la novena, no tiene valor rítmico. Igual cosa sucede en «Alguna parte de lo que yo siento», (v. *infra*), donde *yo* carece de valor rítmico y se suma al verbo que le sigue.

[2] Es posible que, para Garcilaso, *sino* estuviera todavía dividido en *si* y *no* (acentuado); de ser así, este verso no debería clasificarse entre los acentuados sólo en la sílaba cuarta.

[3] Los versos citados en el texto son todos los de Garcilaso que pertenecen indudablemente a los tipos B¹ y B³. En toda su obra sólo encuentro cinco endecasílabos de acentuación inaceptable:

El fruto que con el sudor sembramos...

(Elegía II)

SÁ DE MIRANDA. — Francisco de Sá de Miranda, admirador de Boscán y de Garcilaso, introduce en Portugal el endecasílabo de tipo italiano y lo escribe tanto en portugués como en español. En sus versos castellanos, después de los tipos A y B², el que más abunda es el B³:

> De otren cuidoso, de sí descuidado...
> Con ansia tanta de las mis entrañas... (B¹)
> Pasando d'ellas seguro cercano...
> Aquellos ojos que el alma embaían...
> Con las amigas, mudar la color...
> Zagala altiva con los tus poderes... (B¹)
> Vengan los pejes poblar los currales,
> pasca el ganado los ríos cabdales...
> Son los sospiros de los inocentes... (B¹)
>
> (Égloga XX, *Alejo*)

> Ah, quien me oiere, en mi mal escarmiente...
> Que buen consejo de naturaleza... (B¹)
> Aprisionada, la lengua nos dió...
> A nos se viene; parece Salicio...

> Que ya no me refrenará el temor...
>
> (Canción II)

> Lo menos de lo que en tu sér cupiere...
> Mas todo se convertirá en abrojos...
>
> (Égloga III)

> En lágrimas, como el lluvioso viento...
>
> (Elegía II)

Hay dos versos en que la palabra que decide la acentuación es *un* y no *los*, como antes pensé:

> Descójolos, y de un dolor tamaño...
> Juntándolos, con un cordón los ato...

El verso 42 de la Elegía I aparece de este modo desde la primera edición de las obras de Garcilaso:

> No quedará ya tu alma entera...

La mayor parte de los editores lo conservan así, y Fernando de Herrera lo defiende ingeniosamente contra correcciones que se habían propuesto, diciendo que el verso está incompleto para sugerir, precisamente, que el alma no ha quedado entera. Creo, sin embargo, que Garcilaso habrá escrito once sílabas y que sería aceptable la lección que recojo de anotador anónimo:

> No quedará ya tu alma toda entera.

Sobre la versificación de Garcilaso, consúltese: HAYWARD KENISTON, *Garcilaso de la Vega*, Nueva York, 1922, y NAVARRO TOMÁS, *Palabras sin acento*, págs. 350-351, 356, 362, 364 y 373 (para rectificaciones).

Sin mil enojos, sin lágrimas vistes...
Ojos más tristes que nunca nacieron...
Y que mis fuegos doblaran llorando...
Si amaneciere, será primavera...
Luego las Drías y las Amadrías...(B¹)
Con que la vista del todo perdieron...
Desatinados del todo y sandíos...
Ojos son estos que ansí desbaratan...
Después cantava con los ruisiñores... (B¹)
Seguidas siempre de arrepentimientos... (B¹)
Que henchiste el bosque del són extranjero...

(Primera versión de la égloga *Nemoroso*) [1]

ENDECASÍLABOS ANAPÉSTICOS Y ENDECASÍLABOS CRECIENTES. — De ahí en adelante, el anapéstico (B³) desaparece, porque los poetas españoles lo reconocían como aliado del dodecasílabo en el *arte mayor* y como elemento de la versificación fluctuante en las canciones populares de la época; huyendo de la confusión de metros, desterraron el tipo que entre los italianos es perfectamente legítimo como variante de B¹. Los ejemplos que se encuentran de B³, desde entonces, son esporádicos, y cabe —aquí sí— atribuirlos a descuido, como los versos de acentuación anárquica que suelen descubrirse. Pocos he encontrado, y los cito como curiosidades:

Cantares míos que estáis rebelados...

(Eugenio de Salazar, Soneto a la poetisa de Santo Domingo doña Elvira de Mendoza)

Duro peñasco en do escripto y pintado...

(Gil Polo, *Diana enamorada*, I)

Y a la ciudad del Espíritu Santo...
Lo que merece que todos abonen...

(Juan de Castellanos, *Elegías*, Parte II, Elegía III, Canto IV) [2]

---

[1] Poesías de Francisco de Sá de Miranda, edición de Carolina Michaëlis de Vasconcellos, Halle, 1885. Sá de Miranda todavía tiene versos de acentuación irregular:

Quántas lágrimas por un medio riso...
Adonde con la su lengua esgrimiendo...

(*Nemoroso*)

Sobre su versificación, tanto en castellano como en portugués, consúltese el prólogo de la señora Michaëlis.

[2] Es posible que el tipo B³ fuese normal para Castellanos, porque abunda en las *Elegías;* caso único después de Boscán, Garcilaso y Sá de Miranda.

Oh muerte triste, que así me entristeces...
(Fray Jerónimo Bermúdez, *Nise lastimosa*, I)

Quebró el pincel y vertió las colores...
(Gregorio Silvestre, Soneto «La mano diestra...») [1]

De mí, le dije por qué no venía...
(Calderón, *Casa con dos puertas*, I)

Nos unirá clandestino himeneo...
(Gabriel de Bocángel, *Leandro y Hero*)

Chisgarabís y Don Diego de Noche...
(Quevedo, *Entremés de las sombras*)

¿Por qué? Quizá porque más venturosa...
(Sor Juana Inés de la Cruz, *Sueño*)

Un religioso que apenas podía...
(Fray Matías de Bocanegra, *Canción alegórica*)

¡Ah! no lo es tal, que Damón es honrado...
(Fray Diego González, cit. por Eduardo de la Barra) [2]

El endecasílabo creciente, con una sílaba de exceso, a la manera de los de Petrarca y sus predecesores, no se halla sino por excepción, que también podemos atribuir a inadvertencia:

Hay potramé*dicos*, haya potralcaldes...
(Cervantes, *La elección de los alcaldes*)

LA ACENTUACIÓN EN LA CUARTA SÍLABA: SIGLOS XVI Y XVII. — El endecasílabo acentuado solamente en la cuarta sílaba (B[1]) duró tres siglos con vida normal en castellano. Hay unos pocos poetas que lo evitan: Jorge de Montemayor [3], Gil Polo,

---

[1] A este poeta portugués le atribuyeron Pedro de Cáceres Espinosa y Luis Barahona de Soto el descubrimiento de la verdadera estructura del endecasílabo italiano y castellano; Menéndez y Pelayo *(Antología*, XIII, pág. 384) dice que le atribuyeron el descubrimiento de la «medida yámbica»: si tal pensó o se pensó de él, su práctica lo desmiente, pues en el verso citado coloca un acento en sílaba impar. También empleó el verso acentuado sólo en cuarta sílaba (v. *infra).*

[2] Sobre Góngora, v. *infra.*

[3] En Montemayor sólo hallo este verso que estrictamente debería contarse entre los de acento en cuarta sílaba, pero probablemente el poeta contaba *adonde* como palabra acentuada:

Una comedia adonde su decoro...
(Elegía en la muerte de Feliciano de Silva)

Pablo de Céspedes, Pedro de Oña, Juan de Arquijo, Rioja, y parte del grupo de poetas de Antequera y Granada que figura en las *Flores de poetas ilustres* (1605). Ejemplos, escogidos generalmente entre muchos de cada poeta:

> Comiendo en ella a los enamorados...
>> (Gonzalo Pérez, *La Ulixea*, II)

> Y el verse lejos de su compañía...
>> (Hernando de Acuña, *Fábula de Narciso*)

> Lugar secreto que de mis dolores...
>> (Lomas Cantoral, Soneto «Sombra fresca...»)

> Que con tu ausencia y con desampararme...
> Los altos bienes de mi pensamiento...
>> (Cetina, Soneto «Pues se conforma...»)

> Responde y dice la desconfianza...
>> (Sebastián de Córdoba, Soneto «Nuestra alma...»)

> Que halló en este su descubrimiento...
> Y en esto el miedo y la desconfianza...
>> (Luis Zapata, *Carlo famoso*, XI) [1]

> Amor tus flechas con que enriqueciste...
>> (Gregorio Silvestre, Soneto «En esta sombra»)

> Que fuese, fuera de lo que miraba...
>> (Gregorio Silvestre, *Fábula de Narciso*)

> Son las prisiones y la ligadura...
>> (Camoens, Soneto 283, en castellano) [2]

---

[1] Zapata es versificador muy descuidado y escribe versos como éstos en su *Carlo famoso:*

> Al Emperador sus embajadores... (XI)
> Y sobre ella fué con la capitana... (XII).

[2] Igualmente aparece el tipo B[1] en los versos portugueses de Camoens:

> *Contarei, disse, sem que me reprendam...*
>> *(Os Lusiadas, V)*

El tipo B[1] ha sobrevivido en portugués desde los tiempos de Sá de Miranda:

> *Tornate a Ondelio que la restitua...*
>> (Eloyo de Sá Sotomayor, *Ribeiras do Mondego*, I)

> *E como foste misericordioso...*
>> (Francisco Manuel, *A viola de Talia*, tercetos IV)

Poned manzanas a mi cabecera
y otros olores con que me consuele...
(Arias Montano, Paráfrasis del *Cantar*, III)

Veré las causas, y de los estíos...
(Fray Luis de León, *A Felipe Ruiz*)

Bailes ordena, mientras su Vulcano...
Hermosa sales y resplandeciente...
El risco agudo y el despeñadero...
(Fray Luis de León, Odas de Horacio) [1]

A su albedrío y a mi descontento...
(El Brocense, Soneto «Oh pasos locos...»)

Y alega un salmo con que lo atestigua...
(Alcázar, *Poesías festivas*, soneto V)

E là do pégo da concavidade...
(Frei Manoel de Santa María Itaparica, *Descrição
da Ilha de Itaparica*)

As recebemos dos antepasados...
(Frei Basilio da Gama, *O Uraguay*)

Líamos ambos por curiosidade...
(João de Deus, *Francesca*)

Cuspido ás praias pelas tempestades...
(Theophilo Braga, *O sepulcro de Virgilio*)

A Via Lactea se desenrolava...
(Olavo Bilac, *Via Lactea*)

É liso o lago que nos desfeava...
(Eugenio de Castro, Soneto *Muitos annos depois*)

Tem un soluço de arrepentimento...
Formando un ponto de interrogação...
(Guillerme de Almeida, Soneto XIII, de *Nós*)

Se le encuentra, además, en la moderna poesía gallega:

Os desleigados que te escarneceron...
(Curros Enríquez, *Aires d'a miña terra*, introducción).

[1] Hay en Fray Luis versos imperfectos, como éstos que cita Navarro Tomás *(Palabras sin acento,* pág. 361-362):

Ponían sobre su boca las manos...
Cansado, cuando llegó habían pasado...
¿Qué pierde para que por blanco opuesto...?

O estos otros:

Esta flauta, con que el Alexi hermoso...
(Égloga V de Virgilio)

De Lesbo, que si a tu jüicio es dino...
(Oda I, libro I, de Horacio)

Puede tomar lo que le conviniere...
(Timoneda, Octava a los representantes)

Idea viva de mis pensamientos...
(Bermúdez, *Nise lastimosa*, I)

Traspuesto el sol de tu conocimiento...
(Malón de Chaide, *Parce mihi* de Job)

Egicia, y gloria de su confianza...
(Herrera, *Por la victoria de Lepanto*)

En sus caballos y en la muchedumbre...
(Herrera, *Pérdida de don Sebastián*)

Hiende el caballo desapoderado...
Mas de la suerte, como si del cielo...
Las ricas minas, y los caudalosos...
Piensas sacar de mi desasosiego...
(Ercilla, *Araucana*) [1]

Asienta pueblos con sus oficiales...
Y tal el oro de su nacimiento...
Donde faltaron las enfermedades...

[1] Es significativo encontrar estos versos en Ercilla, que apenas usa otro endecasílabo que el de acento en sexta (tipo A). El de acento en cuarta y octava (B²) no es en *La Araucana* mucho más frecuente que el de acento sólo en cuarta (B¹). Excepcionalmente se encuentra algún verso mal hecho:

Apenas en la deseada arena... (XV)

El chileno Pedro de Oña, que comienza su carrera como discípulo de Ercilla, en su *Arauco domado* (1596) sólo emplea el tipo A. En ocasiones escribe versos que deberían contarse entre los del tipo B¹, porque los vocablos en que figura el esperado (y por él supuesto) acento de la sexta es inacentuado en realidad:

Para salir con cuanto pretendiera...
Sonaban ya por donde discurría...

En *El vasauro*, poema terminado en 1635, emplea a veces el verso acentuado en las sílabas cuarta y octava o tipo B² (pero no predomina: hay que rectificar la afirmación de don Rodolfo Oroz en su edición del poema, Santiago de Chile, 1941, pág. LXXXVI); del acentuado sólo en cuarta (B¹) he encontrado ejemplos dudosos, versos en que, como en el *Arauco domado*, se atribuye acento a palabras que no lo tienen *(quien, cuyo, donde, cuando,* relativos; *hasta, mientras)*:

De engaños, y haya quien te comunique... (I)
Las borlas, tela, y hasta deshaciendo... (III)
Su fiel constancia, cuando de Lucía... (VI)
Por él veniste a donde la cortina... (X)
Nace Luis, a cuyo nacimiento... (X)
Ay, cuántas veces, mientras lo escribías... (X)

Mas no faltaron las calamidades...
Estaban todos, atemorizados...
Diego García con la pesadumbre...
Indios feroces y desvergonzados...

(Juan de Castellanos, *Elegías*, parte II;
Elegía III, canto IV) [1]

Esta es grandeza, que de las grandezas...

(Saavedra Guzmán, Soneto a Valbuena)

Y era creer que te contentarías...

(Francisco de Terrazas, *Epístola*)

Aura, templanza, y a las sonorosas...

(Francisco de la Torre, Soneto «Vuelve Céfiro...»)

Y pues me dejan, por lo que llevaron...

(Francisco de Figueroa, Versos a Montano)

Entre la turba que sacrificaba
A la cuitada que pereceaba...
A tal merced, y que se me ofreciera...

(Pedro Sánchez de Viana, *Metamorfosis de Ovidio*, X)

Si dar queremos a los consonantes...

(Juan de la Cueva, *Ejemplar poético*, II)

Den el perdón al que los ofendiere...

(Fray Diego Murillo, *Palabras de Cristo en la cruz*)

Y lo intrincado y lo dificultoso...

(Barahona de Soto, Sátira I)

Ya que me faltan para dibujaros...
Hermosa frente, en cuyo señorío...
Por fin del mundo, y de la hermosura... [2]

(Gálvez de Montalvo, *El pastor de Filida*, III)

Consigo raudos arrebatarían...

(Hernández de Velasco, *Eneida*, I)

La ansia y pasión que te desasosiega...

(Rey de Artieda, Epístola sobre la comedia)

---

[1] Aparte de emplear este tipo de verso, Castellanos es muy desmañado versificador. Ejemplos tomados del mismo canto:

> Se pasaron a Barraquicimeto...
> Por mandato de la Real Audiencia...
> Que el sol por término se les daría...

[2] *H* aspirada en *hermosura*.

Las altas ondas en el occidente...
(Espinel, *La casa de la memoria*)

La cruz, de yesca para sus enojos...
(Ledesma, Soneto sobre Longinos)

Mi dama, pienso que con su presencia...
(Tárrega, *El prado de Valencia*, I)

Y así, cual padre de misericordia...
(Virués, *Monserrate*, I)

Bien lo han mostrado sus ofrecimientos...
(Miguel Sánchez, *La guarda cuidadosa*, I)

Habréislo sido de mi desventura...
(Damián Vegas, *Comedia Jacobina*, III)

Este lugar! de mis navegaciones...
(Medrano, Canción «Oh mil veces...»)

El triste día se le representa...
(Juan de Arjona, *Tebaida*, I)

Haciendo en esto a la naturaleza...
(Cairasco de Figueroa, *Canto de la Curiosidad*)

Por propria insignia de tu simulacro...
(Lupercio Leonardo, Canción a Felipe II)

Con presupuesto de arrepentimiento...
(Velázquez de Velasco, Salmo 37)

Esto te pido, por lo que aprovecha...
(Dr. Garay, Epístola a Fabia)

Si al cedro vieres ensoberbecerse...
(Pérez de Herrera, *Menosprecio de las cosas caducas*)

Ásperas, blandas con el aspereza...
(Lope de Salinas, Canción «Los claros ojos...»)

Mozas de Lesbos, las que me incitastes...
(Diego Mejía, *Safo a Faón*)

Luego caería en arrepentimiento...
(Luis de Ribera, *De la virtud heroica*)

Al fin veréis que para el alboroto...
      (Esquilache, Carta al Conde de Lemos) [1]

En aquel libro de sus Confesiones...
      (Agustín de Rojas, Loa en alabanza del Jueves)

Y medrantando a los que le seguían...
La necia turba de los rapacillos...
      (Rodrigo Caro, *Días geniales o lúdricos*)

Fingir palabras en su coyuntura...
      (Cascales, *Tablas poéticas*)

Sólo licencia, con que le promete...
      (Gómez de Huerta, *Florando de Castilla*)

Castigan justos, y tus presunciones...
Que infiel se llama la desconfianza...
      (Díaz Callecerrada, *Endimión*, I)

Si yo conozco en mi naturaleza...
      (Guillén de Castro, *La piedad en la justicia*, II)

Y aquella vena con que lo dictaba...
Y la mayor a sus iniquidades...
Sin un Homero que lo celebrase...
Oh musa mía, para mi consuelo...
      (Clarinda, peruana, *Discurso en loor de la poesía*)

Que las más veces la desconfianza...
      (Amarilis, peruana, *Epístola a Belardo*)

Veleras selvas en su movimiento...
Escucha atento si la trabajosa...
(Juan de Ayllón, Poema de los mártires del Japón)

Silvestres galas de la primavera...
De bellas ninfas, las que con decoro...
      (Mira de Amescua, *Acteón y Diana*) [2]

Emulación de la naturaleza...
      (Cardenio, *La estrella de Sevilla*, III)

Y aquel abismo de misericordias...
(Francisco de Aldana, Epístola a Bernardino de Mendoza)

---

[1] Es el único ejemplo con que he tropezado en toda la obra de Esquilache.
[2] En esta fábula de Mira de Amescua hallo este verso imperfecto:

    La carga del no acostumbrado peso...

La providencia, con lo venidero...
Y si los pasas al entendimiento...
(Pedro Espinosa, *Soledad del Duque de Medina Sidonia*)

En tu bondad que en mi merecimiento...
Con pecadores y son publicanos...
A hacer salvos a los pecadores...
(Espinosa, Salmo «Cristo mi redentor...»)

Al desempeño de su profecía...
(Espinosa, Soneto «Encendió luminarias...»)

De dos esposos, y los coronaban...
(Feliciana Enríquez de Guzmán, *Soneto*)

Del ser que tienes por naturaleza...
(Tejada Páez, *El aire*)

De atormentados y atormentadores...
Y así, admirada de su hermosura... [1]
(Fray Diego de Hojeda, *La Cristíada*, VI)

Espía muda de los horizontes...
(Anastasio Pantaleón de Ribera, *Fábula de Eco*)

Que no entró en diosas arrepentimiento...
(Lic. Dueñas, Canción «Quedó conmigo...»)

Introduciendo la desconfianza...
Que las disculpen si la desvanecen...
(Luis de Ulloa, *Raquel*)

Igual, Señor, a tu misericordia...
(Cosme de los Reyes, Canción «Viniste de la altura...»)

De amor no quita la correspondencia...
(Pedro de Salas, Canción «Vuela, afila tus alas...»)

Dejó por jueces y gobernadores...
(Luis Vélez de Guevara, *El ollero de Ocaña*, III)

De mis costumbres y de mis empleos...
(Quevedo, Sátira *Riesgos del matrimonio*)

Monstruo te admira la naturaleza...
(Salas Barbadillo, *La estafeta de Momo*, XXXII)

---

[1] Hojeda aspiraba la *h* de *hermosura*.

En el sagrario del conocimiento...
>(Villamediana, *Sonetos amorosos*, X)

Más mis ofensas que mi sufrimiento...
>(Villamediana, Soneto «Cuando en mi obstinación...»)

Mas quiero ir antes a mi casería...
Mas tú, Señor de la naturaleza...
¿Crees tú que Dafne nos aconsejara...?
Quizá engañada con la semejanza...
Cual ese tuyo, que si lo creyeras...
De su furor, de la desesperada...
Quizá engañada con la semejanza...
>(Jáuregui, *Aminta*)

Admiración de la naturaleza...
>(Castillo Solórzano, «La soberana gracia...»)

Y entre sus ruegos y amonestaciones...
>(Juan de Salinas, Diálogo de Carillo y Bras)

Siempre se olvida del matalotaje...
>(Quiñones de Benavente, *Los cuatro galanes*)

De la fiereza que representaba...
>(Villaviciosa, *La Mosquea*, VII)

Y hace que vivan en su precipicio...
>(Bocángel, *Leandro y Hero*)

Por la lujuria en que se precipita...
>(Villegas, Elegía IV)

Que ni te culpen por desaliñado...
>(Cubillo, Avisos «Fabio, tu carta...»)

Iba la ninfa que se las pelaba...
>(Jacinto Polo, *Fábula de Apolo y Dafne*)

Que no permites en tu compañía...
>(Rebolledo, Trenos de Jeremías, I)

Mas basten burlas, que si se ofreciera...
>(Montalván, *Como padre y como rey*, III)

Dosel florido de la primavera...
>(Calderón, *Mañanas de abril y mayo*, I)

Satisfacciones y desenojarte...
>(Calderón, *Casa con dos puertas*, I)

Áspid de celos a mi primavera...
(Calderón, *El médico de su honra*, I)

Rompiendo leyes a naturaleza...
(Jerónimo de Cáncer, *Fábula del Minolauro*)

Con que luchabas y te defendías...
(Francisco Manuel, Epístola a Licio)

Siendo impecable por naturaleza...
(Luis de Tejeda, *La cena*)

Y efectos sean de tus sentimientos...
(Luis de Tejeda, *El peregrino en Babilonia*)

Labran techumbres para sus alturas...
(Pineda Bascuñán, *Cautiverio feliz*, I, 15)

De las grandezas con que los oprimen...
(Hernando Domínguez Camargo, *San Ignacio*, el banquete)

No tengas cuenta con los revoltosos...
(Antonio Henríquez Gómez, *El pasajero*)

Aquel abrazo de naturaleza...
(López de Zárate, Égloga de Silvio y Anfriso)

Sino rigor, con que le solemnizas...
(Trillo y Figueroa, Soneto IX)

Al que hace el gusto el agradecimiento...
(Moreto, *El parecido en la corte*, III)

En ver las plazas, y le considero...
(Diamante, *El valor no tiene edad*, I)

Y Adonis gime las del peregrino...
Moderna envidia de las rozagantes...
(Carlos de Sigüenza y Góngora, *Primavera indiana*) [1]

El alma aumenta sus melancolías...
(Martínez Meneses, *El tercero de su afrenta*, I)

Que de las costas de la Andalucía...
(Juan Vélez de Guevara, *El mancebón de los palacios*, III)

---

[1] Hallo en el poema este verso imperfecto:

A las breñas que con caduco muro...

Es el inducas de las tentaciones...
>   (Solís, *Hermafrodito y Salmacis*)

El pobre llega, con declamaciones...
>   (Juan del Valle Caviedes, *Beatas*)

Quien le acompaña, para la pendencia...
>   (Fernando de Zárate, *Mudarse por mejorarse*, III)

Hijo de Venus y de sus maldades...
>   (Agustín de Salazar, Silva de *La aurora*)

Y no aquí sólo mi superstición...
>   (Bances Candamo, *Las mesas de la fortuna*)

Cuando a aspirante en lo que mereciste...
>   (Conde de la Granja, Soneto en *Flor de Academias*)

LA ACENTUACIÓN EN LA CUARTA SÍLABA: MUESTRAS DE SU ABUNDANCIA. — Doy ahora grupos de ejemplos tomados de unos cuantos poetas, a fin de que se vea que esta práctica era sistemática y no casual.

Lope de Vega (recuérdese que en las comedias están en reducida minoría los endecasílabos con relación a los octosílabos):

Vi un receptor de la chancillería...
De chimeneas ni de caballetes...
>   (*La noche toledana*)

Y así, vas lejos de mi pensamiento...
De Extremadura. Y en Guadalajara...
>   (*Peribáñez*)

Hechura suya y sus aficionados...
En el donaire, para que tuviera...
>   (*Don Juan de Austria en Flandes*)

Del Hacedor de la naturaleza...
Monstruo será de la naturaleza..
>   (*La hermosa Ester*, I)

No quiere el rey, ni aun en naturaleza...
>   (*Barlaán y Josafat*, I)

Suya la llama en el Deuteronomio...
Y que le vengue de sus enemigos...
>   (*La buena guarda*, I)

Son muy antiguas las enemistades...
(Las mocedades de Bernardo, I)

Que pesa mucho en el entendimiento...
(Los Benavides, III)

Haz que se acerque la de la patena...
(El villano en su rincón, I)

El mal, la pena y el entendimiento...
(Los Vargas de Castilla, III)

Encomendado que en su sacrificio...
(La Santa Liga, II)

¿Mas que tenemos entretenimiento?..
(La niña de plata, III)

Las nuevas minas y la plataforma...
Por acudir a las dificultades...
(El asalto de Mastrique)

En ellos tienen el entendimiento...
(El halcón de Federico, II)

Que no es milagro en la naturaleza...
Y que me dijo que le perdonase...
(El anzuelo de Fenisa)

El que nació con mis obligaciones...
¿Tú, no mandaste que me entretuviese?...
(La inocente Laura, I)

Malas palabras y desabrimientos...
(La viuda valenciana)

Que los planetas y los elementos...
(Los locos de Valencia)

Admiración de la naturaleza...
(Los locos por el cielo, III)

Que tú no ignoras por dificultosas...
(El cardenal de Belén, I)

Las ironías y adubitaciones...
(Arte nuevo de hacer comedias)

310

Juan Ruiz de Alarcón:

> Y en éstos sirvo, que de su fortuna...
> E a Dios pluguiera que su aventuranza...
>
> *(Los pechos privilegiados)*

> Lleve conmigo mis inclinaciones...
> Y porque excede a la naturaleza...
>
> *(La cueva de Salamanca*, I)

> Imprima en ellos agradecimientos...
>
> *(No hay mal que por bien no venga*, III)

> Donde ya libre de que me pudiera...
> Desconocido, para que asegure...
>
> *(La culpa busca la pena*, I)

> Que no refiero porque la supiste...
>
> *(Los empeños de un engaño*, II)

> Mis pensamientos, mis inclinaciones...
> Y dirá hablando a los facinerosos...
> Este silencio cuando notificas...
> Y echaron suertes por mis vestiduras...
>
> *(El Anticristo)*

Tirso de Molina:

> La madre tierra como a su despojo...
>
> *(El condenado por desconfiado*, I)

> Teje coronas para sus mujeres...
> Y don Enrique de la fortaleza...
>
> *(La prudencia en la mujer*, I)

> Murió Leonela de San Severino...
>
> *(Palabras y plumas*, I)

> Cuerdo castigo de mi inadvertencia...
>
> *(Amar por razón de estado*, II)

> Ya no se estiman las conversaciones...
>
> *(No hay peor sordo..*, II)

> Señales dar de mi agradecimiento...
>
> *(El amor y la amistad*, I)

> Si no de ingrato, de desalumbrado...
>
> *(El Àmor médico*, II)

311

Nunca es valiente la jurispericia...

(*Santo y sastre*, III)

Descanso en, brazos de tu cortesía...

(*Los lagos de San Vicente*, I)

Sansón, Alcides y Sardanapalo...

(*La república al revés*, I)

Trajo las suyas el de Calatrava...
Dicen que todos resucitaremos...

(*La reina de los reyes*)

Y yo también de las persecuciones...

(*La elección por la virtud*, II)

Gana blasones que te inmortalicen...

(*La vida de Herodes*, I)

Fabio, mi hermano, que al de Monferrato...

(*Ventura te dé Dios, hijo*)

Ocasionaron las oposiciones...
Dejó en silencio los que conspiraban...

(*Todo es dar en una cosa*)

Pues si enloquece una desconfïanza...

(*La fingida Arcadia*, III)

Cervantes:

Fué en mis alforjas mi repostería...

(*Viaje del Parnaso*, I) [1]

Oh flor y fruto de los bailarines...
Váyanse todos por lo que cantare...

(*El rufián viudo*)

Cierra la piedra de tu sepultura...
Y agora temo que la sepultura...
Que pisa aquel que de su pensamiento...
El desengaño de mi pensamiento...
Hago buen rostro a la desconfïanza...
Y los despojos de mis pensamientos...

---

[1] En el *Viaje*, III, el verso «Fuera melindres, y cese la entena...» debe leerse, probablemente, como propone don Ricardo Rojas, «Fuera melindres, ícese la entena».

Con el valor de tus merecimientos...
Dará mil muestras de tu desvarío...
No hay que hacer caso de su sentimiento...

(*Galatea*, I-III)

Eugenio de Salazar:

La erudición de tus *Anotaciones*...
Con su elegancia y sus resoluciones...

(Epístola a Herrera)

Y para que ella le comunicase...
Por la cabeza de su monarquía...
Piden remedio para sus dolores...
De su majada y su recogimiento...

(*Descripción de la laguna de México*)

De humores malos con melancolía...
Limosna pide con encogimiento...
Otros que piensan sin detenimiento...
Pidiendo injustas remuneraciones...
Y dar remate a mis comparaciones...
Finge mil ascos y revolvimientos...

(*Sátira contra los abusos de la Corte*)

Juan Rufo, en *La Austríada* (1584):

Que juntas tuvo con las teologales...
El poder libre de los vencedores...
Dieron lugar a que la exorbitancia...
Y nuestras guerras y peregrinajes...
La instancia misma con que se apelaba...
Era argumento en que se comprobaba...
Así miraban desde Talanquera...
Los más comunes y particulares...
Es Almanzor, y por la femenina...
Os hace fuertes la naturaleza...
Los pertinaces de los convertidos...   (Canto I)
La furia horrible de los torbellinos...
Previstos cursos de constelaciones...
Y mal armadas en invernaderos...
La preeminencia del anticiparse...
Que noche fuese, y la del Nascimiento...
La cual fué causa que los foragidos...
Marchando a priesa con sus escuadrones...
Al són de gaitas y de tamborinos...
Con qué palabras te agradeceremos... (Canto II) [1]

---

[1] Son raros en Rufo los versos imperfectos:

Fabricando de su desconfianza... (Canto IV)

Probablemente contaba *desde* como palabra acentuada en este verso:

Sin pena, porque aun desde que mamaban... (I).

Alonso de Acevedo, en *La creación del Mundo* (1615):

> Con solas fuerzas de filosofía...
> De los secretos de naturaleza...
> De plata y oro y la circunferencia...
> Oh luz, fiel guía de los navegantes...
> Ni señalada con los horizontes...
> Del Crïador de la naturaleza...
> Está a porfía con el artificio...
> Con las vigilias del desasosiego...
> Sobre el bajel de la filosofía...   (Canto I)
> Del veloz cielo la circunferencia...
> El cual del aire con las frïaldades...
> Y de sus rayos con la muchedumbre...
> Que los topacios que resplandecían...
> Con que nos fuerzan a que concedamos...
> Y de los Sinas entre las regiones...
> Inundaciones y esterilidades...
> Cuando al principio de sus resplandores...
> Y tantos son cuantas exhalaciones... (Canto II) [1]

Fray José de Valdivielso, en la *Vida de San José:*

> Las círreas aguas ni la compañía...
> Y él mismo es limpio por naturaleza...
> Un nombre igual a su merecimiento... (Canto I)
> Tiempo de gracia y de misericordia...
> Perdió mi gracia por su inobediencia...
> Los coronistas, los historiadores...
> Los héroes fuertes, los legisladores
> y de sus patrias los libertadores...
> Lleno de luto y de melancolía...
> A quien la gracia y la naturaleza...
> Amor divino que en las soberanas... (Canto II)

Luis de Góngora:

> Purpúreas rosas sobre Galatea...
> Segur se hizo de sus azucenas...
>
> *(Polifemo)*
>
> Al padre en tanto de su primavera...
> La mayor gloria de su monarquía...
> La hiedra acusa, que del levantado...

---

[1] Una que otra vez tiene Acevedo versos imperfectos:

> Rompe el cielo con tus alas ventosas... (Canto II)
> Y el que por su naturaleza flaca...
> Porque como de su naturaleza...
> Saturno desde su morada fría... (VI)

La ceremonia en su recibimiento...
Gracias no pocas a la vigilancia...

(*Panegírico al Duque de Lerma*)

La alta cenefa, lo majestüoso...
Más de fierezas que de cortesía...
Los mismos autos el de sus cristales...
De los serranos que correspondido...
El menos ágil, cuanto comarcanos...
Pisar quería, cuando el populoso...
Cenizas hizo las que su memoria...
El vello, flores de su primavera...
La blanca espuma, cuantos la tijera...
Entre opulencias y necesidades...
Pisó del viento lo que del ejido...
Lo grave tanto, que lo precipita...
Liberalmente, de los pescadores...
Conservarán el desvanecimiento...
El lagrimoso reconocimiento...
Felices años, y la humedecida...
Éfire luego, la que en el torcido...
A la barquilla, donde la esperaban...
Bebió no sólo, mas la desatada...
Mientras ocupan a sus naturales...

(*Soledades*)

El sueño, autor de representaciones...
(Soneto «Varia imaginación...»)

Y se la ha puesto sobre su cabeza...
(Soneto «Por niñear...»)

Que eran en marzo los caniculares...
(Soneto «Duélete de esa puente...»)

Más con el silbo que con el cayado...
(Soneto «Sacro pastor...»)

Que el mayor mártir de los españoles...
(Soneto «Sacros, altos...»)

Y las reliquias de su atrevimiento...
(Soneto «Verdes hermanas...»)

Mi rostro tiñes de melancolía...
(Soneto «Herido el blanco pie...»)

Mal vadeados de los pensamientos...
(Soneto «Cosas, Celalba mía...»)

315

Es sucio Esgueva para compañero...
Señora tía, de Cagalarache...
No, que en ladrando con su artillería ..
(Soneto «De dónde bueno...»)

Nunca yo tope con sus señorías...
(Soneto «Señores Corteggiantes...»)

No vi más fuerte sino el levantado...
(Soneto «Llegué, señora tía...»)

Soga de gozques contra forastero...
(Soneto «Pisó las calles...»)

De fiera menos que de peregrino...
(Soneto «Restituye a tu mudo...»)

Entre los remos y entre las cadenas...
(Soneto «Florido en años...»)

Suple las frutas de que se corona...
(Soneto «Mis albarcoques...»)

Escondió a otros la de tu serpiente...
(Soneto «Los rayos...»)

Pues de más ojos que desvanecida...
(Soneto «Ser pudiera...»)

Oh, aquel dichoso, que, la poderosa...
(Soneto «En este occidental...»)

Oh, cuánto tarda lo que se desea...
(Soneto «Camina mi pensión...»)

Sino galanes del Andalucía...
En el torneo de la valentía...
(Soneto «Hermosas damas...»)[1]

---

[1] El primer verso de este soneto debería contarse en el tipo B[1]:

Hermosas damas, si la pasión ciega...

Pero es posible que, para el poeta, el acento de *pasión*, en la novena sílaba, compensara la ausencia de acento en la octava:

Casos semejantes son estos versos del *Polifemo:*

Luciente paga de la mejor fruta...
Y el garzón viendo, cuantas mover pudo...

Y éste de las *Soledades:*

Alegre pisan la que si no era...

Repugna a leyes de naturaleza...
No hay elemento como el empedrado...
(Soneto —atribuído— «Quedando con tal peso...»)[1]

Bartolomé Leonardo de Argensola:

Y el no acudir de los setentrionales...
Fuerzas tenían, pero divididas...
Y esto sin fraudes y sin simonías...
Señal, oh Euterpe, que con el deseo..
Lo excusa luego, porque considera...

(A Euterpe)[2]

Que en los umbrales de la adolescencia...
Arando surcos en los materiales...
Le da otros plazos y contemporiza...
Se opone a Dios y a la naturaleza...
Y digo al fin que si los aborreces...

(Sátira «Dícesme Nuño...»)[3]

---

[1] Es extraño encontrar en este sabio artífice estos versos imperfectos:

Señas diera de su arrebatamiento...

(Soledades, I)

Ni de las peregrinaciones rota...
(Soneto, «Montaña inaccesible...»)

Coturnos de oro el pie, armiños vestida...
(Soneto «La aurora...»)

En el último, el problema es la sinalefa forzada entre la palabra *pie,* que lleva el acento central del verso, o debiera llevarlo, y la palabra *armiños,* cuyo acento viene a quedar contiguo al de *pie.*

El verso que en mi trabajo de 1919 di como ejemplo de acentuación en cuarta y séptima sílabas (B[3]):

Jaspe luciente, si pálida insidia...

no pertenece al tipo. D. Dámaso Alonso, en el estudio mencionado en nota anterior, corrigió mi error y señaló la recta lectura:

Jaspe luciente, sí, pálida insidia...

Pero sí son del tipo B[3] estos dos:

Tribuno humilde, si no ofrecimiento...
(Soneto «Corona de Ayamonte...»)

A ver un toro que en un nacimiento...
(Soneto «Salí, señor don Pedro...»)

[2] En otra versión hay diferencia de palabras, pero se mantiene el tipo de verso:

Y la que hoy dura en los setentrionales...
Fuerzas mostraban, pero divididas...

[3] En otra versión:

Da nuevos plazos y contemporiza...
A las de Dios y la naturaleza...

Como en la corte me la represento...
En la abundancia de tu patrimonio...
Nueces y almendras en sus ataúdes...
(*A Don Francisco de Eraso*)

Y no me aguarde la tumultüaria...
Y ésta no es tanta que me desanime...
En el ropaje de las vestiduras...
Se acreditase con la demasía...
(Epístola «Con tu licencia...»)

No es la más grave de las servidumbres...
(Soneto «Tu aliento, Herminia...»)

Huye a tus manos, y con osadía...
(Soneto «Ese pájaro, Cintia...»)

Fiel y segura para mi sosiego...
(Soneto «Huye de ti...»)

Alguna parte de los eslabones...
(Soneto «¿Estás libre, Damón?...»)

Algunas veces se nos permitía...
Mas oh, Señor, cuando se nos conceda...
Y aquellos mismos que a la servidumbre...
(*Super flumina*)

Contra el caudillo que desamparaste...
Tu fuerza entregas a sus influencias...
(Epístola «No te pienso pedir...»)

Del capirote y el de las pihuelas...
Te fertiliza, sin que la fortuna...
Así en los partos del entendimiento...
De estos jüicios, sino por experto...
(Sátira «Don Juan, ya que me he puesto...»)

Bernardo de Valbuena:

Hermosos soles de mi primavera...
Que hay en los cofres de la hermosura... (I)
Al mismo corte de tus invenciones... (II)
Saqué una hortera para mi Tirrena... (IV)
Dos pastorcillos que entre los pastores...
Ahora, en tanto que con la corteza...
Tengo guardadas, para que con ellas...
Y estos ya dichos, por que de tu mano... (V)
Si yo dijese que de mis fatigas...
Dulce regalo de mi pensamiento... (VIII)

Aquí la muerte, por que de mi vida... (IX)
En esta sombra, mientras que tejía... (X)
(Siglo de oro)

De no ajustarse a tu merecimiento...
Arco defienden los que en sus regiones... (I)
Se acaba, muere, y desde la bocina... (III)
El oro hilado que con las voltarias... (IV)
(La grandeza mexicana)

Tristes tragedias a los lastimosos... (I)
Ingrata Gila, pues por complacerte...
Mas la inconstante, cuyo fundamento... (VI)
En una cueva, donde la violencia... (VIII)
Dulcia llamada, cuya gentileza... (XI)
(El Bernardo)

Francisco de Rojas Zorrilla:

Sin que recele sus temeridades...
Mi hermano sale con el Almirante...
Ya estoy herida de tus sinrazones...
(Peligrar en los remedios)

No tu silencio por desconsolarme... ..
(Los bandos de Verona, III)

Tan satisfechas mis temeridades...
(Progne y Filomela, III)

Indignaréme con el amenaza...
Del curso propio con que se movía...
(Entre bobos anda el juego)

Yo dije siempre que le aborrecía...
(No hay ser padre siendo rey)

Doctrina das a la filosofía...
(Del rey abajo ninguno, III)

Pues son precisas las obligaciones...
(Donde hay agravios no hay celos, III)

Sor Juana Inés de la Cruz:

Si no saliera por la comisura...
Y es algo menos en su ligereza...
Que el tal no sabe lo que se murmura...
(Retrato de Lizarda)

319

Amor empieza por desasosiego...

(Soneto que empieza así)

La última línea de lo despreciado...

(Soneto «Cuando mi error...»)

Poner bellezas en mi entendimiento...

(Soneto «En perseguirme...»)

Si déste busco el agradecimiento...

(Soneto «Que no me quiere Fabio...»)

Los simulacros que la Estimativa...
Sino que daban a la fantasía...
En sí, mañosa, las representaba...
Los que unos hizo de naturaleza...
Pobre con ella en las neutralidades...
Ciencia formar de las universales...
Discurso fía su aprovechamiento...
Continuo curso de la disciplina...
De humor terrestre, que a su nutrimiento...
Da las espaldas al entendimiento...
De investigar a la naturaleza...
Abiertas sendas al entendimiento...

(Sueño)

Mira que juzgo que precipitada...

(Auto del Divino Narciso) [1]

LA ACENTUACIÓN EN LA CUARTA SÍLABA; SIGLO XVIII. — Durante el siglo XVIII el tipo B[1] perdura, y es caso digno de señalarse el que abunde hasta en los preceptistas como Luzán y Hermosilla:

Cuando era menos mi melancolía...

(Cañizares, El honor da entendimiento, I)

Que ha de ser catre de la primavera...

(Zamora, El hechizado por fuerza, III)

Que fija el giro de las estaciones...

(Peralta Barnuevo, Lima fundada, II)

---

[1] En largos años de familiaridad con la obra de Sor Juana, sólo le he encontrado este verso imperfecto, en El divino Narciso:

La ocultemos, por que el gemido ronco...

El lucimiento, con que se emularon...
(Luzán, *Juicio de Paris*)

La justa saña del conocimiento...
(Jorge Pitillas, Sátira I)

Que el hombre mire por sus circunstancias...
Suben los diablos por escotillones...
(Ramón de la Cruz, *El Muñuelo*)

Aquella tigre que precipitados...
(Porcel, *El Adonis*, égloga IV)

Contase asombros de su continente...
(Francisco Ruiz de León, *La Hernandía*, I)

El oro apartas de los resplandores...
(Cayetano Cabrera Quintero, Sátira VIII de Horacio)

Anuncio fausto de beneficiencia...
(Somoza, Soneto XV)

Adornar basta la naturaleza...
(Meléndez, cita de Benot) [1]

Y señalando a la que fervorosa...
(Vaca de Guzmán, *El triunfo sobre el oro*)

Favor pedimos los que redimiste...
(Fray Diego González, *Te Deum*)

Serán eternos, inmortalizando...
(García de la Huerta, *Los bereberes*)

Más que la incasta reedificadora...
(Nicolás de Moratín, Sátira II)

Con vana audacia, y el Omnipotente...
(Cadalso, pasaje de Milton)

Será, y estéril tu arrepentimiento...
(Jovellanos, Epístola a Arnesto)

---

[1] BENOT, en su tratado de *Prosodia y versificación castellanas*, tomo III, págs. 159-163, cita como «versos mal hechos» muchos del tipo B¹, especialmente del siglo XVIII: Pitillas, Fray Diego González, García de la Huerta, Escóiquiz, Samaniego, Iriarte, Jovellanos, Leandro de Moratín, Hermosilla, Arriaza, Juan Gualberto González. No dice de dónde los toma. Personalmente, nunca he tropezado con el tipo B¹ en la obra de Meléndez, a pesar de que el verso citado arriba lo mencionan Hermosilla y Juan Gualberto González antes que Benot.

Más compañía que su pensamiento...

(Samaniego, *La lechera*)

Y tanto piensas que me costaría...

(Iriarte, *La hormiga y la pulga*)

Naranjas chinas, y en las soberanas...

(Iglesias, Égloga I)

Ya con constancia belerofontea...

(Forner, *Sátira contra los vicios de la poesía*)

El mismo exceso de la desventura...

(Escóiquiz, *Paraíso perdido*, II)

La nueva secta de sensiblería...

(Vargas y Ponce, *Proclama de un solterón*)

Con sus cabezas y las de sus hijos...
De los troyanos y de sus esposas...

(Hermosilla, *Ilíada*)

Y sin la ayuda de los inmortales...
Luego no existe en la naturaleza...

(Marchena, *De natura rerum*, I)

Tranquilo en tanto que la numerosa...

(Leandro de Moratín, *Los pedantes*) [1]

Duermes entre ellos, y tu respetuosa...
Sin gasto alguno de naturaleza...
Voy a cumplirlos, os aseguraba...

(Manuel María de Arjona, Sátiras de Horacio, I, 1)

La turba vil de sus adoradores...

(Blanco White, Epístola a Forner)

Abarca y ciñe las extremidades...

(González Carvajal, Salmo XCIV)

---

[1] Moratín el hijo usa el tipo B[1] sólo en poesías escritas en su juventud. Después lo abandona.

El tipo desaparece poco después de 1800: ya no se encuentra, por ejemplo, en Quintana ni en Gallego [1]. En los primeros años del siglo XIX es más común en poetas americanos que en españoles:

> Subsiste el todo, y que los elementos...
> Y quién dirá de sus indefinibles...
>
> (Olmedo, *Ensayos sobre el hombre*)

> Muchas regiones, bajo los auspicios...
>
> (Bello, *A la vacuna*, 1806) [2]

> Esta es la voz de la naturaleza...
>
> (Camilo Henríquez, «En esta oscuridad...»)

> Librar su imperio de los españoles...
>
> (Zequeira, *Batalla naval de Cortés*)

> A proporción de los merecimientos...
>
> (Sartorio, Himno de San Pedro Damiano)

> Esta mañana que se levantó...
>
> (Anastasio de Ochoa, *La respuesta concisa*)

> Por tus servicios y lo que mereces...
> Y eran presagio de lo que serías...
> Esos tus ojos misericordiosos...
> Venid, veréis la Pacificadora...

---

[1] JUAN GUALBERTO GONZÁLEZ, en sus *Apuntes sobre versificación caste-llana comparada con la latina (Obras completas,* tomo III, Madrid, 1844: v. pág. 23), dice: «Aunque en buenos poetas antiguos y modernos se encuentran innumerables endecasílabos sin acento desde la cuarta hasta la décima, lo cual bastaría para defenderlos, hoy parece que están generalmente desechados y que sólo por necesidad o por descuido se hacen algunos todavía». Cita once ejemplos, comenzando en Garcilaso y terminando en Hermosilla; cita además versos de Horacio que, leídos con sola atención a los acentos, resultarían parecidos:

> *Sive facturus per inhospitalem...*
> *Crispe Sallusti nisi temperato...*

[2] Todavía en su vejez Bello escribe en *La oración por todos* (1843):

> Profunda sima adonde se derrumba...

Es muy probable que considerara que *adonde*, palabra trisílaba, debiera contarse como palabra plenamente acentuada, aunque sólo lo está débilmente. Recuérdese que él condenaba los versos del tipo B[1] como insuficientemente acentuados.

En José María Heredia, versión del canto *Al Sol* de Osián, hallo este verso semejante:

> Te regocijas. Cuando las borrascas...

Que poco tiempo se concedería...
Nuevas miradas de misericordia...
Y que obra fué de tu sabiduría...

(Navarrete, *Poema de la paz*)

En vano, en vano la filosofía...
Para dar curso a la filosofía...
Y el hombre, dueño de su pensamiento...

(Juan Cruz Varela, *A la libertad de imprenta*)

Mi tierno llanto, o sin que me anegarás...

(Francisco Ortega, *La música*) [1]

Afortunados los que perecisteis...

(José María Heredia, fragmento de la *Eneida*, publicado en 1830)

A devorar mi cerebro cansado...

(Santiago Vidarte, de Puerto Rico, *Insomnio*, 1846)

LA ACENTUACIÓN EN LA CUARTA SÍLABA: SU RAREZA EN EL SIGLO XIX. — Después, a lo largo del siglo XIX, versos del tipo B[1] sólo aparecen como rarezas esporádicas, explicables como inadvertencia, o bien, en poetas como Espronceda, o Batres, o Hartzenbusch, o Javier de Burgos, o Manuel Acuña, como influencia de la lectura de poetas de siglos anteriores:

Allí vi al César. Por sus beneficios...

(Hidalgo, Égloga I de Virgilio)

Encubre el velo de melancolía...

(Esteban Echeverría, *El y ella*)

En un tratado de filosofía...
Llegó aterrando a la secretaría...
Y oyen discursos sin que satisfagan...

(Espronceda, *El diablo mundo*, III)

Se ve, se siente. La filosofía...
Entonces vino el arrepentimiento...
Y tu alto nombre a la inmortalidad...

(Francisco Muñoz Del Monte)

No me limito a la literatura...
De la moral y la filosofía...
Cargó con él a la Recolección...
Inútilmente los economistas...
En el valor y en el desembarazo...

(José Batres Montúfar)

[1] Consúltese mi trabajo *La métrica de los poetas mexicanos en la época de la independencia.*

En las regiones de la eternidad...
(Fernando Calderón, *El torneo*, III)

Del paraíso en sus melancolías...
(Juan Carlos Gómez, *El tiempo*)

Cuentos de Homero y de Maricastaña...
(Campoamor, *El tren expreso*)

Sola ya, madre de los pecadores...
(Nicolás Ureña de Mendoza, *Día de Dolores*)

Si abre sus senos para guarecerte...
(Hartzenbusch, *Los amantes de Teruel*, IV, edición de 1836)

Murió la Grecia, y sobre sus escombros...
(Guillermo Matta, *Un cuento endemoniado*)

Él me contuvo cuando despechado...
Viejo precito, para que malgaste...
Por la mañana, para que a la tarde...
Y con qué objeto la desenvainaba...
(Burgos, Sátiras de Horacio)

Copa empinaba desde el mediodía...
(Miguel Antonio Caro, Epístolas de Horacio, I, 14)

La imitación de sus antepasados...
A los que, amigos del anacronismo...
Bajo la losa del escepticismo...
(Manuel Acuña)

La cual no es otra como con acierto...
Que no le amabas, sino que me consta...
Nombre le da, y como si empezase...
(Jaime Clark, traducción de *Hamlet*)

Partido el disco con que se abroquela...
(Jenaro Alenda, *Batracomiomaquia*)

Pero aun es joven, cual si con sus manos...
(Zorrilla de San Martín, *Tabaré*, I)

---

[1] Estas muestras pueden parecer muchas, pero son todas las que he encontrado en autores del siglo XIX a lo largo de muchos años de familiaridad con la poesía de España y América, mientras que en cualquier poeta de los siglos XVI, XVII o XVIII se hallan en gran número, según demuestro con las citas de Lope, Tirso, Ruiz de Alarcón, Cervantes, Rufo, Acevedo, Valdivielso, Valbuena, Salazar, Bartolomé de Argensola, Góngora, Rojas Zorrilla y Sor Juana Inés de la Cruz.

EL ENDECASÍLABO ANAPÉSTICO EN LA POESÍA POPULAR. — El endecasílabo anapéstico (B³), que los sucesores de Boscán y su grupo evitaron cuidadosamente, tuvo vida propia en los siglos XVI y XVII: no se usó como verso definido, independiente, pero sí como una de las formas que entraban en la versificación fluctuante de las canciones populares, especialmente en las emparentadas con las de origen gallego:

> — Molinico ¿por qué no mueles?
> — Porque me beben el agua los bueyes.

> — Toledano, alzo berenjena.
> — Yo no las como, que soy de Llerena.

> Esta cinta, de amor toda,
> quien me la dió ¿para qué me la toma?

> Por una vez que mis ojos alcé,
> dicen que yo le maté...

> Lo que me quise me quise me tengo,
> lo que me quise me tengo yo.

> — ¿San Juan el Verde pasó por aquí?
> — Más ha de un año que nunca le vi.

> ¡Valame Dios que las ánsares vuelan!
> ¡Valame Dios que saben volar!

> Vayan cautivos el rey y la reina...

> Seis reales dan por el tordo de Juana,
> seis por el pico y seis por la lana.

> Yo que lo sé, que lo vi, que lo digo,
> yo que lo vi, que lo digo, lo sé.

Los poetas cultos, desde el siglo XVII, adoptan esta versificación fluctuante en canciones de corte popular que intercalan en novelas y en comedias o como estribillos en composiciones líricas:

> Molinito que mueles amores...
> muele favores, no muelas cuidados,
> pues que te hicieron tan bello los cielos...
>
> (Lope, *San Isidro*, I)

> Que las almas heladas enciende
> y es de sus penas descanso y alivio...
>
> (Lope, *El Cardenal de Belén*, 1)

> Florecitas que Rut bella pisa,
> mientras sus ojos regadas os ven...
>
> (Tirso, *La mejor espigadera*)

326

Ruiseñor que volando vas,
cantando finezas, cantando favores,
¡oh, cuánta pena y envidia me das!
Pero no, que si cantas amores
tú tendrás celos y tú llorarás...

> (Calderón, *Los dos amantes del cielo*, I)

¡Ay, cómo gime, mas ay, cómo suena,
gime y suena
el remo a que nos condena
el niño Amor!...

> (Góngora, «Contando estaban sus rayos...»)

Marizápalos era muchacha
muy adorada de Pedro Martín...

> (Jerónimo Camargo)

¡Para la Maya, que es linda y galana!...

> (Quiñones de Benavente, entremés de *La Maya*)

En Calderón esta versificación se regulariza, después de gran
variedad de ensayos, y acaba por suprimir el endecasílabo (B³),
reduciéndose a decasílabos y dodecasílabos combinados a veces
con hexasílabos:

Sierpecilla escamada de flores,
intenta correr,
cuando luego detienen sus pasos
prisiones suaves de rosa y clavel...

> (Calderón, *El castillo de Lindabridis*, III)

Si no han vuelto hasta ahora los ojos
que todos llevaron los novios tras sí...

> (Francisco Manuel, Letra para cantar) [1]

---

[1] Esta combinación deca-dodecasílaba reapareció en la época del *modernismo*, acompañada a veces del quebrado de seis sílabas:

Que me deje una estrella en los labios
y un tenue perfume de nardo en el alma...
> (JUANA BORRERO, *Última rima*)

Otra vez, hasta el nido sombrío
do mueres de frío, sin alma y sin voz,
en un triste y desierto paraje,
ha venido a dorar tu plumaje
un rayo de sol...
> (DULCE MARÍA BORRERO, *Nueva vida*)

327

La poesía popular no adoptó esta regularidad y tendió a mantener el endecasílabo anapéstico como eje de la versificación en canciones de las que comúnmente se llaman de gaita gallega:

> Tanto bailé con la hija del cura,
> tanto bailé que me dió calentura...

Se halla también en letras de la *danza prima* de Asturias:

> ¡Ay pobre Juana de cuerpo garrido!...
> Muerto le dejo a la orilla del río... [1]

EL ENDECASÍLABO ANAPÉSTICO EN LA POESÍA CULTA: SIGLOS XVIII Y XIX. — Además, como verso independiente se empezó a cultivar el endecasílabo anapéstico en el siglo XVIII y así sobrevivió, pero como especie de metro raro que sólo aparecía de tarde en tarde:

> Cierta criada la casa barría...
> Cierto Ricacho, labrando una casa...

> (Iriarte)

> Suban al cerco de Olimpo luciente...
> Huyan los años en rápido vuelo,
> goce la tierra durable consuelo,
> mire a los hombres piadoso el Señor...

> (Leandro de Moratín, *Los padres del Limbo*)

> Pues otra vez de la bárbara guerra
> lejos retumba el profundo rugir...

> (Heredia, *Himno de guerra*, 1826)

> Aben Amet, al partir de Granada,
> su corazón desgarrado sintió...

> (Traductor desconocido de la *Romance mauresque* de Martínez de la Rosa en su *Aben Humeya*, versión francesa primitiva)

---

[1] Consúltense: MILÁ, *Del decasílabo y endecasílabo anapésticos* y *De la poesía popular gallega*, en el tomo V de sus *Obras;* mi estudio *la poesía castellana de versos fluctuantes*, capítulo II, parágrafos 10-11, 16, 20 y 23, capítulo III, parágrafos, 7, 10, 20 y 23, capítulo IV, parágrafos 4-6, 10 y 18, capítulo V, parágrafos 1-10; y el trabajo de JULIO VICUÑA CIFUENTES, *Sobre dos formas eld endecasílabo a minori*, en sus *Estudios de métrica española*, Santiago de Chile, 1929 (a pesar de sus caprichos de preceptista e insuficiencia de información).

Entre la bruma y espesa neblina,
entre el celaje que vela la mar...

(¿Camprodón o Ramos Carrión?, *Marina*, I)

Brillan las nubes en nácar y en oro...

(Antonio Arnao, *Canción*) [1]

Como esa espuma que el viento formó...

(Perrín y Palacios, *Sobre las olas*)

EL ENDECASÍLABO ANAPÉSTICO DESDE RUBÉN DARÍO. — Cuando Darío resucita este tipo de endecasílabo en el *Pórtico* al libro *En tropel* de Salvador Rueda (1892):

Libre la frente que el casco rehusa,
toda desnuda en la gloria del día,
alza su tirso de rosas la musa
bajo el gran sol de la eterna armonía...,

provoca la conocida discusión en que *Clarín* revela haber olvidado sus clásicos y conocer poco los cantares de gaita, mientras Menéndez y Pelayo los evocó inmediatamente [2].

Darío se permite libertades en el metro: a veces suprime el acento en la sílaba séptima:

Que él daba al viento con su cornamusa...
Las muelles danzas en las alcatifas...

y se atreve a introducir el endecasílabo creciente, agregando una sílaba inerte después del acento en la cuarta:

Caja de música de duelo y placer...

Manuel González Prada escribió buen número de composiciones en endecasílabos anapésticos: el *Rondel* «Tiene la Luna caprichos de niña...», el *Pántum* «Alzando el himno triunfal de la vida...», el *Ritmo sin rima* «¿Son inviolables doncellas los léxicos?...», el *Rondel* «Es la mañana la alegre chiquilla...»

---

[1] Consúltense: EDUARDO DE LA BARRA, *El endecasílabo dactílico*, Rosario, 1895 (justifica el tipo B³, pero no se da cuenta de que el tipo B¹ había tenido curso normal); mi nota *La versificación de Heredia*, en la *Revista de Filología Hispánica*, 1942, IV, 171-172.

[2] Consúltese el artículo *Dilucidaciones*, de Darío, al final de su libro *El canto errante*, Madrid, 1907.

Hay muchos cultivadores del anapéstico después de su ruidosa reaparición. Lugones, al final de *Las cigarras:*

> Fútil cantora, sonora cigarra,
> en la alegría de tu aire pueril
> crispa su prima gentil mi guitarra,
> bate su parche mi azul tamboril.

Eduardo Marquina, en pasajes de *Vendimión* y en los versos laudatorios para *La casa de la primavera,* de Martínez Sierra:

> Esta caudal plenitud de bonanza...

Unamuno, en uno de los cantos de su *Romancero del destierro,* el que comienza:

> Logre morir con los ojos abiertos...

Enrique Banchs, en la *Balada del puñado de sol:*

> — ¿Llenas están las herradas, mis hijas?
> — Madre, lo están, las llenamos al colmo...

Gabriela Mistral, en el *Recado para las Antillas:*

> Anda el café como un alma vehemente...

Jorge Guillén, en *Noche encendida:*

> Tiempo ¿prefieres la noche encendida?...

Rafael Alberti, en *Madrid por Cataluña:*

> Todos cantando pronuncien tu nombre...

y en *España,* de la *Invitación a un viaje sonoro* (1944):

> Lloren aquí los laúdes de España...

Eugenio Florit, en *Viejos versos de hoy:*

> Este sentir que la vida se acaba
> y ya no ver más que niebla en redor...

RETORNO AL ENDECASÍLABO DE GARCILASO. — Con Rubén Darío el endecasílabo vuelve a la situación en que se hallaba con Garcilaso: se mezclan libremente los cuatro tipos (A, B¹, B² y B³):

Monsieur Prudhomme y Homais no saben nada.
Hay Chipres, Pafos, Tempes y Amatuntes,
donde el amor de mi madrina, un hada,
tus frescos labios a los míos juntes.
Sones de bandolín. El rojo vino
conduce un paje rojo. ¿Amas los sones
del bandolín, y un amor florentino?
Serás la reina en los decamerones.
Un coro de poetas y pintores
cuenta historias picantes. Con maligna
sonrisa alegre aprueban los señores.
Clelia enrojece. Una dueña se signa...

(*Divagación*, 1894.)

Sus rosas aun me dejan su fragancia,
una fragancia de melancolía...
Sino cuando en la dulce primavera
era la hora de la melodía...
Y vigor natural, y sin falsía,
y sin comedia, y sin literatura...
Tal fué mi intento, hacer del alma pura
mía, una estrella, una fuente sonora,
con el horror de la literatura
y loco de crepúsculo y de aurora...

(Pórtico de *Cantos de vida y esperanza*, 1905.)

Cabellos largos en la bohardilla,
noches de insomnio al blancor del invierno,
pan de dolor con la sal de lo eterno,
y ojos de ardor en que Juvencia brilla...

(*Balada en honor de las musas de carne y hueso*)

Mortificaron con las disciplinas
y los cilicios la carne mortal
y opusieron orando las divinas
ansias celestes al furor sexual...
Herido el cuerpo bajo los sayales,
el espíritu ardiente en amor sacro...
y fueron castos por la santidad...

331

>   Poder matar el orgullo perverso
>   y el palpitar de la carne maligna...
>
>   (*La Cartuja*) [1]

Esta renovación, Rubén Darío la hace él solo, sin participación de sus compañeros en la iniciación del movimiento *modernista*, Martí, Gutiérrez Nájera, Casal, Silva. El grupo inmediato sí adopta el endecasílabo renovado [2]:

>   Complicidad con la naturaleza...
>   Metamorfosis de su cabellera...
>   Que ha fatigado a la filosofía...
>
>   (Amado Nervo)
>
>   Se va la luz. Y la naturaleza...
>   La flor azul de la melancolía...
>
>   (Luis Urbina)
>
>   Si no surgieran junto a la piragua...
>   A la ventura que lo diviniza...
>   Que sobre el surco se arremolinaba...
>   La operación de la desgranadora...
>
>   (Leopoldo Lugones)
>
>   El gesto oscuro de los leñadores......
>   Abrióse el lecho de tus primaveras...
>   Ondeó la danza de las bayaderas...
>   Nirvana gris de la naturaleza...
>
>   (Julio Herrera y Reissig)
>
>   Limpia canción, mas bajo la ventana...
>   Que se desmayan y que se despegan...
>   Inesperado en la policromía...
>   Jugo de acíbar para el pensamiento...
>
>   (Enrique González Martínez)

---

[1] VICUÑA CIFUENTES, en sus *Estudios de métrica española*, pág. 113, dice (atribuyéndolo, sin fundamento, al crítico uruguayo Lauxar) que sólo hay diez endecasílabos de acento en cuarta (B¹) en toda la obra de Darío. Cualquiera puede comprobar que hay más; los hay en gran parte de las composiciones en o con endecasílabos (que no son muchas) después de *Prosas profanas*: además de las cuatro que cito, y que contienen trece de esos versos, v. *Ama tu verso*, *Los tres Reyes Magos*, *Soneto a Cervantes*, *En el país de las alegorías*, *Carne, celeste carne...*, *Canto a la Argentina*, *Balada sobre la sencillez de las rosas perfectas*, el soneto *Español*, *Pax*.

[2] Coincidencia: José María de Heredia, el poeta cubano que escribía en francés, el autor de *Los trofeos*, compuso en 1903 unos sonetos en homenaje a su primo y homónimo «el cantor del Niágara», con motivo de su centenario, y en ellos aparece un endecasílabo de acento sólo en cuarta, fruto de su familiaridad con los clásicos castellanos:

>   Al evocar a los conquistadores...

Y mulas pardas en las sementeras...
Dicta lecciones de Caballería...
Ese arbolillo en que nadie repara...

(Antonio Machado)

Primera mancha de los azahares...
El oro viejo de su cabellera...
Los currutacos y las mirliflores...

(Manuel Machado)

Aire de cumbre es el que se respira...
Tape su polvo mis pobres orejas...
Su escalofrío me tupe de calma...
Sentada mira sobre el altozano...

(Unamuno)

El pie que vence y el entendimiento...
Y el aire vago de la madrugada...
En el paisaje de la primavera...
Los olivares de la madrugada...

(Juan Ramón Jiménez)

Y las dos torres de la catedral...
Los hombres secos y reconcentrados...

(Valle Inclán)

La mariposa en su policromía...
Desapareció tras de la serranía...
Y comprendimos que sus lilïales...

(Guillermo Valencia)

Y lecho azul de la imaginación...
Crea el dolor y el arrepentimiento...
Deja de ser, para que te deploren...

(Eduardo Marquina)

Sé de una calle junto al hospital...
En primavera: los convalecientes...
Te hace más tersa y dorada la piel...
Dentro de mí palpitante la siento...
¿Visteis a Shelley, le visteis de cerca?...

(Enrique Díez Canedo)

Para las piedras y para las rosas...
Del corazón de la naturaleza...

(Francisco Villaespesa)

Me infunde un soplo de soberanía
de predominio y de solemnidad...

(José Santos Chocano)

Como se ve, en la renovación predominaba el tipo de acentuación en cuarta sílaba sobre el tipo anapéstico. Actualmente hay poetas que sólo mezclan tres tipos (A, B^1 y B^2)

> ¡Toda real en las apariciones.
> Hacia la gloria del galán temprano
> van en volandas blancas algazaras...
>
> (Jorge Guillén, *Galán temprano*)

> Arde en sus ojos la revelación.
> La luz serena bajo la pantalla
> ¡cómo apacigua aún mi corazón!...
> ¿Que nada sabes ni mi angustia induces?
> ¡Cierra tus ojos como cicatrices!...
>
> (Rafael Alberto Arrieta, *Revelación*)

> Rigen la vida silenciosas leyes
> de una honradez total, con ese ritmo
> seguro de los días y las noches,
> de los inviernos y de los estíos...
>
> (Arturo Capdevila, *Canto de bendición*)

> Cuando a altas horas de la madrugada
> torno a mi barrio con el ceño áspero,
> gusto de contemplar mis cuatro pinos...
>
> (Fernández Moreno, *Pinos*)

> Es preciso caer, quemar jardines...
> Ahogar la bestia entre los querubines...
> La rosa inmensa, la ciudad quebrada...
>
> (Sara de Ibáñez, *Soliloquios del soldado*, V)

> En un haz de parábolas maduras...
> Flor y decoro de la geometría...
> La claridad de la circunferencia...
> En danza inmóvil y en azar de acero...
>
> (Eduardo González Lanuza, *Égloga III*)

> Tengo mi río —sin cesar me alcanza...
> Con aventuras y descubrimientos,
> entre piedras y pájaros y lumbres...
>
> (Vicente Barbieri, *Estancias de agonía*, XVI)

Otros poetas mezclan los cuatro tipos:

> Un monte negro que se contornea
> siempre, para alcanzar el otro monte...
> ¡Hasta el momento de la sien ardiendo,
> del cascabel de la antigua demencia
> y de la trampa en el vórtice rojo!
>
> (Gabriela Mistral, *La fuga*)

El vino clava sus espigas negras
y sus erizos lúgubres pasea
entre puñales, entre mediasnoches...
Y el vino huye por las carreteras,
por las iglesias, entre los carbones,
y se caen sus plumas de amaranto,
y se disfraza de azufre su boca...

(Pablo Neruda, *Estatuto del vino)* [1]

De los antepasados que se asoman
al palco de este cuadro de familia
con qué limpieza cinematográfica...
Los paisajes prendidos al recuerdo
con alfileres de anuncios eléctricos...
Para la autopsia de las lunas muertas...

(Jaime Torres Bodet, *Canción de cuna*)

Y en el agua cabellos, flores, plumas,
a la deriva de la ventolina,
huyendo, verdes, de la voz del fauno...

(Rafael Alberti, *Reflejo*)

—Dí, ¿tú qué harás el Primero de Mayo?...
—Que empuje a España valerosamente
a conquistar de nuevo su paisaje...

(Alberti, *Primero de Mayo de 1938*)

Es interesante advertir que el verso de acentos en cuarta y octava sílabas (B²) ha perdido mucho terreno: hay poetas que no lo emplean con mayor frecuencia que el de acento sólo en la cuarta (B¹), cuya popularidad es grande. Cabe mantener, pues, que para no pocos poetas el endecasílabo ha regresado a sus orígenes medievales: los tipos fundamentales son dos, el de acento en sexta sílaba (A) y el de acento en cuarta (B¹); los tipos acentuados en cuarta y octava (B²) y en cuarta y séptima (B³) aparecen como variantes no muy frecuentes.

NUEVAS LIBERTADES DEL ENDECASÍLABO. — Los poetas del siglo xx no se contentan con devolverle al endecasílabo la situación en que lo dejó Garcilaso; ocasionalmente lo descoyuntan. Uno de los recursos es colocar el acento de la cuarta sílaba en una palabra esdrújula, produciendo así un verso que podría igualmente considerarse como decasílabo con una sílaba de exceso en el medio (los italianos lo llaman *endecasillabo catulliano*, por su

---

[1] Sobre la versificación del poeta chileno, consúltese AMADO ALONSO, *Poesía y estilo de Pablo Neruda*, Buenos Aires, 1940, cap. IV.

semejanza con versos latinos como éste de Catulo: «Minister ve-
tuli puer Falerni»):

> Banda de pájaros en la simiente...
>> (Juan Ramón Jiménez, *Amaneceres*)

> Llegué al epílogo de mis quimeras...
>> (Julio Herrera y Reissig, *Sepelio*)

> Vivir, estímulo de mi terrible...
>> (Juan José Domenchina, *Acibarado fruto*)

> Al cuerpo, en órganos desemejantes...
>> (César Vallejo, *La cólera*)

> Y tú, quedándote tan imprecisa...
>> (María de Villarino, *Tiempo de angustia*, VIII)

> Que con el cántico meditabundo...
> Lo que la música me está diciendo...
> Con lejanísimas inteligencias...
>> (Francisco Luis Bernárdez, *El buque*)

> Viajes buscándote, detrás del viento...
>> (J. R. Wilcock, *Desde antes*)

Esta clase de versos se encontraba antes, pero como descuido:

> Si por pasárseme de la memoria...
> Por asperísimos despeñaderos...
>> (Juan de Castellanos, *Elegías*, parte II, Elegía III, canto IV)

> Tirsi, paréceme que estás turbado...
> Ora consuélate, que comoquiera...
>> (Jáuregui, *Aminta*)

> Licor, gozábase desprevenida...
>> (Núñez de Arce, *La duda*)

Compárense con estos decasílabos de Leandro Fernández de
Moratín:

> Vegas que diáfano fecunda el Arlas...
> Ve los alcázares de Mantua excelsa...

o éstos de Juan Gualberto González:

> Mecenas ínclito, de antiguos reyes
> clara prosapia ¡oh mi refugio!...

A veces el esdrújulo se complica con sinalefa:

> Sería la única inquietud acaso...
>> (Lugones, *Cisnes negros*)

> En una ascética ilusión de Brahma...
>> (Herrera y Reissig, *Enero*)

> Tu amigo Lázaro, el de Betanía...
>> (Unamuno, *El Cristo de Velázquez*)

Otro rasgo frecuente es acentuar la sílaba tercera, a veces también en palabra esdrújula[1]:

> La hebra de oro de la esperanza mía...
>> (Amado Nervo, *La puerta)*

> Una antorcha con que alumbrar la senda...
>> (Urbina, *Así fué*) [2]

> De la copla entre los cañaverales...
>> (Manuel Machado, *La buena canción*)

> De sus tigres, ni la delicadeza...
>> (Jorge Luis Borges, *Del infierno y del cielo*)

> Ni la rosa coronada de espinas,
> ni la rosa de la resurrección...
>> (Xavier Villaurrutia, *Nocturna rosa*)

> Naturales y sobrenaturales...
> Cuya música misericordiosa...
>> (Bernárdez, *El buque*)

> Los espíritus apesadumbrados...
>> (Urbina, *Vieja lágrima*)

> La película caricaturesca...
>> (González Martínez, *Mientras la lluvia cae*)

---

[1] Darío usa este verso, por excepción, en *Torres de Dios* («Rompeolas de las eternidades»), en *Revelación* («y prodigio de las constelaciones») y en *Visión* («se juntaban con las constelaciones»).

[2] Generalmente este verso aparece impreso con acento en *qué;* pero ese acento es falso.

Se llega, por fin, a mayores libertades:

A América su ruiseñor errante...
(J. R. Jiménez, Rubén Darío)

Después queda lo que ya no se nombra...
(Ezequiel Martínez Estrada, Motivos del cielo)

Alma extraña de mi hueco de venas...
(García Lorca, Tu infancia en Mentón)

Y al hundir mis dientes sanos y agudos...
(Juana de Ibarbourou, Merienda)

Insaciable. Rosa de espacio duro...
(Ricardo Molinari, La muerte en la llanura)

Marinero, dame tu blanca vela...
(Genaro Estrada, Retorno al mar)

Sus cándidas mariposas de escarcha...
(José Gorostiza, Preludio)

Muertes, infinitesimales mundos...
(Silvina Ocampo, La siesta)

Espiritualizadísimamente...
(Herrera y Reissig, Idilio espectral) [1]

Ejemplos de maneras libérrimas de tratar el endecasílabo:

A flor de vida van los corazones
como estrellas de mar sobre las aguas
van con la onda furtiva, distintas,
en un romántico juego de gracia...
Algunas saben la ciencia quimérica
y se plasman en peregrinas formas...
Oh victorias que coronan la espuma
con risas quedas y con rosas blancas...
El rudo afán de los conquistadores...
El mástil sin pendón, la frente inmóvil
bajo el prismático fulgor del iris...
Y te llaman con fantásticas liras
desde las sirtes las rubias sirenas....
La más lunática, la más rebelde,

---

[1] En la poesía italiana desde fines del siglo XIX se observan iguales libertades:

Alta, nell' immobilità del gelo...
(PASCOLI, Le due aquile)

hija del arte y de la libertad,
al impulso de un arcano deseo,
el alma a medialuz, sola y distante,
va siguiendo en silencio hora tras hora
la misteriosa estela de tu nave...

(María Eugenia Vaz Ferreira, *El cazador y la estrella*)

Cuando las gotas de sangre en el olmo...
Ocultan en ensueño blanquecino...
El fantasma de la noche olvidaron...
Hay una sangre bermeja en el olmo...
Y en la bruma hay rostros desconocidos...

(José María Eguren, *Lied I*)

Dos robles lloraban como dos niños...
Y en la mágica luz del cielo santo...
De la onda florida de la mañana...
Las risas y las dulces pastorelas...
Amoroso canto de caramillos...

(Eguren, *Los robles*)

Tarde sucia de invierno. El caserío...
Que sube en forma de tirabuzón...
Y debajo de la genuflexión
de la arboleda, somormuja el río...
Como un problema sin definición...
Y el dueño del terruño, indiferente,
rápidamente, muy rápidamente,
baja en su coche por el camellón.

(Luis Carlos López, *Una viñeta*)

Yo que sólo canté de la exquisita
partitura del íntimo decoro,
alzo hoy la voz a la mitad del foro...
Como aguinaldo de juguetería...
Y en el barullo de las estaciones,
con tu mirada de mestiza, pones
la inmensidad sobre los corazones...
Que en tu lengua de amor prueben de ti
la picadura del ajonjolí...
Oigo lo que se fué, lo que aún no toco,
y la hora actual con su vientre de coco...
Joven abuelo, escúchame loarte,
único héroe a la altura del arte...
En piso de metal, vives al día
de milagro, como la lotería...
Suave Patria, vendedora de chía...
Cual muriéndose van las cantadoras
que en las ferias, con el bravío pecho...

(Ramón López Velarde, *Suave Patria*)

339

Suelta mi corazón sus angulosas
palomitas de volatinería,
la iglesia con el atrio de baldosas
y con la cúpula de sillería...
Y más que el humo de las chimeneas
atrae su mirada la blandura
con que saca sobre las azoteas
la arboleda su esponja de verdura...
Mientras borda, primor de sus achaques,
un pañuelo donde se dan el pico
dos palomas como en los almanaques...

(Rega Molina, *Oda provincial*)

Con el neutral y plácido abandono
de las ubres de la naturaleza...
El eminente cocotero yergue
sobre la horizontalidad del agua
su ondulante penacho que a lo lejos...

(Eloy Fariña Núñez, *Canto secular*) [1]

EL ENDECASÍLABO CRECIENTE. — Aparece también el endecasílabo creciente (subrayo la sílaba superflua):

Te salía tu aroma por doquiera...
Llegada la últ*ima*, fuiste la primera...

(Juan Ramón Jiménez, *A mi pena*)

Ceñida a la apariencia y al descuido.
Hebra sonámbu*la*. Espacio ensimismado...

(Mariano Brull, «Aquí la araña atónita...»)

Sobre la espalda flagela*da* del tiempo.
He de encerrar el llanto de las tardes...

(Borges, *Forjadura*)

Socavas *el* horizonte con tu ausencia...
A*co*gedo*ra* como viejo camino...

(Neruda, *Poemas de amor*, XII)

Palabras. Sí, palabras. To*dos* los tallos
del espacio —otro polo, el otro polo...

(Ricardo Molinari, *El desdichado*, I)

Que entre el perfume de las azucenas
posaba en el peluc*he* del banco rojo...

(Rosa Chacel, *Fruto de las ruinas*)

---

[1] Otro ejemplo: Manuel Magallanes Moure, *Tardes de la ciudad.*

EL ENDECASÍLABO COMO EJE DE FLUCTUACIÓN. — El endecasílabo se emplea además como eje de composiciones en versos fluctuantes: renglones de medidas diversas se agrupan alrededor del eje. Así se hace, tanto en poesías de versificación de ritmo cantable como en composiciones de versificación meramente amétrica.

La balada de Juan Ramón Jiménez *Mañana de la cruz* es ejemplo de esta versificación fluctuante acentual (podría decirse que está hecha con endecasílabos crecientes agrupados alrededor de los normales que sirven de eje: subrayo las sílabas de exceso):

> Dios está azul. La flauta y el tambor
> anuncian ya la cruz de primavera.
> ¡Vivan las ro*sas*, las rosas del amor,
> entre el verdor con sol de la pradera!
> Le pregunté: ¿Me dejas que te quiera?
> Me respondió, radiante de pasión:
> Cuando flore*zca* la cruz de primavera
> yo te querré con todo el corazón.
> Ya floreció la cruz de primavera.
> ¡Amor, la cruz, amor, ya floreció!
> Me respondió: ¿Tú quieres que te quiera?
> ¡Y la maña*na* de luz me traspasó!
> *A*legran flauta y tambor nuestra bandera.
> *La* mariposa está aquí con la ilusión.
> ¡Mi novia es la virgen de la era
> y va a quere*rme* con todo el corazón!

Valle Inclán, al adoptar el ritmo de las muiñeiras de Galicia, combina el eneasílabo, el decasílabo, el endecasílabo y el dodecasílabo —cualquiera de ellos puede convertirse en eje— y les añade versos de otras medidas [1]:

---

[1] En gallego se hallan, naturalmente, estas mezclas del endecasílabo con otras medidas:

> Non sei se me da medo,
> se me da compasión;
> parece un pino leixado do vento,
> parece botado do mar de Niñons...
> > (Eduardo Pondal, *Que barba non cuidada*)

> Neto do enxebre e valente gaiteiro...
> dime que notas salen do punteiro
> que tan mal resoan
> no meu corazón...
> > (Manuel Lugris Freire, *A un gaileiro*)

> Si quixeran voar poderían
> pois no mesmo lombo duas azas levan,
> mais preferen voltar paseniño
> depinicando nas froles das veiras...
> > (Eugenio Montes, «Tornan as vacas...»)

Bajo el gran hayedo sombrío
una pastora con dengue de grana
en una gracia de rocío
está hilando su copo de lana...

(*Voces de gesta*, Jornada I, prólogo)

Cómo la sangre del sol matinal
de los vellones del nevero
hace regatos de cristal...

(*Voces de gesta*, Jornada II)

Parece que cavas en mi corazón.
¡No queda un brazo que mueva una honda,
todo se hundió con el sol de este día!
¡Cava, cavador, una cueva bien honda!
¡Con tu esperanza sepulta la mía!...

(*Voces de gesta*, Jornada III)

—¿Esa tu avecilla
canta en Provenza o canta en Castilla?
—Canta en la orilla de todo sendero
y en el albergue de toda villa
y en el alero de toda capilla
y en el postigo de toda taberna!
¡Es el ave que al mundo gobierna!...

(*Cuento de abril*, Jornada III)

Rubén Darío imitó también las formas fluctuantes de la versificación de gaita gallega, y no sólo el endecasílabo aislado:

Gaita galaica, sabes cantar
lo que profundo y dulce nos es...
Canta. Es el tiempo. Haremos danzar
al fino verso de rítmicos pies...
Tiempo de esparcir y de recoger,
tiempo de nacer, tiempo de morir...

De cuando en cuando las adoptan poetas de América:

La barca morena de un pescador,
cansada de bogar,
sobre la playa se puso a rezar...

(José Gorostiza, *Oración*)

Rosalía de Castro escribía versos de esta especie partiéndolos:

As de cantar,
meniña gaiteira,
as de cantar,
que me moiro de pena...

Ay Dios, qué viento frío
mueve la flor del granado este día...

(Molinari, *Analecta*)

Como ejemplos de versificación libre, fluctuante, pero no de ritmos acostumbrados en el canto, en que sirve como eje el endecasílabo, podrían citarse composiciones de Borges *(Las calles, Vanilocuencia, Jardín, Despedida)*, de Alfonso Reyes *(Ifigenia cruel)*, de César Vallejo *(Trilce,* XVIII), de Jorge Carrera Andrade *(Indiada, Boletín del mal tiempo)*, de Eugenio Florit *(Poema de agua y viento, La señal, Tarde presente)*, de Vicente Aleixandre *(La palabra, Muñecas, Ida)*, de León Felipe *(Yo sé dónde está, Esperando a que amanezca)*, de Ricardo Molinari *(Poema del almacén)*, de Conrado Nalé Roxlo *(La esmeralda)*, de Pablo Neruda *(Melancolía en las familias, Maternidad)*, de Salvador Novo *(Viaje)*, de Francisco Giner *(Ausencia,* V), de Héctor Incháustegui Cabral *(Canción suave a los burros de mi pueblo)*, de Octavio Paz *(Bajo tu clara sombra)*.

¡Ah las paredes de la celda!
De ellas me duelen, entretanto, más
las dos largas, que tienen esta noche
algo de madres que ya muertas
llevan por bromurados declives
a un niño de la mano cada una...

(Vallejo, *Trilce*, XVIII)

Se canta en el poema,
por tristeza y olvidanza,
la gota perenne de una estrella
sobre la estalactita de la esperanza.
Y un poco de tristeza en este día
cuelga una lágrima en mi pecho,
porque en mi vida hay una onda
de lago vesperal y gris de cielo...

(Carlos Pellicer, *El puerto*)

Pasamos cerca de la primavera
y más abajo de las noches de luna,
pasamos a la izquierda de la aurora
y ¡ay! sobre todo de espaldas al deseo...
Un camino olvidado
de todos, menos de la brisa
que trae el aura de la ventura,
el polen áspero de los recuerdos
y torbellinos de plumas azules...

(Rosa Chacel, *Encrucijada*)

343

Podrían distinguirse aún dos maneras en esta versificación libre: en la una, el verso fluctúa, como amétrico, y de cuando en cuando se define como endecasílabo métricamente regular; en la otra, el endecasílabo es dominante y va acompañado de otros versos, por lo común más cortos (en ocasiones, los versos acompañantes podrían llamarse endecasílabos disminuídos o aumentados): así en Juan Ramón Jiménez *(Niño en el mar* y el *Nocturno* «Tan inmenso que es...»), en Pedro Salinas *(Suicidio hacia arriba)*, en José Gorostiza *(Muerte sin fin)*, en Carlos Pellicer *(Recinto)*.

OTROS TIPOS DE ENDECASÍLABO. — Otro tipo de endecasílabo empleó Rubén Darío; el de acento en quinta sílaba (tipo C). La poesía galaicoportuguesa lo conocía desde el siglo XIII:

> ¡Ai frores, ai *fror*es do verde pino!
> ¿Se sabedes *no*vas do meu amigo?

Darío lo adopta en su *Balada laudatoria* (1911 ó 1912) al insigne gallego Valle Inclán:

> Del país del sueño, tinieblas, brillos,
> donde crecen plantas, flores extrañas,
> entre los escombros de los castillos,
> junto a las laderas de las montañas,
> donde los pastores en sus cabañas
> rezan cuando al fuego dormita el can,
> y donde las sombras antiguas van
> por cuevas de lobos y de raposas,
> ha traído cosas muy misteriosas
> don Ramón María del Valle Inclán...

Manuel González Prada adoptó también este verso en su composición *El gran doctor:*

> Mar profundo, inmenso mar de las cosas,
> ¿puede acaso el hombre sondar tu abismo?
> ¿Qué del mundo alcanzan a ver sus ojos?
> ¿Sabe si el granito goza y padece?
> ¿Sabe si las flores sienten y piensan? [1]

González Prada, que tantos ensayos de innovación y renovación hizo en el verso, inventó un tipo más de endecasílabo, acentuado en tercera y séptima, con la peculiaridad de que el acento de la tercera va siempre en palabra esdrújula:

---

[1] Aparece en las *Notas* al final de su libro de versos *Exóticas*, Lima, 1911.

Sol del trópico, mi sol adorado,
¿qué del vívido raudal de tu fuego?
Nubes lóbregas te ciñen y ocultan...

(*El rincón florido*) [1]

El poeta dominicano Francisco Muñoz del Monte (1800-1865
ó 1868) empleó una especie de endecasílabo creciente, con una sílaba de exceso después de la cuarta (como solía haberla en los de
Fernán Pérez de Guzmán), en el comienzo de su composición *A
Gertrudis Gómez de Avellaneda:*

Incierta y dé*bil*, saliendo de la cáscara,
implume el a*la*, sin fuego en el mirar...

En el siglo XVII, Sor Juana Inés de la Cruz inventó un tipo de
verso, que a veces ha sido llamado indebidamente endecasílabo,
y que ella empleó en dos composiciones (de ella lo tomaron el poeta hispano-mexicano Agustín de Salazar y Torres y el bogotano
Francisco Álvarez de Velasco); en realidad tiene diez sílabas y
comienza con palabra esdrújula:

Lámina sirva el cielo al retrato,
Lísida, de tu angélica forma...

Vísperas son felices del día...

Resumen. — El verso endecasílabo de las lenguas románicas nace de la adaptación de metros latinos (probablemente
el sáfico y el senario) que a su vez se derivan del griego. Aparece
en francés y en provenzal; del provenzal pasa al italiano, al catalán
y al galaicoportugués.

En castellano, desde el siglo XII hasta el XVI, se ensaya repetidas veces el endecasílabo, como imitación de modelos extranjeros,
pero no se convierte en metro usual, excepto como forma subsi-
diaria que acompaña al dodecasílabo en el arte mayor. Al cabo
de cuatro siglos, Boscán introduce el metro, tomándolo del italiano, y la intervención de Garcilaso lo impone. Desde entonces

---

[1] En su erudita edición de la *Antología poética* de González Prada, México, 1940 (Colección *Clásicos de América*), Carlos García Prada dice que el
maestro peruano «cultivó el endecasílabo de acentos en la tercera, la séptima
y la décima sílabas, como lo hicieron más tarde los modernistas». El verso así
acentuado no lo encuentro en ningún otro poeta, de modo sistemático: sólo
como forma ocasional, que se mezcla con los tipos usuales (v. *supra*). Es de
advertir que González Prada, cuando escribe endecasílabos normales, sólo
emplea los tipos A y B²; nunca mezcla con ellos el B¹, ni el B³, que cultivó separadamente.

es el metro principal, el «verso noble» de nuestro idioma. En portugués, Sá de Miranda, contemporáneo de Boscán y Garcilaso, implanta el endecasílabo de tipo italiano.

En sus orígenes, este verso tiene dos tipos, uno de acento interior en la sexta sílaba (A), otro de acento en la cuarta (B). No debían mezclarse, pero en la práctica se mezclaron. En italiano se hizo normal la mezcla, y los dos tipos se tratan como una unidad: el número de sílabas es igual; la acentuación esencial, si no idéntica, es por lo menos semejante: debe caer en sílaba par, la sexta (A) o la cuarta (B). En realidad, el tipo B se subdivide en tres subtipos, el B^1 (acento sólo en la cuarta sílaba), el B^2 (acentos en la cuarta y en la octava) y el B^3 (acentos en la cuarta y en la séptima). Como singularidad aparece el endecasílabo creciente, con una sílaba de exceso.

Al pasar al castellano, el endecasílabo se altera: no todavía en Boscán y su grupo, que lo escriben como los italianos, pero sí en sus secuaces más jóvenes. De las cuatro formas del verso italiano, sólo se aceptan tres: A, B^1 y B^2. El tipo B^3 se suprime, porque recordaba demasiado el endecasílabo subsidiario del arte mayor. Y el tipo B^1 tenía que usarse mucho menos que A y B^2, en razón de su estructura: no es fácil, o por lo menos cómodo, escribir a menudo series de cinco sílabas en que falte acento. La mayor parte de los poetas lo emplean, y a veces con mucha frecuencia (Juan Rufo, Alonso de Acevedo, Bartolomé de Argensola); unos pocos lo evitan (Montemayor, Gil Polo, Arguijo, Rioja, entre otros). A principios del siglo xix (Leandro de Moratín en su madurez, Quintana, Gallego) se le proscribe. Muy de tarde en tarde reaparece, pero probablemente como descuido, o quizás como arcaísmo (Espronceda, Batres, Burgos).

De hecho, desde mediados del siglo xvi el endecasílabo, en castellano, se siente como metro unitario. El tipo (A) de acento en sexta sílaba y el tipo (B^2) de acentos en cuarta y octava se equivalen para el oído. El tipo (B^1) de acento sólo en la cuarta, a pesar de su persistencia, no tenía otro valor que el de una especie de descanso, de alteración momentánea, que hacía resaltar mejor la estructura fundamental.

A fines del siglo xix, Rubén Darío, renovador fabuloso de la versificación castellana, lleva de nuevo el endecasílabo a la situación de los tiempos de Boscán y Garcilaso: mezcla los cuatro tipos iniciales (A, B^1, B^2 y B^3). Nunca traspasa esos límites. Cultiva a veces separadamente el tipo B^3 y aun adopta las variantes de fluctuación que tiene en gallego («Gaita galaica...»); usó también, fugazmente, y aislado, el tipo (C) acentuado en la quinta sílaba («Del país del sueño tinieblas, brillos...»).

Los discípulos de Darío sí traspasan los límites que él fijó para el endecasílabo normal: poco a poco, el metro sufre toda especie de dislocaciones; ahora, todo es lícito. Pero no todos los poetas se lo permiten todo: unos se detienen donde se detuvo Darío;

otros ni siquiera emplean el tipo (B³) de acentos en cuarta y séptimas sílabas. Finalmente, el endecasílabo sirve de eje en formas de versificación libre.

El tipo (B³) de gaita gallega, desde fines del siglo XVIII (Iriarte y Leandro de Moratín), tiene vida independiente, pero no muy activa. Así se conserva.

III

SOBRE LA HISTORIA DEL ALEJANDRINO

I

El verso alejandrino tiene en castellano larga historia, con cuatro épocas: aparece, nebulosamente, en el siglo XII; se impone, como forma fundamental del mester de clerecía, durante los siglos XIII y XIV [1]; se eclipsa del XV al XVIII, salvo apariciones esporádicas [2] en la poesía culta y en los cantos populares; reaparece a plena luz en el XIX, y alcanza nuevo esplendor con los románticos y los modernistas.

[1] Sobre el alejandrino de los primeros siglos, cf. mi estudio *La poesía castellana de versos fluctuantes*, capítulo I, § 4; el estudio de JOHN DRISCOLL FITZ-GERALD, *Versification of the cuaderna vía*, Nueva York, 1905, y los trabajos de H. H. Arnold mencionados en mi nota sobre la cuaderna vía *(Revista de Filosofía Hispánica*, 1945, VII, págs. 45-47).

[2] Consúltese el erudito estudio de ARTURO MARASSO, *Ensayo sobre el verso alejandrino*, en *Boletín de la Academia Argentina de Letras*, 1939, VII, págs. 63-127. Ejemplos que menciona de los siglos XVI a XVIII: Gil Polo, en la *Diana enamorada*, 1564 (llama a sus alejandrinos *rimas francesas*, pues nadie recordaba la cuaderna vía, salvo excepciones muy contadas, como Gonzalo Argote de Molina, a quien también cita Marasso); Pedro Hurtado de la Vera (¿o Pedro de Faría?), soneto en versos muy mal medidos, en la comedia *Doleria*, 1572; sonetos (¿de quién?) en elogio de *Dos tratados* del insigne protestante español Cipriano de Valera, publicados en Londres, 1588 (influencia francesa); Pedro Espinosa, el conocido soneto en elogio de la Virgen María; Alonso Carrillo, en el *argumento* del *Libro de la erudición poética*, de su hermano Luis, 1611 (versos sin rima; se reimprimen en 1613 partidos en heptasílabos); Ambrosio de Salazar, *La vida del autor*, en pareados, como prólogo de su *Espejo general de la gramática*, impreso en Ruan, 1614 (influencia francesa); en el siglo XVIII, Cándido María Trigueros, Tomás de Iriarte, Tomás Antonio Sánchez (composición en cuaderna vía y lenguaje antiguo, en elogio de Berceo, al publicar sus poemas, 1782), Leandro Fernández de Moratín y hasta el P. Bartolomé Pou (1727-1802), que escribe en su versión de Heródoto un único alejandrino al traducir un verso de la *Odisea:*

En Libia presto apuntan las astas del cordero.

En la cuarta época es común señalar dos períodos: antes y después de las innovaciones que, tras estudiar el modelo francés de Víctor Hugo, introdujeron Francisco Gavidia (1883) y Rubén Darío. En vez de dos períodos, deberían señalarse tres; desde principios del XIX hasta 1838; de ahí hasta Gavidia y Darío; de estos modernistas en adelante. Quizá haya que contar, si la situación actual no se modifica, una nueva fase; desde alrededor de 1920 los poetas emplean poco el alejandrino, y bien podría eclipsarse de nuevo.

Durante la Edad Media, es bien sabido, los poetas españoles que aspiraban a escribir alejandrinos no llegaban fácilmente a la medida exacta de catorce sílabas: sólo Berceo alcanza —las más veces— el fin que se propone, si bien alterando el fluir normal del habla con la supresión total de la sinalefa [1]. Cuando el alejandrino de los siglos XII a XIV realiza plenamente su módulo ideal, su estructura es sencilla: se compone de dos hemistiquios de siete sílabas, que pueden terminar en palabra llana, o esdrújula, o aguda. La acentuación interna de los hemistiquios es libre; puede caer en cualquiera de las sílabas que definen la fisonomía rítmica de este verso, sea en sílabas pares, la segunda o la cuarta o ambas (acentuación yámbica, según la terminología de Bello), sea en sílaba impar, la tercera (acentuación anapéstica):

> La ver*du*ra del prado, la o*lor* de las flores,
> las *som*bras de los *ár*bores de tem*pra*dos sabores.

> (Gonzalo de Berceo)

> Era *vie*ja buhona destas que *ven*den joyas;
> éstas *e*chan el laço, estas *ca*van las foyas...

> (Arcipreste de Hita)

Eran rítmicamente libres los pocos alejandrinos de los siglos XVI y XVII:

Podría agregarse un único alejandrino con que remata Juan María Maury *El festín de Alejandro*, traducido de Dryden:

> Y a fuer de nueva Elena incendia nueva Troya.

En la poesía popular (a la cual no hace referencia Marasso) aparecía de tarde en tarde, durante el siglo XVI, el alejandrino, mezclado con versos distintos, en la poesía de metro fluctuante:

> Aquellas sierras, madre, altas son de subir...
> Lavarm'e yo, cuitada, con penas y dolores...

[1] Cf. los trabajos indicados en nota anterior.

Olor *ten*gan más fino las colo*ra*das rosas...
Floridos *ra*mos mueva el *vien*to sosegado...
Más que el an*ti*guo Néstor teng*áis* larga la vida...

(Gil Polo, *Diana enamorada*) [1]

Y des*pués*, no sabiendo lo que de *mí* sería,
me *vi*ne a*quí* a Ruán por *u*na fantasía...

(Ambrosio de Salazar, *La vida del autor*)

Como el *tris*te piloto que por el *mar* incierto
se *ve*, con *tur*bios ojos, su*je*to de la pena
sobre las *cor*vas olas que vomi*tan*do arena
lo *tie*nen de la espuma sal*pi*cado y cubierto...

(Pedro Espinosa, *Soneto a la Virgen*)

En el siglo XVIII el alejandrino reaparece en Cándido María Trigueros (1736-1800), que lo llamó *pentámetro* (creía haberlo inventado), desde 1774:

Y su*fri*endo en mil tierras y el *re*ino de Neptuno
las *i*ras poderosas de la eno*ja*da Juno...

(*Eneida*, I)

y en Tomás de Iriarte (1750-1791):

Yo le*í*, no sé dónde, que en la *len*gua herbolaria,
salu*dan*do al Tomillo la *hier*ba Parieta*ri*a...
A*pe*nas *me*dio palmo del *sue*lo te levan*tas*...

(Fábula X, *La parietaria y el tomillo*)

La acentuación interna de los hemistiquios es, como se ve, libre. Igualmente en Alberto Lista (1775-1848):

Ya de ful*gen*tes flores se a*dor*na primavera...
Yo tras*pon*go ligero los *cán*tabros collados...
Allí es*tán* sus rediles: a*mor*, yo soy dichoso,
que ya *vue*la a mis brazos la a*ma*da Filis mía...

(*El deseo*)

Se mantiene libre, durante el siglo XIX, en los del prócer chileno Camilo Henríquez (1769-1845):

Los ta*len*tos de Chile yo te *vi* que aplaudías,
pero su *sue*ño y ocio sempi*ter*no sentías...

(*Exhortación al estudio de las ciencias*, ¿1812?)

[1] La mayor parte de los alejandrinos de Gil Polo, puede observarse, son de acentuación yámbica.

¡Salve, *gloria* del mundo, re*pú*blica naciente,
vuela a *ser* el imperiv más *grande* de Occidente!...

(*A Buenos Aires,* ¿1816?)

En los del romántico argentino Esteban Echeverría (1805-1851):

Dic*ho*sos si durasen las *ho*ras *de e*se sueño
como *du*ran y vuelven las del *sueño* común...

(*La Guitarra*)

En los de la cubana Gertrudis Gómez de Avellaneda (1814-1873):

Sola al *pie* de la torre, donde la *voz* tonante
re*su*ena pavorosa de tu se*ñor* fatal...

(*A Polonia,* versión de Hugo, 1840)

En los de Pablo Piferrer (1818-1848):

Y el *ne*gro sumidero en que *bo*ta y retumba...
Más a*llá* está tu patria, un e*ter*no confín...
El *au*ra vespertina que en las *ra*mas suspira...
el *sol* la *ro*ja cúspide por *vez* pos*tre*ra mira...

(*La cascada y la campana*)

En los del mexicano Ignacio Rodríguez Galván (1816-1842):

Hijos de *ta*les padres, por las *sen*das impuras
de ava*ri*cia y torpeza caminar*án* a oscuras
y en *fies*tas crapulosas los hallar*á* la luz...

(*El privado del virrey*)

Todavía en los del novelista andaluz Juan Valera (1824-1905):

De la *sa*bia Minerva maravi*llo*sa fábrica,
¿cómo *se ha* destruído, A*te*nas, tu poder?...

(*Fábula de Euforión*)

En los de José Selgas (1822-1882):

Coro*na*das de lágrimas las *on*das de su velo,
rota sobre los aires su *to*ca virreinal...

(*La nube de verano*)

Y, tardíamente, en Miguel Antonio Caro (1843-1909):

> Le traerían ensueños floridos a la mente
> y olvidados afectos del corazón marchito...
>
> A soñar a la sombra de tus copados árboles,
> de tus bullentes ondas al amoroso ruido...
>
> Mi amor es puro y vago, misterioso y fecundo,
> más hermoso que el cielo, más que la mar profundo...
>
> (*El descubridor*)

Y en otro gran colombiano, Rafael Pombo (1833-1912):

> ¡Qué suerte me ha tocado! ¡qué esclavitud la mía!
> ¡Vivir atado a un libro! ¡trabajar todo el día!...
> Hoy no sabes ser libre. La virtud y la ciencia...
>
> (*El escuelante y la oruga*)
>
> Sorprendida in fraganti cayó la pulga un día...
> Muy poco mal me hiciste, mas ello se te debe
> a que te era imposible hacérmelo mayor...
>
> (*El hombre y la pulga*)
>
> Entonces no se usaban estas carnicerías
> y eran artes incógnitas chorizos y jamón...
>
> (*Chanchito*)

Y hasta en el dramaturgo Echegaray (1832-1916):

> Cuando del viento el ímpetu logra al sauce doblar...
> Y en la marmórea piedra el cincel ha grabado...
>
> (*Noviembre*) [1]

---

[1] En la segunda edición de mi libro *La versificación irregular de la poesía castellana*, Madrid, 1933, pág. 318, atribuí al poeta uruguayo Juan Carlos Gómez (1820-1884) alejandrinos de acentuación libre; no los encuentro ahora en su colección de poesías: si no sufrí equivocación, debí leerlos en una composición no recogida en volumen.

No recuerdo el autor chileno de unos alejandrinos que he visto citados no sé dónde, pero creo que son anteriores a los de Zorrilla:

> Las alhajas que hurtó no encontrándoselé,
> fue puesto en libertad, y a Copiapó se fué...

Hizo también alejandrinos de acentuación libre el argentino José María Cantilo (1816-1872).

II

¿Cuándo empezó la acentuación yámbica rigurosa de los hemistiquios del alejandrino? En *El deseo*, de Lista, está comenzando: solamente la última estrofa de la composición lleva acentuación libre; las anteriores tienen todas acentuación yámbica. Podría esperarse que los clasicistas del siglo xviii hubieran introducido el rigor rítmico, como lo hicieron —por lo menos los últimos, Leandro Fernández de Moratín, Quintana, Gallego, Lista— con el endecasílabo, suprimiendo una de sus formas, la de acento interior sólo en la sílaba cuarta, que se había mantenido desde los tiempos de Boscán y Garcilaso [1]. Pero el alejandrino tuvo escaso favor entre ellos. La acentuación yámbica exclusiva se adopta en el período romántico, y, según parece, la innovación se debe a Zorrilla (1817-1893): los primeros alejandrinos que aparecen en sus obras son los de la plegaria *A María*, que forma parte de la colección inicial de sus poesías, publicadas en 1838:

> Aparta de tus ojos la nube perfumada...

Vienen inmediatamente después los conocidísimos versos de *Las píldoras de Salomón*, en la sexta parte de los *Cantos del trovador* (1840-1841): constituyen el tercer «fragmento», que alcanzó extraordinaria popularidad; no llevaba título, pero después se le ha denominado unas veces *Las nubes*, otras veces *La tempestad:*

> ¿Qué quieren esas nubes que con furor se agrupan
> del aire transparente por la región azul?...
> ¡Cuál rápidas se agolpan! ¡Cuál ruedan y se ensanchan
> y el firmamento trepan en lóbrego montón!...

Poco posteriores a los alejandrinos de *Las píldoras de Salomón* son los de la *Apoteosis de Calderón* (1841):

> Yo oí entre las hojas de mi laurel sonoro
> brotar de un arpa nueva el inspirado són...

y los del «capítulo cuarto» de *La azucena silvestre:*

> ¡Ay triste del viajero que pierde su camino...!

Contemporáneo estricto de Zorrilla, Salvador Bermúdez de Castro (1817-1883) publica en esos mismos años sus *Ensayos poéticos* (1840) donde emplea el alejandrino de acentuación yámbica en las composiciones *Un baño en el Tajo* y *A Toledo*, fechadas am-

---

[1] Cf. mi trabajo sobre *El endecasílabo castellano*.

bas en el año de aparición del volumen [1]. A poca distancia debieron de seguir a Zorrilla, y a Bermúdez de Castro, Gabriel García Tassara (1817-1875) y Ventura Ruiz Aguilera (1820-1881). Hasta la Avellaneda adoptó la nueva forma en su composición *Al mar* y en dos estrofas de *La noche de insomnio y el alba:*

> ¡Ay! de la ar*diente* zona do *tienes* a*l*mo asiento
> tus *r*ayos a mi cuna lan*zaste* abrasador...

En América se difundió la innovación con el argentino José Mármol (1818-1871) y el venezolano Abigaíl Lozano (1821-1866).

III

Durante cuarenta años, desde el éxito de Zorrilla, la mayoría de los poetas consideraron obligatorio la forma que él le dió al alejandrino: en comparación con la libertad anterior, hubo de parecer que el rigor acentual creaba una superior estructura rítmica. Pero sobrevino, después de 1880, la revolución de los *modernistas*, que prefería, a las formas de verso rígidamente acentuadas, las de acentuación libre: así ocurrió con el eneasílabo; para el endecasílabo se restauraron las cuatro formas originarias, las de la primera mitad del siglo XVI, y después se ha llegado a formas descoyuntadas [2]. El alejandrino no podía quedarse intacto.

Cuando Gavidia y Darío descubren, con la lectura de poesía francesa, y particularmente de Hugo, la variedad rítmica de que es capaz el alejandrino, se limitan a devolverle la libertad de acentuación que tenía antes de Zorrilla y a ensayar cortes internos:

> Yo dorm*ía* una noche a la or*i*lla del mar,
> So*p*ló *un* he*l*ado viento que *me hi*zo despertar.
> Desper*té.* Vi la estrella de la mañana. Ardía...
>
> (Gavidia, versión de la *Stella* de Hugo, 1883)

> Trae, al so*plar*, la brisa, ruidos, *b*esos, pasión,
> lleva en*j*am*b*res de arpas, ban*dad*as de preludios...
> Allí el *p*étalo es eco, allí el *f*uego es un ritmo...
>
> (Gavidia, *El idilio de la selva*, 1883)

---

[1] En *Un baño en el Tajo* hay un renglón que —podríamos pensar— viola la rigidez yámbica:

> Corred, plácidas ondas, corred y murmurad...

Pero, probablemente, para el poeta el acento de *corred* dominaba sobre el de *plácidas*.

La violación es franca, pero aislada, en este verso de *A Toledo:*

> Duerme, Toledo, duerme, y en tu a*l*mo*had*a de piedra...

[2] Cf. mi trabajo sobre *El endecasílabo castellano*, parte final.

Además, en la *Sonatina* (¿1893?), Darío emplea otro tipo de alejandrino, con ritmo anapéstico, no menos rígido que el yámbico de Zorrilla; la acentuación interior de cada hemitisquio cae exclusivamente en la sílaba tercera:

> La prin*ce*sa está triste. ¿Qué ten*drá* la princesa?...

Idénticos son los alejandrinos de José Joaquín Pérez (1845-1900) en *La española en América* (1894); es muy poco probable que el poeta dominicano conociese la *Sonatina:*

> Al des*gai*re cruzado el man*tón* de Manila,
> con or*gu*llo y con gracia, como *rei*na y manola,
> en la *cruz* centellante de la *ne*gra pupila
> incen*dian*do las almas, va la ar*dien*te española... [1]

Salvador Rueda (1857-1933) adoptó este alejandrino en el *Preludio* de *La procesión de la naturaleza,* hacia 1909:

> Por mi*tad* del París de arti*fi*cio dorado
> que, de *tan*ta luz ciego, del a*bis*mo va en pos...

En este poema emplea también el alejandrino zorrillesco:

> Un *Niá*gara te cuelga de *cri*nes *he*chas rizos...
>
> *(El caballo)*

> Los *ár*boles fre*né*ticos de *to*das las ciudades...
>
> *(La carrera de árboles)*

Nunca parece haber mezclado libremente el tipo yámbico y el anapéstico.

Después, Rubén Darío desarticuló completamente el alejandrino, haciendo alternar versos en que se mantiene la cesura con versos en que se suprime, y hasta versos de trece sílabas:

> Y los moluscos reminiscencias de mujeres...
> ¿Ha nacido el apocalíptico Anticristo?...

---

[1] El alejandrino clásico francés, el de Corneille y Racine, tendía de preferencia a este ritmo anapéstico, con cuatro acentos:

> *Mais tout* dort, *et l'armée, et les* vents *et Neptune...*

Consúltese MAURICE GRAMMONT, *Le vers français,* 4ª edición, París, 1937, y la obra clásica de BECQ DE FOUQUIÈRES, *Traité général de versification française.*

Coronada con el laurel del rey del día...
Cuando surgen de su prisión los olvidados...
Y el duelo de mi corazón, triste de fiestas...
Significas en mi primavera pasada...
De ir a tientas, en intermitentes espantos...
Pasó ya el tiempo de la juvenil sonrisa...
Y por caso de cerebración inconsciente...

A veces se destacan tres acentos que dividen el verso en tres grupos rítmicos:

Y tú, paloma arrulladora y montañera...
En los instantes del silencio misterioso...
Todo lo que hay en la divina primavera...
Huérfano esquife, árbol insigne, oscuro nido...
Ojos de víboras, de luces fascinantes...
Dichoso el árbol, que es apenas sensitivo...
Que el soñador imperial meditabundo...
Del ruiseñor primaveral y matinal...
Tarda en venir a este dolor adonde vienes...
Sueña, hijo mío, todavía, y cuando crezcas...
Cristalizamos en palabra y pensamiento... [1]

IV

Desde el siglo XVIII se intenta en castellano el llamado «alejandrino de trece sílabas», especie de alejandrino sin cesura: el primer hemistiquio debía terminar en palabra aguda o bien en

---

[1] El modelo de Darío para estos descoyuntamientos fué principalmente Verlaine:

> *Et le vieux tremble sa plainte sempiternelle...*
> *Tu consoles et tu berces, et le chagrin...*
> *Et tout le cirque des civilisations...*
> *Et l'extase perpétuelle et la science...*
> *De cette Science intruse dans la maison...*
> *Oiseau sur ce pâle roseau fleuri jadis...*
> *Et quelque responsabilité d'Empereur...*
> *Depuis Eden pour jusqu'à Ce Jour Irrité...*

En Verlaine abundan, además, los alejandrinos tripartitos:

> *De mes ennuis, de mes dégouts, de mes détresses...*
> *De la douceur, de la douceur, de la douceur...*
> *L'oubli qu'on cherche en des breuvages exécrés...*
> *Je suis indigne, mais je sais votre clémence.....*
> *Regrets sans fin, ennuis profonds, poignants remords...'*
> *En composant des acrostiches indolentes...*

Sobre el alejandrino descoyuntado en Juan Ramón Jiménez («Menos puro que tu vestido blanco, el aire...»; «¡Qué nobleza la de tu palidez indolente!»), cf. ENRIQUE DÍEZ CANEDO, *Juan Ramón Jiménez en su obra*, México, 1944, págs. 46-47.

palabra llana cuya sílaba final hiciese sinalefa con la inicial del hemistiquio siguiente:

> En *cier*ta catedral una cam*pa*na había
> que *só*lo se tocaba al*gún* solemne día...
> Cuatro *gol*pes o tres so*lía dar* no más...
> Celeb*ra*da fué siempre en *to*da la comarca...
>
> (Iriarte, Fábula VII, *La campana y el esquilón*)

Después lo emplea Leandro Fernández de Moratín (1760-1828):

> La *be*lla que prendó con gra*cio*so reír
> mi *tier*no corazón alte*ran*do su paz...

Todavía en 1842 lo ensayaba de nuevo, llamándolo *tredeca-sílabo*, el infatigable y poco afortunado experimentador Sinibaldo de Mas (1809-1868):

> Fra*gan*te y rubicunda, entre sus *ho*jas bellas,
> es la *ro*sa al nacer de *cé*lica figura...

Y hasta en 1894 reaparece en el opúsculo *Al lector*, del uruguayo Roberto de las Carreras:

> ¡Vi*vir*! He a*quí* una cosa ex*tra*ña como el hombre,
> que nos *cau*sa, lector, bas*tan*te pesadumbre...

Andrés Bello, en su tratado de *Ortología y métrica* (1835), lo llama *alejandrino a la francesa* y lo distingue del normal: uno y otro eran raros todavía entonces [1]. Tratadistas posteriores le niegan el derecho a la vida [2]. En principio esta negativa es arbitraria y obecede a prejuicios retóricos; la intención de los poetas

---

[1] En su tratado de *Ortología y métrica*, Bello dice que el *alejandrino a la francesa* «consta de trece sílabas» y lo clasifica entre los versos yámbicos; pero agrega que «el número de sílabas de que consta... pudiera adaptarse lo mismo al ritmo anapéstico que al yámbico, y, en efecto, se le ve pasar algunas veces del yambo al anapesto» (así lo demuestran las sílabas que he subrayado en los versos citados en el texto).

Señala Bello después como verso distinto «el alejandrino de los antiguos poetas castellanos», es decir, los del mester de clerecía, y dice que «no era... simple, sino compuesto de dos versos heptasílabos de acentuación yámbica»: afirmación gratuita, la del ritmo yámbico, que sorprende en quien la hace. En ediciones de su tratado posteriores a 1835, Bello agregó ejemplos de alejandrinos de Salvador Bermúdez de Castro y Fernando Velarde.

[2] Cf. Julio Vicuña Cifuentes, *Estudios de métrica española*, Santiago de Chile, 1929, págs. 13-175 y 151-156, y especialmente 35, nota.

debe acatarse, y así lo hizo Bello. Pero la verdad es que los versos citados resultan ambiguos: siempre pueden leerse como si tuvieran catorce sílabas, haciendo hincapié en la cesura cuando el primer hemistiquio es de terminación aguda y no haciendo sinalefa cuando la terminación es llana. El intento, pues, fracasó. La Avellaneda sí acertó a escribir versos de trece sílabas que no podían confundirse con los de catorce, en dos estrofas de *La noche de insomnio y el alba*. Pueden leerse como de estructura similar a la del alejandrino:

> Yo palpito, tu gloria / mirando sublime,
> noble autor de los vivos / y varios colores...

Pero es probable que el ritmo concebido por la poetisa haya sido otro:

> Yo palpi/to tu glo/ria miran/do sublime,
> noble autor/ de los vi/vos y va/rios colores...

Igual metro usó Ventura Ruiz Aguilera en *El árbol de la libertad:*

> Aún vagaba en mi boca sonrisa de niño
> cuando cerca del árbol sagrado pasé...

Los poetas del movimiento modernista lo adoptaron después, y ya no evitaron, como la Avellaneda y Ruiz Aguilera, las formas ambiguas de Iriarte y Moratín: establecido el eje de trece sílabas, resulta obligatorio prescindir de la cesura en los hemistiquios de final agudo y de la sinalefa en los de final llano. Así en el boliviano Ricardo Jaimes Freyre (1870-1933):

> Canta Lok en la oscura región desolada
> y hay vapores de sangre en el canto de Lok...

En Rubén Darío, soneto *Urna votiva:*

> Sobre el caro despojo esta urna cincelo...
> en la copa que guarda rocío del cielo...
> Una alondra fugaz sorprendida en su vuelo...
> Una estatua de Diana en la selva nativa...
> En el mármol divino que brinda Carrara...

Y en el chileno Pedro Antonio González (1863-1903):

> Yo mecí los embriones de todos los mundos...
> y la sombra de Dios en las aguas del caos...
>
> *(Occidentales)*

359

Enrique Díez Canedo (1879-1944) traduce a Francis Jammes en versos de trece sílabas que los acentos dividen en tres secciones:

Dentro de *poco* nevará. Me acuerdo *bien*...
¿A qué pen*sar* y hablar, en*tonces?* ¡Qué *gracioso!*...
¿Y dónde es*tán* en este ins*tante* mis tris*tezas?*...

Igualmente el argentino Francisco Luis Bernárdez en su *Alabanza didáctica de un toro:*

Para can*tarte*, dicta*dor* de la lla*nura*,
hincha sus *líricos* pul*mones* cada *verso*...

En *La canción de la vida*, el mexicano Enrique González Martínez (n. 1871) combina el verso de trece sílabas tripartito con el de nueve, enlazándose rítmicamente con él:

La vida está / cantando afuera...
En el jardín / hay un olor / de primavera...

A pesar de la importancia de los poetas que lo emplean, el verso de trece sílabas no ha alcanzado popularidad.

IV

LA MÉTRICA DE LOS POETAS MEXICANOS EN LA
ÉPOCA DE LA INDEPENDENCIA

Los últimos años del siglo xviii y primeros del xix no son, en la literatura española, período de gran renovación. En España, sin embargo, la poesía de Quintana y de Gallego, inspirada por la agitación política en que vivía Europa desde la Revolución Francesa, presagiaba, por su inquietud, la futura revolución literaria: el romanticismo. Pero en la forma no había modificaciones importantes. En la métrica se notaban ligeros cambios: Quintana imponía la oda o silva sin división de estrofas y el uso de versos sin rima en mitad de ellas; Arriaza ponía de moda la *octavilla* u octava imperfecta; y D. Tomás de Iriarte y D. Leandro Fernández de Moratín habían ensayado nuevas combinaciones métricas, que no se aprovecharon en el romanticismo, sino más bien hoy, en el *modernismo* iniciado en América.

En México, durante esta época, predominan, como durante los tres siglos anteriores, el verso endecasílabo, importado de Italia, y el octosílabo, típico del idioma.

El primero se usa con o sin el eptasílabo, en silvas, liras y estrofas de más o menos versos (nunca tan largas como en las canciones clásicas de Herrera, Caro y los Argensolas); en soneto, en octava real, en romance y en metro *suelto* o *blanco*. Con el pentasílabo, en sáficos y adónicos. El octosílabo se emplea en redondillas, quintillas, décimas y romances.

La versificación es en general descuidada, aun en los mejores poetas; se abusa de la sinéresis (ya lo indicó Menéndez y Pelayo en Navarrete), como en el tiempo de aparición del endecasílabo en España, en Boscán, Hurtado de Mendoza y Cetina. Es común atribuir a los defectos de pronunciación americana del idioma el abuso de la sinéresis, y la observación no es inexacta respecto de México, donde se suele contraer con exceso cualquier grupo de vocales, aun alterándolas; pero en verdad, la sinéresis se empleó mucho en España, a la vez que el hiato, por influencia del uso italiano, que a menudo abre diptongos y cierra adiptongos, especialmente aquellos en que entra la *i:*

> Delfica deitá dovria la fronda...
> A cui esperienza grazia serba...
> Con l'armonia che temperi e discerni...
> (Dante, *Paradiso*, I)

Así en castellano:

> Oh claras ondas, cómo veo presente...
> Podrían tornar, de enfermo y descontento...
> Por montes y por selvas a Diana...
> Seguía la caza con estudio y gana...
> (Garcilaso, *Égloga*, II)

> Treguas al ejercicio sean robusto...
> Donde espumoso el mar siciliano...
> (Góngora, *Polifemo*)

> Si trae las fuertes armas por despojos...
> (Lupercio Leonardo, Canción *Tan ofendido...*)

> Volvía la vista rústica y salvaje...
> Sin acordarme que es el día prescrito...
> (Jáuregui, *Aminta*, I)

En esta materia de hiatos y sinéresis, como en todas las que se refieren a la ortología y la métrica de nuestro idioma, los tratadistas, preocupados con reglas latinas y con ejemplos italianos, dieron muy tarde con la verdad: en rigor, a D. Andrés Bello se deben las bases definitivas (pero no mucho más que las bases) para el estudio de la versificación castellana; y todavía queda mucho por hacer [1]. Así, si bien en el siglo XVIII los tratadistas llegaron a fijar los defectos de la sinéresis (que había sabido evitar Fernando de Herrera), aún en nuestros días se acepta equivocadamente como canon la obligación del hiato en grupos de vocales que forman verdaderos diptongos, como en *cruel, sonriente, criador, confiado;* simple resto de italianismo.

Los poetas mexicanos abusaban, efectivamente, de la sinéresis, cuando ya no se toleraba en España. El error no deja de ser notado, y los directores del *Diario de México* (uno de cuyos fundadores, el dominicano D. Jacobo de Villaurrutia, tuvo sus pun-

---

[1] Sobre los hiatos y sinéresis hay muchas noticias en la imperfecta pero útil obra de FELIPE ROBLES DÉGANO, *Ortología clásica de la lengua castellana.*

tas de innovador gramatical) subrayan en ocasiones las palabras en que se comete sinéresis discordante; pero los poetas siguen en s trece, aun Barquera, que perteneció al periódico censor:

> Guíalas al templo de la Sión sagrada...
> *(Invocación, Diario,* 1.º de enero de 1814)

El desuso de esta arcaica licencia se debió, más que al bien intencionado pero inútil empeño del *Diario,* a la difusión de los trabajos de D. Mariano José Sicilia, propagados en México, principalmente, por D. Andrés Quintana Roo (sin duda uno de los hombres más cultos de su tiempo), y que todavía en 1843 servían de modelo a D. Francisco Ortega para sus *lecciones* de prosodia.

El endecasílabo se maneja con perfección (salvo la sinéresis), y rara vez se intercala entre sus formas ortodoxas la anapéstica, vulgarmente llamada de gaita gallega. Sólo se encuentra en versificadores descuidados:

> Piden los manes del héroe extremeño...
> (Antonio Salgado, Soneto, *Diario,* 2 de noviembre de 1810)

En cambio es común a todos los versificadores mexicanos el endecasílabo con acento sólo en la cuarta sílaba; forma de origen acaso provenzal, usada en España desde Boscán y Garcilaso, desde Herrera y Fray Luis de León, desde Lope y los Argensolas, hasta Leandro Fernández de Moratín y Manuel María de Arjona, y que nada tenía de inconsciente, según he comprobado antes (trabajo sobre *El verso endecasílabo,* en el libro de *Horas de estudio)* y según ha ratificado D. Marcelino Menéndez y Pelayo:

> Cuál es el numen misericordioso...
> Fueron engaños de su fantasía...
> (Navarrete, *La Divina Providencia)*

> A proporción de los merecimientos...
> (Sartorio, traducción del Himno de la *Gloria del Paraíso,* de San Pedro Damiano)

> Esta mañana que se levantó...
> (Anastasio de Ochoa, *La respuesta concisa)*

> A dos coyotes plenipotenciarios...
> Cuantas mujeres descontentadizas...
> (José María Moreno, *El coyote y la zorra)*

> Que unos son todos en la sepultura...
> (Francisco Palacios, Soneto, *Diario,* 25 de septiembre de 1807)

363

Pueda escribir a mis conciudadanos...
(Mariano Barazábal, Oda, *Diario*, 14 de octubre de 1808)

Y que las picas de los danzarines...
(José Rafael Larrañaga, Égloga V de Virgilio)

Que oirán la voz de sus conocimientos...
(Agustín Pomposo Fernández de San Salvador, *Mopso agradecido...*, Diario, 16 de enero de 1810)

Mi tierno llanto, o sin que me anegaras...
(Francisco Ortega, *La música*)

La fresca sombra que le cobijaba...
(José Ignacio Basurto, Fábula)

Afuera luces del entendimiento...
(Soneto anónimo, *Diario*, 4 de noviembre de 1806)

No soy yo gato mal intencionado...
(Fernández de Lizardi, Fábula VIII)

Ya evitan esta forma algunos, como Juan María Lacunza y Sánchez de Tagle, pero aún en éste se encuentran aproximaciones:

El abandono de lo más querido...
(*La pasión de Cristo*, de Metastasio, II)

La regla de acentuar las sílabas cuarta y octava en los sáficos adónicos se descuida casi siempre:

Tres veces visten verde prodigioso
de Guadalupe cerros y riberas...
(Juan de Dios Uribe, *Himno a la Guadalupana*)

Huyan las penas, huyan las congojas,
respire todo generales gozos...
Salve mil veces, celestial imagen,
consuelo dulce de los mexicanos;
recibe grata de mi plectro humilde
los tonos safos.
(Barquera, Oda, *Diario*, 21 de diciembre de 1805)

Versos que generalmente se usan mal son el decasílabo y el eneasílabo (raro este último):

Lidia bella, muchachita blanca
más que la leche y que cándido lirio...

(Navarrete, traducción de Galo)

¡Oh que dulces, preciosos instantes
en un sueño logré enamorado,
pues juzqué que de mi dueño amado
conseguía mi afecto el favor!
Yo creí que en los brazos amantes
descansaba de mi dulce dueño,
y era todo ficción de mi sueño,
y era todo ficción de mi amor.

(Canción anónima *El sueño*, que parece haber sido
popular; *Diario de México*, 21 de octubre de 1810)

Llegó a casa el anciano diciendo
a la novia que se recogiera...

(Juan José Guido, *Cuento*, *Diario*, 19 de noviembre de 1805)

Otras veces el decasílabo se confunde con el eneasílabo, al punto de que no se sabe en qué metro quiso el autor escribir:

Logró de su jaula escaparse
no sé cómo una vez un lorito
y vuelto a la selva y sus gentes
entre ellas andaba y sus gritos...

(Juan María Lacunza, *Fábula, Diario*, 8 de enero de 1814)

Duerme, duerme, pastorcilla mía,
serranita de mi corazón;
ceda todo a la grata quietud
mientras duerme mi dulce amor...
A la ro... a la ro... ro... ro...

(Mariano Barazábal, *Idilio, Diario*, 25 de febrero de 1812)

El eneasílabo aparece una vez (con el nombre de *novisílabo*),
en metro libre, manejado con soltura por un poeta desconocido:

¡Ay triste! Tu favor constante,
la risa, el ademán sensible,
aquel mirar gracioso y tierno
que yo buscara ciego siempre...

(Arneto de Mosvos, *Timante por la muerte de Filis*,
Diario, 1.º de julio de 1809)

365

Se había olvidado aquel curioso verso de diez sílabas que ensayó Sor Juana Inés de la Cruz:

> Lámina sirva al cielo el retrato,
> Lísida, de tu angélica forma...
> Hécate, no triforme, mas llena...

El decasílabo que Moratín llamó *asclepiádeo* aparece rara vez:

> Brillante todo lisonjeaba
> a las pupilas enternecidas...
> (Himno anónimo a Felipe de Jesús, *Diario*, 4 de enero de 1808)

Así mismo el dodecasílabo, manejado con soltura:

> Por esto, señora, al te concebir
> tus ilustres padres, el Supremo Ser
> su divina gracia hizo intervenir...
> (Francisco de Rojas, *Ave María, Diario*, 22 de febrero de 1812)

> El ave en el aire vive con sosiego
> y la salamandra gustosa en el fuego...
> y yo que nací para mis tormentos...
> (Manuel de Medina, *Endechas, Diario*, 1.º de noviembre de 1807)

No hay pruebas de que los poetas mexicanos supiesen del castizo abolengo de este metro de arte mayor que ilustraron Juan de Mena y el Marqués de Santillana; pero sí da muestras de saberlo el militar realista Ramón Roca, culto y brillantísimo poeta granadino que empleó sus fuerzas en una admirable oda al sanguinario Calleja con motivo de la destrucción de Zitácuaro, y a quien perjudicó sobre manera (al grado de haberlo hecho olvidar) su venida a América, donde de seguro moriría, pues los españoles de Europa no le conocieron, y los mexicanos, por explicables razones del momento histórico, le insultaron y desdeñaron (por ejemplo, Bustamante y Mora). Este poeta, que supera en brillo y fuerza poética a cuantos escribían por entonces en México, nativos o europeos (si bien no posee las delicadezas de Navarrete ni el sentido clásico de Ochoa), escribió versos de arte mayor en lenguaje antiguo, tomando por modelo las hermosas pero falsas *Querellas* que se compusieron en el siglo XVII para hacerlas pasar como del rey Alfonso el Sabio:

> A vos que acudido de heroica bravura,
> muy más de que esquadras asaz favorido,
> las nobles fazannas de tal aguerrido

cual Cid o Bernardo vos facen mesura:
a vos, renovando lejana escriptura,
cual vos el recuerdo de grandes cabdillos,
mi pénnola acata, y en metros sencillos
se postra a la vuestra perínclita altura.

Versos cortos se usan con frecuencia, especialmente en romancillos, aun de cuatro sílabas:

> Da mil duros
> y seremos
> dos amantes
> sin ejemplo...

(Ramón Quintana del Azebo, Letrilla, *Diario*, 22 de febrero de 1810)

> Arroyuelo
> que caminas
> a la aldea
> de Clorila

(Navarrete, *Juguetillos a Clorila*)

Las combinaciones métricas más en uso son las mencionadas con relación al endecasílabo y al octosílabo. El asonante está en boga, y se usa en los romancillos y romances, inclusive los endecasílabos, muy de moda para asuntos solemnes; y aun en los sáficos adónicos, cuya libertad original se olvidaba. Los romances octosílabos suelen terminar con un verso endecasílabo (así lo hace en particular Juan María Lacunza); cuando son letrillas, llevan su estribillo independiente, como era general durante los siglos de oro.

Ya aparece, con frecuencia, la *octavilla* u octava imperfecta, que puso de moda Arriaza (tan popular en toda América, y especialmente en México, donde se hizo reimpresión de sus versos), pero de que ya había ejemplos intercalados en las *Silvas a Fany* de Meléndez:

> ¡Con qué quietud, Elena,
> recuerdo aquellos días
> colmados de alegrías
> falaces del amor;
> aquella edad que llena
> de mil gustos fingidos
> tenía mis sentidos
> esclavos del error!

(Ramón Quintana del Azebo, *Diario*, 1.º de julio de 1806)

Esta octavilla había de extenderse bien pronto a toda clase de versos, especialmente a los decasílabos (para los himnos según el ejemplo de Arriaza) y a los endecasílabos. Menéndez y Pelayo declara no saber de dónde surgió esta última forma: por mi parte creo que fue una simple extensión del tipo al verso heroico, y que debió su éxito a su semejanza con la octava real, menos fácil; no puede caber duda de que sea muy anterior a Salvador Bermúdez de Castro, a quien se atribuyó su invención.

El soneto sólo se usa en endecasílabos, sin que nadie recuerde el caso aislado del soneto alejandrino de Pedro Espinosa; pero poco después, hacia 1830, Joaquín María del Castillo y Lanzas escribió un interesante soneto eneasílabo, *El recuerdo* (una de las pocas obras interesantes en sus desabridos *Ocios juveniles*), en verdad tan solitario como el alejandrino del elegante poeta de Antequera:

> Pronto a partir en occidente,
> Su curso diurno terminado,
> Muéstrase ahora el sol fulgente
> De bellas nubes circundado.
> Óyese en trino regalado
> Del ruiseñor la voz doliente,
> Y, murmurando, la corriente
> Rauda desliza por el prado.
> Leves besando tiernas flores
> Zéfiros vuelan, conduciendo
> Sus fragantísimos olores.
> Empero a mí, todo esto viendo,
> ¿Qué falta? Oh Lesbia, tus amores;
> ¡Salid, pues, lágrimas corriendo!

V

RUBÉN DARÍO Y EL SIGLO XV

Durante mucho tiempo, llamó mi atención el carácter «siglo xv» de los *Dezires, layes y canciones* que Rubén Darío agregó a sus *Prosas profanas* (libro de 1896) al reimprimirlas en Europa (en París, 1901). No tenía nada de extraño que el poeta, amigo de experimentar constantemente, ensayara las formas trovadorescas del siglo xv: lo extraño era que, puesto a escoger modelos, no los buscara en los grandes maestros, como Juan de Mena, Santillana, los Manriques, sino en poetas de mucho menor importancia, como Juan de Dueñas, Juan de Torres, Pedro de Santafé, Valtierra. Y sobre todo: ¿dónde había encontrado Darío la peculiar ortografía de esos nombres: Johan, Santa Ffe, Duenyas? ¿Por qué se había creído obligado a escribir *esparça, dezir, ffin, ffinida*.

Antes de 1900, tales peculiaridades ortográficas no se reproducían frecuentemente tratándose del siglo xv: la mayor parte de las antologías modernizaban los textos. Podía pensarse en el *Cancionero de Baena* (edición de Madrid, 1851): pero sólo para desechar inmediatamente la idea, puesto que Dueñas, Torres, Valtierra y Santafé no figuran en aquella colección. Aun más podría pensarse en el *Cancionero de Stúñiga* (edición de Madrid, 1872), ya que allí figuran Dueñas y Torres: pero no se advierte relación entre las composiciones suyas que allí aparecen[1] y las de Darío; y, como se ve, faltan Santafé y Valtierra.

La solución del problema la encontré en el *Cancionero inédito del siglo XV* publicado por Alfonso Pérez Gómez Nieva en Madrid, 1884[2]. Este volumen que no es muy conocido ni merece serlo,

---

[1] De Dueñas, *La nao de amor* y la composición que comienza «La franquesa muy extranna...»; de Torres, las que comienzan «Non sabes, Iohn de Padilla...» y «Oh temprana sepoltura...».

[2] *Colección de poesías de un cancionero inédito del siglo XV existente en la biblioteca de S. M. el rey D. Alfonso XII, con una carta del Excmo. Sr. D. Manuel Cañete, de la Academia Española, y un prólogo, notas y apéndice por A. Pérez Gómez Nieva, Madrid, Tipografía de Alfredo Alonso, calle del Soldado, núm. 8, 1884.*

369

transcribe torpemente textos de trovadores castellanos y aragoneses que en su mayor parte pertenecieron a la corte de Alfonso V de Aragón en Nápoles [1]. Y en este volumen, que caería casualmente en manos de Rubén Darío, halló el poeta de *Prosas profanas* la manera de ser, momentáneamente, «muy siglo xv».

¿Qué tomó Darío de aquellos poetas menores? Apenas la versificación, y, de tarde en tarde, vagas *resonancias* de estilo —las que suelen acompañar a toda forma métrica.

Del castellano de Dueñas toma dos formas de *decires:* una en doce versos, de ocho y de cuatro sílabas, rimas A *a* B A *a* B C C D E D E, con *finida* A *a* B A *a* B (composición «Senyor Don Juan, excelente...»; en Darío: «Reina Venus, soberana...»); otra de siete versos octosílabos, rimas A B A B C C B (composición «Entre todos los cuydados...»; en Darío: «Ponte el traje azul que más...»).

De Juan de Torres, la forma de *lay* en seis versos hexasílabos, rimas *a a b a a b,* luego *b b c b b c* (composición «Ay triste de mí...»; en Darío: «¿Qué pude yo hacer...?»).

De Valtierra, la forma de *canción* octosilábica, con cabeza de cuatro versos rimas, A B B A, y copla de ocho, rimas A B B A C D D C, sirviendo de *fin* los tres últimos versos de la última copla (composición «Enojados de tristura...»; en Darío: «Amor tu ventana enflora...»).

Del aragonés Pedro de Santafé [2] —el poeta de quien hay más composiciones en el *Cancionero* de Pérez Nieva—, tres formas: 1, una canción en octosílabos y tetrasílabos, con cabeza de cuatro versos, rimas A B A *b,* y coplas de ocho, C D C D E B E *b,* repitiéndose como estribillo el verso corto *b* a través de toda la composición (en Santafé: «Senyora, maguer consiento...»; *b:* «No me e'nganyo»; en Darío: «Señora, Amor es violento...»; *b:* «La locura»); 2, otra canción en octosílabos y tetrasílabos, rimas A *a* B B *b* A *a* C *c* A, con *fin* de cinco versos, rimas A *a* B *b* A (composición «Rey Alfonso esmerado...»; en Darío: «A qué comparar la pura...»); y 3, *copla esparza,* octosilábica, ocho versos con rimas A B B A C D D C y *tornada* E F F E (composición «Tanto, senyora, baledes...»; en Darío: «¡La gata blanca! En el lecho...»)

---

[1] Sobre Dueñas, Torres y Santafé, véase MENÉNDEZ Y PELAYO, *Antología de poetas líricos castellanos,* tomo V, páginas CCLVI, CCLXXXV, CCXC, CCXCVI a CCXCVIII, CCC a CCCII; tomo VI, pág. CCCLXXIX; tomo VII, pág. CCLIII. De Dueñas reproduce la *Antología* (tomo II, págs. 145 a 153) *La nao de amor.* FOULCHÉ-DELBOSC recoge todas sus composiciones conocidas —doce— en el tomo II de su *Cancionero castellano del siglo* XV (Madrid, 1915).

[2] En los versos *Por Sancha de Lubián* Santafé se plañe del esfuerzo que le cuesta el señorío de la lengua de Castilla:

Blanda lengua castellana
que por guerra que la haga
tan dulcemente me llaga...

De Santafé proviene también el intercalar un verso en latín en medio de los castellanos *(Tristis est anima mea* en «Pues mi triste corazón...», y *Regnum meum non est de hoc mundo* en «Cerca mi gloria que beo...»; en Darío: «*Mel et lac sub lingua tua,* en «Señora, Amor es violento...»). Al imitar sus formas, Rubén Darío superó con creces a los medianos trovadores del Cancionero: como en ellos había escasa materia poética, desdeñó sus temas de escolástica cortesana. En los *Dezires, layes y canciones* del poeta moderno, la versificación es «muy siglo xv»; pero la materia es, por lo general, «muy siglo xviii», muy llena de «la Grecia de la Francia» (con curiosa mezcla de los nombres latinos y los griegos: Venus, Afrodita, Eros, Juno, Diana...). A veces hay «siglo xvii», Góngora (y, a través de él, Renacimiento italiano, Ariosto y Bernardo Tasso): «la lección que dio a Angélica Medoro»; «el garzón de Ida». Y también frecuentes alusiones al amor hebraico: Ester, Belkiss, la Sulamita —y hasta la cita «Mel et lac...» proviene del *Cantar de los cantares* en la Vulgata latina.

Admirables juegos de ingenio poético, elegantes divagaciones sobre temas de fina sensualidad, a los cuales se mezcla a veces la profunda nota del pesimismo de la carne:

> ...Que en el vino del amor
> hay la amargura del mar.

Corresponden a la fase *Banville* de la obra de Darío: la curiosa exploración de formas caídas en desuso, pero que pueden dar de sí nuevamente elegancia o brillantez, como en los *Caprices,* las *Odelettes* y las *Amethystes* de Banville, o en los versos ingleses, sobre modelo francés, de Andrew Lang y Austin Dobson.

ÍNDICES

ÍNDICE DE TEMAS

ÍNDICE DE AUTORES Y DE OBRAS ANÓNIMAS

ÍNDICE GENERAL

OTROS ESTUDIOS

ESTE LIBRO SE TERMINÓ
DE IMPRIMIR EL DÍA 5 DE
MAYO DE 1961 EN LA
IMPRENTA DE LA UNIVER-
SIDAD DE BUENOS AIRES